GROUP THEORY IN PHYSICS

GROUP THEORY IN PHYSICS

An Introduction to Symmetry Principles, Group Representations, and Special Functions in Classical and Quantum Physics

Wu-Ki Tung

Michigan State University, USA

World Scientific

NEW JERSEY • LONDON • SINGAPORE • BEIJING • SHANGHAI • HONG KONG • TAIPEI • CHENNAI

Published by

World Scientific Publishing Co. Pte. Ltd.
5 Toh Tuck Link, Singapore 596224
USA office: 27 Warren Street, Suite 401-402, Hackensack, NJ 07601
UK office: 57 Shelton Street, Covent Garden, London WC2H 9HE

Library of Congress Cataloging-in-Publication Data
Tung, Wu-Ki.
Group theory in physics.

Bibliography: p.
Includes index.
1. Representations of groups. 2. Symmetry groups.
I. Title.
QC174.17.G7T86 1985 530.1'5222 85-3335
ISBN-13 978-9971-966-56-0 -- ISBN-10 9971-966-56-5
ISBN-13 978-9971-966-57-7 (pbk) -- ISBN-10 9971-966-57-3 (pbk)

British Library Cataloguing-in-Publication Data
A catalogue record for this book is available from the British Library.

First published 1985
Reprinted 1993, 1999, 2003, 2005, 2008, 2010

To
Beatrice, Bruce, and Lei

PREFACE

Group theory provides the natural mathematical language to formulate symmetry principles and to derive their consequences in Mathematics and in Physics. The "special functions" of mathematical physics, which pervade mathematical analysis, classical physics, and quantum mechanics, invariably originate from underlying symmetries of the problem although the traditional presentation of such topics may not expressly emphasize this universal feature. Modern developments in all branches of physics are putting more and more emphasis on the role of symmetries of the underlying physical systems. Thus the use of group theory has become increasingly important in recent years. However, the incorporation of group theory into the undergraduate or graduate physics curriculum of most universities has not kept up with this development. At best, this subject is offered as a special topic course, catering to a restricted class of students. Symptomatic of this unfortunate gap is the lack of suitable textbooks on general group-theoretical methods in physics for all serious students of experimental and theoretical physics at the beginning graduate and advanced undergraduate level. This book is written to meet precisely this need.

There already exist, of course, many books on group theory and its applications in physics. Foremost among these are the old classics by Weyl, Wigner, and Van der Waerden. For applications to atomic and molecular physics, and to crystal lattices in solid state and chemical physics, there are many elementary textbooks emphasizing point groups, space groups, and the rotation group. Reflecting the important role played by group theory in modern elementary particle theory, many current books expound on the theory of Lie groups and Lie algebras with emphasis suitable for high energy theoretical physics. Finally, there are several useful general texts on group theory featuring comprehensiveness and mathematical rigor written for the more mathematically oriented audience. Experience indicates, however, that for most students, it is difficult to find a suitable modern introductory text which is both general and readily understandable.

This book originated from lecture notes of a general course on Mathematical Physics taught to all first-year physics graduate students at the University of Chicago and the Illinois Institute of Technology. The author is not, by any stretch of the imagination, an expert on group theory. The inevitable lack of authority and comprehensiveness is hopefully compensated by some degree of freshness in pedagogy which emphasizes underlying principles and techniques in ways easily appreciated by students. A number of ideas key to the power and beauty of the group theoretical approach are highlighted throughout the book, e.g., invariants and invariant operations; projection operators on function-, vector-, and operator-spaces; orthonormality and completeness properties of representation functions,..., etc. These fundamental features are usually not discussed or emphasized in the more practical elementary texts. Most books written by experts, on the other hand, either are "over the head" of the average student; or take many conceptual points for granted, thus leaving students to their own devices. I make a special effort to elucidate the important group theoretical methods by referring frequently to analogies in elementary topics and techniques familiar to students from basic courses of mathematics and physics. On the rich subject of Lie groups, key ideas are first introduced in the context of simpler groups using easily understandable examples. Only then are they discussed or developed for the more general and more complex cases. This is, of course, in direct contrast to the deductive approach, proceeding from the most abstract (general) to the more concrete (specific), commonly found in mathematical texts. I believe that the motivation provided by concrete examples is very important in developing a real understanding of the abstract theory. The combination of inductive and deductive reasoning adopted in our presentation should be closer to the learning experience of a student (as well as to the process of generalization involved in the creation of the theory by the pioneers) than a purely deductive one.

This book is written primarily for physicists. In addition to stressing the physical motivations for the formalism developed, the notation adopted is close to that of standard physics texts. The main subject is, however, the mathematics of group representation theory, with all its inherent simplicity and elegance. Physical arguments, based on well-known classical and quantum principles, are used to motivate the choice of the mathematical subjects, but not to interfere with their logical development. Unlike many other books, I refrain from extensive coverage of applications to specific fields in physics. Such diversions are often distracting for the coherent presentation of the mathematical theory; and they rarely do justice to the specific topics treated. The examples on physical applications that I do use to illustrate advanced group-theoretical techniques are all of a general nature applicable to a wide range of fields such as atomic, nuclear, and particle physics. They include the classification of arbitrary quantum mechanical states and general scattering amplitudes involving particles with spin (the Jacob-Wick helicity formalism), multipole moments and radiation for electromagnetic transitions in any physical system,..., etc. In spite of their clear group-theoretical origin and great practical usefulness, these topics are rarely discussed in texts on group theory.

Group representation theory is formulated on linear vector spaces. I assume the reader to be familiar with the theory of linear vector spaces at the level required for a standard course on quantum mechanics, or that of the classic book by Halmos. Because of the fundamental importance of this background subject, however, and in order to establish an unambiguous set of notations, I provide a brief summary of notations in Appendix I and a systematic review of the theory of finite dimensional vector spaces in Appendix II. Except for the most well-prepared reader, I recommend that the material of these Appendices be carefully scanned prior to the serious studying of the book proper. In the main text, I choose to emphasize clear presentation of underlying ideas rather than strict mathematical rigor. In particular, technical details that are needed to complete specific proofs, but are otherwise of no general implications, are organized separately into appropriate Appendices.

The introductory Chapter encapsulates the salient features of the group-theoretical approach in a simple, but non-trivial, example—discrete translational symmetry on a one dimensional lattice. Its purpose is to illustrate the flavor and the essence of this approach before the reader is burdened with the formal development of the full formalism. Chapter 2 provides an introduction to basic group theory. Chapter 3 contains the standard group representation theory. Chapter 4 highlights general properties of irreducible sets of vectors and operators which are used throughout the book. It also introduces the powerful projection operator techniques and the Wigner-Eckart Theorem (for any group), both of which figure prominently in all applications. Chapter 5 describes the representation theory of the symmetric (or permutation) groups with the help of Young tableaux and the associated Young symmetrizers. An introduction to symmetry classes of tensors is given, as an example of useful applications of the symmetric group and as preparation for the general representation theory of classical linear groups to be discussed later. Chapter 6 introduces the basic elements of representation theory of continuous groups in the Lie algebra approach by studying the one-parameter rotation and translation groups. Chapter 7 contains a careful treatment of the rotation group in three-dimensional space, SO(3). Chapter 8 establishes the relation between the groups SO(3) and SU(2), then explores several important advanced topics: invariant integration measure, orthonormality and completeness of the D-functions, projection operators and their physical applications, differential equations satisfied by the D-functions, relation to classical special functions of mathematical physics, group-theoretical interpretation of the spherical harmonics, and multipole radiation of the electromagnetic field. These topics are selected to illustrate the power and the breadth of the group-theoretical approach, not only for the special case of the rotation group, but as the prototype of similar applications for other Lie groups. Chapter 9 explores basic techniques in the representation theory of inhomogeneous groups. In the context of the simplest case, the group of motions (Euclidean group) in two dimensions, three different approaches to the problem are introduced: the Lie algebra, the induced representation, and the group contraction methods. Relation of the group representation functions to Bessel functions is established and used to elucidate properties of the latter. Similar topics for the Euclidean group in three dimensions are then discussed. Chapter 10 offers a systematic derivation of the finite-dimensional and the unitary representations of the Lorentz group, and the unitary representations of the Poincaré group. The latter embodies the full continuous space-time symmetry of Einstein's special relativity which underlies contemporary physics (with the exception of the theory of gravity). The relation between finite-dimensional (non-unitary) representations of the Lorentz group and the (infinite-dimensional) unitary representations of the Poincaré group is discussed in detail in the context of relativistic wave functions (fields) and wave equations. Chapter 11 explores space inversion symmetry in two, and three-dimensional Euclidean space, as well as four-dimensional Minkowski space. Applications to general scattering amplitudes and multipole radiation processes are considered. Chapter 12 examines in great detail new issues raised by time reversal invariance and explores their physical consequences. Chapter 13 builds on experience with the various groups studied in previous chapters and develops the general tensorial method for deriving all finite dimensional representations of the classical linear groups $GL(m; C)$, $GL(m; R)$, $U(m, n)$, $SL(m; C)$, $SU(m, n)$, $O(m, n; R)$, and $SO(m, n; R)$. The important roles played by invariant tensors, in defining the groups and in determining the irreducible representations and their properties, is emphasized.

It may be noticed that, point and space groups of crystal lattices are conspicuously missing from the list of topics described above. There are two reasons for this omission: (i) These groups are well covered by many existing books emphasizing applications in solid state and chemical physics. Duplication hardly seems necessary; and (ii) The absence of these groups does not affect the coherent development of the important concepts and techniques needed for the main body of the book. Although a great deal of emphasis has been placed on aspects of the theory of group representation that reveal its crucial links to linear algebra, differential geometry, and harmonic analysis, this is done only by means of concrete examples (involving the rotational, Euclidean, Lorentz, and Poincare groups). I have refrained from treating the vast and rich general theory of Lie groups, as to do so would require a degree of abstraction and mathematical sophistication on the part of the reader beyond that expected of the intended audience. The material covered here should provide a solid foundation for those interested to pursue the general mathematical theory, as well as the burgeoning applications in contemporary theoretical physics, such as various gauge symmetries, the theory of gravity, supersymmetries, supergravity, and the superstring theory.

When used as a textbook, Chapters 1 through 8 (perhaps parts of Chapter 9 as well) fit into a one-semester course at the beginning graduate or advanced undergraduate level. The entire book, supplemented by materials on point groups and some general theory of Lie groups if desired, is suitable for use in a two-semester course on group theory in physics. This book is also designed to be used for self-study. The bibliography near the end of the book comprises commonly available books on group theory and related topics in mathematics and physics which can be of value for reference and for further reading.

My interest in the theory and application of group representations was developed during graduate student years under the influence of Loyal Durand, Charles Sommerfield, and Feza Gürsey. My appreciation of the subject has especially been inspired by the seminal works of Wigner, as is clearly reflected in the selection of topics and in their presentation. The treatment of finite-dimensional representations of the classical groups in the last chapter benefited a lot from a set of informal but incisive lecture notes by Robert Geroch.

It is impossible to overstate my appreciation of the help I have received from many sources which, together, made this book possible. My colleague and friend Porter Johnson has been extremely kind in adopting the first draft of the manuscript for field-testing in his course on mathematical physics. I thank him for making many suggestions on improving the manuscript, and in combing through the text to uncover minor grammatical flaws that still haunt my writing (not being blessed with a native English tongue). Henry Frisch made many cogent comments and suggestions which led to substantial improvements in the presentation of the crucial initial chapters. Debra Karatas went through the entire length of the book and made invaluable suggestions from a student's point of view. Si-jin Qian provided valuable help with proof-reading. And my son Bruce undertook the arduous task of typing the initial draft of the whole book during his busy and critical senior year of high school, as well as many full days of precious vacation time from college. During the period of writing this book, I have been supported by the Illinois Institute of Technology, the National Science Foundation, and the Fermi National Accelerator Laboratory.

Finally, with the deepest affection, I thank all members of my family for their encouragement, understanding, and tolerance throughout this project. To them, I dedicate this book.

Chicago WKT
December, 1984

CONTENTS

CHAPTER 1

INTRODUCTION

Symmetry, Quantum Mechanics, Group Theory, and Special Functions in a Nutshell

The theory of group representation provides the natural mathematical language for describing symmetries of the physical world. Although the mathematics of group theory and the physics of symmetries were not developed simultaneously—as in the case of calculus and mechanics by Newton—the intimate relationship between the two was fully realized and clearly formulated by Wigner and Weyl, among others, before 1930. This close connection is most apparent in the framework of the new quantum mechanics. But much of classical physics, involving symmetries of one kind or another, can also be greatly elucidated by the group-theoretical approach. Specifically, the solutions to equations of classical mathematical physics and "state vectors" of quantum mechanical systems both form linear vector spaces. Symmetries of the underlying physical system require distinctive regularity structures in these vector spaces. These distinctive patterns are determined purely by the group theory of the symmetry and are independent of other details of the system.

Therefore, in addition to furnishing a powerful tool for studying new mathematical and physical problems, the group theoretical approach also adds much insight to the wealth of old results on classical "special functions" of mathematical physics previously derived from rather elaborate analytic methods. Since the 1950's, the application of group theory to physics has become increasingly important. It now permeates every branch of physics, as well as many areas of other physical and life sciences. It has gained equal importance in exploring "internal symmetries" of nature (such as isotopic spin and its many generalizations) as in elucidating traditional discrete and continuous space-time symmetries.

In this introductory chapter we shall use a simple example to illustrate the close relationship between physical symmetries, group theory, and special functions. This is done before entering the formal development of the next few chapters, so that the reader will be aware of the general underlying ideas and the universal features of the group theoretical approach, and will be able to see through the technical details which lie ahead. As with any "simple example", the best one can do is to illustrate the basic ideas in their most transparent setting. The full richness of the subject and the real power of the approach can be revealed only after a full exposition of the theory and its applications.

Since we shall try to illustrate the full scope of concepts with this example, notions of classical and quantum physics as well as linear vector spaces and Fourier analysis are all involved in the following discussion. For readers approaching this subject for the first time, a full appreciation of all the ideas may be more naturally attained by referring back to this chapter from time to time after the initial reading. Starting with Chap. 2, the basic theory is presented *ab initio*; the required mathematical and physical concepts are introduced sequentially as they are needed. The last part of this chapter consists of a brief survey of commonly encountered symmetry groups in physics.

Our notational conventions are explained in Appendix I. For reference throughout the book, a rather detailed summary of the theory of linear vector spaces is provided in Appendix II. Some readers may find it useful to go over these two Appendices quickly beforehand, so that all basic concepts and techniques will be at hand when needed. The Dirac notation for vectors and operators on vector spaces is used because of its clarity and elegance. Refer to Appendices I & II for an introduction to this notation if it is not familiar initially.

References in the text are indicated by the names of first authors enclosed in square brackets. In keeping with the introductory nature of this book, no effort is made to cite original literature. References are selected primarily for their pedagogical value and easy accessibility. With the exception of two classical exemplary papers, all references are well-known treatises or textbooks. They are listed at the end of the book.

1.1 Particle on a One-dimensional Lattice

Consider a physical system consisting of a single particle on a one-dimensional lattice with lattice spacing b. For definiteness, we shall refer to this particle as an "electron". The name is totally irrelevant to the concepts to be introduced. The dynamics of the system will be governed by a *Hamiltonian*

(1.1-1) $$H = p^2/2m + V(x)$$

where m represents the mass and p the momentum of the electron. The potential function $V(x)$ satisfies the periodicity condition

(1.1-2) $$V(x + nb) = V(x) \qquad \text{for all } n = \text{integer.}$$

We shall not be concerned with the detailed shape of V, which may be very complex [see Fig. 1.1].

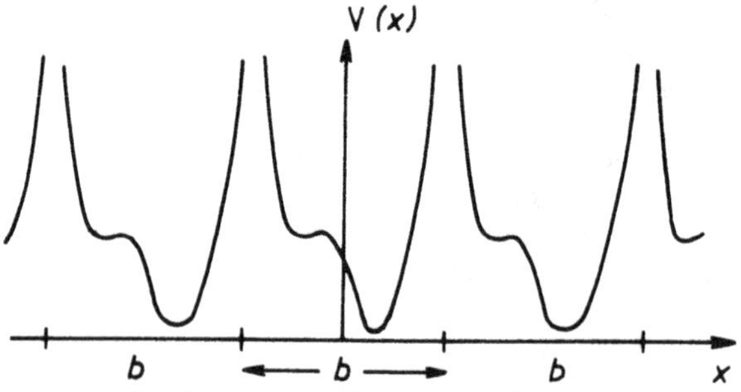

Fig. 1.1 A periodic potential function.

Translational Symmetry (discrete)

The above system has an obvious *symmetry*. The Hamiltonian is *invariant* under translations along the lattice by any integral multiple (n) of the lattice spacing b

(1.1-3) $$x \to x' = x + nb$$

It is self-evident that two identical physical systems related to each other by such a translation (for any n) should behave in exactly the same way. Alternatively, we may say: a given system must appear to behave in an equivalent manner with respect to two observers related to each other by such a translation.[1] We now try to formulate this principle in mathematical language. To be specific, we use the language of quantum mechanics.

Let $|\psi\rangle$ be an arbitrary physical "state vector" of our system. How will it be affected by a symmetry operation given by Eq. (1.1-3)? Let us denote by $|\psi'\rangle$ the "transformed state" after the specified translation. The correspondence $|\psi\rangle \to |\psi'\rangle$ defines an operator, denoted by $T(n)$, in the vector space of physical states V_{ph}. Thus, for each discrete translation of the lattice system, we obtain a "transformation" on the physical states,

(1.1-4) $$|\psi\rangle \longrightarrow |\psi'\rangle = T(n)|\psi\rangle \qquad \text{for all } |\psi\rangle \in V_{ph} \quad .$$

Since this is a symmetry operation, the two sets of vectors $\{|\psi'\rangle\}$ and $\{|\psi\rangle\}$ (for any given $T(n)$) must provide equivalent descriptions of the physical system. This requires $T(n)$ to be a linear transformation. In addition, all physical observables must remain invariant under this transformation. But all physical observables are expressed in terms of scalar products, such as $\langle\phi|\psi\rangle$. Linear transformations which preserve scalar products are induced by *unitary operators*. [Cf. Appendix II] We say that the set of symmetry operations on the lattice is *realized* on the vector space V_{ph} by the set of unitary operators $\{T(n)\}$. Alternatively, we say that the operators $\{T(n)\}$ form a *representation* of the symmetry operations of the Hamiltonian.

In quantum mechanics, physical observables are represented by hermitian operators. In conjunction with the transformation of the state vectors induced by a symmetry operation [cf. Eq. (1.1-4)], each operator A undergoes the transformation

(1.1-5) $$A \longrightarrow A' = T(n)\,A\,T(n)^{-1}$$

In order that the hermitian nature of the operator A be preserved, again we need the symmetry operators $\{T(n)\}$ to be unitary.

Let $|x\rangle$ be an idealized position eigenstate (i.e. a state in which the particle in question is located precisely at x) then it follows from Eq. (1.1-3)

(1.1-6) $$T(n)\,|x\rangle = |x + nb\rangle \quad .$$

[1] These two different ways of envisioning symmetry operations are often referred to as the *active* and the *passive* point of view, respectively. We shall adopt the language of the active point of view. For some readers not familiar with symmetry considerations, it may be easier to adopt the other way of thinking in order to be convinced of, say, the invariance of physically measurable quantities. The equivalence of the two viewpoints is the essence of a symmetry principle.

The invariance of the Hamiltonian follows from[2]

$$T(n)\,V(X)\,T(n)^{-1} = V(X - nb) = V(X) \tag{1.1-7a}$$

(where X denotes the coordinate operator) and from[3]

$$T(n)\,(p^2/2m)\,T(n)^{-1} = p^2/2m \quad . \tag{1.1-7b}$$

The symmetry condition is expressed mathematically as either $T(n)\,H\,T(n)^{-1} = H$ or, equivalently

$$[H, T(n)] = 0 \qquad \text{for all } n = \text{integer.} \tag{1.1-8}$$

The most important step in studying a quantum mechanical system is to solve for the eigenstates of the Hamiltonian. In view of Eq. (1.1-8), the eigenstates of H can be chosen as eigenstates of $T(n)$ as well. This is because mutually commuting operators have a complete set of simultaneous eigenvectors. Of more significance for our purpose is the fact (to be proved in Chap. 3) that simultaneous eigenstates of $T(n)$ are necessarily eigenstates of H. Thus, the dynamical problem of solving for the eigenstates of the Schrödinger equation, involving a yet unspecified potential function, is reduced first to that of solving for the eigenstates of $T(n)$, which is purely kinematical, depending only on the symmetry of the problem. Although this does not solve the original problem completely, it leads to very important simplifications of the problem and to significant insight on the behavior of the system. The next section formulates a systematic procedure to solve the "kinematical" part of the problem referred to above. This is the prototype of group representation theory.

1.2 Representations of the Discrete Translation Operators

The translation operators are required by physical principles and simple geometry to satisfy the following conditions:

$$T(n)\,T(m) = T(n + m) \tag{1.2-1a}$$

i.e. two successive translations by n and m steps respectively are equivalent to a single translation by $n + m$ steps;

$$T(0) = E \tag{1.2-1b}$$

i.e. the null translation corresponds to the identity operator; and

$$T(-n) = T(n)^{-1} \tag{1.2-1c}$$

[2] The first equality can be derived by examining the effects of the operators on the basis vector $|x\rangle$

$$V(X - nb)\,|x\rangle = |x\rangle\, V(x - nb)$$
$$T(n)\,V(X)\,T(n)^{-1}\,|x\rangle = T(n)\,V(X)\,|x - nb\rangle = T(n)\,|x - nb\rangle\, V(x - nb) = |x\rangle\, V(x - nb) \quad .$$

Note that the coordinate operator X assumes the eigenvalue of the eigenvector it operates on. The second equality in Eq. (1.1-7a) follows from Eq. (1.1-2) with the classical function $V(x)$ replaced by the quantum mechanical operator $V(X)$.

[3] Since $p = (\hbar/i)\,d/dx$ in the coordinate representation, it is not affected by the transformation $x \to x + nb$. ($\hbar$ is the Planck constant divided by 2π.)

i.e. each translation has an inverse, corresponding to a translation in the opposite direction by the same number of steps.

These properties identify the algebraic structure of the translation operators as that of a *group*. (See Chap. 2.) This group of discrete translations will be denoted by T^{d}. Two additional conditions are worth noting:

$$T(n)\,T(m) = T(m)\,T(n) \tag{1.2-1d}$$

$$T^{\dagger}(n)\,T(n) = E \tag{1.2-1e}$$

where $T^{\dagger}$ is the hermitian conjugate (or adjoint) operator of T (cf. Definitions II.16 and II.20). The *commutativity* condition (d) follows simply from Eq. (1.2-1a). The *unitarity* condition (e) is a consequence of the physical requirement that $T(n)$ represent symmetry operations under which measurable physical quantities must remain invariant. As mentioned earlier, these quantities are given by scalar products on the space of state vectors in Quantum Mechanics. Scalar products are invariant under unitary transformations (Theorem II.16).

These algebraic relations allow us to determine all possible realizations (or representations) of the operators $T(n)$, by the following quite straightforward steps:

(i) Since all $T(n)$ commute with each other, we can choose a set of basis vectors in V, the vector space of all state vectors, which are simultaneous eigenvectors of $T(n)$ for all n. We denote members of this basis by $|u(\xi)\rangle$ where ξ is a yet unspecified label for the vectors. We have

$$T(n)\,|u(\xi)\rangle = |u(\xi)\rangle\, t_n(\xi) \tag{1.2-2}$$

where $t_n(\xi)$ are the eigenvalues of $T(n)$ corresponding to the eigenvector $|u(\xi)\rangle$.

(ii) Applying the basic relations (a)–(e) (Eqs. (1.2-1a)–(1.2-1e)), to $|u(\xi)\rangle$ and invoking the linear independence of $|u(\xi)\rangle$ for distinct ξ, we obtain:

$$t_n(\xi)\,t_m(\xi) = t_{n+m}(\xi) \tag{1.2-3a}$$

$$t_0(\xi) = 1 \tag{1.2-3b}$$

$$t_{-n}(\xi) = 1/t_n(\xi) \tag{1.2-3c}$$

$$t_n(\xi)\,t_m(\xi) = t_m(\xi)\,t_n(\xi) \tag{1.2-3d}$$

and

$$|t_n(\xi)|^2 = 1 \quad . \tag{1.2-3e}$$

(iii) Condition (1.2-3e) implies

$$t_n(\xi) = e^{-i\phi_n(\xi)} \tag{1.2-4}$$

where $\phi_n(\xi)$ are real numbers and the negative sign is adopted by convention. Eqs. (1.2-3abc) then translate to:

$$\phi_n(\xi) + \phi_m(\xi) = \phi_{n+m}(\xi) \tag{1.2-5a}$$

$$\phi_0(\xi) = 0 \tag{1.2-5b}$$

$$\phi_{-n}(\xi) = -\phi_n(\xi) \quad . \tag{1.2-5c}$$

(iv) The solution to these three equations is obvious, i.e. $\phi_n(\xi) = nf(\xi)$, where f is an arbitrary function. Since ξ is an arbitrary parameter not yet specified, we can choose $f(\xi) = \xi$,

(1.2-6) $$\phi_n(\xi) = n\xi$$

which leads us to:

(1.2-7) $$t_n(\xi) = e^{-in\xi} \quad .$$

This is the complete solution to the original algebraic problem. The set of numbers $\{t_n(\xi)\}$, for any given choice of ξ, are said to form a *representation* of the discrete translation group. Eq. (1.2-7) indicates that $t_n(\xi)$ is periodic in the variable ξ with period 2π. We shall use the basic range $-\pi \le \xi < \pi$.

1.3 Physical Consequences of Translational Symmetry

The mathematical results of the last section can be applied directly to the original physical problem with important consequences. First, since the Hamiltonian of the system commutes with all translational operators, we look for simultaneous eigenvectors of H and $T(n)$. For notational reasons which will become obvious in a moment, we shall introduce a new parameter k related to ξ of the previous section by

(1.3-1) $$k = \xi/b \qquad \left(-\frac{\pi}{b} \le k < \frac{\pi}{b}\right)$$

where b is the lattice spacing. Denoting the energy eigenvalue by E, we have:

(1.3-2) $$H\,|u(E,k)\rangle = |u(E,k)\rangle\, E$$

and

(1.3-3) $$T(n)\,|u(E,k)\rangle = |u(E,k)\rangle\, e^{-iknb} \quad .$$

Let us examine the wave function in the coordinate space representation, which is just the Schrödinger wave function[4]

(1.3-4) $$u_{E,k}(x) = \langle x|u(E,k)\rangle \quad .$$

We can relate $u(x)$ for arbitrary x to the same wave function within the "unit cell" around the origin because the spatially localized states $|x\rangle$ have simple known translational properties. Let

(1.3-5) $$x = nb + y \qquad \left(-\frac{b}{2} \le y < \frac{b}{2}\right)$$

then according to Eq. (1.1-6), $|x\rangle = T(n)|y\rangle$; hence $\langle x| = \langle y|T^{\dagger}(n)$. Making use of

[4] We recall some standard quantum mechanical results in the Dirac notation: let $|u\rangle$ be an arbitrary quantum mechanical state vector, and $\{|q\rangle\}$ be a complete set of orthonormal basis, then the "wave function" of the u-state in the q-representation is $u(q) = \langle q|u\rangle$. In particular, the coordinate space basis is $\{|x\rangle\}$ and the corresponding wave function is the Schrödinger wave function $u(x) = \langle x|u\rangle$. [cf. Messiah, Chap. VIII, Sec. 16; or Schiff, Chap. 6, Sec. 23.] In the present case, the state u depends on the "wave vector" label k (explained later) and the energy eigenvalue E.

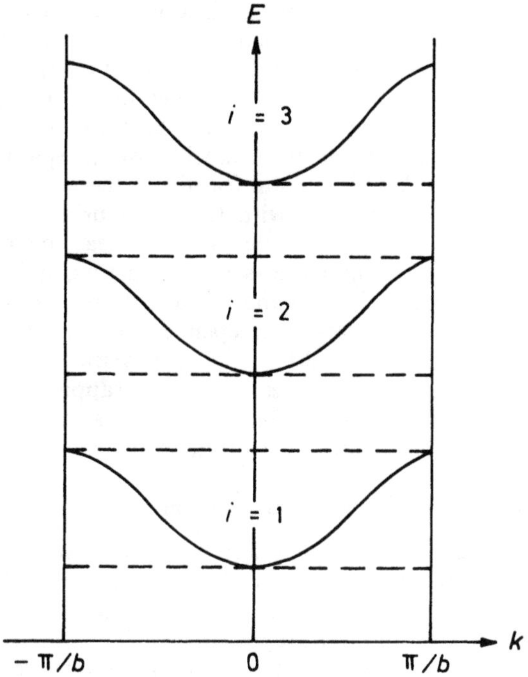

Fig. 1.2 Energy spectrum of a typical one-dimensional lattice system. The energy depends on the wave vector and on i, which labels the bands.

this result, we can express the wave function (1.3-4) as follows:

$$u_{E,k}(x) = \langle y|\, T^{\dagger}(n)\,|u(E,k)\rangle = \langle y|\, T(-n)\,|u(E,k)\rangle$$
$$= \langle y|u(E,k)\rangle\, e^{iknb} = u_{E,k}(y)\, e^{ik(x-y)} \quad .$$

In other words,

(1.3-6) $$u_{E,k}(x)\, e^{-ikx} = u_{E,k}(y)\, e^{-iky}$$

for all x and $-\frac{b}{2} \leq y < \frac{b}{2}$. Thus, if one defines $v_{E,k}(x)$ by

(1.3-7) $$v_{E,k}(x) = u_{E,k}(x)\, e^{-ikx}$$

the new wave function is periodic in x, with period b. This is the well-known *Bloch wave function.* The parameter k has the familiar physical interpretation of being the *wave vector* variable.

When Eq. (1.3-7) is substituted in the original Schrödinger equation, we obtain a *reduced* Schrödinger equation for $v_{E,k}(x)$ with *periodic* boundary conditions. For any given wave vector $-\frac{\pi}{b} \leq k < \frac{\pi}{b}$, one can find a set of energy eigenvalues $E_i(k)$, $i = 1, 2, \ldots$, with corresponding wave functions $v_{i,k}(x)$ by solving the reduced

Schrödinger equation. The detailed forms of $E_i(x)$ clearly depend on the potential function $V(x)$, which we have so far left completely arbitrary. In physically interesting cases, the ranges of $E_i(k)$ for different i do not overlap, at least for some values of i. The energy spectrum—which determines, to a large extent, the physical properties of the system—may look like that depicted in Fig. 1.2. There are allowed ranges of "energy bands" for the electron (labelled by i), separated by forbidden regions called "energy gaps". This general feature of the energy spectra for electrons in periodic potentials, together with the Pauli principle that determines whether the allowed states can or cannot be populated, lead to a basic understanding of the distinction between conductors, semi-conductors, and insulators.

The above discussion makes it clear that such key properties of solids follow entirely from the symmetry of the lattice, independent of any details of the complex interaction between the molecules. Many other physical consequences can be derived such as the effects due to impurities: scattering, trapping,... etc. We shall not pursue them here,[5] except by again emphasizing how a multitude of physically important results follow from symmetry conditions alone.

1.4 The Representation Functions and Fourier Analysis

The results of Sec. 1.2 also illustrate a deep relation between group representation theory and "harmonic analysis", of which the Fourier analysis and various orthogonal polynomials of mathematical physics are particular examples. In this simple case, we can easily recognize the representation functions in Eq. (1.2-7) as the basis functions for the Fourier Series. They satisfy the familiar relations:

(1.4-1)
$$\int_{-\pi}^{\pi} d\xi\, e^{in\xi} e^{-in'\xi} = 2\pi\delta_{n,n'}$$

(1.4-2)
$$\sum_n e^{-in\xi} e^{in\xi'} = \delta(\xi - \xi') \quad .$$

The second equation must be interpreted, of course, in the sense of generalized functions (i.e. both sides occur under an integral expression). In ξ-space, Eq. (1.4-1) expresses the *orthonormality* of the basis functions; whereas Eq. (1.4-2) expresses their *completeness* (for functions defined in the interval $-\pi < \xi < \pi$, or $-\pi/b \leq k \leq \pi/b$). [cf. Theorem II.13] To be more precise: given any function $f(\xi)$ defined on the interval $(-\pi, \pi)$, one can write it as a linear combination of the representation functions $e^{-in\xi}$,

(1.4-3)
$$f(\xi) = \sum_n e^{-in\xi} f_n \quad ;$$

and the coefficients f_n are given by,

(1.4-4)
$$f_n = \frac{1}{2\pi} \int_{-\pi}^{\pi} d\xi\, e^{in\xi} f(\xi) \quad .$$

It is worth noting that the continuous variable ξ over the range $(-\pi, \pi)$ and the discrete index $n = 0, \pm 1, \pm 2, \ldots$ play symmetric roles. One may alternatively regard Eq. (1.4-4) as an expansion of the function f_n defined on the lattice, in terms of the

[5] For interesting discussions, see [Feynman], or [Gasiorowicz].

representation functions $e^{in\xi}$ summed over the continuous label ξ with coefficient $f(\xi)$. Eq. (1.4-3) then serves as the defining equation of the coefficient for a given function f_n.

For most symmetry groups in physics, the above result can be generalized: the group representation matrices form an orthonormal and complete set of functions in the function space of the relevant variables. This far-reaching result forms the basis of most important applications of group theory to physics as well as to other branches of mathematics. As the representation functions may become relatively complex for larger groups, the geometrical interpretation associated with the underlying symmetry will prove invaluable in providing insight in the understanding of the relevant mathematics and the physical consequences.

1.5 Symmetry Groups of Physics

The above example illustrates the following general features of the application of group theory to physical symmetries:

(i) Since the Hamiltonian is invariant under symmetry operations, H commutes with all the symmetry group operators. Hence eigenstates of H are also basis vectors of representations of the symmetry group. (Sec. 1.1)

(ii) The representations of the relevant group can be found by general mathematical methods. The results are inherent to the symmetry, and independent of details of the physical system. (Sec. 1.2)

(iii) The physical interpretation of the group-theoretic results leads to valuable information on the energy spectrum of the system and on the pattern of energy degeneracies among many other consequences not discussed explicitly here. (Sec. 1.3)

(iv) The representation functions form orthonormal and complete sets in the function space of solutions to the physical problem. Physically interesting quantities (e.g. wave functions, transition and scattering amplitudes, physical operators... etc.) can be expanded in terms of these functions. (Sec. 1.4)

Not discussed in this simple example, but of equal importance in applications, is the systematic treatment of deviations from the symmetry pattern when the physical symmetry is broken by specific perturbations.

We now enumerate some of the commonly encountered symmetries in physics to indicate the scope of our subject.

(i) Continuous Space-Time Symmetries

(a) Translations in Space, $\mathbf{x} \to \mathbf{x} + \mathbf{a}$, where $\mathbf{a}$ is a constant 3-vector: This symmetry, applicable to all isolated systems, is based on the assumption of *homogeneity of space*, i.e. every region of space is equivalent to every other, or alternatively, physical phenomena must be reproducible from one location to another. The conservation of linear momentum is a well known consequence of this symmetry. [Goldstein], [Landau (1), (2)]

(b) Translations in Time, $t \to t + a_0$, where a_0 is a constant: This symmetry, applicable also to isolated systems, is a statement of *homogeneity of time*, i.e. given the same initial conditions, the behavior of a physical system is independent of the absolute time—in other words, physical phenomena are reproducible at different times. The conservation of energy can be easily derived from it. [Goldstein], [Landau (1), (2)]

(c) Rotations in 3-Dimensional Space, $x^i \to x'^i = R^i{}_j x^j$ where $i,j = 1,2,3$, $\{x^i\}$ are the 3-components of a vector, and (R) is a 3×3 (orthogonal) rotation matrix: This symmetry reflects the *isotropy of space*, i.e. the behavior of isolated systems must be independent of the orientation of the system in space. It leads to the conservation of angular momentum. [Goldstein], [Landau (1), (2)]

(d) Lorentz Transformations,

$$\begin{pmatrix} t \\ \mathbf{x} \end{pmatrix} \longrightarrow \Lambda \begin{pmatrix} t' \\ \mathbf{x}' \end{pmatrix}$$

where Λ is a 4×4 Lorentz matrix and $\mathbf{x}$ stands for a three component column vector: This symmetry embodies the generalization of the classical, separate space and time symmetries into a single *space-time symmetry*, now known as Einstein's *special relativity*. [Goldstein], [Landau (3)]

(ii) Discrete Space Time Symmetries

(a) Space Inversion (or Parity transformation), $\mathbf{x} \to -\mathbf{x}$: This symmetry is equivalent to the reflection in a plane (i.e. mirror symmetry), as one can be obtained from the other by combining with a rotation through angle π. Most interactions in nature obey this symmetry, but the "weak interaction" (responsible for radioactive decays and other "weak" processes) does not. [Commins], [Sakurai]

(b) Time Reversal Transformation, $t \to -t$: This is similar to the space inversion. The symmetry is respected by all known forces except in isolated instances (e.g. neutral "K-meson" decay) which are not yet well-understood. [Commins], [Sakurai]

(c) Discrete translations on a Lattice. This example has been discussed in detail earlier in this Chapter.

(d) Discrete Rotational Symmetry of a Lattice (Point Groups): These are subsets of the 3-dimensional rotation- and reflection-transformations which leave a given lattice structure invariant. There are 32 crystallographic point groups. In conjunction with the discrete translations, they form the *space groups* which are the basic symmetry groups of solid state physics.

(iii) Permutation Symmetry
Systems containing more than one identical particles are invariant under the interchange of these particles. The permutations form a symmetry group. If these particles have several degrees of freedom, the group theoretical analysis is essential to extract symmetry properties of the permissible physical states. (Bose-Einstein and Fermi-Dirac statistics, Pauli exclusion principle,... etc.)

(iv) Gauge Invariance and Charge Conservation
Both classical and quantum mechanical formulation of the interaction of electromagnetic fields with charged particles are invariant under a "gauge trans-

formation". This symmetry is intimately related to the law of conservation of charge. [Landau (3)]

(v) Internal Symmetries of Nuclear and Elementary Particle Physics
The most familiar symmetry of this kind is the "isotopic spin" invariance of nuclear physics. This type of symmetry has been generalized and refined greatly in modern day elementary particle physics. All known fundamental forces of nature are now formulated in terms of "gauge theories" with appropriate internal symmetry groups, e.g. the $SU(2) \times U(1)$ theory of unified weak and electromagnetic interactions, and the $SU(3)_c$ theory of strong interaction (Quantum Chromodynamics).

We shall not study all these symmetry groups in detail. Rather, we shall concentrate on general group theoretical techniques which can be readily extended to large classes of applications. The next three chapters provide the general theory of groups and group representations. Many of the simpler discrete groups are discussed as examples. Chapter 5 concerns the permutation, or symmetric groups. In addition to being symmetry groups of physical systems, these groups are important as tools for studying other finite and continuous groups. In Chap. 6 we study one-parameter continuous groups which form the basis for the general theory of continuous (or Lie) groups. Chapter 7 contains a systematic treatment of the 3-dimensional rotation group and angular momentum. Chapter 8 extends the theory in several directions to develop the full power of the group-theoretical approach in the context of the rotation group and SU(2). Chapter 9 discusses the groups of motion in 2- and 3-dimensional Euclidean space—groups which combine translations with rotations. Chapter 10 extends this study to the 4-dimensional Minkowski space, and analyzes the structure and the physical applications of the Lorentz and Poincaré group. Chapters 11 and 12 cover the added features when spatial inversion and time reversal are incorporated into the theory. Chapter 13 provides a simple introduction to classical linear groups which have found a variety of applications in physics.

CHAPTER 2

BASIC GROUP THEORY

Bearing in mind the concrete examples of symmetry groups in physics just described, we shall present in this chapter the key elements of group theory which form the basis of all later applications. In order to convey the simplicity of the basic group structure, we shall stay close to the essentials in the exposition.

2.1 Basic Definitions and Simple Examples

Definition 2.1 (A Group): A set $\{G: a, b, c \ldots\}$ is said to form a *group* if there is an operation $\cdot$, called *group multiplication*, which associates any given (ordered) pair of elements a, $b \in G$ with a well-defined *product* $a \cdot b$ which is also an element of G, such that the following conditions are satisfied:

(i) The operation $\cdot$ is *associative*, i.e. $a \cdot (b \cdot c) = (a \cdot b) \cdot c$ for all a, b, $c \in G$;

(ii) Among the elements of G, there is an element e, called the *identity*, which has the property that $a \cdot e = a$ for all $a \in G$;

(iii) For each $a \in G$, there is an element $a^{-1} \in G$, called the *inverse* of a, which has the property that $a \cdot a^{-1} = e$.

All three of the above conditions are essential. From these axioms, one can derive useful, elementary consequences such as: $e^{-1} = e$; $a^{-1} \cdot a = e$; and $e \cdot a = a$, for all $a \in G$. (Notice the order of the elements in comparison to (ii) and (iii) respectively.) The proofs are non-trivial but standard. [See Problem 2.1] For simplicity, the group multiplication symbol $\cdot$ will be omitted whenever no confusion is likely to arise (just as in the multiplication of ordinary numbers).

Example 1: The simplest group consists of only one element: the identity element e. The inverse of e is e and the group multiplication rule is $ee = e$. It is straightforward to see that all the group axioms are satisfied. The number 1 with the usual multiplication constitutes such a group, which we shall denote by C_1.

Example 2: The next simplest group has two elements, one of which must be the identity; we denote them by $\{e, a\}$. According to the properties of e, we must have $ee = e$ and $ea = ae = a$. Thus only aa needs to be specified. Is $aa = e$ or is $aa = a$? The second possibility is untenable because multiplication on both sides by a^{-1} would lead to $a = e$, which is false. The rules of multiplication can be summarized succinctly in a *group multiplication table* [Table 2.1]. This group shall be designated C_2. It should be obvious that the numbers $+1$ (e) and -1 (a) form just such a group with respect to the usual multiplication. Interesting examples of C_2 appear in all branches of physics and mathematics: e.g. the transposition of two objects together with the identity form a 2-element permutation

Table 2.1 Group Multiplication Table of C_2

	e	a
e	e	a
a	a	e

Table 2.2 Group Multiplication Table of C_3

e	a	b
a	b	e
b	e	a

group having just this structure; likewise, the spatial inversion (parity) transformation (i.e. $\mathbf{x} \to -\mathbf{x}$) and the identity also form such a group.

Example 3: There is one and only one three-element group [cf. Problem 2.2] called C_3. The multiplication table is given in Table 2.2. (In comparison to Table 2.1, we have omitted the (redundant) row and column which label the group elements.) Since $a^{-1} = b$, we can denote the three elements by $\{e, a, a^{-1}\}$, with the requirement that $a^3 = e$. Concrete examples of the group C_3 are: (i) the numbers $(1, e^{i2\pi/3}, e^{-i2\pi/3})$ with the usual rules of multiplication, (ii) the symmetry operations of the equilateral triangle $\triangle$ in the plane, i.e. rotations by angles 0, $2\pi/3$, and $4\pi/3$.

All three simple groups mentioned so far are examples of *cyclic groups* C_n which have the general structure $\{e, a, a^2, \ldots, a^{n-1}; a^n = e\}$ where n can be any positive integer. The rows and columns of the multiplication table of such a group are cyclic permutations of each other; hence the name.

Definition 2.2 (Abelian Group): An *abelian group* G is one for which the group multiplication is commutative, i.e. $ab = ba$ for all $a,b \in G$.

Definition 2.3 (Order): The *order* of a group is the number of elements of the group (if it is finite).

The cyclic groups C_n described above are of order n $(=1, 2, \ldots)$ and they are all abelian. Most interesting groups are not abelian, however.

Example 4: The simplest non-cyclic group is of order 4. It is usually called the *four-group* or the *dihedral group* and denoted by D_2. If we denote the four elements by $\{e, a, b, c\}$, the multiplication table is given by Table 2.3.

It is helpful to visualize this (abelian) group by its association to a geometrical symmetry (which may be realized by a physical system, such as a molecule). For this purpose, consider the configuration of Fig. 2.1, and the following symmetry transformations on this figure: (i) leaving the figure unchanged, (ii) reflection about the vertical axis (1, 3), (iii) reflection about the horizontal axis (2, 4), and

Table 2.3 Group Multiplication Table of D_2

e	a	b	c
a	e	c	b
b	c	e	a
c	b	a	e

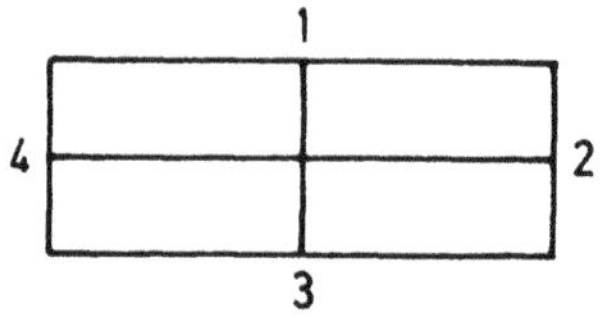

Fig. 2.1 A configuration with D_2 symmetry.

(iv) rotation of the figure, in the plane, around the center by π. Successive applications of any two of these transformations produce the same effect as one of the original transformations, thereby defining a group multiplication rule. It is straightforward to check that the multiplication table obtained through these geometric constructions reproduces Table 2.3.

2.2 Further Examples, Subgroups

The smallest *non-abelian group* is of order 6. It can be generated from the symmetry transformations of the geometric configuration Fig. 2.2 consisting of: (i) the identity transformation, (ii) reflections about the axes $(1, 1')$, $(2, 2')$, $(3, 3')$, and (iii) rotations around the center by angles $2\pi/3$, and $4\pi/3$. Notice that all six transformations leave the triangular configuration unchanged except for the labels $(1, 2, 3)$. They form the *dihedral group* D_3. The reflections interchange two of the labels, leaving the remaining one unchanged. For instance, reflection about the $(3, 3')$ axis leads to the interchange of 1 and 2,... and so on. Hence, we denote these three operations by (12), (23), and (31), respectively. Rotations (counter-clockwise) by $2\pi/3$ and $4\pi/3$ lead to cyclic permutation of all three labels. They will be denoted by (321) and (123) respectively. One can see that there is a one-to-one correspondence between these symmetry transformations and the permutations of the three labels which form the permutation group S_3 to be discussed in the next section. One can easily verify that, for instance, the transformations (12) and (123), applied in succession, is equal to either (31) or (23), depending on the order of application. The group is therefore non-abelian.

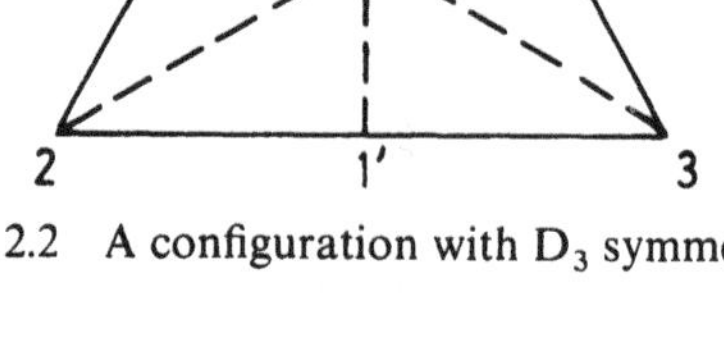

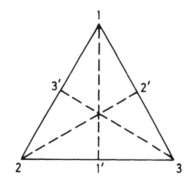

Fig. 2.2 A configuration with D_3 symmetry.

In the next two chapters, we shall repeatedly use the group D_3 as a useful example to illustrate important general theorems and definitions. It is therefore important to construct the group multiplication table [Problem 2.3]. We give the result in Table 2.4.

Table 2.4 Group Multiplication Table of D_3 (or S_3)

e	(12)	(23)	(31)	(123)	(321)
(12)	e	(123)	(321)	(23)	(31)
(23)	(321)	e	(123)	(31)	(12)
(31)	(123)	(321)	e	(12)	(23)
(123)	(31)	(12)	(23)	(321)	e
(321)	(23)	(31)	(12)	e	(123)

Definition 2.4 (Subgroup): A subset H of a group G which forms a group (according to Def. 2.1) under the same multiplication law as G is said to form a *subgroup* of G.

Example 1: The four-group of Sec. 2.1 has three distinct subgroups consisting of the elements $\{e,a\}$, $\{e,b\}$, and $\{e,c\}$ respectively. The square of a, for instance, is e. Hence $\{e,a\}$ coincides with the group C_2. The same is true for the other two subsets.

Example 2: The group S_3 has four distinct subgroups consisting of the elements $\{e,(12)\}$, $\{e,(23)\}$, $\{e,(31)\}$, and $\{e,(123),(321)\}$ respectively. The first three subgroups are again identical to the C_2 group. The last one, which is of order 3, has the structure of C_3. This can be seen most readily by referring to the geometrical transformations discussed above in connection with Fig. 2.2: each reflection about a given axis, together with the identity, form a subgroup; the two rotations, together with the identity, form another.

Many physically significant groups contain an *infinite* number of elements. We studied one such example consisting of discrete translations on a one-dimensional lattice in Chap. 1. The group elements $T(n)$ in that case are specified by the integer label n which assume all possible values $0, \pm 1, \pm 2, \ldots$. We denote this group by T^d. It can be easily seen that the subset of elements $\{T(ml);\ m = \text{fixed positive integer},\ l = 0, \pm 1, \pm 2, \ldots\}$ forms a subgroup T^d_m of the full group T^d for any m. The subgroup T^d_m consists of all translations of multiples m of the lattice spacing.

In many other applications, the group elements carry labels which are continuous parameters. These are *continuous groups. Groups of rotations* in Euclidean spaces, and *groups of continuous translations* are prominent examples which will be studied in detail in later chapters. Before their formal introduction, we shall mention them from time to time as examples. For this purpose, we shall refer to the groups of rotations in 2- and 3-dimensional space as R(2) and R(3); and the combined groups of rotations and translations in the same spaces as E_2 and E_3 respectively. The latter two are examples of *Euclidean groups.*

Any set of invertible $n \times n$ matrices, which includes the unit matrix and which is closed under matrix multiplication, forms a *matrix group*. Important examples are:

(i) the *general linear group* GL(n) consisting of all invertible $n \times n$ matrices;

(ii) the *unitary group* U(n) consisting of all unitary matrices, i.e. $n \times n$ matrices U which satisfies $UU^\dagger = 1$;

(iii) the *special unitary group* SU(n) consisting of unitary matrices with *unit determinant*; and

(iv) the *orthogonal group* O(n) consisting of *real* orthogonal matrices, or $n \times n$ real matrices satisfying $OO^T = 1$.

These are examples of *classical groups* which occupy a central place in group representation theory and have many applications in various branches of mathematics and physics. Clearly, SU(n) and O(n) are subgroups of U(n) which, in turn, is a subgroup of GL(n).

2.3 The Rearrangement Lemma and the Symmetric (Permutation) Group

The existence of an inverse for every element is a crucial feature of a group. A direct consequence of this property is the rearrangement lemma, which will be used repeatedly in the derivation of important results.

Rearrangement Lemma: If $p, b, c \in G$ and $pb = pc$ then $b = c$.

Proof: Multiply both sides of the equation by p^{-1}. QED

This result means: if b and c are distinct elements of G, then pb and pc are also distinct. Therefore, if all the elements of G are arranged in a sequence and are multiplied on the left by a given element p, the resulting sequence is just a rearrangement of the original one. The same, of course, applies to multiplication on the right.

Let us consider the case of a finite group of order n. We shall denote elements of the group by $\{g_1, g_2, \ldots, g_n\}$. Multiplication of each of these elements by a fixed element h results in $\{hg_1, hg_2, \ldots, hg_n\} = \{g_{h_1}, g_{h_2}, \ldots, g_{h_n}\}$ where $(h_1, h_2, \ldots, h_n)$ is a permutation of the numbers $(1, 2, \ldots, n)$ determined by h. We find, therefore, a natural relationship between a group element $h \in G$ and a permutation characterized by $(h_1, h_2, \ldots, h_n)$.[1]

As this correspondence is crucial in group theory, we shall introduce the *group of permutations* here. An arbitrary permutation of n objects will be denoted by

$$p = \begin{pmatrix} 1 & 2 & 3 & \cdots & n \\ p_1 & p_2 & p_3 & \cdots & p_n \end{pmatrix}$$

where each entry in the first row is to be replaced by the corresponding one in the second row. The set of $n!$ permutations of n objects form a group S_n called the *permutation group* or the *symmetric group*. It is not hard to see that one permutation followed by a second results in another permutation. This defines the group

[1] This relation can be made even more explicit as follows: The elements of G are labelled $\{g_i; i = 1, \ldots, n\}$, hg_i is an element of G determined from the group multiplication rule. Let h_i be the integer label of this particular element, i.e. $g_{h_i} = hg_i$. This determines the sequence of numbers $(h_1, \ldots, h_n)$. According to the rearrangement lemma, g_{h_i} and g_{h_j} are distinct if i and j are distinct. It follows that all the entries in $(h_1, h_2, \ldots, h_n)$ are distinct. Hence these numbers are just a permutation of $(1, 2, \ldots, n)$.

multiplication. The identity element corresponds to no permutation, i.e.

$$e = \begin{pmatrix} 1 & 2 & \cdots & n \\ 1 & 2 & \cdots & n \end{pmatrix} \quad .$$

The inverse to p is just

$$p^{-1} = \begin{pmatrix} p_1 & p_2 & \cdots & p_n \\ 1 & 2 & \cdots & n \end{pmatrix} \quad .$$

The verification of the associative nature of group multiplication will be left to the reader.

A more compact and convenient notation for permutations is based on the *cycle structure* which can be explained most clearly by an example. Consider the permutation

$$p = \begin{pmatrix} 1 & 2 & 3 & 4 & 5 & 6 \\ 3 & 5 & 4 & 1 & 2 & 6 \end{pmatrix}$$

of six objects. Since 1 is replaced by 3 which is replaced by 4 which is, in turn, replaced by 1, these three objects form a *three-cycle* to be denoted by (134). Similarly, 2 and 5 form a *two-cycle* which will be denoted by (25). The object 6 is not disturbed, it forms a *one-cycle*. The *cycle notation* (134)(25)(6) uniquely specifies the permutation. In this notation, the identity element consists of n one-cycles, and the inverse of $(p_1, p_2, \ldots, p_m)$ is simply the same numbers in reverse order i.e. $(p_m, p_{m-1}, \ldots, p_1)$. It is clear that the absolute position of a given number in the cycle is not important; only the cyclical order of the whole sequence counts. The observant reader may have noticed that we have already "sneaked in" this notation in our description of the group S_3 in Sec. 2.2.

Definition 2.5 (Isomorphism): Two groups G and G' are said to be *isomorphic* if there exists a one-to-one correspondence between their elements which preserves the law of group multiplication. In other words, if $g_i \in G \leftrightarrow g_i' \in G'$ and $g_1 g_2 = g_3$ in G, then $g_1' g_2' = g_3'$ in G' and vice versa.

Examples: (i) All three examples of C_2 given in Sec. 2.1 are isomorphic to each other—the group multiplication tables are identical to each other; (ii) The group consisting of the numbers $\{\pm 1, \pm i\}$ with respect to the usual multiplication is isomorphic to the cyclic group of order 4, C_4; and (iii) The dihedral group D_3 given in Sec. 2.2 is isomorphic to the symmetric group S_3 defined above.

Theorem 2.1 (Cayley): Every group G of order n is isomorphic to a subgroup of S_n.

Proof: The Rearrangement Lemma provided us with the correspondence from G to S_n:

(2.3-1) $$a \in G \longrightarrow p_a = \begin{pmatrix} 1 & 2 & \cdots & n \\ a_1 & a_2 & \cdots & a_n \end{pmatrix} \in S_n \quad ,$$

where the indices $\{a_i\}$ are determined from the defining identity (cf. footnote 1 after the Rearrangement Lemma):

(2.3-2) $$g_{a_i} \equiv a g_i, \qquad i = 1, 2, \ldots, n \quad .$$

Let $ab = c$ in G. We have correspondingly,

$$p_a p_b = \begin{pmatrix} 1 & 2 & \cdots & n \\ a_1 & a_2 & \cdots & a_n \end{pmatrix} \cdot \begin{pmatrix} 1 & 2 & \cdots & n \\ b_1 & b_2 & \cdots & b_n \end{pmatrix}$$

$$= \begin{pmatrix} b_1 & b_2 & \cdots & b_n \\ a_{b_1} & a_{b_2} & \cdots & a_{b_n} \end{pmatrix} \cdot \begin{pmatrix} 1 & 2 & \cdots & n \\ b_1 & b_2 & \cdots & b_n \end{pmatrix} = \begin{pmatrix} 1 & 2 & \cdots & n \\ a_{b_1} & a_{b_2} & \cdots & a_{b_n} \end{pmatrix} .$$

But according to Eq. (2.3-2),

(2.3-3) $$g_{a_{b_i}} = a g_{b_i} = a(bg_i) = (ab)g_i = cg_i = g_{c_i} .$$

We conclude that the right-hand side of the above equation is just

$$p_c = \begin{pmatrix} 1 & 2 & \cdots & n \\ c_1 & c_2 & \cdots & c_n \end{pmatrix} .$$

Hence, $ab = c$ in G implies $p_a p_b = p_c$ in S_n; in other words, the mapping $a \in G \to p_a \in S_n$ preserves group multiplication. It follows that the permutations

$$p_a = \begin{pmatrix} 1 & 2 & \cdots & n \\ a_1 & a_2 & \cdots & a_n \end{pmatrix}$$

for all $a \in G$ form a subgroup of S_n which is isomorphic to G. QED

Example 1: The cyclic group of order 3 $\{C_3: e, a, b = a^2\}$ is isomorphic to the subgroup of S_3 consisting of the elements $\{e, (123), (321)\}$. We work this example out explicitly in order to clarify the general proof given above. If the three elements of C_3 are labelled alternatively as (g_1, g_2, g_3), then multiplying on the left by e $(=g_1)$ leaves this set unchanged. Thus $e \in C_3 \to e = (1)(2)(3) \in S_3$. Next, multiplying the group elements by a $(=g_2)$ yields the re-arranged set $(a, b, e) = (g_2, g_3, g_1)$. Hence the set of numbers (a_1, a_2, a_3) is $(2, 3, 1)$, and we obtain

$$a \in C_3 \longrightarrow p_a = \begin{pmatrix} 1 & 2 & 3 \\ 2 & 3 & 1 \end{pmatrix} \in S_3 .$$

In the cycle-notation, $p_a = (123)$. Similarly, multiplication by the element b $(=g_3)$ yields (g_3, g_1, g_2), hence $(b_1, b_2, b_3) = (3, 1, 2)$ and $b \in C_3 \to p_b = (321) \in S_3$. The verification of the isomorphism of the two groups is straightforward.

Example 2: The dihedral group $\{D_2: e, a, b, c\}$ of Sec. 2.1 is isomorphic to the subgroup of S_4 consisting of the elements $\{e$, (12)(34), (13)(24), (14)(23)$\}$. The reader is encouraged to verify this result in the manner described in the previous example.

Example 3: The group $\{C_4: e = a^4, a, a^2, a^3\}$ is isomorphic to the subgroup of S_4 consisting of the elements $\{e$, (1234), (13)(24), (4321)$\}$.

An interesting general feature of the correspondence (2.3-1) due to the Rearrangement Lemma is that no element other than the identity in a subgroup of S_n which is isomorphic to a group of order n in the specified way can contain one-cycles.[2]

[2] The presence of a one-cycle means that a particular group element is unchanged upon left multiplication by another element which is not the identity. This contradicts the Rearrangement Lemma.

Furthermore, the cycles which do occur in any permutation associated with a given group element must all be of the same length.[3] This is clearly true in all the examples cited above. An interesting consequence of this result is that: if the order n of a group is a prime number, then the corresponding subgroup of S_n can only contain unfactorized full n-cycles. These correspond to elements of the cyclic group of order n. Therefore, we have the following theorem.

Theorem 2.2: If the order n of a group is a prime number, it must be isomorphic to C_n.

Therefore, as long as n is prime, there can only be one group of this order, no matter how large n is. This result may appear somewhat unexpected considering the simple criteria defining a group. It is an illustration of the tight structure imposed by the group axioms. This theme of the ability to obtain useful specific structures from general group-theoretical considerations underlies the entire group representation theory to be explored in this book.

2.4 Classes and Invariant Subgroups

The elements of a group G can be partitioned into conjugate classes and cosets. These constitute different ways to sort the group elements which will prove to be useful in studying the structure of the group and the representation theory.

Definition 2.6 (Conjugate Elements): An element $b \in G$ is said to be *conjugate* to $a \in G$ if there exists another group element $p \in G$ such that $b = pap^{-1}$. We shall denote the conjugation relation by the symbol $\sim$.

Example: In the permutation group S_3, the element (12) is conjugate to (31) because $(23)(12)(23)^{-1} = (31)$. Likewise, (123) is conjugate to (321) since $(12)(123)(12)^{-1} = (321)$. Conjugation is an *equivalence relation*: i.e. (i) each element is conjugate to itself $a \sim a$ (reflexive); (ii) if $a \sim b$, then $b \sim a$ (symmetric); and (iii) if $a \sim b$ and $b \sim c$, then $a \sim c$ (transitive). These three basic properties can be established straightforwardly. Let us verify the last one. If $a \sim b$ and $b \sim c$, then there exist $p,q \in G$ such that $a = pbp^{-1}$ and $b = qcq^{-1}$. It follows then $a = pqcq^{-1}p^{-1} = (pq)c(pq)^{-1}$, or $a \sim c$. It is well known that any equivalence relation provides a unique way to classify the elements of a set.

Definition 2.7 (Conjugate Class): Elements of a group which are conjugate to each other are said to form a (conjugate) *class*.

Each element of a group belongs to one and only one class. The identity element forms a class all by itself. [Problem 2.4] For matrix groups, all elements in the same class are related to each other by some "similarity transformation". [cf. Eq. (II.3-6) and Theorem II.7]

[3] The proof of this statement can be easily formulated after examining an example. Assume that a particular group element g is mapped to a permutation p_g which contains two cycles of different lengths, say $p_g = (13)(245)\ldots$. Since g^2 must be in the group, so must $p_g{}^2$ be in the corresponding subgroup of S_n. But the square of a two-cycle is the identity, hence $p_g{}^2 = (1)(3)(254)\ldots$. This is impossible since one-cycles are not allowed by the Rearrangement Lemma. In general, if any element contains two cycles of differing length, say (l_1, l_2) with $l_1 < l_2$, then the l_1-th power of this element will create the same contradiction as above.

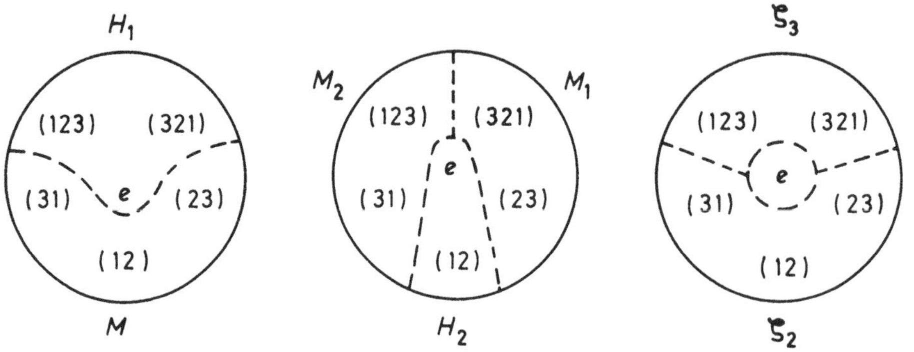

Fig. 2.3 (a) left cosets of H_1 (b) left cosets of H_2 (c) classes of S_3.

Example 1: Elements of the permutation group S_3 can be divided into the following three classes: the identity $\zeta_1 = e$, the class of two-cycles $\zeta_2 = \{(12), (23), (31)\}$, and the class of three-cycles $\zeta_3 = \{(123), (321)\}$. [cf. Fig. 2.3] This example illustrates a general result for the general symmetric groups: permutations with the same cycle structure belong to the same class. To prove this assertion, we only have to note that the permutation qpq^{-1} differs from p only in that the label-numbers $\{p_i\}$ in the cycle notation for p are replaced by $\{p_{q_i}\}$, leaving the cycle structure unchanged. For example: $(23)(12)(23)^{-1} = (13)$, $(123)(12)(123)^{-1} = (23)$, $(12)(123)(12)^{-1} = (213) = (321), \ldots$ etc.

Example 2: In the group of 3-dimensional rotations R(3), let $R_{\hat{n}}(\psi)$ denote a rotation around the $\hat{n}$ axis by the angle ψ. Then the rotations $\{R_{\hat{n}};\ \text{all}\ \hat{n}\}$ for a given ψ form a class. This is because, for an arbitrary R, $R \cdot R_{\hat{n}}(\psi) \cdot R^{-1} = R_{\hat{n}'}(\psi)$ where $\hat{n}' = R\hat{n}$ is in the direction determined by rotating $\hat{n}$ by R. In other words, all rotations by the same angle but about different axes belong to the same class. This certainly makes sense. For details, see Chap. 7.

Example 3: In the Euclidean group E_3, in addition to the rotations described above, let $T_{\hat{n}}(b)$ denote a translation along the direction $\hat{n}$ by the distance b. Then, similarly to Example 2, the translations $\{T_{\hat{n}}(b);\ \text{all}\ \hat{n}\}$ for a given b form a class. The reason is: $R \cdot T_{\hat{n}}(b) \cdot R^{-1} = T_{\hat{n}'}(b)$, where $\hat{n}'$ is related to $\hat{n}$ in the same way as before. So, all translations by the same distance but along different directions belong to the same class. This also appears natural. A detailed study of E_3 will be given in Chap. 9.

These three examples should give the reader a good idea about the meaning and the usefulness of the concept of class in group theory.

If H is a subgroup of G and $a \in G$, then $H' = \{aha^{-1};\ h \in H\}$ also forms a subgroup of G. H' is said to be a *conjugate subgroup* to H. Clearly if H and H' are conjugate to each other, then they have the same number of elements. One can also show that either H and H' are isomorphic or they have only the identity element in common.

Definition 2.8 (Invariant Subgroup): An *invariant subgroup* H of G is one which is identical to all its conjugate subgroups.

It is easy to see that a subgroup H is invariant if and only if it contains elements of G in complete classes. It then follows that all subgroups of an abelian group are invariant subgroups.

Examples: (i) The subgroup $H = \{e, a^2\}$ of $C_4 = \{e = a^4, a, a^2, a^3\}$ is an invariant subgroup; (ii) For S_3, $\{e, (123), (321)\}$ form an invariant subgroup, but $\{e, (12)\}$ do not; (iii) The subgroup T^d_m of the discrete translation group T^d (cf. Sec. 2.2) is an invariant subgroup for any given integer m.

Let us examine the second of these examples explicitly. $\{e, (123), (321)\}$ is an invariant subgroup because it contains the identity and the entire class of three-cycles. Every possible conjugate element of this set must be in these two classes, hence be in the original set. For instance, $(12)\{e, (123), (321)\}(12)^{-1} = \{e, (321), (123)\}$, $(123)\{e, (123), (321)\}(123)^{-1} = \{e, (123), (321)\}, \ldots$, where an abbreviated but self-evident notation is used. In contrast, $\{e, (12)\}$ is not an invariant subgroup because it only contains one of the three two-cycles. One finds immediately that $(23)\{e, (12)\}(23)^{-1} = \{e, (31)\}$, hence one of the conjugate subgroups of $\{e, (12)\}$ is $\{e, (31)\}$ which is distinct from itself. Similarly, $\{e, (23)\}$ is another distinct conjugate subgroup. The reader is encouraged to work out the other examples in the same manner.

Every group G has at least two trivial invariant subgroups: $\{e\}$ and G itself. If non-trivial invariant subgroups exist, the full group can be "simplified" or "factorized" in ways to be discussed later. Consequently, it is natural to adopt the following definition.

Definition 2.9 (Simple and Semi-simple Groups): A group is *simple* if it does not contain any non-trivial invariant subgroup. A group is *semi-simple* if it does not contain any abelian invariant subgroup.

Examples: (i) The cyclic groups C_n with n = prime number are simple groups; (ii) C_n with n = non-prime number are neither simple nor semi-simple. For example, $C_4 = \{e, a, a^2, a^3\}$ has a subgroup $\{e, a^2\}$ which is invariant and abelian; (iii) The group S_3 is neither simple nor semi-simple, it has an abelian invariant group $\{e, (123), (321)\}$; (iv) The three-dimensional rotation group SO(3) is simple, but the two-dimensional rotation group is not. (Surprise?) The latter has an infinite number of abelian invariant subgroups consisting of discrete rotations by angles which are rational fractions of 2π. [See Chap. 6]

2.5 Cosets and Factor (Quotient) groups

Definition 2.10 (Cosets): Let $H = \{h_1, h_2, \ldots\}$ be a subgroup of G and let p be an element of G (one which is *not* in H), then the set of elements $pH = \{ph_1, ph_2, \ldots\}$ is called a *left coset* of H. Similarly, $Hp = \{h_1 p, h_2 p, \ldots\}$ is a *right coset* of H.

Everything we shall discuss concerning left cosets has its counterpart for right cosets. It is only necessary to discuss the former case explicitly. Aside from H itself (obtained if $p \in H$ in Definition 2.10), cosets are *not* subgroups (because they do not contain the identity element!). Each coset has exactly the same number of distinct elements as H, as a consequence of the rearrangement lemma.

Lemma: Two left cosets of a subgroup H either coincide completely, or else have no elements in common at all.

Proof: Let pH and qH be the two cosets. Assume $ph_i = qh_j$ for some $h_i, h_j \in H$. Then $q^{-1}p = h_j h_i^{-1}$ is an element of H. This implies that $q^{-1}pH$ must coincide with H, i.e. $q^{-1}pH = H$. It follows then $pH = qH$. Of course, if no h_i, h_j satisfying $ph_i = qh_j$ exist, then pH and qH must be disjoint by definition. QED

Given a subgroup H of order n_H, the distinct left cosets of H partition the elements of the full group G into disjoint sets of n_H each.

Theorem 2.3 (Lagrange): The order of a finite group must be an integer multiple of the order of any of its subgroups.

Examples: Consider the permutation group S_3: (i) The subgroup $\{H_1: e, (123), (321)\}$ has one coset $\{M: (12), (23), (31)\}$ obtained by multiplying the elements of H_1 from the left with any one of (12), (23), or (31);
(ii) The subgroup $\{H_2: e, (12)\}$ has two left cosets: $\{M_1: (23), (321)\}$, obtained from H_2 by multiplication with either (23) or (321), and $\{M_2: (31), (123)\}$, obtained from H_2 by multiplication with either (31) or (123). We illustrate schematically the partitioning of the elements of S_3 according to cosets and classes in Fig. 2.3. We will use these results later.

The cosets of invariant subgroups are particularly simple and useful. To begin with, if H is an invariant subgroup, its left cosets are also right cosets. ($pHp^{-1} = H$ implies $pH = Hp$.) The partitioning of the elements of the full group G into cosets is unique, and a "factorization" of G based on this partitioning becomes natural. (It will be helpful to bear in mind the special case of Fig. 2.3a in the following discussion.) Let us consider the cosets of an invariant subgroup H as elements of a new group. The multiplication of two cosets pH and qH is defined as the coset consisting of all products $ph_i qh_j = (pq)h_k$, where $h_k = (q^{-1}h_i q)h_j \in H$ provided h_i, $h_j \in H$ and $p, q \in G$. Since $pH \cdot qH = (pq)H$, it becomes obvious that (i) $H = eH$ plays the role of the identity element; (ii) $p^{-1}H$ is the inverse of pH; and (iii) $pH(qH \cdot rH) = (pH \cdot qH) \cdot rH = (pqr)H$. In other words, we have the following theorem.

Theorem 2.4: If H is an invariant subgroup of G, the set of cosets endowed with the law of multiplication $pH \cdot qH = (pq)H$ form a group, called the *factor* (or *quotient*) *group* of G. The factor group is denoted by G/H, it is of order n_G/n_H.

Example 1: Consider the invariant subgroup $H = \{e, a^2\}$ of the cyclic group C_4. H and the coset $M = \{a, a^3\}$ form the factor group C_4/H. Applying the rule of multiplication of cosets described above, it is straightforward to verify that $HM = M = MH$, $HH = H$, and $MM = H$. We see that both the subgroup H and the factor group C_4/H are of order 2 and are isomorphic to C_2.

Example 2: In the case of the permutation group S_3, $H = \{e, (123), (321)\}$ represents an invariant subgroup. (cf. Fig. 2.3a) G/H consists of two elements: H and $M = \{(12), (23), (31)\}$. We have: $HM = H \cdot (ij)H = (ij)H = M = MH$, and $HH = MM = H$. Therefore, G/H is also isomorphic to the cyclic group of order 2, C_2.

Example 3: Consider the discrete translation group $T^d \equiv \Gamma$ and one of its invariant subgroups Γ_m. The cosets are Γ_m, $T(1)\Gamma_m$, $T(2)\Gamma_m, \ldots,$ $T(m-1)\Gamma_m$ ($T(m)\Gamma_m = \Gamma_m$). Hence the factor group Γ/Γ_m is isomorphic to the cyclic group

C_m. Infinite groups, such as this one, do not behave exactly like finite ones. For instance, Γ and Γ_m are, in fact, isomorphic to each other (if we establish the one-to-one correspondence $T(n) \leftrightarrow T(mn)$) even though Γ/Γ_m is non-trivial.

Example 4: We state without proof (cf. Chap. 9) that the translations in 3-dimensional space form an invariant subgroup of the Euclidean group E_3; and the factor group is isomorphic to the group of rotations. This fact forms the basis of important techniques to analyze the Euclidean group and its generalization to 4-dimensional space-time—the Poincaré group. The later will be described in Chap. 10.

2.6 Homomorphisms

Definition 2.11 (homomorphism): A *homomorphism* from a group G to another group G' is a mapping (not necessarily one-to-one) which preserves group multiplication. In other words, if $g_i \in G \to g_i' \in G'$ and $g_1 g_2 = g_3$, then $g_1' g_2' = g_3'$.

Clearly, isomorphism (Definition 2.5) is a special case of homomorphism. The entire theory of group representations is built on homomorphisms of abstract groups (often symmetry groups of physics) to groups of linear operators or matrices on vector spaces (for our purposes, spaces of physical states). [cf. Chap. 1]

Example: The mapping from S_3 to C_2 depicted in Fig. 2.4 is a homomorphism. This follows from the fact that the product of any two elements from H or from M results in an element in H, whereas the product of one element from H with one element from M results in an element in M. This example illustrates the general result that if G has an invariant subgroup H, then there exists a natural homomorphism from G to the factor group G/H: $g \in G \to gH \in G/H$. Group multiplication is preserved by definition. This result can be turned around to yield the following interesting theorem.

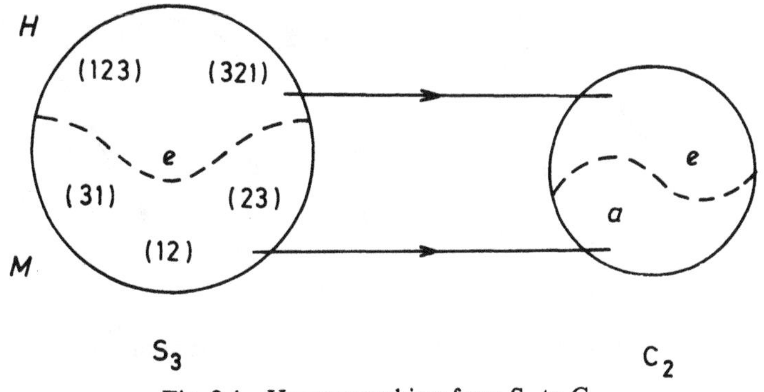

Fig. 2.4 Homomorphism from S_3 to C_2.

Theorem 2.5: Let f be a homomorphism from G to G'. Denote by K the set of all elements of G which are mapped to the identity element of G', i.e. $K = \{a \in G; a \xrightarrow{f} e' \in G'\}$. Then K forms an invariant subgroup of G. Furthermore, the factor group G/K is isomorphic to G'.

Proof: (i) If $a, b \in K$, then $ab \xrightarrow{f} e' \cdot e' = e'$. Hence $ab \in K$. For a homomorphism, we must have $e \in G \xrightarrow{f} e' \in G'$ and $g^{-1} \xrightarrow{f} g'^{-1}$ (if $g \xrightarrow{f} g'$). Hence $e \in K$, and if $a \in K$ then $a^{-1} \xrightarrow{f} (e')^{-1} = e'$ which implies that $a^{-1} \in K$. Therefore, K is a subgroup.

(ii) Let $a \in K$ and g be any element of G. We have: $gag^{-1} \xrightarrow{f} g'e'(g^{-1})' = g'e'g'^{-1} = e'$. Hence $gag^{-1} \in K$ for all $g \in G$. This means that K is an invariant subgroup.

(iii) The elements of the factor group G/K are cosets pK. Consider the mapping $pK \xrightarrow{\rho} p' \in G'$ (where $p \xrightarrow{f} p'$). If $\rho(pK) = \rho(qK)$, then $\rho(q^{-1}pK) = \rho(q^{-1}K \cdot pK) = \rho(q^{-1}K)\rho(pK) = \rho^{-1}(qK)\rho(pK) = e'$ which implies that $q^{-1}pK = K$ or $qK = pK$. Thus the mapping is one-to-one. Group multiplication is preserved by ρ, as $\rho(pK)\rho(qK) = p'q' = (pq)' = \rho(pqK)$. Therefore, ρ is an isomorphism. K is often called the *kernel* or *center* of the homomorphism f. We show schematically the content of this theorem in Fig. 2.5a and Fig. 2.5b. QED

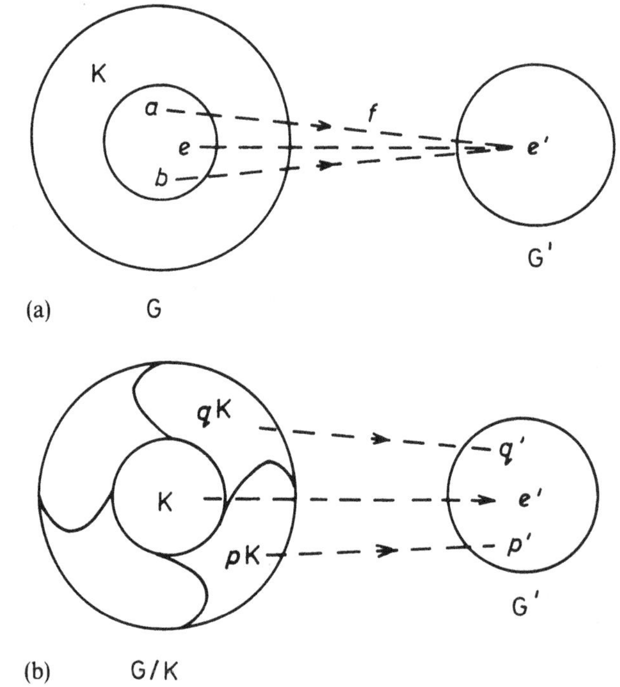

Fig. 2.5 (a) homomorphism $G \to G'$ (b) isomorphism $\frac{G}{K} \leftrightarrow G'$.

2.7 Direct Products

Many physically useful symmetry groups are *direct products* of simpler groups. When this is the case, it suffices to know the structure and the representations of the smaller groups.

Definition 2.12 (Direct Product Group): Let H_1 and H_2 be subgroups of a group G with the following properties: (i) every element of H_1 commutes with any element of H_2, i.e. $h_1 h_2 = h_2 h_1$ for all $h_1 \in H_1$ and $h_2 \in H_2$; and (ii) every element g of G can be written uniquely as $g = h_1 h_2$ where $h_1 \in H_1$ and $h_2 \in H_2$. In this case, G is said to be the direct product of H_1 and H_2; symbolically, $G = H_1 \otimes H_2$.

Example 1: Consider the group C_6 with elements $\{e = a^6, a, a^2, a^3, a^4, a^5\}$, and the subgroups $H_1 = \{e, a^3\}$ and $H_2 = \{e, a^2, a^4\}$. Criterion (i) above is trivially satisfied because the group is abelian, and (ii) can be verified by noting that $e = ee$, $a = a^3a^4$, $a^2 = ea^2$, $a^3 = a^3e$, $a^4 = ea^4$, $a^5 = a^3a^2$ where in each case the first factor on the direct product of H_1 and H_2. Since $H_1 \simeq C_2$ and $H_2 \simeq C_3$, we obtain $C_6 \simeq C_2 \otimes C_3$. (The symbol $\simeq$ signifies isomorphism.)

Example 2: Consider the group O(3) consisting of all linear transformations of 3-dimensional Euclidean space which leave the origin fixed and which leave the length of vectors unchanged. We shall state without proof that this group consists of all 3-dimensional rotations R, the spatial inversion (parity) transformation I_s and their products (cf. chap. 11). It is not hard to see that $I_sR = RI_s$ for all R. Hence the *full orthogonal group* O(3) is the direct product of the subgroups consisting of $\{R\}$ and (e, I_s) respectively.

If $G = H_1 \otimes H_2$, then both H_1 and H_2 must be invariant subgroups of G. The reason is that, if $g = h_1 h_2 \in G$, h_1 and $a_1 \in H_1$, and $h_2 \in H_2$, then $g a_1 g^{-1} = h_1 h_2 a_1 h_2{}^{-1} h_1{}^{-1} = h_1 a_1 h_1{}^{-1} \in H_1$ for all g and a_1. (Obviously, we also have $g a_2 g^{-1} \in H_2$ for all $g \in G$ and $a_2 \in H_2$.) Now, we can form the quotient group G/H_2 (G/H_1) and prove that it is isomorphic to H_1 (H_2), i.e. $G/H_2 \simeq H_1$ $(G/H_1 \simeq H_2)$. This is not too surprising, as suggested by the terminologies such as "product" and "quotient". However, one must be sure to verify all these intuitive ideas. For instance, the converse to the above is not true! Let H be an invariant subgroup of G, and $H' = G/H$. It does not follow that $G = H \otimes H'$. To give a concrete example, S_3 has an invariant subgroup $H = \{e, (123), (321)\}$. The quotient group S_3/H is isomorphic to any one of the subgroups $H_i = \{e, (jk)\}$ $(i, j, k =$ cyclic permutation of 1, 2, 3). But S_3 is not the direct product of H and H_i, since the elements of H and H_i do not commute.

Problems

2.1 Prove that the identities (i) $e^{-1} = e$, (ii) $a^{-1}a = e$, and (iii) $ea = a$ for all $a \in G$ follow from the basic axioms of Definition 1.

2.2 Show that there is only one group of order three, using a step-by-step procedure to construct the group multiplication table.

2.3 Construct the multiplication table of the permutation group S_3 using the cycle structure notation. (The geometrical interpretation represented by Fig. 2.2 should be of great help.)

2.4 Show that every element of a group belongs to one and only one class, and the identity element forms a class by itself.

2.5 Enumerate the subgroups and classes of the group S_4. Which of the subgroups are invariant ones? Find the factor groups of the invariant subgroups.

2.6 Let H be any subgroup of G, which is not necessarily invariant. Is it possible to *define* products of left cosets directly by the equation $pH \cdot qH = (pq)H$, hence obtain a "factor group" consisting of left cosets? Apply this definition to the special case of $H = \{e, (12)\}$ for S_3, and point out logical difficulties if there are any.

2.7 Prove that $G = H_1 \otimes H_2$ implies $G/H_1 \simeq H_2$ and $G/H_2 \simeq H_1$, where $\simeq$ means "isomorphic to".

2.8 Consider the dihedral group D_4 which is the symmetry group of the square, consisting of rotations around the center and reflections about the vertical, horizontal, and the diagonal axes. Enumerate the group elements, the classes, the subgroups, and the invariant subgroups. Identify the factor groups. Is the full group the direct product of some of its subgroups?

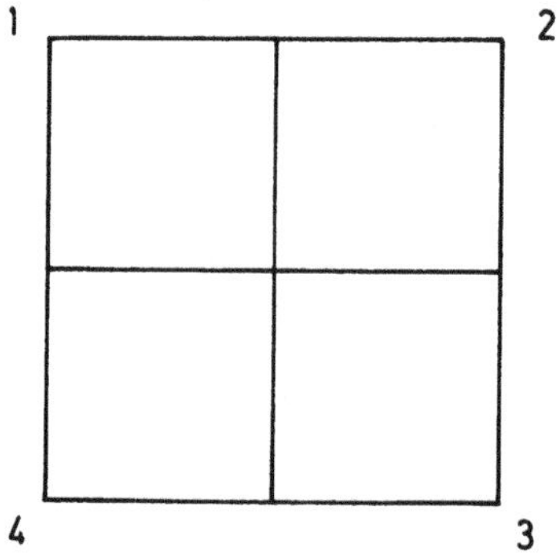

Fig. 2.6 Configuration with D_4 symmetry.

CHAPTER 3

GROUP REPRESENTATIONS

In geometrical and physical applications, group theory is closely associated with symmetry transformations of the systems under study. In classical physics, the interest lies in the effect of the symmetry transformations on the solutions to the partial differential or integral equations of "mathematical physics". These solutions usually form a linear vector space.[1] With the advent of quantum mechanics, this connection becomes more explicit, as linear vector space is adopted as the formal mathematical framework for the underlying theory. The interest in group theory, therefore, centers on the *realization* of group transformations as linear transformations on vector spaces of classical and quantum physics.

We assume the reader to be familiar with the theory of linear vector spaces. For reference, however, and for the purpose of introducing consistent and convenient notation, we provide a review of key notions and results of the theory of linear vector spaces in Appendix II. A summary of the notation used throughout the book is given in Appendix I. In the following, we shall use the terms "linear transformations" and "operators" interchangeably. For definiteness, we shall explicitly use finite-dimensional vector spaces in our discussions, although most results hold for physically useful inifinite-dimensional (Hilbert) spaces as well. Unless stated otherwise, we take the vector spaces to be defined over the complex number field.

3.1 Representations

The multiplication of linear transformations on a linear vector space is, in general, associative, but not necessarily commutative [cf. Appendix II]. Hence it is basically a "group multiplication". A set of invertible linear transformations, closed with respect to operator multiplication, satisfies the group axioms. Such a set forms a *group of linear transformations*, or *group of operators*.

Definition 3.1 (Representations of a Group): If there is a homomorphism from a group G to a group of operators $U(G)$ on a linear vector space V, we say that $U(G)$ forms a *representation* of the group G. The *dimension of the representation* is the dimension of the vector space V. A representation is said to be *faithful* if the homomorphism is also an isomorphism (i.e. it is also one-to-one). A *degenerate representation* is one which is not faithful.

Let us be more specific: the representation is a mapping

$$g \in G \xrightarrow{U} U(g)$$

[1] This point of view was the unifying theme of the classical, influential book of Courant and Hilbert on Mathematical Methods of Physics [Courant].

where $U(g)$ is an operator on V, such that

$$U(g_1)U(g_2) = U(g_1 g_2), \tag{3.1-1}$$

i.e. the (representation) operators satisfy the same rules of multiplication as the original group elements.

Consider the case of a finite-dimensional representation. Choose a set of basis vectors $\{\hat{\mathbf{e}}_i, i = 1, 2, \ldots, n\}$ on V. The operators $U(g)$ are then realized as $n \times n$ matrices $D(g)$ as follows:

$$U(g)|e_i\rangle = |e_j\rangle D(g)^j{}_i, \qquad g \in G \quad . \tag{3.1-2}$$

[Reminder: (i) the index j is implicitly summed from 1 to n; (ii) for the matrix $D(g)$, the first index (j) is the row-label and the second index (i) is the column-label. See Appendix I for details of the notation used.] Let us examine how the basic property of the representation operators, Eq. (3.1-1), can be expressed in terms of the $\{D(g); g \in G\}$ matrices. Apply the operators on both sides of Eq. (3.1-1) to the basis vectors, and we obtain

$$\begin{aligned} U(g_1)U(g_2)|e_i\rangle &= U(g_1)|e_j\rangle D(g_2)^j{}_i = |e_k\rangle D(g_1)^k{}_j D(g_2)^j{}_i \\ &= U(g_1 g_2)|e_i\rangle = |e_k\rangle D(g_1 g_2)^k{}_i \quad . \end{aligned}$$

Since $\{e_i\}$ form a basis, we conclude

$$D(g_1)D(g_2) = D(g_1 g_2) \tag{3.1-3}$$

where matrix multiplication is implied. Since $D(G) = \{D(g), g \in G\}$ satisfy the same algebra as $U(G)$ [cf. Appendix II], the group of matrices $D(G)$ forms a *matrix representation* of G.

Example 1. There is a trivial 1-dimensional representation for every group G: let $V = C$ (the space of complex numbers), and $U(g) = 1$ for all $g \in G$. Clearly $U(g_1)U(g_2) = 1 \cdot 1 = 1 = U(g_1 g_2)$, hence $g \in G \to 1$ forms a representation.

Example 2: Let G be a group of matrices (such as GL(n), $U(n)$ mentioned in Chap. 2), $V = C$ (the space of complex numbers), and $U(g) = \det g$. This defines a non-trivial one-dimensional representation since $(\det g_1)(\det g_2) = \det(g_1 g_2)$ is a basic property of matrices.

Example 3: We recall that, for any given real number ξ in the interval $(-\pi < \xi \le \pi)$, the numbers $\{e^{-in\xi}, n = 0, \pm 1, \pm 2, \ldots\}$ form a (one-dimensional) representation of the discrete translation group in one spatial dimension, as discussed in detail in Chap. 1.

Example 4: Let G be the dihedral group D_2 consisting of e (identity), h (reflection about the Y-axis), v (reflection about the X-axis), and r (rotation by π around the origin) as described at the end of Sec. 2.1 (cf. Table 2.3 and Fig. 2.1); and let V_2 be the two-dimensional Euclidean space with basis vectors $(\hat{\mathbf{e}}_1, \hat{\mathbf{e}}_2)$. By referring to Fig. 3.1a, and making use of the definition Eq. (3.1-2), we easily infer:

$$\begin{aligned} D(e) &= \begin{pmatrix} 1 & 0 \\ 0 & 1 \end{pmatrix} \qquad D(h) = \begin{pmatrix} -1 & 0 \\ 0 & 1 \end{pmatrix} \\ D(v) &= \begin{pmatrix} 1 & 0 \\ 0 & -1 \end{pmatrix} \qquad D(r) = \begin{pmatrix} -1 & 0 \\ 0 & -1 \end{pmatrix} \quad . \end{aligned} \tag{3.1-4}$$

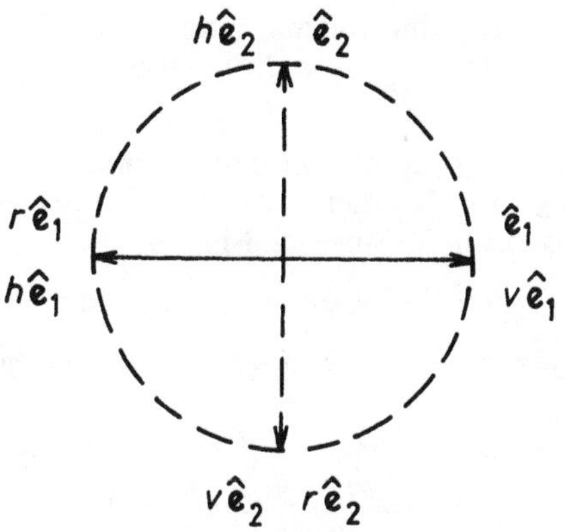

(a) D_2 transformations

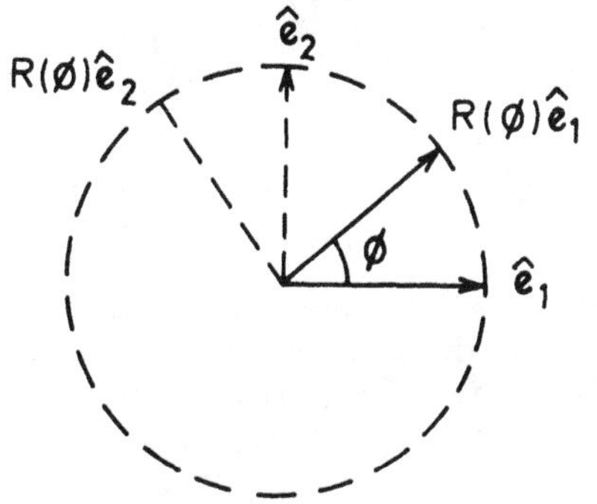

(b) Rotations

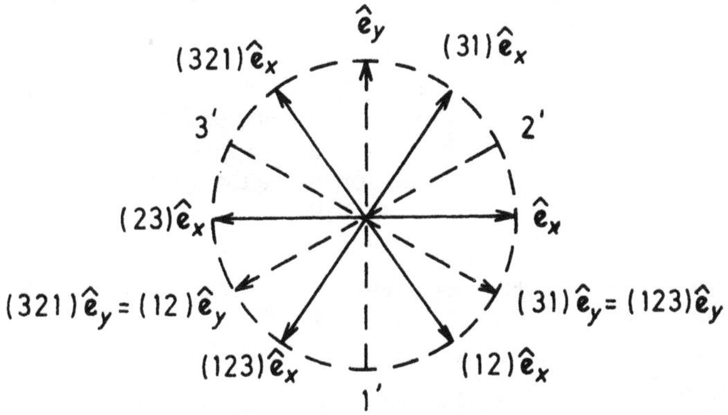

(c) D_3 transformations

Fig. 3.1 Realizations of three different groups in two-dimensional space.

It is straightforward to verify that the mapping $g \to D(g)$ is a homomorphism (cf. Table 2.3), hence these matrices form a 2-dimensional representation of the D_2 group.

Example 5: Let G be the group of continuous rotations in a plane around the origin O, $G = \{R(\phi), 0 \le \phi < 2\pi\}$. Let V_2 be the same two-dimensional Euclidean space as in the previous example. Since (cf. Fig. 3.1b)

(3.1-5)
$$\hat{\mathbf{e}}_1' = U(\phi)\hat{\mathbf{e}}_1 = \hat{\mathbf{e}}_1 \cdot \cos\phi + \hat{\mathbf{e}}_2 \cdot \sin\phi$$
$$\hat{\mathbf{e}}_2' = U(\phi)\hat{\mathbf{e}}_2 = \hat{\mathbf{e}}_1 \cdot (-\sin\phi) + \hat{\mathbf{e}}_2 \cdot \cos\phi$$

we obtain[2]:

(3.1-6)
$$D(\phi) = \begin{pmatrix} \cos\phi & -\sin\phi \\ \sin\phi & \cos\phi \end{pmatrix} \quad .$$

Note that if $\mathbf{x}$ is an arbitrary vector in V_2, $\mathbf{x} = \hat{\mathbf{e}}_i x^i$, then

(3.1-7)
$$\mathbf{x}' = U(\phi)\mathbf{x} = \hat{\mathbf{e}}_j x'^j$$
$$x'^j = D(\phi)^j{}_i x^i \quad ;$$

or,

(3.1-8)
$$\begin{pmatrix} x'^1 \\ x'^2 \end{pmatrix} = \begin{pmatrix} \cos\phi & -\sin\phi \\ \sin\phi & \cos\phi \end{pmatrix} \begin{pmatrix} x^1 \\ x^2 \end{pmatrix} \quad .$$

Applying two rotations by angles ϕ and θ in succession, one can verify that the matrix product $D(\theta)D(\phi)$ is the same as that of a single rotation by $(\phi + \theta)$, $D(\phi + \theta)$ [cf. Eq. (3.1-3)]. Thus, $\{U(\phi)\}$ provide a two-dimensional representation of the rotation group $\{R(\phi) \in R(2)\}$. Correspondingly, $\{D(\phi)\}$ is the matrix realization of $\{U(\phi)\}$ with respect to the specific set of basis $\{\hat{\mathbf{e}}_i\}$.

Example 6: Let G be the dihedral group D_3 consisting of three reflections and three rotations as described in Sec. 2.2 (cf. Fig. 2.2). Again, choose V_2 to be the 2-dimensional Euclidean space as above. The two basis vectors $\{\hat{\mathbf{e}}_i\}$ transform under group operations as depicted in Fig. 3.1c. (The group elements are labelled according to Sec. 2.2. To avoid confusion about the numerical indices, the basis vectors are denoted by $(\hat{\mathbf{e}}_x, \hat{\mathbf{e}}_y)$ in this graph.) Expressing the transformed vectors $U(g)\hat{\mathbf{e}}_i$ in terms of the original basis vectors according to Eq. (3.1-2), one obtains six 2-dimensional matrices $\{D(g)\}$ which form a representation of the group D_3. [Problem 3.1] Since the group D_3 is isomorphic to the symmetric group S_3, these matrices provide a representation of S_3 as well.

[2] The signs of $\sin\phi$ in Eq. (3.1-6) might appear to be backwards, but they are not. Explicitly, according to Eq. (3.1-2) [see also Appendix II, Eqs. (II.3-1) and (II.3-3)],

$$U(\phi)|e_1\rangle = |e_1\rangle D(\phi)^1{}_1 + |e_2\rangle D(\phi)^2{}_1 \quad ;$$
$$U(\phi)|e_2\rangle = |e_1\rangle D(\phi)^1{}_2 + |e_2\rangle D(\phi)^2{}_2 \quad .$$

Comparing with Eq. (3.1-5), we can identify the matrix elements $D(\phi)^j{}_i$ precisely as given in Eq. (3.1-6). It is important for the reader to develop proficiency with matrix manipulations in the rest of the book. Appendices I and II are designed to provide help if needed.

The last three examples illustrate that different groups may be realized on the same vector space. Here, the 2-dimensional Euclidean space V_2 is seen to provide representations for the two finite groups D_2, D_3 as well as the continuous (hence infinite) group R(2).

Example 7: Let V_f be the space of complex-valued linear homogeneous functions f of two real variables (x, y):

$$f(x, y) = a\,x + b\,y \tag{3.1-9}$$

where (a, b) are arbitrary complex coefficients. If we interpret (x, y) as the components of a vector $\mathbf{x}$ in a 2-dimensional Euclidean space V_2, $(x, y) \equiv (x^1, x^2)$, then group operations from any of the three previous examples will induce the following transformation in the function space V_f:

$$f \xrightarrow{g \in G} f'(x^1, x^2) \equiv f(x'^1, x'^2) \tag{3.1-10}$$

where $\mathbf{x}' = U(g^{-1})\,\mathbf{x}$ [cf. Eq. (3.1-7)]. It is straightforward to show that the mapping (in the function space V_f) defined by Eq. (3.1-10) is a homomorphism; for if $g''g' = g$ then

$$\begin{aligned} f &\xrightarrow{g'} f' \qquad & f'(\mathbf{x}) &= f[U(g')^{-1}\mathbf{x}] \\ f' &\xrightarrow{g''} f'' \qquad & f''(\mathbf{x}) &= f'[U(g'')^{-1}\mathbf{x}] \end{aligned} \tag{3.1-11}$$

Substituting f' from the first equation to the right-hand side of the second, we obtain:

$$f''(\mathbf{x}) = f[U(g')^{-1}U(g'')^{-1}\mathbf{x}] = f[U(g''g')^{-1}\mathbf{x}] = f[U(g)^{-1}\mathbf{x}] \tag{3.1-12}$$

or,

$$f \xrightarrow{g = g''g'} f'' \qquad f''(\mathbf{x}) = f[U(g)^{-1}\mathbf{x}] \quad .$$

Therefore, the set of transformations defined by (3.1-10) forms a representation of the group G. The function space V_f in this case is 2-dimensional, and (due to the linear nature of the function f) the representations realized on V_f are actually the same as the ones realized on $\{\mathbf{x} \in V_2\}$ described in the previous three examples. [Prove!]

There are, of course, other function spaces defined over (x, y) which are of arbitrarily high dimensions. One can obtain rather complicated representations of the group G in question on those higher dimensional spaces. We shall discuss some examples of this kind in later sections. Group representations on function spaces are very important in physical applications. The transformation properties of "Wave Functions" in classical (string, sound, fluids,...) and quantum (Schrodinger, Dirac,...) systems as well as "Fields" (Electromagnetic, Gauge,...) under space-time and "internal" symmetry groups are central to modern physics and will occupy much of our attention.

Theorem 3.1: (i) If the group G has a non-trivial invariant subgroup H, then any representation of the factor group $K = G/H$ is also a representation of G. This representation must be degenerate; (ii) Conversely, if $U(G)$ is a degenerate representation of G, then G has at least one invariant subgroup H such that $U(G)$ defines a faithful representation of the factor group G/H.

Proof: (i) The mapping $g \in G \to k = gH \in K$ followed by $k \to U(k)$ on V is a homomorphism from G to the group of linear transformations $U(K)$. It, therefore, forms a representation. If H is a non-trivial invariant subgroup, then the first step of the above mapping is many-to-one. Hence the representation is not faithful. (ii) The proof follows from Theorem 2.5 of Chap. 2. QED

An immediate corollary of this theorem is that all representations (except the trivial one) of simple groups are faithful.

Example: We learned in Chap. 2 that the symmetric (permutation) group S_3 has an invariant subgroup consisting of $\{e, (123), (321)\}$. The factor group is isomorphic to $C_2 = \{e, a\}$. The group C_2 has the rather simple representation $(e, a \to 1, -1)$. This induces a one-dimensional representation of S_3 which assigns 1 to the elements $\{e, (123), (321)\}$ and -1 to $\{(12), (23), (31)\}$. The reader should verify for himself that this assignment indeed preserves the operation of group multiplication. (cf. Table 2.4)

3.2 Irreducible, Inequivalent Representations

A fact of fundamental importance is that for most groups of interest, the possible ways of realization of the group (i.e. possible representations) are limited and can be enumerated. Therefore, once the symmetry group is specified, the structure of the vector spaces of physical interest is determined to a large extent. In order to enumerate all possible representations, it is important to distinguish between essentially different (or "inequivalent") representations from redundant (or "equivalent") ones. What types of redundancy are there? We shall describe two of them.

Let $U(G)$ be a representation of the group G on the vector space V, and S be any non-singular (i.e. invertible) operator on V. ($U(G)$ stands, collectively, for the operators $\{U(g), g \in G\}$.) Then it is obvious that $U'(G) = S\,U(G)S^{-1}$ also form a representation of G on V. The new representation is of the same dimension as the original one. The relation between the two representations is identical to that between two matrix representations of the same operators with respect to two different bases on V. The two sets of operators $U(G)$ and $U'(G)$ are said to be related by the "similarity transformation" S. [cf. Appendix II]

Definition 3.2 (Equivalence of Representations): Two representations of a group G related by a similarity transformation are said to be *equivalent*.

Equivalent representations form an equivalence class. It suffices to know just one member of this class. The others can be generated by performing all possible similarity transformations. In enumerating possible representations of a group, we need only concern ourselves with inequivalent representations.

How can one tell whether two given representations of a group are equivalent or not? The answer can be found, obviously, by seeking characterizations of the representation which are invariant under similarity transformations. One such characterization is the trace. [Definition II.14]

Definition 3.3 (Characters of a Representation): The *character* $\chi(g)$ of $g \in G$ in a representation $U(G)$ is defined to be $\chi(g) = \mathrm{Tr}\, U(g)$. If $D(G)$ is a matrix realization of $U(G)$, then

$$\chi(g) = \sum_i D(g)^i{}_i \quad .$$

All group elements in a given class of G (cf. Sec. 2.4) have the same characters, because $\mathrm{Tr}\, D(p)\, D(g)\, D(p^{-1}) = \mathrm{Tr}\, D(g)$. Therefore, the group character is a function of the class-label only.

A second type of redundancy concerns direct sum representations. The most obvious form of such a representation is as follows: Let $U(G)$ be a representation of the group G on a vector space V_n. If for some choice of basis on V_n, the matrix representation of $U(G)$ appear in the form:

$$D(g) = \begin{pmatrix} D_1(g) & O \\ O & D_2(g) \end{pmatrix} \qquad \text{for all } g \in G \tag{3.2-1}$$

where $D_1(g)$ are $m \times m$, $D_2(g)$ are $(n-m) \times (n-m)$ square matrices and the two $\boldsymbol{O}$'s are $m \times (n-m)$ and $(n-m) \times m$ rectangular null-matrices, then $D(G)$ is the direct sum of $D_1(G)$ and $D_2(G)$. Since

$$D(g)\, D(g') = \begin{pmatrix} D_1(g)\, D_1(g') & O \\ O & D_2(g)\, D_2(g') \end{pmatrix} \qquad \text{for all } g, g' \in G \, .$$

$D(G)$ does not contain any new information other than that already contained in $D_1(G)$ and $D_2(G)$. In practice, direct sums may not be immediately identifiable as above, because the block-diagonal form of the representation matrices can be obscured by a similarity transformation as the result of using a different basis. In order to identify a direct sum properly, we first introduce a few useful terms.

Definition 3.4 (Invariant Subspace): Let $U(G)$ be a representation of G on the vector space V, and V_1 be a subspace of V with the property that $U(g)\,|x\rangle \in V_1$ for all $\mathbf{x} \in V_1$ and $g \in G$. V_1 is said to be an *invariant subspace* of V with respect to $U(G)$. An invariant subspace is *minimal* or *proper* if it does not contain any non-trivial invariant subspace with respect to $U(G)$.

Examples of trivial invariant subspaces of V with respect to $U(G)$ are: (i) the space V itself, and (ii) the subspace consisting only of the null vector.

Definition 3.5 (Irreducible Representations): A representation $U(G)$ on V is *irreducible* if there is no non-trivial invariant subspace in V with respect to $U(G)$. Otherwise, the representation is *reducible*. In the latter case, if the orthogonal complement[3] of the invariant subspace is also invariant with respect to $U(G)$, then the representation is said to be *fully reducible* or *decomposable*.

Example 1: Consider the action of the dihedral group D_2 on the 2-dimensional Euclidean space V_2 as described in Example 4 of the previous section. The 1-dimensional subspace spanned by $\hat{\mathbf{e}}_1$ is invariant under all four group operations. [cf. Eq. (3.1-4) and Fig. 3.1a] It is therefore an invariant subspace with respect to D_2.

[3] If V_1 is a subspace of V, the *orthogonal complement* of V_1 consists of all vectors in V which are orthogonal to every vector in V_1. For finite-dimensional vector spaces, at least, the orthogonal complement of V_1 also forms a subspace, called V_2 say, and we have $V = V_1 \oplus V_2$.

The same is true for the 1-dimensional subspace spanned by $\hat{\mathbf{e}}_2$. The 2-dimensional representation of the group given by Eq. (3.1-4) is therefore a reducible representation. The representations defined on the 1-dimensional invariant subspaces are irreducible as these spaces are minimal.

Example 2: The 1-dimensional subspace spanned by $\hat{\mathbf{e}}_1$ (or $\hat{\mathbf{e}}_2$) is not invariant under the group R(2). [cf. Example 5 of Sec. 1] However, if we form the following linear combinations of (complex) vectors,

$$\hat{\mathbf{e}}_{\pm} = \frac{1}{\sqrt{2}}(\mp\hat{\mathbf{e}}_1 - i\hat{\mathbf{e}}_2) \quad ; \tag{3.2-2}$$

it is straightforward to show that:

$$\begin{aligned} U(\phi)\hat{\mathbf{e}}_+ &= \hat{\mathbf{e}}_+ e^{-i\phi} \\ U(\phi)\hat{\mathbf{e}}_- &= \hat{\mathbf{e}}_- e^{i\phi} \end{aligned} \quad . \tag{3.2-3}$$

Therefore, the 1-dimensional spaces spanned by $\hat{\mathbf{e}}_{\pm}$ are individually invariant under the rotation group R(2). The 2-dimensional representation given by Eq. (3.1-6) can be simplified if we make a change of basis to the eigenvectors $\hat{\mathbf{e}}_{\pm}$. With respect to the new basis,

$$D'(\phi) = \begin{pmatrix} e^{-i\phi} & 0 \\ 0 & e^{+i\phi} \end{pmatrix} \quad . \tag{3.2-4}$$

The $D'(\phi)$ matrices can be obtained from the $D(\phi)$ matrices of Eq. (3.1-6) by a similarity transformation S, which is just the transformation from the original basis $\{\hat{\mathbf{e}}_1, \hat{\mathbf{e}}_2\}$ to the new basis $\{\hat{\mathbf{e}}_+, \hat{\mathbf{e}}_-\}$ given by Eq. (3.2-2). [cf. Eqs. (II.3-5), (II.3-6)]

Example 3: The reader should be able to convince himself (after working out Problem 3.1) that the 2-dimensional space V_2 is minimal with respect to the dihedral group D_3. Therefore, the 2-dimensional representation of D_3 (hence S_3) described in Example 6 of Sec. 1 is an irreducible representation.

Let us look at the general matrix form of a reducible representation. If V_1 is a n_1-dimensional invariant subspace with respect to $U(G)$, we can always choose a set of basis vectors $\{\hat{\mathbf{e}}_i, i = 1, \ldots, n\}$ in V such that the first n_1 vectors are in V_1 (Theorem II.3). Since, for all $g \in G$,

$$U(g)|e_i\rangle = |e_j\rangle D(g)^j{}_i \in V_1 \qquad \text{for } i = 1, \ldots, n_1$$

we conclude that $D(g)^j{}_i = O$ for $i = 1, \ldots, n_1$ and $j = n_1 + 1, \ldots, n$. Therefore, the matrix representation is of the form:

$$D(g) = \begin{pmatrix} D_1(g) & D'(g) \\ O & D_2(g) \end{pmatrix} \tag{3.2-5}$$

where $D_1(g)$ and $D_2(g)$ are square matrices of dimension n_1 and $n_2 = n - n_1$ respectively and $D'(g)$ is a $n_1 \times n_2$ rectangular matrix. One can verify that if $D(g)$ and $D(g')$ are both of this form, then their product $D(gg')$ is also of this form, and that $D_i(gg') = D_i(g)D_i(g')$ for $i = 1, 2$. Thus, all essential properties of $D(G)$ are already contained in the simpler representations $D_1(G)$ and $D_2(G)$. It is therefore natural that our study of group representations be directed primarily to irreducible representations.

The basis vectors $\{\hat{\mathbf{e}}_i, i = n_1 + 1, \ldots, n_1 + n_2\}$ span the subspace V_2 complementary to V_1. If V_2 is also invariant with respect to $U(G)$ (i.e. $U(G)$ is decomposable), then a repeat of the above argument leads to the conclusion that $D'(g)$ of Eq. (3.2-5) must vanish. Therefore, $D(g)$ reduces to the block diagonal form Eq. (3.2-1).

We see that if $U(G)$ is a representation of the group G on V and V^μ is an invariant subspace of V with respect to G, then by restricting the action of $U(G)$ to V^μ, we obtain a lower-dimension representation $U^\mu(G)$. If the subspace V^μ cannot be further reduced, $U^\mu(G)$ is an irreducible representation, and we say that V^μ is a *proper* or *irreducible invariant subspace* with respect to G.

3.3 Unitary Representations

Definition 3.6 (Unitary Representation): If the group representation space is an inner product space (cf. Appendix II.5), and if the operators $U(g)$ are unitary for all $g \in G$, then the representation $U(G)$ is said to be a *unitary representation.*

Because symmetry transformations are naturally associated with unitary operators (which preserve lengths, angles, and scalar products), unitary representations play a central role in studying symmetry groups. They acquire added importance as the result of two useful theorems.

Theorem 3.2: If a unitary representation is reducible, then it is also decomposable (i.e. fully reducible).

Proof: Let $U(G)$ be a reducible representation of G on the inner product space V. Let V_1 be an invariant subspace (of dimension n_1) with respect to $U(G)$. We can choose an orthonormal basis of V $\{\hat{\mathbf{e}}_i, i = 1, 2, \ldots\}$ such that $\hat{\mathbf{e}}_i \in V_1$ for $i = 1, 2, \ldots, n_1$. The orthogonal complement of V_1 is spanned by $\{\hat{\mathbf{e}}_i, i = n_1 + 1, n_1 + 2, \ldots\}$, and shall be denoted by V_2. We need to prove that V_2 is also invariant with respect to $U(G)$. This can be established in two steps: (i) Since V_1 is invariant, $|e_i(g)\rangle \equiv U(g)|e_i\rangle \in V_1$ for $i = 1, \ldots, n$; (ii) Since $U(G)$ is unitary, $\langle e^j(g)|e_i(g)\rangle = 0$ for all $j = n_1 + 1, n_1 + 2, \ldots$ and $i = 1, \ldots, n_1$. This means $\hat{\mathbf{e}}_j(g)$ are in V_2, the orthogonal complement of V_1. Since any vector $\mathbf{x} \in V_2$ is a linear combination of $\{\hat{\mathbf{e}}_j, j = n_1 + 1, \ldots\}$, $U(g)|x\rangle$ must also be in V_2. QED

Theorem 3.3: Every representation $D(G)$ of a finite group on an inner product space is equivalent to a unitary representation.

In order to prove this theorem, we need to find a non-singular operator S such that $SD(g)S^{-1} = U(g)$ is unitary for all $g \in G$. S can be chosen to be one of those operators which satisfy the following equation:

$$(x, y) \equiv \langle Sx|Sy\rangle = \sum_g \langle D(g)x|D(g)y\rangle \qquad \text{for all } \mathbf{x}, \mathbf{y} \in V \quad . \tag{3.3-1}$$

The existence of S is easily established by noting that (*i*) (x, y) satisfies the axioms of the definition for a new scalar product (Problem 3.4); and (*ii*) S represents the transformation from a basis orthonormal with respect to the scalar product $\langle \mid \rangle$ to another basis orthonormal with respect to the new scalar product $(,)$. To show that $U(g)$ is unitary for such a choice of S, note:

$$\begin{aligned} \langle U(g)x \mid U(g)y \rangle &= \langle SD(g)S^{-1}x \mid SD(g)S^{-1}y \rangle \\ &= \sum_{g'} \langle D(g')D(g)S^{-1}x \mid D(g')D(g)S^{-1}y \rangle \\ &= \sum_{g''} \langle D(g'')S^{-1}x \mid D(g'')S^{-1}y \rangle \\ &= (S^{-1}x, S^{-1}y) = \langle x \mid y \rangle \quad . \end{aligned} \tag{3.3.-2}$$

The second, fourth, and last equalities in this derivation follow from Eq. (3.3-1), the third equality is a consequence of the Rearrangement Lemma. Since Eq. (3.3-2) holds for all $\mathbf{x}, \mathbf{y} \in V$ and $g \in G$, the representation $U(G)$ is indeed a unitary one.

Although we restricted the statement of the Theorem 3.3 to finite groups, the proof suggests that it remains valid for any group provided the summation over group elements in Eq. (3.3-1) can be properly defined and such that the Rearrangement Lemma holds. Examples of continuous groups (which are necessarily infinite) with the required property which occur in physical applications are rotation groups in n-dimensional Euclidean space, the unitary group $U(n)$, and the special unitary groups $SU(n)$.

An immediate corollary of Theorems 3.2 and 3.3 is that all reducible representations of finite groups are fully reducible. Let V_1 and V_2 be complementary invariant subspaces with respect to $U(G)$, and $U_1(G)$, $U_2(G)$ denote the operators which coincide with $U(G)$ on these subspaces, then clearly $V = V_1 \oplus V_2$ in the sense of vector spaces, and $U(g) = U_1(g) \oplus U_2(g)$ in the sense of operators (see Appendix II) for all $g \in G$.

Definitión 3.7 (Direct Sum Representation): Given the above situation, the representation $U(G)$ is said to be the *direct sum representation* of $U_1(G)$ (on V_1) and $U_2(G)$ (on V_2).

If either V_1 or V_2 is reducible with respect to G, then it can be further decomposed. This process can be repeated until the representation $U(G)$ is fully reduced. If during this reduction, an irreducible representation $U^1(G)$ occurs a_1 times, $U^2(G)$ a_2 times, ... etc., we write:

$$\begin{aligned} U(G) &= \underbrace{U^1(G) \oplus \cdots \oplus U^1(G)}_{a_1 \text{ terms}} \oplus \underbrace{U^2(G) \oplus \cdots \oplus U^2(G)}_{a_2 \text{ terms}} \oplus \cdots \\ &= \sum_{\mu \oplus} a_\mu U^\mu(G) \quad . \end{aligned} \tag{3.3-3}$$

In Eq. (3.3-3), $U^\mu(G)$ on the right-hand side denotes *inequivalent irreducible representations* labelled by μ. With the proper choice of bases, $U(G)$ will appear in block-diagonal form with $U^\mu(G)$ appearing as diagonal blocks. Direct sum representations and the decomposition of reducible representations are of central importance in theory and in application; many examples will be given when we discuss specific groups. •

How does one recognize a reducible representation if its apparent matrix realization does not appear in block-diagonal form? This question will be automatically answered as we proceed to investigate the remarkable properties of the inequivalent irreducible representations.

3.4 Schur's Lemmas

In order to prove the central theorems of group representation theory (and also for later use), we must discuss two powerful lemmas derived by Schur at the beginning of this century.

Schur's Lemma 1: Let $U(G)$ be an irreducible representation of a group G on the vector space V, and A be an arbitrary operator on V. If A commutes with all the operators $\{U(g), g \in G\}$, i.e. $AU(g) = U(g)A$, then A must be a multiple of the identity operator E, i.e. $A = \lambda E$ where λ is a number.
Before delving into the proof of this lemma, let us consider a simple consequence of this lemma which illustrates the power of this result. Other important consequences will arise later.

Theorem 3.4: Irreducible representations of any abelian group must be of dimension one.

Proof: Let $U(G)$ be an irreducible representation of the abelian group G. Denote by p a fixed element of G. Due to the abelian nature of the group, we have $U(p)U(g) = U(g)U(p)$ for all $g \in G$. According to Schur's Lemma, $U(p) = \lambda_p E$. This applies to all $p \in G$. Hence, the representation $U(G)$ is equivalent to the one dimensional representation $p \to \lambda_p \in \mathrm{C}$ for all $p \in G$. QED

Examples of irreducible representations of simpler abelian groups will be given in Sec. 3.5 [cf. Tables 3.1 and 3.2].

Proof of Schur's Lemma 1: (i) Without loss of generality, we can take $U(G)$ to be unitary and A to be hermitian. [If $U(G)$ is not unitary, we can make it into one by a similarity transformation (Theorem 3.3). If A is not hermitian, we can always decompose it into two hermitian operators $A_+ = (A + A^\dagger)/2$, $A_- = (A - A^\dagger)/2i$, and consider these separately before combining them again in $A\ (= A_+ + iA_-)$]; (ii) A basis of V, $\{\hat{\mathbf{u}}_{\alpha,i}\}$, can be chosen to consist of the eigenvectors of A, i.e.

$$A|u_{\alpha,i}\rangle = |u_{\alpha,i}\rangle\,\lambda_i$$

where λ_i are the eigenvalues of A, and α represents additional labels needed to specify the basis vectors fully. The set $\{\hat{\mathbf{u}}_{\alpha,i}\}$ may be chosen to be orthonormal; (iii) For any given i, denote by V^i the subspace spanned by $\{\hat{\mathbf{u}}_{\alpha,i}; \alpha = 1, 2, \ldots\}$; we can prove that V^i are invariant subspaces with respect to $U(G)$. The reason is $|U(g)u_{\alpha,i}\rangle \in \mathrm{V}^i$, as a consequence of the fact that it is also an eigenvector of A with the same eigenvalue λ_i, i.e.

$$A\,U(g)|u_{\alpha,i}\rangle = U(g)\,A\,|u_{\alpha,i}\rangle = U(g)\,|u_{\alpha,i}\rangle\,\lambda_i \qquad ;$$

(iv) But $U(G)$ is irreducible on V: the vector space V does not contain any non-trivial invariant subspace (Definition 3.5). Consequently, the invariant subspace V^i

must coincide with V itself, i.e. $V^i = V$. It follows that A has only one eigenvalue, and $A = \lambda E$. QED

The second lemma of Schur compares two irreducible representations of a given group.

Schur's Lemma 2: Let $U(G)$ and $U'(G)$ be two irreducible representations of G on the vector spaces V and V′ respectively, and let A be a linear transformation from V′ to V which satisfies $AU'(g) = U(g)A$ for all $g \in G$. It follows then, either (i) $A = 0$, or (ii) V and V′ are isomorphic and $U(G)$ is equivalent to $U'(G)$.

To help visualize the content of this theorem and the proof that follows, consider the schematic diagram Fig. (3.2a). Notice that both $AU'(G)$ and $U(G)A$ are transformations from V′ to V. The equality of the two is represented graphically by the closing of the quadrangle.

Proof of Schur's Lemma 2: (i) Denote by R the *range* of A, i.e. $R = \{\mathbf{x} \in V; \mathbf{x} = A\mathbf{x}' \text{ for some } \mathbf{x}' \in V'\}$. (cf. Fig. 3.2b) R is an invariant subspace of V with respect to $U(G)$ because given any $|x\rangle \in V$, $U(g)|x\rangle = U(g)A|x'\rangle = AU'(g)|x'\rangle = A|U'(g)x'\rangle \in R$ for all $g \in G$. But if $U(G)$ is an irreducible representation, we must have either $R = 0$ (hence $A = 0$) or $R = V$ (i.e. the mapping A is "onto") [cf. Definition 3.5]. (ii) Now, consider (in V′) the *null space* N′ of A: $N' = \{\mathbf{x}' \in V'; A\mathbf{x}' = 0\}$. (see Fig. 3.2c) N′ is an invariant subspace of V′ with respect to $U'(G)$ because if $|x'\rangle \in N'$ then $AU'(g)|x'\rangle = U(g)A|x'\rangle = U(g)|0\rangle = 0$, implying $U'(g)|x'\rangle \in N'$, for all $g \in G$. Since $U'(G)$ is irreducible, we must have either $N' = V'$ (hence $A = 0$) or $N' = 0$. In the second case, $A|x'\rangle = A|y'\rangle$ implies $|x'\rangle = |y'\rangle$. Hence the mapping A is one-to-one. Combining (*i*) and (*ii*), we see that either $A = 0$ or it establishes an isomorphism between V and V′. In the latter case, we have also $U(G) = AU'(G)A^{-1}$. QED

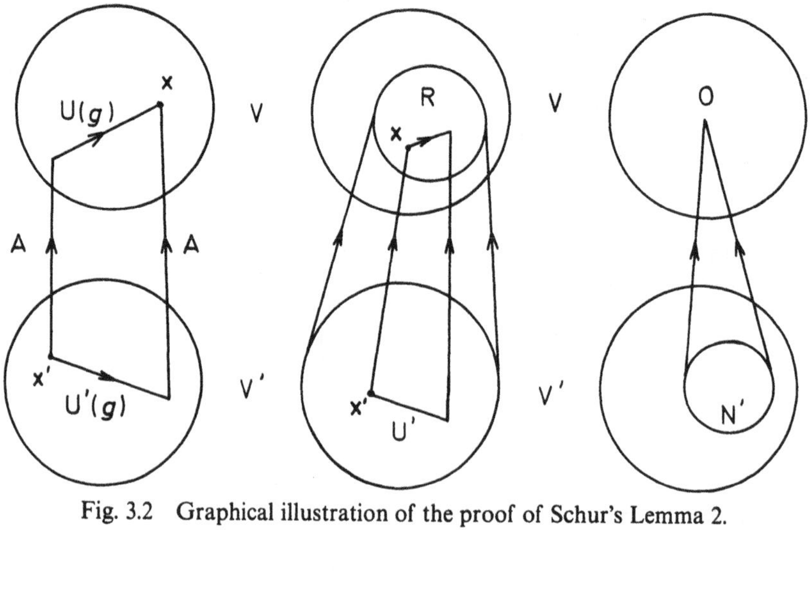

Fig. 3.2 Graphical illustration of the proof of Schur's Lemma 2.

3.5 Orthonormality and Completeness Relations of Irreducible Representation Matrices

We are now ready to present the central results of group representation theory. First, let us agree on a list of notation,

n_G: order of the group G;
μ, ν: labels for inequivalent, irreducible representations of G;
n_μ: the dimension of the μ-representation;
$D^\mu(g)$: the matrix corresponding to $g \in G$ in the μ-representation with respect to an orthonormal basis;
χ_i^μ: character of class ζ_i elements in the μ-representation;
n_i: number of elements in the class ζ_i;
n_c: number of classes in the group G $(i = 1, 2, \ldots, n_c)$.

Theorem 3.5 (Orthonormality of Irreducible Representation Matrices): With the symbols defined above, the following *orthonormality condition* holds,

(3.5-1) $$\frac{n_\mu}{n_G} \sum_g D_\mu^\dagger(g)^k{}_i D^\nu(g)^j{}_l = \delta_\mu^\nu \delta_i^j \delta_l^k$$

where, by convention, $D_\mu^\dagger(g)^k{}_i = [D^\mu(g)^i{}_k]^*$. [The convention for the placement of the indices is established in Appendix I.]

Please note that this important theorem applies only to irreducible representations (labelled by μ, ν). The sum is over all group elements of G. The reason to call this an orthonormality condition is that if, for fixed (ν, j, l), we regard $D^\nu(g)^j{}_l (n_\nu/n_G)^{1/2}$ as a n_G component vector (with g ranging over G), then this equation is just the usual orthonormality relation for vectors.[4] The proof of this rather remarkable theorem will be given after we sample some of its consequences.

This theorem simplifies when applied to any abelian group: since all irreducible representations are one dimensional, we have,

(3.5-2) $$n_G^{-1} \sum_g d_\mu^\dagger(g) \, d^\nu(g) = \delta_\mu^\nu$$

where $d^\nu(g)$ are c-numbers.[5] We can make use of these relations to construct new irreducible representations from known ones.

Example 1: Consider the simplest non-trivial group C_2 (cf. Table 2.1). The identity representation d_1 is given by $(e, a) \xrightarrow{d_1} (1, 1)$. (This notation stands for: $d_1(e) = 1$ and $d_1(a) = 1$. The short-hand notation is natural because, according to the above discussion, we want to regard $d_1(e)$ and $d_1(a)$ as two components of a "vector".) If a second, inequivalent representation d_2 is also regarded as a vector with two components, then it must be orthonormal to $(1, 1)$, according to Theorem 3.5. The only two-component vector which is orthogonal to $(1, 1)$ and also properly normalized is $(1, -1)$. Therefore, the only candidate for a second irreducible representation is $(e, a) \xrightarrow{d_2} (1, -1)$. It is easily verified that this is indeed an

[4] Explicitly, one can introduce the notation $\langle g | \mu, j, l \rangle = \sqrt{\frac{n_\mu}{n_G}} D^\mu(g)^j{}_l$ and write Eq. (3.5-1) as $\sum_g \langle \mu, i, k | g \rangle \langle g | \nu, j, l \rangle = \delta^\nu{}_\mu \delta^j{}_i \delta^k{}_l$ which is a more familiar form of orthonomality relation.

[5] A *c-number* is a complex number; it is usually used in a context to contrast with operators or matrices.

Table 3.1 Inequivalent Irreducible Representations of C_2

μ \ g	e	a
1	1	1
2	1	-1

irreducible representation. There is no other irreducible representation of C_2. We can summarize the results in Table 3.1.

This example gives us a first glimpse of the usefulness of Theorem 3.5, quite apart from its theoretical value: we can deduce new, inequivalent irreducible representations of a group from knowledge of the simpler ones (such as the identity representation above)—by the requirement of orthonormality. When combined with other handles on the simpler representations (such as Theorem 3.1), we can obtain a wealth of information about irreducible representations of the simpler groups.

Example 2: Consider the dihedral group D_2 [cf. Table 2.3]. The trivial irreducible representation is $\{e, a, b, c\} \to \{1, 1, 1, 1\}$. The elements $\{e, a\}$ form an invariant subgroup. The factor group consists of $\{(e, a), (b, c)\}$ and is isomorphic to C_2. (There is only one group of order 2.) According to Example 1, this factor group has two inequivalent irreducible representations. Using Theorem 3.1, we obtain two induced representations of the full group D_2. The first one is again the identity representation. The second one is $\{e, a, b, c\} \xrightarrow{d_2} \{1, 1, -1, -1\}$. Applying the same procedure to the invariant subgroups with elements $\{e, b\}$, and $\{e, c\}$, we obtain two more irreducible representations: $\{e, a, b, c\} \xrightarrow{d_3} \{1, -1, 1, -1\}$ and $\xrightarrow{d_4} \{1, -1, -1, 1\}$. It is easily seen that these representation vectors do satisfy the required orthonormality condition, and no other irreducible representation is allowed by that condition. These representations are summarized in Table 3.2.

Table 3.2 Inequivalent Irreducible Representations of D_2

μ \ g	e	a	b	c
1	1	1	1	1
2	1	1	-1	-1
3	1	-1	1	-1
4	1	-1	-1	1

Example 3: We have already seen (in Chap. 1) the orthonormality relation at work in the case of the infinite abelian group $T^d = \{T(n), n = 1, 2, \ldots\}$ consisting of all discrete translations. The representations are given by $T(n) \to e^{-in\xi}$, where ξ serves as

the representation label. Eq. (1.4-2), then, is the expression of the orthonormality relation (3.5-2) with the correspondence $\mu, \nu \to \xi, \xi'$ and $g \to n$.
We pointed out in Chap. 1 that this relation coincides with the classical Fourier Theorem for periodic functions. Theorem 3.5 represents a significant extension of that important and powerful result. We shall emphasize this central result a number of times throughout this book.

Proof of Theorem 3.5: (i) Let X be any $n_\mu \times n_\nu$ matrix and define

(3.5-3) $$M_x = \sum_g D_\mu^\dagger(g)\, X\, D^\nu(g) \qquad [D_\mu^\dagger(g) = D_\mu^{-1}(g)] \quad .$$

Then $D_\mu^{-1}(p)\, M_x\, D^\nu(p) = M_x$ for all $p \in G$ (as the result of the Rearrangement Lemma). According to the second Schur's Lemma, either $\mu \neq \nu$ and $M_x = 0$, or $\mu = \nu$ and $M_x = c_x E$ where c_x is a constant and E is the unit matrix; (ii) Choose X to be one of the $n_\nu n_\mu$ matrices X_l^k $(k = 1, \ldots, n_\nu;\ l = 1, \ldots, n_\mu)$ with matrix elements $(X_l^k)^i{}_j = \delta_j^k\, \delta_l^i$. We obtain

$$(M_l^k)^m{}_n = \sum_g D_\mu{}^\dagger(g)^m{}_i (X_l^k)^i{}_j\, D^\nu(g)^j{}_n = \sum_g D_\mu{}^\dagger(g)^m{}_l\, D^\mu(g)^k{}_n \quad .$$

According to (i), the left-hand side is equal to zero if $\mu \neq \nu$. This proves the part of Theorem 3.5 concerning $\mu \neq \nu$. In the case $\mu = \nu$, the left-hand side must be equal to $c_l^k\, \delta_n^m$ where c_l^k are constants. They can be determined by taking the trace of both sides of the above equation. On the left-hand side, one obtains $n_\mu c_l^k$; on the right-hand side, one obtains $\sum_g [D^\mu(g)\, D_\mu^\dagger(g)]^k{}_l = n_G\, \delta_l^k$. Therefore, $c_l^k = (n_\mu/n_G)\, \delta_l^k$. QED

Corollary 1: The number of inequivalent irreducible representations of a finite group is restricted by the condition: $\sum_\mu n_\mu{}^2 \leq n_G$.

Proof: As mentioned earlier, we can regard $D^\mu(g)^i{}_j, g \in G$ as the n_G components of a set of orthogonal "vectors" labelled by (μ, i, j). Since the labels (i, j) take $n_\mu{}^2$ values, $\sum_\mu n_\mu{}^2$ represents the number of "vectors" in this set, whereas n_G is the number of components of each such vector. The inequality then follows from the well-known fact that the number of mutually orthogonal (hence linearly independent) vectors must be less than the dimension of the vector space (which is just n_G). QED

It is this important result which makes it possible to set the main objective for group representation theory as that of finding *all* the possible inequivalent irreducible representations for the groups of interest. The most remarkable fact is, in fact, that the above inequality is always saturated: i.e. $\sum_\mu n_\mu{}^2 = n_G$. Thus, the n_G-component vectors $D^\mu(g)^i{}_j$ labelled by (μ, i, j) are a *complete set* in addition to being orthogonal.

Theorem 3.6 (Completeness of Irreducible Representation Matrices): (i) The dimensionality parameters $\{n_\mu\}$ for the inequivalent irreducible representations satisfy:

(3.5-4) $$\sum_\mu n_\mu{}^2 = n_G;$$

(ii) The corresponding representation matrices satisfy the *Completeness Relation*[6]:

(3.5-5)
$$\sum_{\mu,l,k} \frac{n_\mu}{n_G} D^\mu(g)^l{}_k D^\dagger_\mu(g')^k{}_l = \delta_{gg'} \quad .$$

The proof of Eq. (3.5-4) will be deferred until we introduce the notion of the regular representation later in this chapter (See Theorem 3.11). If this result is accepted, then the set of orthonormal vectors labelled by (μ, l, k) and with components equal to $D^\mu(g)^l{}_k$ must be complete—because the number of independent vectors in the set is equal to the dimension of the vector space. The completeness relation, according to Theorem II.13, can be written in the form of Eq. (3.5-5).

For abelian groups, all irreducible representations are one-dimensional, hence $n_\mu = 1$ for all μ. We expect, therefore, that there are n_G inequivalent irreducible representations. This is, of course, seen to be the case for the groups C_2 and D_2, as illustrated in Table 3.1 and 3.2 respectively. It is also simple to see that the row vectors (labelled by μ) form complete orthogonal sets.

This result can also be generalized to infinite groups if the required summation can be meaningfully carried out. We again mention the example of the discrete transformation group T^d. Eq. (1.4-1) is the expression of completeness for the representation functions for that particular case.

The orthonormality and completeness relations for $D^\mu(g)^i{}_j$ are very important theoretical results. However, the representation matrices themselves are basis-dependent, and hence bring in much detail which is not intrinsic to the irreducible representation $(U^\mu(G))$ itself. For this reason, it is much more fruitful to move on to the corresponding relations concerning group characters, which are basis-independent.

3.6 Orthonormality and Completeness Relations of Irreducible Characters

Recall that the characters of a representation $U(G)$ are traces of the operators $U(g)$ [Definition 3.3], and they are independent of the choice of basis in the representation space. All group elements in a given class have the same character in a given representation.

Lemma: Let $U^\mu(G)$ be an irreducible representation of G. Then the sum of $U^\mu(g)$ over any class of group elements is given by:

(3.6-1)
$$\sum_{h \in \zeta_i} U^\mu(h) = \frac{n_i}{n_\mu} \chi_i^\mu E$$

where ζ_i denotes the class i, E is the identity operator and the other quantities are defined earlier in Sec. 3.5.

Proof: Denote the left-hand side of the above equation by A_i: then $U^\mu(g) A_i U^\mu(g)^{-1} = A_i$, as the product merely rearranges the order of the summation, which is immaterial. (We use, of course, the fact that if $h \in \zeta_i$, then $ghg^{-1} \in \zeta_i$ for all $g \in G$.) According to Schur's Lemma 1, A_i must be proportional to the identity operator, $A_i = c_i E$. We can evaluate c_i by taking the trace of both sides of this equation. The left-hand side yields $n_i \chi_i^\mu$, the right-hand side yields $c_i n_\mu$. QED

Theorem 3.7 (Orthonormality and Completeness of Group Characters): The characters of inequivalent irreducible representations of a group G satisfy the

[6] In the notation introduced in the footnote of p. 39, this completeness relation takes the more familiar form:

$$\sum_{\mu,l,k} \langle g|\mu,l,k\rangle\langle \mu,l,k|g'\rangle = \delta^g{}_{g'} .$$

following relations:

(3.6-2) $$\sum_i \frac{n_i}{n_G} \chi_\mu^{\dagger i} \chi_i^\nu = \delta_\mu^\nu \qquad \text{(orthonormality)}$$

(3.6-3) $$\frac{n_i}{n_G} \sum_\mu \chi_i^\mu \chi_\mu^{\dagger j} = \delta_i^j \qquad \text{(completeness)}$$

where, by convention, $\chi_\mu^{\dagger i} = (\chi_i^\mu)^*$. The summation on i is, of course, over the distinct classes of the group; and the summation on μ is over all the inequivalent irreducible representations.

Proof: (i) We start from Theorem 3.5. Setting $i = k, j = l$, and summing over both indices, we obtain on the left-hand side, (n_μ/n_G) times $\sum_g \chi_\mu^\dagger(g)\chi^\nu(g) = \sum_i n_i \chi_\mu^{\dagger i} \chi_i^\nu$; and on the right-hand side, $n_\mu \delta_\mu^\nu$. The orthonormality relation thus follows; (ii) Turn to Theorem 3.6. Sum g over group elements of the class ζ_i, and g' over the class ζ_j, According to the lemma just proved, we should obtain, on the left-hand side $(n_i n_j/n_G)$ times $\sum_\mu \chi_i^\mu \chi_\mu^{\dagger j} \mathrm{Tr} E/n_\mu = \sum_\mu \chi_i^\mu \chi_\mu^{\dagger j}$. While, on the right-hand side, we obtain $n_i \delta_i^j$. This proves the completeness relation. QED

The orthonormality and completeness relations become even more transparent if we define *normalized characters*,

(3.6-4) $$\tilde{\chi}_i \equiv (n_i/n_G)^{1/2} \chi_i \quad .$$

Using implicit summation convention [cf. Appendix I], Theorem 3.7 appears simply as:

(3.6-5) $$\tilde{\chi}_\mu^{\dagger i} \tilde{\chi}_i^\nu = \delta_\mu^\nu$$

(3.6-6) $$\tilde{\chi}_i^\mu \tilde{\chi}_\mu^{\dagger j} = \delta_i^j \quad .$$

(Compare with Theorem II.13.) If $\{\tilde{\chi}_i, i = 1, 2, \ldots, n_c\}$ are interpreted as components of a vector $\tilde{\chi}$, Eq. (3.6-5) can be further simplified to $\tilde{\chi}_\mu^\dagger \cdot \tilde{\chi}^\nu = \delta_\mu^\nu$, where $\cdot$ indicates that a "scalar product" in the n_c-dimensional vector space is taken. These notational conveniences will prove useful in some of the subsequent discussions.

An important consequence of Theorem 3.7 is the following corollary.

Corollary: The number of inequivalent irreducible representations for any finite group G is equal to the number of distinct classes of G (i.e. n_c). In other words, χ_i^μ is a $n_c \times n_c$ square matrix if we designate μ as the row index and i as the column index. A table of this matrix for any given G is called the *character table*.

Example: For abelian groups, each group element forms a class by itself and all irreducible representations are one-dimensional, hence $D^\mu(g) = \chi_i^\mu$. Therefore, tables of $D^\mu(g)$ (such as Tables 3.1 and 3.2) are also character tables for the corresponding group (C_2 and D_2 respectively).

In general, because the characters χ_i^μ are much simpler than the representation matrices $D^\mu(g)^k{}_l$, and because they are intrinsic to the representations (i.e. independent of the arbitrary choice of basis), they are much more useful in the studying of irreducible representations of groups.

Example: Let us find all the irreducible representations of the non-abelian group S_3. (i) S_3 has three classes: the 1-cycle {e}, the 2-cycles {(12), (23), (31)}, and the 3-cycles {(123), (321)}. Hence, there are three inequivalent irreducible representations. (ii) We know, a priori, that there is the trivial (identity) representation $p \to E$ for all $p \in S_3$. Let us label it as $\mu = 1$. The three characters are (1, 1, 1). (iii) From the example following Theorem 3.1, we know of a second one-dimensional (irreducible) representation of S_3 which has the characters (1, −1, 1) for the 1-, 2-, and 3-cycles respectively. We label this representation by $\mu = 2$. (iv) The last irreducible representation ($\mu = 3$) must be 2-dimensional, since Theorem 3.6 requires $n_G = 6 = 1 + 1 + {n_3}^2$. The three characters $({\chi_i}^3, i = 1, 2, 3)$ can be determined as follows: (a) $\chi_1^3 = \mathrm{Tr}D(e) = \mathrm{Tr}E = 2$; (b) from the orthonormality and completeness relations, one can deduce that $\chi_2^3 = 0$, and $\chi_3^3 = -1$. The character table for S_3 is summarized in the following:

Table 3.3 Character Table of the Group S_3

μ \ i	1	2	3
1	1	1	1
2	1	−1	1
3	2	0	−1

Note that for any representation, the character for the identity element (say, $i = 1$) is equal to the dimension of the representation. Hence the first column of the character table reveals the dimension of all the irreducible representations. The most important uses of the character table for practical applications, however, are derived from the following Theorems.

Theorem 3.8: In the reduction of a given representation $U(G)$ of group G into its irreducible components, the number of times (a_ν) that the irreducible representation $U^\nu(G)$ occurs [cf. Eq. (3.3-3)] can be determined from the formula:

$$a_\nu = \sum_i \chi_\nu^{\dagger i} \chi_i n_i / n_G = \tilde{\chi}_\nu^\dagger \cdot \tilde{\chi} \quad . \tag{3.6-7}$$

Example: Consider the following matrix representation $D(G)$ of the group C_2:

$$e \longrightarrow \begin{pmatrix} 1 & 0 \\ 0 & 1 \end{pmatrix} \qquad a \longrightarrow \begin{pmatrix} 0 & 1 \\ 1 & 0 \end{pmatrix} \quad .$$

(Verify that this is indeed a representation!) The characters are $\chi_i = (2, 0)$. The character table for the irreducible representations is given by Table 3.1. In fact, $\chi_i^{\mu=1} = (1, 1)$, $\chi_i^{\mu=2} = (1, -1)$. Thus, according to the above theorem, $a_1 = 1$ and $a_2 = 1$, i.e. each of the irreducible representations occurs once in the reduction of the 2-dimensional representation. We leave as an exercise to prove that, through a similarity transformation, this representation can be brought to the fully reduced (diagonal) form

$$e \longrightarrow \begin{pmatrix} 1 & 0 \\ 0 & 1 \end{pmatrix} \quad \text{and} \quad a \longrightarrow \begin{pmatrix} 1 & 0 \\ 0 & -1 \end{pmatrix} \quad \text{[Problem 3.6].}$$

This form explicitly shows that $D(G)$ is a direct sum of the two irreducible representations.

Proof of Theorem 3.8: Take the trace of Eq. (3.3-3), and we obtain $\chi_i = \sum_\mu a_\mu \chi_i^\mu$, or upon multiplication by $(n_i/n_G)^{1/2}$, $\tilde{\chi} = \sum_\mu a_\mu \tilde{\chi}^\mu$. Taking the scalar product on both sides with $\tilde{\chi}_\nu{}^\dagger$, and applying the orthonormality property of $\tilde{\chi}^\mu$ [Theorem 3.7 part (i)], we obtain $\tilde{\chi}_\nu{}^\dagger \tilde{\chi} = a_\nu$. QED

Theorem 3.9 (Condition for Irreducibility): A necessary and sufficient condition for a representation $U(G)$ with characters $\{\chi_i\}$ to be irreducible is that $\sum_i n_i |\chi_i|^2 = n_G$ (i.e. $\tilde{\chi}^\dagger \cdot \tilde{\chi} = 1$).

Proof: If a_μ denotes the number of times that the irreducible representation $U^\mu(G)$ is contained in $U(G)$, we have:

$$\tilde{\chi}^\dagger \cdot \tilde{\chi} = (a_\mu \tilde{\chi}^\mu)^\dagger \cdot (a_\nu \tilde{\chi}^\nu) = a^{\mu *} a_\nu \tilde{\chi}_\mu{}^\dagger \cdot \tilde{\chi}^\nu = a^{\mu *} a_\nu \delta^\nu_\mu = \sum_\mu |a_\mu|^2 \quad .$$

If $U(G)$ is equivalent to an irreducible representation ν, then $a_\nu = 1$ and $a_\mu = 0$ for $\mu \neq \nu$. Hence $\tilde{\chi}^\dagger \cdot \tilde{\chi} = 1$ and the condition of the theorem is satisfied. Conversely, if this condition is satisfied, we must have $\sum_\mu |a_\mu|^2 = 1$. Since $a_\mu = 0, 1, 2, \ldots$, the only way this can be fulfilled is if $a_\nu = 1$ for some ν and $a_\mu = 0$ for all $\mu \neq \nu$. QED

Because of the many uses of group characters, character tables for all useful symmetry groups have been evaluated and are readily available. In particular, character tables of all crystallographic *point-groups* are given in all books which concern the application of group theory to solid state physics. [Hamermesh, Tinkham]

3.7 The Regular Representation

The *Regular Representation* defined on the *Group Algebra* plays an important role in the development of the group representation theory, as will be evident from our subsequent discussion. In order not to be distracted by what might appear to be a somewhat abstract and technical subject, we only discuss the bare essentials in this section. A more systematic treatment of this subject is given in Appendix III. (The results will be needed in Chap. 5 on the symmetric group.)

Let G be a finite group with elements $\{g_i, i = 1, \ldots, n_G\}$. The group multiplication rule $g_i g_j = g_k$ can be written formally as

$$g_i g_j = g_m \Delta^m_{ij} \tag{3.7-1}$$

where $\Delta^m_{ij} = 1$ or 0 depending on whether $m = k$ or $m \neq k$.

Theorem 3.10 (The Regular Representation): The matrices $(\Delta_i)^k{}_j = \Delta^k_{ij}$, $i = 1, \ldots, n_G$, form a representation of the group G. It is called the *regular representation*.

Proof: To avoid being confused by the many indices, we shall change our notation a little bit: let $a, b, c \in G$ such that $ab = c$, and $ag_k = g_m\Delta^m_{ak}\ldots$ etc. Then,

$$abg_j = a\,g_m\Delta^m_{bj} = g_k\,\Delta^k_{am}\Delta^m_{bj}$$

and

$$cg_j = g_k\Delta^k_{cj} \quad .$$

Since the left-hand sides of these two equations are equal, the right-hand sides must also be. This implies

$$\Delta^k_{am}\Delta^m_{bj} = \Delta^k_{cj}. \tag{3.7-2}$$

Omitting matrix element indices we have, $(\Delta_a)(\Delta_b) = (\Delta_c)$, i.e. these matrices form a representation of G. QED

Before discussing the important consequences of the regular representation, it is worth pointing out that Theorem 3.10 is really just a different incarnation of Cayley's Theorem of Chap. 2 (Theorem 2.1). A straightforward comparison of the correspondence $a \in G \to p_a \in S_n$ specified by Eq. (2.3-1) and the mapping $a \to \Delta_a$ given above reveals that

$$(\Delta_a)^k{}_m = \delta^k_{a_m} \tag{3.7-3}$$

where the integers a_k are determined by Eq. (2.3-2). This provides us with an alternative proof of Theorem 3.10: we have

$$(\Delta_a)^k{}_m(\Delta_b)^m{}_j = \delta^k_{a_m}\delta^m_{b_j} = \delta^k_{a_{b_j}} = \delta^k_{c_j} = (\Delta_c)^k{}_j$$

where the third equality follows from Eq. (2.3-3), and the rest are just definitions.

The significance of the regular representation lies in the fact that all inequivalent irreducible representations of the group are contained in it; furthermore, the number of times each irreducible representation appears is precisely equal to its own dimension. To see this, let us evaluate the characters of the regular representation: $\chi^R_b = \mathrm{Tr}(\Delta_b) = \Delta^k_{bk}$. When $b = e$ (the identity), $\chi^R_e = \Delta^k_{ek} = n_G$ (since $\Delta^k_{ej} = \delta^k{}_j$). When $b \neq e$, $bg_k \neq g_k$; therefore all the diagonal matrix elements of Δ_b vanish and $\chi^R_b = \Delta^k_{bk} = 0$ for all k $(=1,\ldots,n_G)$ and $b \in G$. Applying Theorem 3.8, we find that the number of times the irreducible representation μ occurs in the regular representation is given by:

$$a^R_\mu = \sum_i \chi^{\dagger i}_\mu \chi^R_i (n_i/n_G) = \chi^{e\dagger}_\mu \chi^R_e (n_e/n_G) = n_\mu n_G n_G{}^{-1} = n_\mu \quad . \tag{3.7-4}$$

As previously defined, n_μ is the dimension of the μ-representation.

Theorem 3.11 (Decomposition of the Regular Representation): (i) The regular representation contains every inequivalent irreducible representation μ precisely n_μ times, and (ii)

$$\sum_\mu n_\mu{}^2 = n_G \quad . \tag{3.7-5}$$

Proof: (i) See the discussion preceding the theorem; (ii) Using the above result, we have $\Delta^R_e = \sum_\mu n_\mu U^\mu(e)$. Taking the trace, we obtain $\chi^R_e = n_G = \sum_\mu n_\mu{}^2$. QED

The last result is just the missing element in the proof of Theorem 3.6 on the completeness relation for the irreducible representation matrices. This restores the logical completeness of our presentation.

Example: Consider the group $C_2 = \{e, a\}$. According to the above discussion, the regular representation matrices are

$$\Delta_e = \begin{pmatrix} 1 & 0 \\ 0 & 1 \end{pmatrix} \qquad \Delta_a = \begin{pmatrix} 0 & 1 \\ 1 & 0 \end{pmatrix} \quad . \tag{3.7-6}$$

The characters are:

$$\chi_e^{\mathbf{R}} = 2 \qquad \chi_a^{\mathbf{R}} = 0 \quad .$$

Making use of the character table of the irreducible representations of C_2 (cf. Table 3.1), we obtain

$$a_{\mu=1}^{\mathbf{R}} = 1 \qquad a_{\mu=2}^{\mathbf{R}} = 1 \quad .$$

Therefore the regular representation contains each of the irreducible representations exactly once.

By a similarity transformation, $\Delta_i' = S\Delta_i S^{-1}$, the matrices of Eq. (3.7-6) can be diagonalized:

$$\Delta_e' = \begin{pmatrix} 1 & 0 \\ 0 & 1 \end{pmatrix} \qquad \Delta_a' = \begin{pmatrix} 1 & 0 \\ 0 & -1 \end{pmatrix} \tag{3.7-7}$$

where

$$S = \begin{pmatrix} 1 & 1 \\ -1 & 1 \end{pmatrix}$$

is used. Eq. (3.7-7) makes explicit the reduction of the regular representation into its irreducible components.

As a consequence of Theorem 3.11, one can obtain all the inequivalent irreducible representations of any finite group G, by systematically reducing the corresponding regular representation into its irreducible components. With an appropriate choice of basis vectors, as illustrated in the above example, the representation matrices in the regular representation can be all brought to the block-diagonal form

$$\begin{pmatrix} 1 & & & & & & \\ & D^2 & & & & & \\ & & D^2 & & & & \\ & & & \ddots & & & \\ & & & & D^{n_c} & & \\ & & & & & \ddots & \\ & & & & & & D^{n_c} \\ & \underbrace{\qquad\qquad}_{n_2 \text{ Blocks}} & & \cdots & \underbrace{\qquad\qquad}_{n_c \text{ Blocks}} & & \end{pmatrix} \quad .$$

Note that the first irreducible representation ($\mu = 1$) is always the 1-dimensional identity representation. The above expression explicitly displays the content of Theorem 3.11.

In the first part of Chap. 5, the reduction of the regular representation will be worked out in detail for a non-trivial example—the permutation group S_3. To prepare our way for that study, and for the general analysis, we need to examine the regular representation space a little more closely. By the way the representation is introduced, the space has as its basis the group elements $\{g_m \in G\}$—the right-hand side of Eq. (3.7-1) contains an explicit summation over the basis element label m. [Although there is actually no sum since all but one coefficients vanish.] Conceptually, we have thereby introduced a new mathematical structure which, on the one hand, is a linear vector space (with respect to forming linear combinations) and, on the other hand, has a well-defined multiplication rule (based on the original group structure). This new mathematical construct is called the *group algebra*. A systematic method for the reduction of the regular representation on the group algebra space can be formulated in terms of irreducible projection operators called *idempotents*. This method is employed to derive all irreducible representations of the general permutation group S_n in the second part of Chap. 5. An introduction to the basic theory of group algebra necessary for that analysis is presented in Appendix III rather than here because it represents a somewhat more advanced topic than the rest of this chapter. The group algebra is also called the group ring.

3.8 Direct Product Representations, Clebsch-Gordan Coefficients

Vector spaces which occur in physical applications are often *direct products* of smaller vector spaces that correspond to different degrees of freedom of the physical system (e.g. translations and rotations of a rigid body, or orbital and spin motion of a particle such as the electron). We shall define the direct product of two representations, and study the relationship between representations of a symmetry group realized on the product space and those defined on the component spaces.

Definition 3.8 (Direct Product Vector Space): Let U and V be inner product spaces and $\{\hat{\mathbf{u}}_i;\, i = 1,\ldots,n_u\}$ and $\{\hat{\mathbf{v}}_j;\, j = 1,\ldots,n_v\}$ be orthonormal bases in the two spaces respectively. Then the *direct product space* $W = U \times V$ consists of all linear combinations of the orthonormal basis vectors $\{\hat{\mathbf{w}}_k;\, k = (i,j);\, i = 1,\ldots,n_u;\, j = 1,\ldots,n_v\}$ where $\hat{\mathbf{w}}_k$ can be regarded as the "formal product" $\hat{\mathbf{w}}_k = \hat{\mathbf{u}}_i \cdot \hat{\mathbf{v}}_j$.[7] By definition:

(i) $\langle w^{k'} | w_k \rangle = \delta^{k'}{}_k = \delta^{i'}{}_i \delta^{j'}{}_j$ where $k' = (i', j')$ and $k = (i, j)$;

(ii) $W = \{\mathbf{x};\, |x\rangle = |w_k\rangle\, x^k\}$ where the complex numbers x^k are the components of x;

(iii) $\langle x | y \rangle \equiv x_k^\dagger\, y^k$ where $x_k^\dagger = (x^k)^*$.

Example: Let $\mathbf{x}_1$ be the coordinate vector of "particle 1". Similarly, let $\mathbf{x}_2$ be the coordinate vector of "particle 2". Then the two-particle system consisting of par-

[7] It is possible to define the direct product without reference to specific bases. One makes use of the space consisting of all linear transformations from V to U. [Halmos] The above formulation is adopted because it is just as general, and it stays closer to the way such products arise in physical applications.

ticles 1 and 2 are characterized classically by the coordinates $(\mathbf{x}_1, \mathbf{x}_2)$. In quantum mechanics, let $|\psi_s\rangle$, $s = 1,2$, denote the state vectors of particle s in the quantum mechanical Hilbert spaces $\tilde{\mathrm{H}}_s$, and let $\{|x_s\rangle\}$ be the basis vectors in the "coordinate representation". We have,

$$|\psi_s\rangle = \int |\mathbf{x}\rangle \, \psi_s(\mathbf{x}) \, d^3x \qquad s = 1,2,$$

where $\psi_s(\mathbf{x})$ is the Schrödinger wave function of particle s. [Messiah, Schiff] Then the states of the combined two-particle system are elements of the direct product space $\tilde{\mathrm{H}}_1 \times \tilde{\mathrm{H}}_2$ with coordinate basis vectors $\{|\mathbf{x}_1, \mathbf{x}_2\rangle\}$ and state vectors

$$|\Psi\rangle = \int |\mathbf{x}_1, \mathbf{x}_2\rangle \, \Psi(\mathbf{x}_1, \mathbf{x}_2) \, d^3x_1 \, d^3x_2$$

where $\Psi(\mathbf{x}_1, \mathbf{x}_2)$ is the c-number Schrödinger wave function of the two-particle system.

To each pair of operators (A, B) defined on the vector spaces U and V respectively there is a natural *direct product operator*, $D \equiv A \times B$, defined on $\mathrm{W} = \mathrm{U} \times \mathrm{V}$ which is determined by its action on the direct product basis vectors $\{\hat{\mathbf{w}}_k\}$ (cf. Definition 3.8) as,

$$D|\mathbf{w}_k\rangle = |\mathbf{w}_{k'}\rangle D^{k'}{}_k \qquad D^{k'}{}_k \equiv A^{i'}{}_i B^{j'}{}_j \tag{3.8-1}$$

where $A^{i'}{}_i$ $(B^{j'}{}_j)$ are matrix elements of A (B) on the subspace U (V) with respect to to the bases $\{\hat{\mathbf{u}}_i\}$ $(\{\hat{\mathbf{v}}_j\})$ and $k = (i,j)$, $k' = (i',j')$. In most applications, the operators A and B are related in the sense that they correspond to the same physical operator realized in the two different vector spaces U and V. In that case, the operator D also corresponds to the same operator realized on the direct product space U × V. For instance, in the example given above, the operators A, B, and D could be the quantum mechanical momentum operator p_z for particles 1, 2, and the combined two-particle system respectively. Likewise, they could be the Hamiltonian, or one of the angular momentum operators for the respective systems.

We now apply these concepts to the theory of group representations. Let G be a symmetry group of a physical system (e.g. rotations in 3-space), and W be the direct product space of physical solutions consisting of two sets of degrees of freedom U, V (e.g. orbital motion of two different particles). Suppose $D^{\mu}(G)$ and $D^{\nu}(G)$ are the representations of G on U and V respectively. Then the operators $D^{\mu \times \nu}(g) = D^{\mu}(g) \times D^{\nu}(g)$ on W with $g \in G$ also form a representation of the group G. [Prove that $g \in G \to D(g)$ is a homomorphism.]

Definition 3.9 (Direct Product Representation): The representation $D^{\mu \times \nu}(G)$ defined above on the space W is called the *direct product representation* of $D^{\mu}(G)$ (on U) and $D^{\mu}(G)$ (on V).

It is straightforward to verify that the group characters of the direct product representation $D^{\mu \times \nu}$ are equal to the product of the characters of the two representations D^{μ} and D^{ν}: i.e.

$$\chi^{\mu \times \nu} = \chi^{\mu} \chi^{\nu} \tag{3.8-2}$$

where an implicit class-label (previously denoted by i) is not displayed. Indeed, $\chi^{\mu\times\nu} = \mathrm{Tr}D^{\mu\times\nu}(g) = D^{\mu\times\nu}(g)^k{}_k = D^\mu(g)^i{}_i D^\nu(g)^j{}_j = \chi^\mu\chi^\nu$, where g is any group element belonging to the class under consideration. Suppose $D^\mu(G)$ and $D^\nu(G)$ are irreducible representations of the group G of dimension n_μ and n_ν, respectively, then $D^{\mu\times\nu}(G)$ is a representation of dimension $n_\mu \times n_\nu$, and it is usually reducible. The number of times a_λ that a given irreducible representation $D^\lambda(G)$ occurs in $D^{\mu\times\nu}(G)$ is given by Theorem 3.8: $a_\lambda^{\mu\times\nu} = \tilde{\chi}_\lambda^\dagger\tilde{\chi}^{\mu\times\nu} = \sum_i (\chi_i^\lambda)^* \chi_i^\mu \chi_i^\nu n_i/n_G$.

Example: Consider the product representations $D^\mu \times D^\nu$ of the symmetric group S_3 where D^μ and D^ν are the three irreducible representations discussed previously. By consulting the character table (Table 3.3), it is obvious that $D^{1\times 1} \sim D^1$, $D^{1\times 2} \sim D^2$, $D^{2\times 2} \sim D^1$, $D^{1\times 3} \sim D^3$, and $D^{2\times 3} \sim D^3$, where $\sim$ stands for "equivalent to". What about $D^{3\times 3}$? This is a four-dimensional representation; hence it must be reducible. Applying the formula of the last paragraph, we obtain: $a_1 = a_2 = (4 + 0 + 2)/6 = 1$, and $a_3 = (8 + 0 - 2)/6 = 1$. Hence the representations D^1, D^2, and D^3 occur once each in the reduction of $D^{3\times 3}$.

Let D^μ (defined on U) and D^ν (defined on V) be irreducible representations. The product representation $D^{\mu\times\nu}$ (defined on W = U $\times$ V) is in general reducible; it can be decomposed as $D^{\mu\times\nu} \sim \sum_{\lambda\oplus} a_\lambda D^\lambda$. In other words, the vector space W can be decomposed into a direct sum of invariant subspaces W_α^λ where λ is the label for irreducible representations, and α $(=1,\ldots,a_\lambda)$ distinguishes the spaces which correspond to the same λ. A new basis in W can be chosen such that the first n_1 basis vectors are in $W_1{}^1$, the next n_1 are in $W_2{}^1, \ldots$, etc. With respect to the new basis, the representation matrices are all in block-diagonal form.

To be specific, let us denote the new basis vectors by $\{\hat{w}_{\alpha l}^\lambda;\ l = 1,\ldots,n_\lambda;\ \alpha = 1,\ldots,a_\lambda;$ and $\lambda =$ irreducible representation label$\}$. We assume, as usual, that they are orthonormal. These vectors are related to the original basis vectors $\{\hat{w}_k = \hat{w}_{i,j}; i = 1,\ldots,n_\mu; j = 1,\ldots,n_\nu\}$ by a unitary transformation,

$$|w_{\alpha l}^\lambda\rangle = \sum_{i,j} |w_{i,j}\rangle \langle i, j(\mu,\nu)\alpha, \lambda, l\rangle \tag{3.8-3}$$

where $\langle i, j(\mu,\nu)\alpha, \lambda, l\rangle$ are (complex number) elements of the transformation matrix with (i, j) as the "row index" and (α, λ, l) as the "column index". The labels (μ, ν) in the middle serve to identify this transformation matrix as being the one for $D^{\mu\times\nu}$ to D^λ; they are fixed.

Definition 3.10 (Clebsch-Gordan Coefficients): The matrix elements $\langle i, j(\mu,\nu)\alpha, \lambda, l\rangle$ defined by Eq. (3.8-3) are called *Clebsch-Gordan Coefficients.*

Theorem 3.12 (Orthonormality and Completeness of Clebsch-Gordan Coefficients): The Clebsch-Gordan coefficients satisfy the following orthonormality and completeness relations:

$$\sum_{\alpha\lambda l} \langle i', j'(\mu,\nu)\alpha, \lambda, l\rangle \langle \alpha, \lambda, l(\mu,\nu)i, j\rangle = \delta^{i'}{}_i \delta^{j'}{}_j \tag{3.8-4}$$

and

$$\sum_{i,j} \langle \alpha', \lambda', l'(\mu,\nu)i, j\rangle \langle i, j(\mu,\nu)\alpha, \lambda, l\rangle = \delta^{\alpha'}{}_\alpha \delta^{\lambda'}{}_\lambda \delta^{l'}{}_l \tag{3.8-5}$$

where $\langle \alpha, \lambda, l(\mu,\nu)i, j\rangle \equiv \langle i, j(\mu,\nu)\alpha, \lambda, l\rangle^*$.

Proof: These relations are direct consequences of the orthonormality and completeness of the bases $\{\hat{w}_{i,j}\}$ and $\{\hat{w}^{\lambda}_{\alpha l}\}$. [cf. (i) and (ii) of Theorem II.13] QED

Clearly, the inverse of Eq. (3.8-3) is:

(3.8-6) $$|w_{i,j}\rangle = \sum_{\alpha\lambda l} |w^{\lambda}_{\alpha l}\rangle \langle \alpha, \lambda, l(\mu, \nu) i, j\rangle \quad .$$

The defining properties of the two bases are:

(3.8-7) $$U(g)\,|w_{i,j}\rangle = |w_{i',j'}\rangle\, D^{\mu}(g)^{i'}{}_{i}\, D^{\nu}(g)^{j'}{}_{j}$$

and

(3.8-8) $$U(g)\,|w^{\lambda}_{\alpha l}\rangle = |w^{\lambda}_{\alpha l'}\rangle\, D^{\lambda}(g)^{l'}{}_{l} \quad .$$

Let us use Eq. (3.8-6) on the left-hand side Eq. (3.8-7):

$$\begin{aligned} U(g)\,|i, j\rangle &= U(g)\,|\alpha, \lambda, l\rangle \langle \alpha, \lambda, l|i, j\rangle = |\alpha, \lambda, l'\rangle D^{\lambda}(g)^{l'}{}_{l} \langle \alpha, \lambda, l|i, j\rangle \\ &= |i'j'\rangle \langle i'j'|\alpha, \lambda, l'\rangle\, D^{\lambda}(g)^{l'}{}_{l} \langle \alpha, \lambda, l|i, j\rangle \end{aligned}$$

where three abbreviations are adopted to simplify the expressions: (i) the summation sign is omitted—all repeated indices are summed; (ii) the letter w is omitted for the basis vectors—only the labels are necessary to identify the vectors; and (iii) the fixed labels (μ, ν) are omitted in the Clebsch-Gordan coefficients and replaced with a $|$. Comparing the last result with the right-hand side of Eq. (3.8-7), and making use of the linear independence of the basis vectors $\{\hat{w}_{i,j}\}$, we obtain a useful theorem.

Theorem 3.13 (Reduction of Product Representation): The similarity transformation composed of Clebsch-Gordan coefficients decomposes the direct product representation $D^{\mu\times\nu}$ into its irreducible components. The following reciprocal relations hold:

(3.8-9) $$D^{\mu}(g)^{i'}{}_{i}\, D^{\nu}(g)^{j'}{}_{j} = \langle i'j'|\alpha, \lambda, l'\rangle\, D^{\lambda}(g)^{l'}{}_{l} \langle \alpha, \lambda, l|i, j\rangle \quad ;$$

(3.8-10) $$\delta^{\alpha'}_{\alpha}\, \delta^{\lambda}_{\lambda'}\, D^{\lambda}(g)^{l'}{}_{l} = \langle \alpha', \lambda', l'|i', j'\rangle\, D^{\mu}(g)^{i'}{}_{i}\, D^{\nu}(g)^{j'}{}_{j} \langle i, j|\alpha, \lambda, l\rangle \quad .$$

The last equation makes explicit the block-diagonal form of the direct product representation in the new basis: the similarity-transformed matrix (right-hand side) is diagonal in two of the three labels—λ, α (left-hand side).

The proof of Eq. (3.8-9) is provided in the discussion preceding the theorem. The reciprocal formula, Eq. (3.8-10), can be derived in a similar way—by substituting Eq. (3.8-3) in Eq. (3.8-8). (It also follows from Eq. (3.8-9) in conjunction with the orthonormality and completeness property of the Clebsch-Gordan coefficients, Theorem 3.12.)

Physically, direct products arise when one considers the behavior of systems involving two or more degrees of freedom under symmetry operations, or when one explores the regularities of transition amplitudes of physical processes implied by the underlying symmetry (or, sometimes, "broken-symmetry"). The "additition" of angular momenta of a two-particle system, or of the orbital- and spin-angular momenta of a single particle, is the most often encountered example of a direct product representation (of the rotation group). We shall study it in detail in Chap. 7. The Wigner-Eckart theorem (to be introduced in the next chapter) which provides the most important method to uncover symmetry-related regularities in matrix elements of physical observables, is derived from the reduction of direct product representations to their irreducible parts. For those who have not had previous experience with these applications, it may be desirable to come back to this section after studying Chap. 7, so that the content and the power of the general results may be better appreciated.

Problems

3.1 Consider the six transformations associated with the dihedral group D_3 defined in Chap. 2 (cf. Fig. 2.2). Let V be the 2-dimensional Euclidean space spanned by $\hat{e}_x$ and $\hat{e}_y$ as shown. Write down the matrix representation of elements of D_3 on V with respect to this Cartesian basis.

3.2 Show that the 2-dimensional representation of rotations in the plane given in Example 5 of Sec. 3.1 can be decomposed into two 1-dimensional representations.

3.3 In Example 7 of Sec. 3.1, show that the mapping in function space defined by Eq. (3.1-10) forms a representation of the relevant group G if $x'^i = D^T(g)^i{}_j x^j$, where $\{D^T(g), g \in G\}$ are the transposes of representation matrices of the group G (such as those described in Examples 4, 5, 6 in the same section).

3.4 Prove that if $D(G)$ is any representation of a finite group G on an inner product space V, and **x**, **y** $\in$ V, then

$$(\mathrm{x}, \mathrm{y}) \equiv \sum_{g \in G} \langle D(g)x | D(g)y \rangle$$

defines a new scalar product on V. (Verify that the axioms of Appendix II.5 are satisfied.)

3.5 Find one set of (unitary) representation matrices $D^\mu(p), p \in S_3$, for the $\mu = 3$, two-dimensional irreducible representation of the group S_3. [Hint: Examine the solution to Problem 1, check the irreducibility, unitarity,... etc.]

3.6 Find the similarity transformation which reduces the 2-dimensional representation of C_2 given in the Example following Theorem 3.8 into diagonal form.

3.7 Consider the 6-dimensional function space V consisting of polynomials of degree 2 in two real variables (x, y):

$$f(x, y) = a x^2 + b xy + c y^2 + d x + e y + h$$

where $a, b, \ldots h$ are complex constants. If (x, y) transform under the dihedral group D_3 as the coordinates of a 2-vector as described in Example 6 of Sec. 3.1 [cf. Problem 1], then we obtain a 6-dimensional representation of D_3 on V. Identify the various invariant subspaces of V under D_3, and the corresponding irreducible representations that are contained in this 6-dimensional representation.

3.8 Let (x_1, y_1) and (x_2, y_2) be coordinates of two 2-vectors which transform independently under D_3 transformations as in Problems 1 and 7. Consider the function space V spanned by the monomials x_1x_2, x_1y_2, y_1x_2, y_1y_2. Show that the realization of the group D_3 on this 4-dimensional space is the direct product representation of that of Problem 1 with itself.

3.9 Reduce the 4-dimensional representation of the group D_3 (hence S_3) obtained in the previous problem into its irreducible components. Evaluate the Clebsch-Gordan coefficients.

3.10 The tetrahedral group consists of all rotations which leave the regular tetrahedron invariant. This group has four 3-fold axes, and three 2-fold axes. Enumerate the group elements, the distinct classes, and any invariant subgroups. Describe the irreducible representations and construct the character table.

3.11 Construct the character table for the group S_4. [Hint: Make use of the irreducible representations of any factor groups that may exist. Then complete the table by using the orthonormality and completeness relations.]

3.12 Analyze the irreducible representations of the dihedral group D_4 [cf. Problem 2.8]: (i) Enumerate the irreducible representations, and (ii) Construct the character table for these representations.

CHAPTER 4

GENERAL PROPERTIES OF IRREDUCIBLE VECTORS AND OPERATORS

Whenever a physical system possesses a symmetry, the basic solutions to the classical equations or the basis state vectors of the corresponding quantum-mechanical problem are naturally classified according to the irreducible representations of the symmetry. This is done in all fields of physics from the elementary to the advanced, whether or not group theoretical language is used explicitly. For instance, the frequent occurrence of the spherical harmonics Y_{lm} in solutions for both classical mathematical physics and quantum mechanics just reflects the underlying spherical symmetry of the physical systems being studied (as will become evident when we discuss in detail the symmetry group R_3 in Chaps. 7 and 8). This intimate relationship is also illustrated in Chap. 1, where the physically useful Bloch wave functions for an electron on any lattice are shown to correspond to irreducible representation functions of the underlying symmetry group—the discrete translation group.

Of equal importance is the fact that physical observables, such as position, momentum, electromagnetic field,... etc. are also classified according to the irreducible representations of the underlying symmetry groups. Under symmetry transformations, they transform in a definite way specified by group representation theory, just as do state vectors. Elementary examples of this general result are: components of **x** (position) and **p** (momentum) transform as vectors under rotations; components of $T_{\mu\nu}$ (energy-momentum), $F_{\mu\nu}$ (electromagnetic field) transform as second rank tensors under homogeneous Lorentz transformations, ... etc.

A systematic study of the consequences of the above-described properties of state vectors and physical observables allows the full structure due to symmetry to be exposed and utilized. In this chapter, we define irreducible sets of state vectors and operators, formulate a general procedure to decompose arbitrary vectors and operators into their irreducible components, and study the full range of implications on physically measurable quantities due to a symmetry group. This general formalism will then be applied to specific groups to be discussed in the remainder of the book.

4.1 Irreducible Basis Vectors

Let $U(G)$ be a representation defined on an inner product vector space V. (Unless specified otherwise, we always assume that the representations are unitary; cf. Theorem 3.3.) Let V_μ be an invariant subspace with respect to $U(G)$, and

$\{\hat{\mathbf{e}}_i^\mu; i = 1, \ldots, n_\mu\}$ be a set of orthonormal basis vectors of V_μ. By definition,

$$U(g)|e_i^\mu\rangle = |e_j^\mu\rangle\, D^\mu(g)^j{}_i \qquad g \in G \tag{4.1-1}$$

where $D^\mu(G)$ is an irreducible (matrix) representation of G.

Definition 4.1: Any set of vectors $\{\hat{\mathbf{e}}_i^\mu, i = 1, \ldots, n_\mu\}$ which transform under $U(G)$ as in Eq. (4.1-1) is said to be an *irreducible set* transforming according to the μ-representation.

The orthonormality and completeness relations satisfied by the irreducible representation matrices lead to useful consequences for the irreducible basis vectors and the decomposition of arbitrary vectors into their irreducible components.

Theorem 4.1: Let $\{\hat{\mathbf{u}}_i^\mu, i = 1, \ldots, n_\mu\}$ and $\{\hat{\mathbf{v}}_j^\nu, j = 1, \ldots, n_\nu\}$ be two sets of irreducible basis vectors with respect to a group G in a vector space V. If the two representations labelled by μ and ν respectively are not equivalent, then the two invariant subspaces spanned by these bases are orthogonal to each other.

Proof: Since we assume that the bases are orthonormal and that the representations are unitary, we have:

$$\begin{aligned}\langle v_\nu^j | u_i^\mu\rangle &= \langle v_\nu^j|\, U^\dagger(g)\, U(g)\, | u_i^\mu\rangle \\ &= D_\nu^\dagger(g)^j{}_k \langle v_\nu^k | u_l^\mu\rangle\, D^\mu(g)^l{}_i = n_G^{-1} \sum_g D_\nu^\dagger(g)^j{}_k D^\mu(g)^l{}_i \langle v_\nu^k | u_l^\mu\rangle \\ &= n_\mu^{-1}\, \delta_\nu^\mu\, \delta_i^j\, \delta_l^k \langle v_\nu^k | u_l^\mu\rangle = \delta_\nu^\mu\, \delta_i^j n_\mu^{-1} \langle v_\nu^k | u_k^\mu\rangle\end{aligned}$$

where the first equality follows from $U^\dagger U = E$, the second from Eq. (4.1-1), the third from averaging over all group elements, and the fourth from Theorem 3.5. We see, therefore, if $\mu \neq \nu$, every vector from one basis must be orthogonal to every vector from the other. It follows then that all vectors in one invariant subspace are orthogonal to all vectors in the other. QED

This powerful result can be regarded as a generalization of the familiar fact that eigenvectors of a hermitian operator corresponding to different eigenvalues are orthogonal to each other. The reader may wonder, what can be said when $\mu = \nu$ (i.e. the two representations are equivalent). There are two possibilities: (*i*) If the subspaces spanned by $\{\hat{\mathbf{u}}_i\}$ and $\{\hat{\mathbf{v}}_i\}$ do not overlap, then $\langle v^j | u_i\rangle = 0$ (typically, the two spaces are distinguished by the eigenvalues of some other operator outside the group under consideration); and (*ii*) If the intersection of the two subspaces is not null, then they must coincide. In this case the two bases are related by $|\hat{u}_i\rangle = |\hat{v}_j\rangle S^j{}_i$, where S is a unitary matrix (indeed, $\langle v^j | u_i\rangle = S^j{}_i$).

Examples: Consider the Hilbert space of electron wave functions in a hydrogen atom. Apply the above considerations to the symmetry group R_3—the group of rotations. The following facts, easily verified by consulting any book on elementary quantum mechanics, illustrate fully the general results described above: States corresponding to different angular momenta (i.e. different irreducible representations of R_3) are necessarily orthogonal to each other, irrespective of the "radial quantum number". States corresponding to the same angular momenta are also mutually orthogonal if they correspond to different radial quantum numbers. Non-vanishing scalar products are obtained only if both the angular momenta and the radial quantum numbers are the same. [Messiah, Schiff]

4.2 The Reduction of Vectors—Projection Operators for Irreducible Components

In applications, it is important to be able to express any arbitrary vector in terms of irreducible basis vectors, and to be able to transform from one irreducible basis (with respect to one symmetry group or subgroup) to another irreducible basis. Given the symmetry group and its irreducible representations, both of these objectives can be achieved using the projection operator method. The basic idea is as simple as projecting out the component of an arbitrary vector $|x\rangle$ along the unit vector $|e_i\rangle$ by means of the projection operator $E_i = |e_i\rangle\langle e_i|$:

$$E_i|x\rangle = |e_i\rangle\langle e_i|x\rangle = |e_i\rangle x^i.$$

The details are, however, more involved as we now discuss.

Theorem 4.2: Let $U(G)$ be a representation of the group G on a vector space V, and $D^\mu(G)$ be an irreducible matrix representation of G. Define operators

$$\mathrm{P}^j_{\mu i} = (n_\mu/n_G)\sum_g D^{-1}_\mu(g)^j{}_i\, U(g) \quad . \tag{4.2-1}$$

Then given any $|x\rangle \in$ V, the set of vectors $\{\mathrm{P}^j_{\mu i}|x\rangle, i = 1,\dots,n_\mu\}$, with fixed j, transform irreducibly according to the μ-representation (provided they are not all null).

Proof: Omitting the normalization factor (n_μ/n_G), we have

$$\begin{aligned} U(g)\,\mathrm{P}^j_{\mu i}|x\rangle &= \sum_{g'} U(g)U(g')|x\rangle\, D^{-1}_\mu(g')^j{}_i \\ &= \sum_{g'} U(gg')|x\rangle\, D^{-1}_\mu(g')^j{}_i = \sum_{g''} U(g'')|x\rangle\, D^{-1}_\mu(g^{-1}g'')^j{}_i \\ &= \left[\sum_{g''} U(g'')|x\rangle\, D^{-1}_\mu(g'')^j{}_k\right] D^{-1}_\mu(g^{-1})^k{}_i \\ &= \mathrm{P}^j_{\mu k}|x\rangle\, D^\mu(g)^k{}_i \qquad \text{(no sum over } \mu). \end{aligned}$$

The third equality makes use of the Rearrangement Lemma; the others only make use of the fact that $U(G)$ and $D^\mu(G)$ are operator and matrix representations of the group respectively. QED

Thus, starting with any vector $|x\rangle \in$ V, we can generate an irreducible invariant subspace corresponding to the μ-representation, with $\{\mathrm{P}^j_{\mu i}|x\rangle, i = 1,\dots,n_\mu\}$ as basis. (The basis vectors, as defined, are orthogonal but not normalized; they can be easily normalized, if desired.) The operators $\mathrm{P}^j_{\mu i}$ are generalized projection operators (as will become clear after the following two theorems); they are extremely useful and will be called upon frequently in later parts of the book. For the rest of this section, we shall assume $D(G)$ to be unitary, and use $D^\dagger(g)$ in place of $D^{-1}(g)$.

Theorem 4.3: Let $\{\hat{e}^\nu_k, k = 1,\dots,n_\nu\}$ be a set of irreducible basis vectors, and $\mathrm{P}^j_{\mu i}$ be operators defined in Theorem 4.2. Then

$$\mathrm{P}^j_{\mu i}|e^\nu_k\rangle = |e^\nu_i\rangle\, \delta^\nu_\mu\, \delta^j_k \quad . \tag{4.2-2}$$

Proof: We have,

$$\begin{aligned} P^j_{\mu i}|e^\nu_k\rangle &= (n_\mu/n_G)\sum_g U(g)|e^\nu_k\rangle D^\dagger_\mu(g)^j{}_i \\ &= |e^\nu_l\rangle (n_\nu/n_G)\sum_g D^\nu(g)^l{}_k D^\dagger_\mu(g)^j{}_i \\ &= |e^\nu_l\rangle \delta^\nu_\mu \delta^l_i \delta^j_k = |e^\nu_i\rangle \delta^\nu_\mu \delta^j_k \quad . \end{aligned}$$

In this derivation, the third equality makes use of the orthonormality condition (Theorem 3.5) of the irreducible matrix representations; the other steps are all straightforward. QED

Thus, if $\mu \neq \nu$, $P^j_{\mu i}|e^\nu_k\rangle = 0$; and if $\mu = \nu$, $P^j_{\mu i}|e^\nu_k\rangle = |e^\mu_i\rangle \delta^j_k$.

Corollary 1:

(4.2-3) $$P^j_{\mu i} P^l_{\nu k} = \delta^\nu_\mu \delta^j_k P^l_{\mu i} \quad .$$

Proof: Since $\{P^l_{\nu k}|x\rangle, k = 1,\ldots,n_\nu\}$ is an irreducible set, according to Theorem 4.3: $P^j_{\mu i} P^l_{\nu k}|x\rangle = P^l_{\nu i}|x\rangle \delta^\nu_\mu \delta^j_k$ for all $|x\rangle \in V$. QED

Corollary 2: The n_G operators $U(g)$, $g \in G$, can be written as linear combinations of $P^j_{\mu i}$ ($\mu = 1,\ldots,n_c; i,j = 1,\ldots,n_\mu$):

(4.2-4) $$U(g) = \sum_{\mu,i,j} P^j_{\mu i} D^\mu(g)^i{}_j \quad .$$

This is just the inverse of the defining equation of $P^j_{\mu i}$. It can be easily proved using the orthonormality of the $D(G)$ matrices.

Corollary 3: The following identity holds:

(4.2-5) $$U(g) P^l_{\nu k} = \sum_i P^l_{\nu i} D^\nu(g)^i{}_k \quad .$$

This relation follows directly from Equations (4.2-3) and (4.2-4). It is, of course, merely a restatement of Theorem 4.2 in pure operator form.

Definition 4.2: The set of operators $P_{\mu i} \equiv P^{j=i}_{\mu i}$ and $P_\mu \equiv \sum_i P_{\mu i}$ are said to be the *projection operators* onto the basis vector $\hat{e}^\mu_i$ and the irreducible invariant space V_μ (spanned by $\{\hat{e}^\mu_i, i = 1,\ldots,n_\mu\}$) respectively.

We must establish that $P_{\mu i}$ are indeed projection operators. This follows directly from Corollary 1 and the definition of $P_{\mu i}$:

$$P_{\mu i} P_{\nu k} = P^i_{\mu i} P^k_{\nu k} = P^i_{\mu i} \delta^\nu_\mu \delta^k_i = P_{\mu i} \delta^\nu_\mu \delta^k_i \quad .$$

(N.B. There is no summation over any of the repeated indices in this equation—a rare departure from our usual convention.) Similarly,

$$P_\mu P_\nu = \sum_{i,k} P_{\mu i} P_{\nu k} = \sum_{i,k} P_{\mu i} \delta^\nu_\mu \delta^k_i = \delta^\nu_\mu \sum_i P_{\mu i} = \delta^\nu_\mu P_\mu \quad .$$

Theorem 4.4: The projection operators P_μ and $P_{\mu i}$ are *complete* in the sense that $\sum_\mu P_\mu = E$ (the identity operator).

Proof: Let $\{\hat{e}^\nu_k\}$ be the basis vectors for any of the irreducible invariant subspaces of V. According to Theorem 4.3:

$$P_{\mu i}|e^\nu_k\rangle = P^i_{\mu i}|e^\nu_k\rangle = |e^\nu_i\rangle\,\delta^\nu_\mu\,\delta^i_k \quad ;$$

and

$$P_\mu|e^\nu_k\rangle = |e^\nu_k\rangle\,\delta^\nu_\mu, \quad \text{hence} \quad \sum_\mu P_\mu|e^\nu_k\rangle = |e^\nu_k\rangle \quad .$$

As this holds for all irreducible basis vectors, $\sum_\mu P_\mu = E$ provided the space V is fully reducible (as we always assume it is). QED

To summarize: If $U(G)$ is a representation of G on V, then V is a direct sum of irreducible invariant spaces, $V = \sum_{\mu,\alpha,\oplus} V_\mu^{\ \alpha}$ where μ is the irreducible representation label ($\mu = 1, \ldots, n_c$; n_c = number of distinct classes), and $\alpha = 1, \ldots, a_\mu$ (a_μ = number of occurrences of the μ-representations in the reduction of $U(G)$). A complete set of basis vectors corresponding to this reduction can be labelled as $|\alpha, \mu, i\rangle$ where $i = 1, \ldots, n_\mu$ (n_μ = dimension of the μ-representation). The effects of the above-defined operators on these vectors are:

(4.2-6) $$P_\mu\,|\alpha, \nu, k\rangle = |\alpha, \nu, k\rangle\,\delta^\mu_\nu$$

(4.2-7) $$P_{\mu i}\,|\alpha, \nu, k\rangle = |\alpha, \nu, k\rangle\,\delta^\mu_\nu\,\delta^i_k$$

(4.2-8) $$P^j_{\mu i}\,|\alpha, \nu, k\rangle = |\alpha, \nu, i\rangle\,\delta^\mu_\nu\,\delta^j_k \quad .$$

Although $P^j_{\mu i}$ are not projection operators in the strict sense, they are the most useful among the three because they can be used to construct irreducible basis vectors from arbitrary vectors according to Theorem 4.2. (N.B. The projection operators $P_{\mu i}$ do not have this property.)

Example 1: Let V be the space of square integrable functions $f(x)$ of the variable x, and G be the group $\{e, I_s\}$ where I_s, the space inversion operation, changes x to $-x$. Since G is isomorphic to C_2, it has two one-dimensional irreducible representations (given by Table 3.1). The two projection operators are: $P_1 = E + U(I_s)$ and $P_2 = E - U(I_s)$, where we have used $U(e) = E$. (For one-dimensional representations, the i, j indices on $P^j_{\mu i}$ are, of course, unnecessary.) Given any function $f(x)$, the "parity" operator $U(I_s)$ transforms it into $f(-x)$. Hence $P_1 f(x) = f(x) + f(-x) \equiv f_+(x)$, and $P_2 f(x) = f(x) - f(-x) \equiv f_-(x)$. It is apparent that $f_+(x)$ and $f_-(x)$ each span an irreducible invariant subspace under G—$f_+(x)$ is even under parity and $f_-(x)$ is odd. Thus, we arrive at the obvious conclusion that, for a system with space inversion symmetry, it is advantageous to use either even or odd functions in the function space. For this case, the employment of group-theoretical apparatus is clearly unnecessary. The example is given only to illustrate that this method reproduces conventional wisdom for simple systems.

Example 2: Let V be the space of state-vectors for a particle on a one-dimensional lattice, and G be the symmetry group of discrete translations T^d, as discussed in Chap. 1. We have learned that the irreducible representations are labelled by $k(-\pi/b \leq k \leq \pi/b)$, and the representation functions are $\{e^{-iknb}\}$. Starting with a localized state $|y\rangle$ where $-b/2 \le y \le b/2$, we can project out its irreducible components

$$|k, y\rangle = P_k |y\rangle = \sum_n T(n)|y\rangle e^{iknb} = \sum_n |nb + y > e^{iknb} \quad . \tag{4.2-9}$$

These states are eigenstates of translations with eigenvalue e^{-ikmb}: $T(m)|k, y\rangle = \sum_n T(m+n)|y\rangle e^{iknb} = \sum_{n'} T(n')|y\rangle e^{ik(n'-m)b} = |k, y\rangle e^{-ikmb}$, confirming Eq. (1.3-3). The last expression in Eq. (4.2-9) for $|k, y\rangle$ indicates that the probabilities for finding the electron in any of the "cells" on the lattice are equal to each other (i.e. relative probability $= |e^{iknb}|^2 = 1$). These states are *normal mode* states analogous to plane wave states in continuum quantum mechanics. We mention in passing that if $|x\rangle = |lb + y\rangle$ for any integer l, then $P_k|x\rangle = |k, y\rangle e^{-iklb}$. This is just a multiple of the state obtained above in Eq.. (4.2-9). [Problem 4.1] Hence, to obtain all distinct irreducible states, it suffices to start with localized states within just one unit cell and apply the projection operators.

The last example illustrates how the projection operators can be used to transform from a given basis ($|x\rangle = |nb + y\rangle \equiv |n, y\rangle$, representing localized states) to an irreducible basis ($|k, y\rangle = P_k|0, y\rangle$, representing normal modes). The localized states may represent the physical system at some initial (or intermediate) time. In order to predict the time development of these states, it is necessary to express them in terms of the normal mode vectors, because only the latter have simple time evolution behavior—as a consequence of the commutativity of the Hamiltonian with symmetry transformations. This fact underlines the importance of the systematic utilization of irreducible basis for all applicable symmetries of a given physical system. We shall use this type of transformation of bases extensively in later chapters when we study the irreducible representations of many symmetry groups.

A second type of application concerns the reduction of direct product representations to their irreducible components, and the evaluation of Clebsch-Gordan coefficients. Let G be a symmetry group, $D^\mu(G)$ ($\mu = 1, 2, \ldots, n_c$) be an irreducible representation realized on the vector space V_μ with basis $\{\hat{e}^\mu_i, i = 1, 2, \ldots, n_\mu\}$. Consider the direct product representation $D^{\mu\times\nu}$ realized on $V_\mu \times V_\nu$. How do we find the irreducible invariant subspaces of $V_\mu \times V_\nu$ described in Sec. 3.8? One systematic method is to use the projection operators of this section. Specifically, we can start with the original basis vectors $|k, l\rangle = \hat{e}^\mu_k \times \hat{e}^\nu_l$, and apply the projection operators: $P^j_{\lambda i}|k, l\rangle$. For fixed (λ, j, k, l), the n_λ vectors ($i = 1, \ldots, n_\lambda$) span a irreducible invariant subspace (provided the projection does not yield null vectors). By selecting different sets of (λ, j, k, l), one can generate all the irreducible invariant subspaces. The transformation matrix between the original and the new basis gives the Clebsch-Gordan coefficients. A concrete example of using this procedure to reduce $D^{3\times 3}(S_3)$ is given as an exercise [cf. Problem 4.2].

4.3 Irreducible Operators and the Wigner-Eckart Theorem

Under symmetry group transformations, operators on the vector space of physical solutions also transform in definite ways. They are naturally classified according to the irreducible representations of the symmetry group as for the basis vectors. The systematic exploitation of the transformation properties of the operators and the (state) vectors leads to immense simplification in the structure of physically measurable quantities. This structure is manifested in the Wigner-Eckart Theorem which represents the highlight of this section.

Definition 4.3: A set of operators $\{O^\mu_i, i = 1, \ldots, n_\mu\}$ on a vector space V transforming under a symmetry group G as:

$$U(g)\, O^\mu_i\, U(g)^{-1} = O^\mu_j\, D^\mu(g)^j{}_i \quad , \tag{4.3-1}$$

where $g \in G$, and $D^\mu(G)$ is an irreducible matrix representation, is said to be (a set of) *irreducible operators* corresponding to the μ-representation. They are sometimes also referred to as *irreducible tensors.*

Given $\{O^\mu_i\}$ and $\{\hat{\mathbf{e}}^\nu_j\}$ as irreducible operators and vectors respectively, how does the set of vectors $O^\mu_i\,|\,e^\nu_j\rangle$ behave under group transformations? We have,

$$\begin{aligned} U(g)\, O^\mu_i |e^\nu_j\rangle &= U(g)\, O^\mu_i U(g)^{-1} U(g)\,|e^\nu_j\rangle \\ &= O^\mu_k\,|e^\nu_l\rangle\, D^\mu(g)^k{}_i D^\nu(g)^l{}_j \quad , \end{aligned} \tag{4.3-2}$$

i.e. these states transform according to the direct product representation $D^{\mu\times\nu}$. Following the discussions of Sec. 3.8, we can express this set of vectors in terms of irreducible vectors $|w^\lambda_{\alpha l}\rangle$ [cf. Eq. (3.8-6)] as,

$$O^\mu_i\,|e^\nu_j\rangle = \sum_{\alpha,\lambda,l} |w^\lambda_{\alpha l}\rangle\langle \alpha, \lambda, l(\mu, \nu) i, j\rangle \quad . \tag{4.3-3}$$

We can now evaluate the matrix element $\langle e^l_\lambda\,|O^\mu_i\,|e^\nu_j\rangle$ making use of Theorem 4.1, and arrive at the far-reaching result:

Theorem 4.5 (Wigner-Eckart): Let $\{O^\mu_i\}$ be a set of irreducible tensor operators, then

$$\langle e^l_\lambda\,|O^\mu_i\,|e^\nu_j\rangle = \sum_\alpha \langle \alpha, \lambda, l(\mu, \nu) i, j\rangle\langle \lambda | O^\mu | \nu\rangle_\alpha \tag{4.3-4}$$

where $\langle \lambda | O^\mu | \nu\rangle_\alpha \equiv n_\lambda^{-1} \sum_k \langle e^k_\lambda | w^\lambda_{\alpha k}\rangle$ is called the *reduced matrix element.*

The significance of this celebrated theorem lies in the fact that the multitude of matrix elements on the left-hand side are all determined by a few reduced matrix elements. The Clebsch-Gordan coefficients on the right-hand side (which contain all the i-, j-, and l- dependence) are specified by group representation theory, hence can be looked up in published tables. The specific properties of the states and the operator only enter the reduced matrix elements. In many important applications, such as 3-dimensional rotational symmetry, each irreducible representation (λ) only occurs once in the reduction of the direct product ($\mu \times \nu$); then $\alpha = 1$ and there is only one reduced matrix element for each (μ, ν, λ). Under normal circumstances, the regularities exhibited by the Wigner-Eckart theorem exhaust all the structure of the relevant matrix elements required by invariance under the symmetry group.

To illustrate the usefulness of the Wigner-Eckart theorem, we sketch its application to electromagnetic transitions in atoms (visible light, x-ray) and nuclei (γ-ray). Since the electromagnetic interaction is invariant under 3-dimensional rotation, the symmetry group is the rotation group $\mathbf{R}_3$ [see Chapters 7 and 8 for details]. The electromagnetic transitions involve the emission of a "photon" of angular momentum (s, λ) while the atomic nuclear system jumps from an initial state

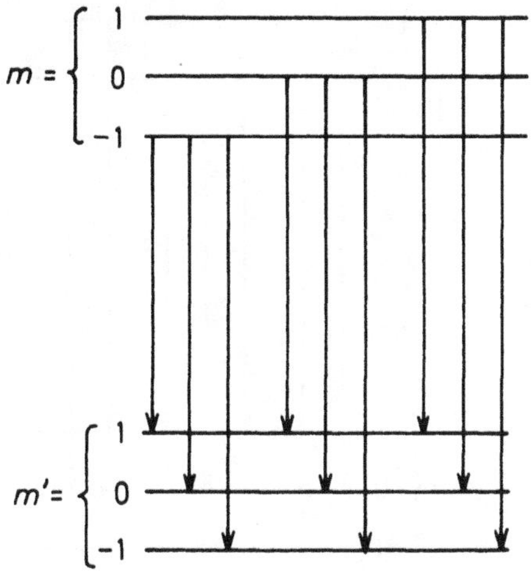

Fig. 4.1 Possible transitions without symmetry consideration.

of angular momentum $|j, m\rangle$ to a final state of angular momentum $|j', m'\rangle$. In each case, the first "quantum number" s (or j, or j') corresponds to the magnitude of angular momentum, the second λ (or m, or m') to its component along an arbitrary chosen "quantization axis", and λ takes on $2s + 1$ values: $-s, -s + 1, \ldots, s$ (similarly for m and m'). The energy levels for the initial and final states, and the a priori possible transitions are depicted in Fig. 4.1 for the case of $j = j' = 1$, and we shall assume $s = 1$ as well.

The probability (intensity) for each transition is, according to quantum mechanics [Messiah, Schiff], proportional to $|f|^2$ where $f = \langle j'm'|O^s_\lambda|jm\rangle$ where O^s_λ is "multipole transition operator" [cf. Sec. 8.7] for the process. This permits the use of the Wigner-Eckart theorem which implies $f = f_0 \langle j', m'(s, j)\lambda, m\rangle$ where f_0 is the "reduced matrix element", and $\langle j, m(s, j)\lambda, m\rangle$ is the relevant Clebsch-Gordan coefficient. [α in Theorem 4.5 is identical to 1 for the group R_3.] As a consequence, all 9 potential transitions are determined by one constant f_0. The Clebsch-Gordan coefficients $\langle 1, m'(1, 1)\lambda, m\rangle$ vanish unless $m' = \lambda + m$, and the non-zero elements are given in Table 4.1. From this information we can predict that, unless there are other

Table 4.1 Clebsch-Gordan coefficients $\langle 1, m'(1, 1)\, m' - m, m\rangle$

m' \ m	-1	0	1
-1	$\sqrt{\frac{1}{2}}$	$\sqrt{\frac{1}{3}}$	0
0	$-\sqrt{\frac{1}{2}}$	$-\sqrt{\frac{1}{3}}$	$\sqrt{\frac{1}{2}}$
1	0	$\sqrt{\frac{1}{3}}$	$-\sqrt{\frac{1}{2}}$

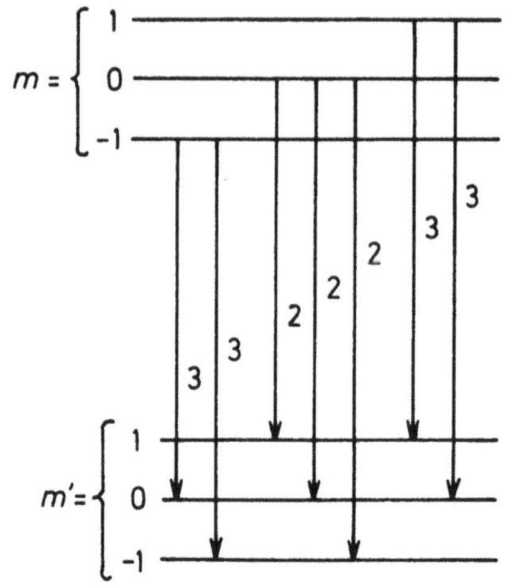

Fig. 4.2 Allowed transitions and branching ratios.

reasons forbidding the transition, there should be 7 distinct transitions. These are depicted in Fig. 4.2 with their relative intensities (also called "branching ratios") labelling the lines. [In reality, there is also space inversion symmetry (parity conservation), which forbids about half of the transitions shown in Fig. 4.2. We shall reconsider this example in Chap. 11.]

Problems

4.1 Let $G = \mathrm{T}^{\mathrm{d}}$ be the discrete translational symmetry group, V be the vector space of one particle on the one-dimensional lattice of Chap. 1, and P_k be the projection operator to the irreducible representation described in this chapter. If $|x\rangle = |nb + y\rangle$, $n =$ integer and $-b/2 < y \leq b/2$, prove that $\mathrm{P}_k|x\rangle = \mathrm{P}_k|y\rangle e^{-iknb}$ so that $\mathrm{P}_k|x\rangle e^{ikx} = \mathrm{P}_k|y\rangle e^{iky}$. Compare with Eq. (1.3-6).

4.2 Let $G = \mathrm{S}_3$ and $\mathrm{V} = \mathrm{V}_2 \times \mathrm{V}_2$ where V_2 is the two-dimensional vector space of Problem 3.1. Starting with basis vectors $\hat{\mathbf{e}}_x\hat{\mathbf{e}}_x, \hat{\mathbf{e}}_x\hat{\mathbf{e}}_y, \hat{\mathbf{e}}_y\hat{\mathbf{e}}_x$, and $\hat{\mathbf{e}}_y\hat{\mathbf{e}}_y$, construct four new basis vectors which transform irreducibly under S_3. Use the projection operator technique.

4.3 Prove that the operators $\mathrm{P}^i_{\mu j}$ have the following property: $\mathrm{P}^{j\,\dagger}_{\mu i} = \mathrm{P}^i_{\mu j}$.

4.4 Prove that:

$$\text{(i)}\quad \mathrm{P}^{j\,\dagger}_{\mu i}\,\mathrm{P}^{j}_{\mu i} = \mathrm{P}_{\mu i} \quad ;$$

and

$$\text{(ii)}\quad \mathrm{P}_{\mu i}\,\mathrm{P}^{l}_{\sigma k}\,\mathrm{P}_{\nu j} = \delta_{\mu\sigma}\,\delta_{\sigma\nu}\,\delta^{l}_{j}\,\delta_{ik}\,\mathrm{P}^{l}_{\sigma k} \quad .$$

Use (ii) to interpret $P^{l}_{\sigma k}$ as the "transfer operator" from vectors of type $|\sigma l\rangle$ to the type $|\sigma k\rangle$.

4.5 Suppressing the irreducible label μ and matrix indices (i, j), Definition 4.3 for irreducible operators can be written as

$$U(g)O\,U(g)^{-1} = O\,D(g)$$

where $\{D(g);\, g \in G\}$ form a representation of the group G. Consider replacing the right-hand side of this equation by the following alternatives, in turn:

$$\text{(i)}\;\; O\,D(g)^* \qquad \text{(ii)}\;\; O\,D(g^{-1}) \qquad \text{(iii)}\;\; O\,D(g)^\dagger$$
$$\text{(iv)}\;\; D(g)^{\mathrm{T}}O \qquad \text{(v)}\;\; D(g^{-1})O \qquad \text{(vi)}\;\; D(g)^\dagger\,O \quad ,$$

where the order of appearance of the two factors is important because of the implied matrix multiplication. In which of the six cases do we get true representations of the group G on the space of the linear operators $\{O^\mu_i\}$; thereby obtain viable alternatives to the original definition? Among the original definition and the alternatives, which ones are equivalent to each other if (a) $D(G)$ is unitary, (b) $D(G)$ is equivalent to $D(G)^*$, (c) $D(G)$ is both unitary and equivalent to $D(G)^*$?

CHAPTER 5

REPRESENTATIONS OF THE SYMMETRIC GROUPS

The symmetric or permutation groups S_n and their representations are important for a number of reasons. First, recall that all finite groups of order n are subgroups of S_n (Cayley's Theorem, Sec. 2.3). Knowledge of the representations of S_n can, therefore, be useful in the study of representations of other finite groups. Secondly, as we shall see, the irreducible representations of S_n provide a valuable tool to analyze the irreducible representations of the important classical continuous groups—such as GL(m), U(m), and SU(m) (m = integer)—through tensor analysis. Furthermore, permutation symmetry is of direct relevance to physical systems consisting of identical particles. Therefore, the study of group theory in both mathematics and physics requires a reasonable familiarity with the representations of S_n.

We have discussed, in previous chapters, the representations of the simpler symmetric groups S_2 ($=C_2$) and S_3 for the purpose of illustrating general group representation theory methods. In this chapter, we shall construct all inequivalent irreducible representations of S_n for an arbitrary n. Section 1 describes the one dimensional representations of S_n from two alternative points of view. The basic tools for the general analysis are introduced in Secs. 2 and 3; they consist of Young diagrams, Young tableaux, and the associated symmetrizers, anti-symmetrizers, and irreducible symmetrizers. The case of S_3 is worked out in detail to illustrate the use of these tools in a concrete example, and to motivate the general method. The main theorems on the irreducible representations of S_n are discussed in Sec. 4. It is shown that the irreducible symmetrizers provide the necessary projection operators (called idempotents) to generate all such representations on the group algebra space. In fact, this method leads to the complete decomposition of the regular representation of S_n. The last section (Sec. 5) explores the power of the same symmetrizers applied to another important area of group representation theory—the analysis of finite dimensional irreducible representations of the general linear group GL(m). This significant application of the Young symmetrizers is based on the intricate complementary roles played by the two groups S_n and GL(m) on the space of nth-rank tensors in m-dimensional space. Tensors of specific symmetries and symmetry classes, which have a wide range of use, are introduced. This section will provide the basis for a systematic study of the representations of the classical groups to be given in Chap. 13.

For the sake of clarity, we shall emphasize the precise presentation of the methodology and the results rather than details of the derivations. To this end, most of the technical material and lengthy proofs which are not needed in any other parts of the book will be relegated to Appendix IV. For those who are mainly interested in the applications of Young tableaux, it will not be detrimental to skip these proofs and take the stated theorems on faith. Since use is made of properties of idempotents on the group algebra space in the discussion of the theorems, some knowledge of the content of Appendix III is desirable. If a full understanding of the details is desired, then Appendix III is a prerequisite and Appendix IV is a corequisite.

5.1 One-Dimensional Representations

Every symmetric group S_n has a non-trivial invariant subgroup A_n consisting of all even permutations. (An *even permutation* is one which is equivalent to an even number of simple transpositions.) This subgroup is called the *alternating group*. The factor group S_n/A_n is isomorphic to C_2. It follows that every S_n has two one-dimensional irreducible representations which are induced by the two representations of C_2. [cf. Table 3.1] The first is the identity representation. The second assigns to each permutation p the number $(-1)^p$ which is 1 if p is "even" and -1 if p is "odd". We shall refer to $(-1)^p$ as the *parity* of the permutation p.

An alternative way of deriving the one-dimensional representations of S_n is by means of the idempotents (i.e. projection operators on the group algebra; cf. Appendix III).

Theorem 5.1: The *symmetrizer* $s = \sum_p p$ and the *anti-symmetrizer* $a = \sum_p (-1)^p p$ of the group S_n are essentially idempotent and primitive.

Proof: Using the rearrangement lemma, it is straightforward to show that $qs = sq = s$ for all $q \in S_n$. It follows then that $ss = n!\, s$, and $sqs = ss = n!\, s$. According to the discussions of Appendix III, s is essentially idempotent and primitive. Similarly, for the anti-symmetrizer, we have $qa = aq = (-1)^q a$, which implies $aa = n!\, a$ and $aqa = (-1)^q n!\, a$ for all $q \in S_n$. The same result then follows. QED

According to Appendix III.3, s and a generate irreducible representations of S_n on the group algebra. Since $sqa = sa = 0$ for all $q \in S_n$, the two representations are inequivalent. The basis vectors of the irreducible representations are of the form $|q\,s\rangle$ and $|q\,a\rangle$ respectively. But since $qs = s$ and $qa = (-1)^q a$ for all $q \in S_n$, both representations are one-dimensional and the matrix elements are 1 and $(-1)^q$ respectively. Thus we reproduce the previous results.

5.2 Partitions and Young Diagrams

In order to generate primitive idempotents for all the irreducible representations of S_n, it is convenient to introduce Young Diagrams. We begin with the idea of "partitions".

Definition 5.1 (Partition of n, Young Diagram): (i) A *partition* $\lambda \equiv \{\lambda_1, \lambda_2, \ldots, \lambda_r\}$ of the integer n is a sequence of positive integers λ_i, arranged in descending order, whose sum is equal to n: $\lambda_i \geq \lambda_{i+1}$, $i = 1, \ldots, r-1$; and $\sum_{i=1}^{r} \lambda_i = n$.

(ii) Two partitions λ, μ are *equal* if $\lambda_i = \mu_i$ for all i.

(iii) $\lambda > \mu$ ($\lambda < \mu$) if the first non-zero number in the sequence $(\lambda_i - \mu_i)$ is positive (negative).

(iv) A partition λ is represented graphically by a *Young Diagram* which consists of n squares arranged in r rows, the ith one of which contains λ_i squares.

Example 1:   For the case $n = 3$, there are three distinct partitions: $\{3\}$, $\{2,1\}$, and $\{1,1,1\}$. The corresponding Young diagrams are

Example 2:   For the case of $n = 4$, there are five distinct partitions: $\{4\}$, $\{3,1\}$, $\{2,2\}$, $\{2,1,1\}$, and $\{1,1,1,1\}$. The corresponding Young diagrams are

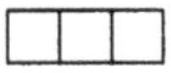

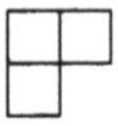

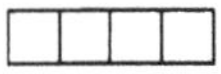

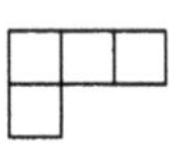

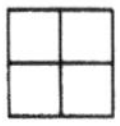

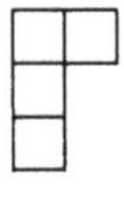

There is a one-to-one correspondence between the partitions of n and the classes of group elements in S_n. Recall that every class S_n is characterized by a given "cycle structure" consisting of, say, ν_1 1-cycles, ν_2 2-cycles, ... etc. Since the numbers $1, 2, \ldots, n$ fill all the cycles, we must have: $n = \nu_1 + 2\nu_2 + 3\nu_3 + \cdots = (\nu_1 + \nu_2 + \cdots) + (\nu_2 + \nu_3 + \cdots) + (\nu_3 + \cdots) + \cdots$. If we equate the parentheses of the last expression to $\lambda_1, \lambda_2, \lambda_3, \ldots$ etc., clearly $\lambda_1 \geq \lambda_{i+1}$ and $\sum_i \lambda_i = n$. Thus $\lambda \equiv \{\lambda_i\}$ is a partition of n.

Theorem 5.2:   The number of distinct Young diagrams for any given n is equal to the number of classes of S_n—which is, in turn, equal to the number of inequivalent irreducible representations of S_n. [Cf. Corollary to Theorem 3.7.]

Example: For S_3, the class $\{e\}$ corresponds to $\nu_1 = 3$, $\nu_2 = \nu_3 = 0$; the class $\{(12), (23), (31)\}$ to $\nu_1 = \nu_2 = 1$, $\nu_3 = 0$; and the class $\{(123), (321)\}$ to $\nu_1 = \nu_2 = 0$, $\nu_3 = 1$. The corresponding $(\lambda_1, \lambda_2, \lambda_3)$ are $(3, 0, 0)$, $(2, 1, 0)$, and $(1, 1, 1)$ respectively—as given before.

Definition 5.2 (Young Tableau, Normal Tableau, Standard Tableau):   (i) A *Young Tableau* is obtained by filling the squares of a Young diagram with numbers $1, 2, \ldots, n$ in any order, each number being used only once;
(ii) A *normal Young tableau* is one in which the numbers $1, 2, \ldots, n$ appear in order from left to right and from the top row to the bottom row;
(iii) A *standard Young tableau* is one in which the numbers in each row appear increasing (not necessarily in strict order) to the right and those in each column appear increasing to the bottom.

Example: $\begin{array}{|c|c|c|}\hline 1 & 2 & 3 \\\hline 4 \\\cline{1-1}\end{array}$, $\begin{array}{|c|c|}\hline 1 & 2 \\\hline 3 & 4 \\\hline\end{array}$ are normal tableaux and $\begin{array}{|c|c|c|}\hline 1 & 2 & 4 \\\hline 3 \\\cline{1-1}\end{array}$, $\begin{array}{|c|c|}\hline 1 & 3 \\\hline 2 & 4 \\\hline\end{array}$ are standard tableaux of S_4.

We shall refer to the normal Young tableau associated with a partition λ by the symbol Θ_λ. An arbitrary tableau can be obtained from the corresponding Θ_λ by applying an appropriate permutation p on the numbers $1, 2, \ldots, n$ in the boxes; hence it can be uniquely referred to as Θ_λ^p. Symbolically, we represent this relationship by: $\Theta_\lambda^p = p\,\Theta_\lambda$. It should be quite obvious that $q\,\Theta_\lambda^p = \Theta_\lambda^{qp}$.

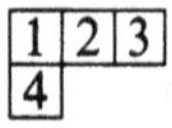

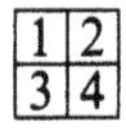

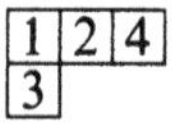

5.3 Symmetrizers and Anti-Symmetrizers of Young Tableaux

To each Young tableau, one can define a primitive idempotent which generates an irreducible representation of S_n on the group algebra space. These idempotents are constructed from corresponding "symmetrizers" and "anti-symmetrizers", which, in turn, are built from "horizontal" and "vertical" permutations. We introduce them in logical order.

Definition 5.3 (Horizontal and Vertical Permutations): Given a Young tableau Θ^p_λ, we define *horizontal permutations* $\{h^p_\lambda\}$ which leave invariant the sets of numbers appearing in the same row of Θ^p_λ. Similarly, we define *vertical peermutations* $\{v^p_\lambda\}$ which leave invariant the sets of numbers appearing in the same column of Θ^p_λ.

It is easy to see that the cycles comprising a horizontal permutation h^p_λ must only contain numbers which appear in the same row of the corresponding Young diagram Θ^p_λ. Likewise, the cycles in a vertical permutation v^p_λ must only involve numbers in the same column.

Definition 5.4 (Symmetrizer, Anti-symmetrizer, Irreducible Symmetrizer): The *symmetrizer* s^p_λ, the *anti-symmetrizer* a^p_λ, and the *irreducible symmetrizer* e^p_λ associated with the Young tableau Θ^p_λ are defined as:

$$s^p_\lambda = \sum_h h^p_\lambda \qquad \text{(sum over all horizontal permutations);}$$

$$a^p_\lambda = \sum_v (-1)^{v_\lambda} v^p_\lambda \qquad \text{(sum over all vertical permutations);}$$

$$e^p_\lambda = \sum_{h,v} (-1)^{v_\lambda} h^p_\lambda v^p_\lambda \qquad \text{(sum over all } h^p_\lambda \text{ and } v^p_\lambda\text{).}$$

The irreducible symmetrizer e^p_λ will sometimes be called a *Young Symmetrizer*.
Example: We evaluate symmetrizers and anti-symmetrizers associated with the *normal* Young tableaux of the group S_3,

$\Theta_1 = \boxed{1}\boxed{2}\boxed{3}$: All p are h_λ; only e is a v_λ. Hence $s_1 = \sum_p p = s$ (symmetrizers of the full group); $a_1 = e$; and $e_1 = es = s$.

$\Theta_2 = \begin{array}{|c|c|}\hline 1 & 2 \\ \hline 3 & \\ \cline{1-1}\end{array}$: Now, e, (12) are h_λ; e, (31) are v_λ. Hence $s_2 = e + (12)$; $a_2 = e - (31)$; and $e_2 = s_2 a_2 = e + (12) - (31) - (321)$.

$\Theta_3 = \begin{array}{|c|}\hline 1 \\ \hline 2 \\ \hline 3 \\ \hline\end{array}$: Only e is a h_λ, all p are v_λ. Hence $s_3 = e$; $a_3 = \sum_p (-1)^p p = a$; and $e_3 = ea = a$.

Similarly, for the only remaining standard tableau,

$\Theta^{(23)}_2 = \begin{array}{|c|c|}\hline 1 & 3 \\ \hline 2 & \\ \cline{1-1}\end{array}$: The h_λ are e, (31); the v_λ are e, (12); hence $s^{(23)}_2 = e + (31)$; $a^{(23)}_2 = e - (12)$; and $e^{(23)}_2 = e + (31) - (12) - (123)$.

Based on this example, we make a series of observations which will prove to be useful for subsequent development.

(i) For each tableau Θ_λ, the horizontal permutations $\{h_\lambda\}$ and the vertical permutations $\{v_\lambda\}$ each form a subgroup of S_n;

(ii) Since s_λ and a_λ are the (total) symmetrizer and anti-symmetrizer of the respective subgroups, they clearly satisfy the relations, $s_\lambda h_\lambda = h_\lambda s_\lambda = s_\lambda$, $a_\lambda v_\lambda = v_\lambda a_\lambda = (-1)^{v_\lambda} a_\lambda$; $s_\lambda s_\lambda = n_\lambda s_\lambda$; $a_\lambda a_\lambda = n_\lambda a_\lambda$ (where $n_\lambda = \lambda_1!\lambda_2!\cdots\lambda_n!$). Thus s_λ and a_λ are idempotents [cf. Appendix III]. They are, however, in general, not primitive idempotents.

(iii) e_λ are primitive idempotents. This is evident for $e_1 = s$ and $e_3 = a$. We leave it as an exercise [cf. Problem 5.3] for the reader to verify by explicit calculation that e_2 and $e_2^{(23)}$ are also primitive idempotents.

(iv) We already know that e_1 and e_3 generate the two inequivalent one-dimensional representations of S_3. Likewise, e_2 generates the two-dimensional irreducible representation of S_3 mentioned in Chap. 3. [See Table 3.3 and Problem 3.5.] We can verify that right multiplication by e_2 on $p \in S_3$ generates a two-dimensional subspace of the group algebra. Indeed,

$$
\begin{aligned}
&ee_2 = e_2 \qquad\qquad (12)e_2 = e_2 \\
&(23)e_2 = (23) + (321) - (123) - (12) \equiv r_2 \\
&(31)e_2 = (31) + (123) - e - (23) = -e_2 - r_2 \\
&(123)e_2 = (123) + (31) - (23) - e = -e_2 - r_2 \\
&(321)e_2 = (321) + (23) - (12) - (123) = r_2
\end{aligned}
$$

and the subspace (or left ideal) is spanned by e_2 and r_2. (The choice of the basis vectors, of course, is arbitrary.) We conclude that the symmetrizers of the normal Young tableaux generate all irreducible representations of the group.

(v) It is equally straightforward to verify that $e_2^{(23)}$ also generates a two-dimensional irreducible representation. It is, by necessity, *equivalent* to the one described above (as S_3 has only one such representation). We note, however, the invariant subspace (i.e. left ideal) generated by $e_2^{(23)}$ is distinct from the previous one. It is spanned by $e_2^{(23)}$ and $r_2^{(23)} = (123) + (23) - (31) - (321)$; it does not overlap with any of the left ideals generated by the other tableaux.

(vi) The four left ideals generated by the idempotents of the four standard Young tableaux e_1, e_2, $e_2^{(23)}$, and e_3 together span the whole group algebra space $\tilde{S}_3$. In other words, $\tilde{S}_3$ is the direct sum of these (non-overlapping) left ideals. The identity element has the following decomposition:

$$
e = \frac{1}{6} e_1 + \frac{1}{3} e_2 + \frac{1}{3} e_2^{(23)} + \frac{1}{6} e_3 \quad . \tag{5.3-1}
$$

Thus, the regular representation of S_3 is fully reduced by using the irreducible symmetrizers associated with the standard Young tableaux.

5.4 Irreducible Representations of S_n

Based on the experience with the S_3 example discussed above, we now develop the central theorems of the theory of irreducible representations of S_n. The symmetrizers and anti-symmetrizers associated with Young tableaux form the basis to construct primitive idempotents according to the general method described in Appendix III. To avoid obscuring the essential results by too many technical details, we relegate to Appendix IV a number of lemmas whose sole use to us is to help prove the following theorems. To simplify the notation, a superscript p to Θ_λ, s_λ, a_λ, and e_λ is omitted in most of the following discussions: all results apply to an arbitrary Young tableau although the explicit notation may suggest a normal tableau.

Theorem 5.3: The symmetrizers associated with a Young tableau Θ_λ have the following properties:

(5.4-1) $$s_\lambda r\, a_\lambda = \xi e_\lambda \qquad \text{for every } r \in \tilde{S}_n$$

(5.4-2) $$e_\lambda{}^2 = \eta\, e_\lambda$$

where ξ and η are two ordinary numbers. Furthermore, $\eta \neq 0$ hence e_λ is essentially idempotent.

Proof: (i) Let h_λ (v_λ) be an arbitrary horizontal (vertical) permutation associated with Θ_λ; it follows from simple identities established in Lemma IV.2 that,

$$h_\lambda(s_\lambda r\, a_\lambda)v_\lambda = (h_\lambda s_\lambda)r(a_\lambda v_\lambda) = (s_\lambda r\, v_\lambda)(-1)^{v_\lambda} \quad .$$

Lemma IV.5 then ensures that $s_\lambda r\, a_\lambda = \xi\, e_\lambda$.
(ii) Since $e_\lambda{}^2 = (s_\lambda a_\lambda)(s_\lambda a_\lambda) = s_\lambda(a_\lambda s_\lambda)a_\lambda$, the first part of this theorem guarantees that the right-hand side is proportional to e_λ. Hence $e_\lambda{}^2 = \eta\, e_\lambda$.
(iii) To check whether $\eta = 0$, we need to examine the proof of Lemma IV.5 in some detail. As applied to the case at hand, the factor η is equal to the coefficient of the identity term in the expansion of $e_\lambda{}^2 = \sum h_\lambda v_\lambda h_\lambda' v_\lambda' (-1)^{v_\lambda}(-1)^{v_\lambda'}$ in terms of group elements. But since e is the common element of the two subgroups $\{v_\lambda\}$ and $\{h_\lambda\}$, it appears at least once in the expansion. Furthermore, if it occurs more than once in the above sum, the contribution is always positive. Therefore the relevant coefficient is always a non-vanishing positive integer, and e_λ is essentially idempotent. QED

Theorem 5.4: The "irreducible symmetrizer" e_λ associated with the Young tableau Θ_λ is a primitive idempotent. It generates an irreducible representation of S_n on the group algebra space.

Proof: We already know e_λ is an idempotent. Making use of Theorem 5.3 above, we easily establish

$$e_\lambda r\, e_\lambda = s_\lambda(a_\lambda r\, s_\lambda)a_\lambda = \xi\, e_\lambda$$

for all $r \in \tilde{S}_n$. By the criterion of Theorem III.3, e_λ is a primitive idempotent. QED

We remind the reader that in the previous section we have seen several examples of these irreducible symmetrizers at work for the group S_3: e_1 and e_3 for the one-dimensional representations, e_2 and $e_2^{(23)}$ for two equivalent two-dimensional representations.

Theorem 5.5: The irreducible representations generated by e_λ and $e_\lambda{}^p$, $p \in S_n$, are equivalent.

Proof: This result can be established by applying Theorem III.4. We simply note: $e_\lambda{}^p = p\, e_\lambda p^{-1}$, hence $e_\lambda{}^p\, p\, e_\lambda = p\, e_\lambda p^{-1}\, p\, e_\lambda = \eta\, p\, e_\lambda$ which is non-vanishing. QED

For an example of this result, we again recall the two-dimensional representations generated by e_2 and $e_2^{(23)}$ for S_3.

Theorem 5.6: Two irreducible symmetrizers e_λ and e_μ generate inequivalent (irreducible) representations if the corresponding Young diagrams are different (i.e. if $\lambda \neq \mu$).

Proof: With no loss of generality, assume $\lambda > \mu$. Let p be any element of S_n, then

$$e_\mu p e_\lambda = e_\mu (p e_\lambda p^{-1}) p = (e_\mu e_\lambda^p) p = 0$$

where the last equality is a consequence of Lemma IV.6. It follows that,

$$e_\mu r e_\lambda = 0 \qquad \text{for all } r \in \tilde{S}_n$$

as r is a linear combination of $p \in S_n$. By theorem III.4, the two primitive idempotents e_μ and e_λ generate inequivalent representations. QED

We have seen, in the case of S_3, that e_1, e_2, and e_3—which are associated with distinct Young diagrams—do generate inequivalent representations.

Corollary: If $\lambda \neq \mu$, then $e_\lambda^p e_\mu^q = 0$, for all $p, q \in S_n$.

When $\lambda < \mu$, the result is proved in Lemma IV.6. When $\lambda > \mu$, the proof is left as an exercise [Problem 5.4].

Theorem 5.7 (Irreducible Representations of S_n): The irreducible symmetrizers $\{e_\lambda\}$ associated with the normal Young tableaux $\{\Theta_\lambda\}$ generate all the inequivalent irreducible representations of S_n.

Proof: This very important result is an obvious consequence of the following observations:

(i) The number of inequivalent irreducible representations of S_n is equal to the number of Young diagrams [Theorem 5.2];
(ii) There is one e_λ associated with each Young diagram (corresponding to the normal tableau); and
(iii) Every e_λ generates an inequivalent irreducible representation [Theorem 5.6].
QED

To conclude, we state without proof the theorem governing the complete decomposition of the regular representation of S_n. [Boerner, Miller]

Theorem 5.8 (Decomposition of the Regular Representation of S_n): (i) The left ideals generated by the idempotents associated with distinct *standard* Young tableaux are linearly independent; (ii) the direct sum of the left ideals generated by all standard tableaux spans the whole group algebra space $\tilde{S}_n$.

5.5 Symmetry Classes of Tensors

An important application of the Young-tableau method and the irreducible representations of S_n concerns the construction and the classification of irreducible tensors in physics and in mathematics.

Let V_m be a m-dimensional vector space, and $\{g\}$ be the set of invertible linear transformations on V_m. With respect to the law of multiplication for linear transformations, $\{g\}$ forms a group commonly called the *general linear group* GL(m, C). In this chapter, we shall refer to this group simply as G_m. Given any basis

$\{|i\rangle, i = 1,2,\ldots,m\}$ on V_m, a natural matrix representation of G_m is obtained by:

$$g\,|i\rangle = |j\rangle\, g^j{}_i \tag{5.5-1}$$

where $(g^j{}_i)$ are elements of an invertible $m \times m$ matrix (i.e. $\det g \neq 0$).

Definition 5.5 (Tensor Space): The direct product space $V_m \times V_m \times \cdots \times V_m$ involving n factors of V shall be referred to as the *tensor space* and denoted by V^n_m.

Given a basis $\{|i\rangle\}$ on V_m, a natural basis for V^n_m is obtained in the form:

$$|i_1 i_2 \cdots i_n\rangle = |i_1\rangle \cdot |i_2\rangle \cdots |i_n\rangle \quad . \tag{5.5-2}$$

When no confusion is likely to arise, we shall refer to this basis simply as $\{|i\rangle_n\}$. An arbitrary element x of the tensor space V^n_m has the decomposition,

$$|x\rangle = |i_1\, i_2 \cdots i_n\rangle\, x^{i_1 i_2 \cdots i_n} \tag{5.5-3}$$

where $\{x^{i_1 i_2 \cdots i_n}\} \equiv \{x^{\{i\}}\}$ are the *tensor components* of x. The above equation shall often be abbreviated as:

$$|x\rangle = |i\rangle_n\, x^{\{i\}} \quad . \tag{5.5-4}$$

Elements of the group G_m (defined on V_m) induce the following linear transformations on the tensor space V^n_m.

$$g|i\rangle_n = |j\rangle_n\, D(g)^{\{j\}}{}_{\{i\}} \tag{5.5-5}$$

where

$$D(g)^{\{j\}}{}_{\{i\}} = g^{j_1}{}_{i_1}\, g^{j_2}{}_{i_2} \ldots g^{j_n}{}_{i_n} \tag{5.5-6}$$

for all $g \in G_m$. It can easily be verified that $\{D(g)\}$ forms a $(n \cdot m)$-dimensional representation of G_m, and that for any $|x\rangle \in V^n_m$,

$$g\,|x\rangle = |x_g\rangle = |j\rangle_n x_g{}^{\{j\}} \tag{5.5-7}$$

where

$$x_g{}^{\{j\}} = D(g)^{\{j\}}{}_{\{i\}}\, x^{\{i\}} \tag{5.5-8}$$

where the simplified notation of Eqs. (5.5-4)–(5.5-6) is used.

Independently, the symmetric group S_n also has a natural realization on the tensor space V^n_m. In particular, consider the mapping $p \in S_n \to p =$ linear transformation on V^n_m defined by,

$$p\,|x\rangle = |x_p\rangle, \tag{5.5-9}$$

where $|x\rangle, |x_p\rangle \in V^n_m$ and

$$x_p{}^{i_1 i_2 \cdots i_n} = x^{i_{p1} i_{p2} \ldots i_{pn}} \quad . \tag{5.5-10}$$

In terms of the basis vectors $\{|i\rangle_n\}$, the action of p goes as

$$p\,|i_1\, i_2 \cdots i_n\rangle = |i_{p_1^{-1}}\, i_{p_2^{-1}} \cdots i_{p_n^{-1}}\rangle = |i_{p^{-1}}\rangle_n \quad . \tag{5.5-11}$$

Therefore, if we write

$$p\,|i\rangle_n = |j\rangle_n\, D(p)^{\{j\}}{}_{\{i\}} \tag{5.5-12}$$

then

(5.5-13) $$D(p)^{\{j\}}_{\{i\}} = \delta^{j_1}_{i_{p_1^{-1}}} \cdots \delta^{j_n}_{i_{p_n^{-1}}} = \delta^{j_{p1}}_{i_1} \cdots \delta^{j_{pn}}_{i_n} \quad .$$

The last equality involves permuting the n δ-factors by p. The reader should verify that Eq. (5.5-9), or equivalently (5.5-11), does provide a representation of the group S_n. [Problem 5.5]

Both the representations discussed above, $D[G_m]$ for the linear group and $D[S_n]$ for the symmetric group, are in general reducible. As S_n is a finite group, we know from the theorems of Chap. 3 that $D[S_n]$ can be decomposed into irreducible representations. In fact, we shall see shortly that the irreducible symmetrizers associated with Young tableaux provide an effective method to achieve this decomposition. On the other hand, the group G_m is an infinite group. A general reducible representation of G_m is not guaranteed to be fully decomposible. We shall demonstrate, however, that the reduction of the tensor space V^n_m by Young symmetrizers from the $\tilde{S}_n$ algebra leads naturally to a full decomposition of $D[G_m]$. This interesting and useful result is a consequence of the fact that linear transformations on V^n_m representing $\{g \in G_m\}$ and $\{p \in S_n\}$ commute with each other, and each type of operator constitutes essentially the "maximal set" which has this property.

It is useful to bear in mind the above observation as we begin to establish the relevant theory. The underlying principle behind these results is very similar to, and in fact is a generalization of, the familiar facts that: (i) a complete set of commuting operators on a vector space share common eigenvectors; and (ii) a decomposition of reducible subspaces with respect to some subset of the commuting operators often leads naturally to diagonalization of the remaining operator(s). We have made use of this principle to diagonalize the Hamiltonian for a general one-dimensional lattice by taking advantage of the discrete translational symmetry group. Similarly, as is often done in the solution to physical problems involving spherical symmetry, the Hamiltonian is diagonalized by decomposing first with respect to angular momentum operators.

Lemma 5.1: The representation matrices $D(G_m)$, Eq. (5.5-6), and $D(S_n)$, Eq. (5.5-13) satisfy the following symmetry relation:

(5.5-14) $$D^{\{j\}}_{\{i\}} = D^{\{j_q\}}_{\{i_q\}}$$

where $\{i_q\} = (i_{q_1} i_{q_2} \cdots i_{q_n})$ and $q = \begin{pmatrix} 1 & 2 & \cdots n \\ q_1 & q_2 & q_n \end{pmatrix} \in S$.

Linear transformations on V^n_m satisfying this condition are said to be *symmetry-preserving*.

Proof: The equality follows from the product form of the matrix elements, Eqs. (5.5-6) and (5.5-13). The value of the products clearly does not depend on the order in which the n-factors are placed. Permuting the n-factors by an arbitrary element (q) of S_n results in the simultaneous reshuffling of the superscripts and the subscripts by the same permutation. QED

Theorem 5.9: The two sets of matrices $\{D(p), p \in S_n\}$ and $\{D(g), g \in G_m\}$ commute with each other.

Proof: Consider the action of pg and gp on the basis vectors in turn:

(i) $pg\,|i\rangle_n = p\,|j\rangle_n D(g)^{\{j\}}{}_{\{i\}} = |j_{p^{-1}}\rangle_n D(g)^{\{j\}}{}_{\{i\}} = |j\rangle_n D(g)^{\{j_p\}}{}_{\{i\}}$;

(ii) $gp\,|i\rangle_n = g\,|i_{p^{-1}}\rangle_n = |j\rangle_n D(g)^{\{j\}}{}_{\{i_{p^{-1}}\}} = |j\rangle_n D(g)^{\{j_p\}}{}_{\{i\}}$.

In the last step of (i) we made use of the fact that $\{j\}$ are dummy summation indices, hence can be labelled in any convenient way. In the last step of (ii) we invoked Lemma 5.1. The equality of the right-hand sides of (i) and (ii) establishes the theorem. QED

Example 1: Consider second rank tensors ($n = 2$) in 2-dimensional space ($m = 2$). the basis vectors will be denoted by $|++\rangle$, $|+-\rangle$, $|-+\rangle$, and $|--\rangle$. Since the group S_2 has only two elements, and the identity element leads to trivial results, we need only to consider $p = (12) \in S_2$ and its interplay with elements of G_2. It is quite straightforward to see that,

$$pg\,|\pm\pm\rangle = p\,|ik\rangle\, g^i{}_\pm\, g^k{}_\pm = |ki\rangle\, g^k{}_\pm\, g^i{}_\pm = gp\,|\pm\pm\rangle$$
$$pg\,|\pm\mp\rangle = p\,|ik\rangle\, g^i{}_\pm\, g^k{}_\mp = |ki\rangle\, g^k{}_\mp\, g^i{}_\pm = g\,|\mp\pm\rangle = gp\,|\pm\mp\rangle.$$

These equalities hold for any element $g \in G_2$.

We shall now decompose the tensor space V^n_m into irreducible subspaces with respect to S_n and G_m, utilizing the irreducible symmetrizers associated with various Young tableaux of S_n. As before, let Θ^p_λ be a particular Young tableau and e^p_λ be the irreducible symmetrizer and L_λ be the left ideal generated by e_λ. The main results will be: (i) a subspace consisting of tensors of the form $r|\alpha\rangle$ for fixed $|\alpha\rangle \in V^n_m$ and arbitrary $r \in L_\lambda$ is irreducibly invariant under S_n; (ii) a subspace consisting of tensors of the form $e^p_\lambda|\alpha\rangle$ for arbitrary $\alpha \in V^n_m$ and fixed Θ^p_λ are irreducibly invariant under G_m; and (iii) the tensor space V^n_m can be decomposed in such a way that the basis vectors are of the "factorized" form $|\lambda, \alpha, a\rangle$ where λ denotes a *symmetry class* specified by a Young diagram, α labels the various irreducible invariant subspaces under S_n, and "a" labels the various irreducible invariant subspaces under G_m.

Definition 5.6 (Tensors of Symmetry Θ^p_λ and Tensors of Symmetry Class λ): To each Young tableau Θ^p_λ we associate *tensors of the symmetry* Θ^p_λ consisting of $\{e^p_\lambda|\alpha\rangle; |\alpha\rangle \in V^n_m\}$. For a given Young diagram characterized by λ, the set of tensors $\{re_\lambda|\alpha\rangle, r \in \tilde{S}_n, \alpha \in V^n_m\}$ is said to belong to the *symmetry class* λ.

We first consider the subspace $T_\lambda(\alpha)$ consisting of tensors $\{re_\lambda|\alpha\rangle, r \in \tilde{S}_n\}$ for a given $|\alpha\rangle$.

Theorem 5.10 (i) $T_\lambda(\alpha)$ is an irreducible invariant subspace with respect to S_n; (ii) if $T_\lambda(\alpha)$ is not empty, then the realization of S_n on $T_\lambda(\alpha)$ coincides with the irreducible representation generated by e_λ on the group algebra $\tilde{S}_n$.

Proof: (i) Let $|x\rangle \in T_\lambda(\alpha)$, then by definition,

$$|x\rangle = re_\lambda|\alpha\rangle \qquad \text{for some } r \in \tilde{S}_n$$

hence,

$$p|x\rangle = pre_\lambda|\alpha\rangle \in T_\lambda(\alpha) \qquad \text{for all } p \in S_n \quad .$$

This means $T_\lambda(\alpha)$ is invariant under S_n.

(ii) Since $T_\lambda(\alpha)$ is not empty, we know $e_\lambda|\alpha\rangle \neq 0$. Let $\{r_i e_\lambda\}$ be a basis of L_λ, then $\{r_i e_\lambda|\alpha\rangle\}$ form a basis of $T_\lambda(\alpha)$. Hence, if

$$p|r_i e_\lambda\rangle = |pr_i e_\lambda\rangle = |r_j e_\lambda\rangle D(p)^j{}_i \qquad \text{on } \tilde{S}_n$$

then,

$$pr_i e_\lambda|\alpha\rangle = r_j e_\lambda|\alpha\rangle D(p)^j{}_i \qquad \text{on } T_\lambda(\alpha)$$

for all $p \in S_n$. Hence the invariant subspace is irreducible, and the representation matrices on $T_\lambda(\alpha)$ coincide with those on $\tilde{S}_n$. QED

Let $\Theta_{\lambda=s} = \square\square\cdots\square$, then $e_s = \sum_p p/n!$ is the total symmetrizer. Since $re_s = e_s$ for all $r \in S_n$, the left ideal L_s is one-dimensional. Correspondingly, for any given element $|\alpha\rangle$ in the tensor space V_m^n, the irreducible subspace $T_s(\alpha)$ consists of all multiples of $e_s|\alpha\rangle$. These are *totally symmetric tensors*, as it is straightforward to verify:

$$e_s|\alpha\rangle\, n! = \sum_p p|i\rangle_n \alpha^{\{i\}} = \sum_p |i_{p^{-1}}\rangle_n \alpha^{\{i\}} = |i\rangle_n \sum_p \alpha^{\{i_p\}} \quad ; \qquad (5.5\text{-}15)$$

hence the components are totally symmetric in the n-indices. The realization of S_n on $T_\lambda(\alpha)$ is the one-dimensional identity representation because all permutations leave a totally symmetric tensor unchanged.

Example 2: Consider third rank tensors ($n = 3$) in two dimensions ($m = 2$). Four distinct totally symmetric tensors can be generated by starting with different elements of $V_2^{n=3}$:

(i) $|\alpha\rangle = |+++\rangle \quad e_s|\alpha\rangle = |+++\rangle \equiv |s,1,1\rangle$
(ii) $|\alpha\rangle = |++-\rangle \quad e_s|\alpha\rangle = [|++-\rangle + |+-+\rangle + |-++\rangle]/3 \equiv |s,2,1\rangle$
(iii) $|\alpha\rangle = |--+\rangle \quad e_s|\alpha\rangle = [|--+\rangle + |-+-\rangle + |+--\rangle]/3 \equiv |s,3,1\rangle$
(iv) $|\alpha\rangle = |---\rangle \quad e_s|\alpha\rangle = |---\rangle \equiv |s,4,1\rangle$.

In the last column, we introduced the labelling scheme for these irreducible tensors which was mentioned in the paragraph preceding Definition 5.6. This classification is used extensively in the following discussions. Each of the above totally symmetric tensors is invariant under all permutations of the S_3 group. Together, they represent all totally symmetric tensors that can be constructed in V_2^3; they are tensors of the symmetry class s, where s represents the Young tableau with one single row. We shall denote the subspace of tensors of the symmetry class s by T'_s.

Can we similarly generate totally anti-symmetric tensors in V_m^n? We leave as an exercise [Problem 5.6] for the reader to show that they exist only if $m \geq n$. The total anti-symmetrizer is $e_a = \sum_p (-1)^p p/n!$. Since $pe_a = (-1)^p e_a$, both L_a and $T_a(\alpha)$ are one-dimensional, and the realization of S_n on $T_a(\alpha)$ corresponds to the one-dimensional representation $p \to (-1)^p$.

Example 3: There is one and only one independent totally anti-symmetric tensor of rank n in n-dimensional space, usually denoted by ε. In two dimensions, its components are $\varepsilon^{12} = -\varepsilon^{21} = 1$, $\varepsilon^{11} = \varepsilon^{22} = 0$. In three dimensions, the components are $\varepsilon^{ijk} = \pm 1$ according to whether (ijk) is an even or odd permutation of (123); else, if any two indices are equal, then $\varepsilon^{ijk} = 0$.

Example 4: Consider second rank tensors ($n = 2$) in m-dimensions ($m \geq 2$),

$$e_s|ii\rangle = |ii\rangle \qquad i = 1, 2, \ldots, m$$

$$e_s|ij\rangle = [|ij\rangle + |ji\rangle]/2 \qquad i \neq j \quad .$$

There are $m(m-1)/2$ distinct anti-symmetric tensors, as

$$e_a|ii\rangle = 0$$

$$e_a|ij\rangle = [|ij\rangle - |ji\rangle]/2 \qquad i \neq j \quad .$$

Let us now turn to tensors with *mixed symmetry.*

Example 5: We return to 3rd rank tensors in 2-dimensions [cf. Example 2]. Consider tensors with symmetry associated with the normal young tableau $\Theta_{\lambda=m}$ and irreducible symmetrizer e_m, where

$$\Theta_m = \begin{array}{|c|c|}\hline 1 & 2 \\ \hline 3 & \\ \cline{1-1}\end{array} \quad \text{and} \quad e_m = [e + (12)][e - (31)]/4 \quad .$$

It is straightforward to show that two independent irreducible invariant subspaces of tensors with mixed symmetry can be generated.

(i) By choosing $|\alpha\rangle = |++-\rangle$, we obtain:

$$\begin{aligned} e_m|\alpha\rangle &= [e + (12)][|++-\rangle - |-++\rangle]/4 \\ &= [2|++-\rangle - |-++\rangle - |+-+\rangle]/4 \equiv |m, 1, 1\rangle \\ (23)e_m|\alpha\rangle &= (23)[2|++-\rangle - |-++\rangle - |+-+\rangle]/4 \\ &= [2|+-+\rangle - |-++\rangle - |++-\rangle]/4 \equiv |m, 1, 2\rangle \quad ; \end{aligned}$$

and, for any $r \in \tilde{S}_3$, $re_m|\alpha\rangle$ is a linear combination of the above two tensors. These two mixed tensors form a basis for $T_{\lambda=m}(1)$.

(ii) By choosing $|\alpha\rangle = |--+\rangle$, we similarly obtain:

$$\begin{aligned} e_m|\alpha\rangle &= [2|--+\rangle - |+--\rangle - |-+-\rangle]/4 \equiv |m, 2, 1\rangle \\ (23)e_m|\alpha\rangle &= [2|-+-\rangle - |+--\rangle - |--+\rangle]/4 \equiv |m, 2, 2\rangle \end{aligned}$$

as the basis for another irreducible invariant subspace of tensors with mixed symmetry $T_{\lambda=m}(2)$.

The realization of the group S_3 on either $T_m(1)$ or $T_m(2)$ corresponds to the 2-dimensional irreducible representation discussed in Sec. 5.2 and described earlier in Chap. 3 [cf. Table 3.3].

The two tensors of mixed symmetry $|m, i, 1\rangle, i = 1, 2$ (first ones of the two sets given above), are two linearly independent tensors of the form $e_m|\alpha\rangle$ with $|\alpha\rangle$ ranging over V_m^n. [Problem 5.8] They are tensors of the symmetry Θ_m. We call the subspace spanned by these vectors $T'_m(1)$. $T'_m(1)$ is an invariant subspace under G_2 since

$$g\, e_m|\alpha\rangle = e_m g|\alpha\rangle \in T'_m(1)$$

for all $|\alpha\rangle \in V_m^n$. One can also show that this invariant subspace is irreducible under G_2. [Problem 5.8]

Similarly, the two tensors $|m,i,2\rangle, i = 1,2$ (second ones of the two sets) are two linearly independent tensors of the form $e_m^{(23)}|\alpha\rangle$—as can easily be verified by noting that $(23)e_m = e_m^{(23)}(23)$. They are tensors of the symmetry $\Theta_m^{(23)}$. We denote the subspace spanned by these tensors by $T'_m(2)$. $T'_m(2)$ is also invariant under group transformations of G_2, and it is irreducible. Together, the two sets $\{T'_m(a), a = 1,2\}$ comprise tensors of the symmetry class m, where m denotes the Young diagram (frame) associated with the normal tableau Θ_m. For the sake of economy of indices, we shall use "α" in place of the label "i" from now on; it is understood that the range of this label is equal to the number of independent tensors that can be generated by $e_\lambda|\alpha\rangle$ with $|\alpha\rangle \in V_m^n$.

We note that for the 8-dimensional tensor space V_2^3, the use of Young symmetrizers (in Examples 2 and 5) leads to the complete decomposition into irreducible tensors $|\lambda,\alpha,a\rangle$ where λ $(=s,m)$ characterizes the symmetry class (Young diagram); "α" labels the distinct (but equivalent) sets of tensors $T_\lambda(\alpha)$ invariant under S_n; and "a" labels the basis elements within each set $T_\lambda(\alpha)$, it is associated with distinct symmetries (tableaux) in the same symmetry class. We have 4 totally symmetric tensors (Example 2) and 2 sets of 2 linearly independent mixed symmetry tensors. The latter can be classified either as belonging to two invariant subspaces under S_3 $\{T_m(\alpha), \alpha = 1,2\}$, or as belonging to two invariant subspaces under G_2 $\{T'_m(a), a = 1,2\}$. The latter comprise of tensors of two distinct symmetries associated with Θ_m and $\Theta_m^{(23)}$.

Bearing in mind these results for V_2^3, we return to the general case.

Theorem 5.11: (i) Two tensor subspaces irreducibly invariant with respect to S_n and belonging to the same symmetry class either overlap completely or they are disjoint; (ii) Two irreducible invariant tensor subspaces corresponding to two distinct symmetry classes are necessarily disjoint.

Proof: (i) Let $T_\lambda(\alpha)$ and $T_\lambda(\beta)$ be two invariant subspaces generated by the same irreducible symmetrizer e_λ. Either they are disjoint or they have at least one non-zero element in common. In the latter case, there are $s, s' \in \tilde{S}_n$ such that

$$s e_\lambda|\alpha\rangle = s' e_\lambda|\beta\rangle \quad .$$

This implies, $rse_\lambda|\alpha\rangle = rs'e_\lambda|\beta\rangle$ for all $r \in \tilde{S}_n$. When r ranges over all $\tilde{S}_n$, so do rs and rs'. Therefore, the left-hand side of the last equation ranges over $T_\lambda(\alpha)$ and the right-hand side ranges over $T_\lambda(\beta)$, hence the two invariant subspaces coincide.

(ii) Given any two subspaces $T_\lambda(\alpha)$ and $T_\mu(\beta)$ invariant under S_n; their intersection is also an invariant subspace. If $T_\lambda(\alpha)$ and $T_\mu(\beta)$ are irreducible, then either the intersection is the null set or it must coincide with both $T_\lambda(\alpha)$ and $T_\mu(\beta)$. If λ and μ correspond to different symmetry classes, then the second possibility is ruled out. Hence $T_\lambda(\alpha)$ and $T_\mu(\beta)$ have no elements in common if $\lambda \neq \mu$. QED

These general results permit the complete decomposition of the tensor space V_m^n into irreducible subspace $T_\lambda(\alpha)$ invariant under S_n. As explained when working on the the example of V_2^3, we shall use α as the label for distinct subspaces corresponding to the same symmetry class λ. The decomposition can be expressed as

$$V_m^n = \sum_{\lambda\oplus} \sum_{\alpha\oplus} T_\lambda(\alpha) \quad . \qquad (5.5\text{-}16)$$

The basis elements of the tensors in the various symmetry classes are denoted by $|\lambda, \alpha, a\rangle$ where a ranges from 1 to the dimension of $T_\lambda(\alpha)$. We can choose these bases in such a way that the representation matrices for S_n on $T_\lambda(\alpha)$ are identical for all α associated with the same λ, or

$$p\,|\lambda, \alpha, a\rangle = |\lambda, \alpha, b\rangle\, D_\lambda(p)^b{}_a \tag{5.5-17}$$

independently of α.

The central result of this section will be that the decomposition of V_m^n according to the symmetry classes of S_n, as described above, automatically provides a complete decomposition with respect to the general linear group G_m as well. We have already seen how this worked out in the case of V_2^3.

Theorem 5.12: If $g \in G_m$ and $\{|\lambda, \alpha, a\rangle\}$ is the set of basis tensors generated according to the above procedure, then the subspaces $T'_\lambda(a)$ spanned by $\{|\lambda, \alpha, a\rangle\}$ with fixed λ and a are invariant with respect to G_m, and the representations of G_m on $T'_\lambda(a)$ are independent of a: i.e.

$$g\,|\lambda, \alpha, a\rangle = |\lambda, \beta, a\rangle\, D_\lambda(g)^\beta{}_\alpha \quad . \tag{5.5-18}$$

Proof: (i) Given $r\,e_\lambda\,|\alpha\rangle \in T_\lambda(\alpha)$ and $g \in G_m$, we have

$$g\,(re_\lambda)\,|\alpha\rangle = (re_\lambda)\,g\,|\alpha\rangle \in T_\lambda(g\alpha) \quad .$$

Hence, the operations of the linear group do not change the symmetry class of the tensor, or

$$g\,|\lambda, \alpha, a\rangle = |\lambda, \beta, b\rangle\, D_\lambda(g)^{\beta b}{}_{\alpha a} \quad ;$$

(ii) We now show that $D_\lambda(g)$ is diagonal in the indices (b, a). To this end, we note, for $g \in G_m$ and $p \in S_n$,

$$g\,p\,|\lambda, \alpha, a\rangle = g\,|\lambda, \alpha, c\rangle\, D_\lambda(p)^c{}_a = |\lambda, \beta, b\rangle\, D_\lambda(g)^{\beta b}{}_{\alpha c}\, D_\lambda(p)^c{}_a \quad ;$$

and

$$p\,g\,|\lambda, \alpha, a\rangle = p\,|\lambda, \beta, c\rangle\, D_\lambda(g)^{\beta c}{}_{\alpha a} = |\lambda, \beta, b\rangle\, D_\lambda(p)^b{}_c\, D_\lambda(g)^{\beta c}{}_{\alpha a} \quad .$$

Since $g\,p = p\,g$ (Theorem 5.9), the two product matrices on the right-hand sides can be equated to each other. For clarity, let us designate quantities in square brackets as matrices in the space of Latin indices, and suppress these indices. We obtain

$$[D_\lambda(g)^\beta{}_\alpha][D_\lambda(p)] = [D_\lambda(p)][D_\lambda(g)^\beta{}_\alpha] \quad . \tag{5.5-19}$$

For given g, this equation holds for all $p \in S_n$. According to Schur's Lemma, the matrix $D_\lambda(g)^{\beta b}{}_{\alpha a}$ must be proportional to the unit matrix in the Latin indices. QED

Theorem 5.13 (Irreducible Representations of G_m): The representations of G_m on the subspace $T'_\lambda(a)$ of V_m^n as described above are irreducible representations.

Proof: Even though the complete proof involves some technical details [Miller], the basic idea behind it is rather easy to understand: since G_m is, so to speak, the most general group of transformations which commutes with S_n on V_m^n, on the subspace

T'_λ the operators $\{D(g), g \in G_m\}$ must be "complete"—they cannot be reducible. More specifically, consider an arbitrary linear transformation A on the vector space $T'_\lambda(a)$. In tensor component notation,

$$x^{\{i\}} \longrightarrow y^{\{i\}} = A^{\{i\}}{}_{\{j\}} x^{\{j\}} \quad .$$

Because $\mathbf{x}$ and $\mathbf{y}$ belong to the same symmetry class, A must be "symmetry preserving" in the sense that,

$$A^{\{i\}}{}_{\{j\}} = A^{\{i_p\}}{}_{\{j_p\}} \qquad \text{for all } p \in S_n \quad . \tag{5.5-20}$$

We know already that the linear transformations representing $g \in G_m$ on V_m^n are symmetry preserving [Lemma 5.1]. It can be established that, even though A does not necessarily factorize as $D(g)$ in Eq. (5.5-6), it can nevertheless be written as a linear combination of $D(g)$. [cf. Lemma IV.7] Since this is true for all linear transformations, $D(g)$ must be irreducible. QED.

A concrete example on how the tensor space V_m^n is decomposed to irreducible invariant subspaces with respect to both S_n and G_m was worked out in detail previously for V_2^3. In the context of Theorems 5.12 and 5.13, we found: (i) associated with totally symmetric tensors ($\lambda = s$), there is an invariant subspace (with respect to G_2) T'_s which is 4-dimensional and has basis vectors $\{|s, \alpha, 1\rangle, \alpha = 1, \ldots, 4\}$ given in Example 2; and (ii) associated with the symmetry class $\lambda = m$, there are two invariant subspaces $T'_m(1)$ and $T'_m(2)$ which give rise to equivalent 2-dimensional irreducible representations of the linear group G_2. [cf. Problem 5.8]

The irreducible representations of G_m provided by tensors of various symmetry classes as described in this section are by no means the only irreducible representations of the general linear group. The main purpose of this exposition is to illustrate the usefulness of the symmetric (or permutation) group in an important class of applications—tensor analysis. In Chapter 13, we shall give a more systematic discussion of finite-dimensional representations of the classical groups which includes GL(m, C) as the most general case. We shall also utilize the tensor method to help evaluate the explicit expression for all representation matrices of the rotation group in Sec. 8.1.

Problems

5.1 Display all the standard Young tableaux of the group S_4. From the result, enumerate the inequivalent irreducible representations of S_4 and specify their dimensions.

5.2 Repeat the above for S_5.

5.3 Verify by explicit calculation that e_2 of the group algebra $\tilde{S}_3$ (given after Definition 5.4) is a primitive idempotent [cf. Appendix III.3].

5.4 Prove that: if $\lambda > \mu$, $e_\lambda^p e_\mu^q = 0$ for all p, $q \in S_n$. [Hint: use Theorem 5.6 and Theorem III.4.]

5.5 Prove that $D(p)$, $p \in S_n$ as defined by Eq. (5.5-13) forms a representation of S_n.

5.6 Prove that there is no nth-rank totally anti-symmetric tensor in m-dimensional space if $n > m$.

5.7 Verify that the mixed symmetry tensors $\{|m, \alpha, a\rangle, a = 1, 2\}$ span an invariant subspace under S_3 in the tensor space V_2^3. [cf. Sec. 5.5, Example 5.]

5.8 (i) Show that in Example 5 of Sec. 5.5 the two vectors $\{|m, i, 1\rangle, i = 1, 2\}$ span the subspace $\{e_m|\alpha\rangle, |\alpha\rangle \in V_2^3\}$. (ii) Show that this subspace is irreducible under G_2.

CHAPTER 6

ONE-DIMENSIONAL CONTINUOUS GROUPS

Continuous groups consist of group elements which are labelled by one or more continuous variables, say $(a_1, a_2, \ldots, a_r)$, where each variable has a well-defined range. Clearly, all continuous groups have an infinite number of elements. On the other hand, not all infinite groups are continuous, as discrete labels for group elements can take an infinite number of values—the discrete translation group of Chap. 1 is an example. The multitude of group elements does not necessarily lead to complications in analyzing the group structure and representation. On the contrary, the analytic properties of group relations (as functions of the continuous variables) can lead to unsurpassed simplicity and beauty which bring together algebra, analysis, geometry, and physics. This chapter explores the simplest examples of continuous groups—the group of rotations in a plane SO(2), and the group of translations in one-dimensional T_1. These groups are one-dimensional (i.e. the group elements only depend on one continuous parameter) and they are necessarily abelian. As a consequence, the exposition will be relatively straightforward. The results and methods developed here will nonetheless form the basis for all subsequent study of continuous groups, since the theory of continuous groups with more than one parameter is formulated in terms of one-parameter subgroups.

The general mathematical theory of continuous groups is usually called the theory of Lie groups. Roughly speaking, a *Lie group* is an infinite group whose elements can be parametrized smoothly and analytically. The definition of these properties requires introducing algebraic and geometric structures beyond group multiplication in pure group theory (which has been our only concern so far for discrete groups). The precise formulation of the general theory of Lie groups requires considerable care; it involves notions of topology and differential geometry. All known continuous symmetry groups of interest in physics, however, are groups of matrices for which the additional algebraic and geometric structures are already familiar. These groups are usually referred to as *linear Lie groups* or *classical Lie groups.* We shall introduce the most important features and techniques of the theory of linear Lie groups by studying the important symmetry groups of space and time, starting from this chapter. Experience with these physically useful examples should provide a good foundation for studying the general theory of Lie groups. [Chevalley, Gilmore, Miller, Pontrjagin, Weyl]

In Sec. 1 we define the group SO(2) and study its general properties. In Sec. 2 we show that all elements of the group can be parametrized in terms of a single quantity—the generator of the group—which is determined by the group structure near the identity element. The irreducible representations of SO(2) are derived in Sec. 3 using eigenvectors of the generator. The role of global properties of the group is discussed. In Sec. 4 the importance of defining an invariant integration measure on the group manifold is explained; a systematic method to derive such a measure is formulated. Using the invariant integration, orthonormality and completeness properties of the representation functions as well as their relation to Fourier analysis are discussed. In Sec. 5, the existence of multi-valued representations and their relation to the topology of the group manifold is explored. In Sec. 6 we turn to the group of continuous translations in one dimension T_1. Similarities and differences to SO(2) and to the group of discrete translations T_d are highlighted. The last section (Sec. 7) focuses on the conjugate roles of the (linear) variables parametrizing the group elements on the one hand, and those characterizing the irreducible representations on the other. For each symmetry group, it is shown that the basis vectors associated with these conjugate variables have well defined physical meaning: they correspond to localized states, and states with definite linear or angular momentum respectively. Thus the generators of continuous symmetry groups are directly identifiable with measurable physical quantities. All ideas introduced in this chapter will find significant generalizations in later chapters.

6.1 The Rotation Group SO(2)

Consider a system symmetric under rotations in a plane, around a fixed point O. Adopt a Cartesian coordinate frame on the plane with $\hat{\mathbf{e}}_1$ and $\hat{\mathbf{e}}_2$ as the orthonormal basis vectors [cf. Fig. 6.1]. Denoting the rotation through angle ϕ by $R(\phi)$, we obtain by elementary geometry [cf. Example 5, Sec. 3.1]:

(6.1-1)
$$\begin{aligned} R(\phi)\hat{\mathbf{e}}_1 &= \hat{\mathbf{e}}_1\cos\phi + \hat{\mathbf{e}}_2\sin\phi \\ R(\phi)\hat{\mathbf{e}}_2 &= -\hat{\mathbf{e}}_1\sin\phi + \hat{\mathbf{e}}_2\cos\phi \quad ; \end{aligned}$$

or equivalently,

(6.1-2)
$$R(\phi)\hat{\mathbf{e}}_i = \hat{\mathbf{e}}_j R(\phi)^j{}_i$$

with the matrix $R(\phi)^j{}_i$ given by

(6.1-3)
$$R(\phi) = \begin{pmatrix} \cos\phi & -\sin\phi \\ \sin\phi & \cos\phi \end{pmatrix} \quad .$$

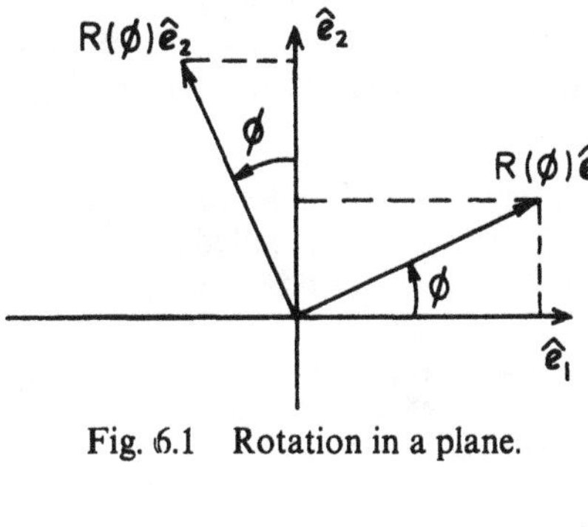

Fig. 6.1 Rotation in a plane.

Let $\mathbf{x}$ be an arbitrary vector in the plane with components (x^1, x^2) with respect to the basis $\{\hat{\mathbf{e}}_i\}$, i.e. $\mathbf{x} = \hat{\mathbf{e}}_i x^i$. Then $\mathbf{x}$ transforms under rotation $\mathbf{R}(\phi)$ according to:

$$\mathbf{x} \to \mathbf{x}' \equiv \mathbf{R}(\phi)\mathbf{x} = \mathbf{R}(\phi)\hat{\mathbf{e}}_i x^i = \hat{\mathbf{e}}_j \mathbf{R}(\phi)^j{}_i x^i$$

Since $\mathbf{x}' \equiv \hat{\mathbf{e}}_j x'^j$, we obtain

(6.1-4) $$x'^j = \mathrm{R}(\phi)^j{}_i x^i \quad .$$

Geometrically, it is obvious that the length of vectors remains invariant under rotations, i.e. $|\mathbf{x}|^2 = x_i x^i = |\mathbf{x}'|^2 = x'_i x'^i$. Using Eq. (6.1-4), we obtain the condition on the rotational matrices:

(6.1-5) $$\mathrm{R}(\phi)\,\mathrm{R}^{\mathrm{T}}(\phi) = E \qquad \text{for all } \phi$$

where R^{T} denotes the transpose of R, and E is the unit matrix. Real matrices satisfying the condition (6.1-5) are called *orthogonal matrices.* It is straightforward to show that the explicit form of $\mathrm{R}(\phi)$ given by (6.1-3) does satisfy this equation.

Eq. (6.1-5) implies that $(\det \mathrm{R}(\phi))^2 = 1$ or $\det \mathrm{R}(\phi) = \pm 1$. The explicit formula for $\mathrm{R}(\phi)$, Eq. (6.1-3) which represents all continuous rotations in the plane, indicates that we must impose the more restrictive condition[1]

(6.1-6) $$\det \mathrm{R}(\phi) = 1 \qquad \text{for all } \phi \quad .$$

Matrices satisfying this determinant condition are said to be *special.* Hence these rotation matrices are *special orthogonal matrices of rank 2*; they are designated as *SO(2) matrices.*

Theorem 6.1: There is a one-to-one correspondence between rotations in a plane and SO(2) matrices.

The proof of this theorem is left as an exercise. [Problem 6.1] This correspondence is a general one, applicable to SO(n) matrices and rotations in the Euclidean space of dimension n for any n.

Two rotation operations can be applied in succession, resulting in an equivalent single rotation. Geometrically, it is obvious that the law of composition is:

(6.1-7) $$\mathrm{R}(\phi_2)\,\mathrm{R}(\phi_1) = \mathrm{R}(\phi_2 + \phi_1)$$

with the understanding that if $\phi_1 + \phi_2$ goes outside the range $(0, 2\pi)$, we have,

(6.1-8) $$\mathrm{R}(\phi) = \mathrm{R}(\phi \pm 2\pi) \quad .$$

Theorem 6.2 (Two-dimensional Rotation Group): With the law of multiplication (6.1-7), and with the definitions that $\mathrm{R}(\phi = 0) = E$ and $\mathrm{R}(\phi)^{-1} = \mathrm{R}(-\phi) = \mathrm{R}(2\pi - \phi)$, the 2-dimensional rotations $\{\mathrm{R}(\phi)\}$ form a group called the R_2 or SO(2) group.

The proof is completely straightforward and will not be spelled out in detail here.

The group elements of SO(2) have been labelled by the continuous real variable ϕ in the domain $0 \le \phi < 2\pi$. This corresponds to all points on the unit circle which

[1] Matrices satisfying Eq. (6.1-5) but with determinant equal to -1 correspond physically to rotations combined with spatial inversion or mirror reflection. This set of matrices is not connected to the identity transformation by a continuous change of parameters. We shall include spatial inversion in our group theoretical analysis in Chap. 11.

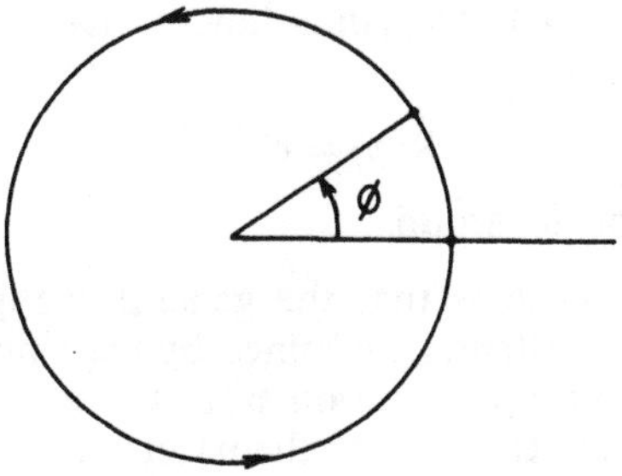

Fig. 6.2 SO(2) group manifold.

defines the "topology" of the group parameter space [cf. Fig. 6.2]. Obviously, this parameterization, although natural, is not unique. Any monotonic function $\xi(\phi)$ of ϕ over the above domain can serve as an alternative label for the group element. The structure of the group and its representations should not be affected by the labelling scheme. We shall come back to the "naturalness" of the variable ϕ and the question of topology in a later section. Both issues are important for the analysis of general continuous groups.

Note that Eq. (6.1-7) implies $R(\phi_1)R(\phi_2) = R(\phi_2)R(\phi_1)$ for all ϕ_1, ϕ_2. Thus, the group SO(2) is abelian.

6.2 The Generator of SO(2)

Although there is an infinite number of group elements in SO(2), its structure is almost trivially determined by its group multiplication rule (6.1-7) and the requirement of continuity. The following simple analysis forms the foundation of the theory of Lie groups.

Consider an infinitesimal SO(2) rotation by the angle $d\phi$. Differentiability of $R(\phi)$ in ϕ requires that $R(d\phi)$ differs from $R(0) = E$ by only a quantity of order $d\phi$ which we define by the relation

(6.2-1) $$R(d\phi) \equiv E - i\,d\phi J$$

where the factor $(-i)$ is included by convention and for later convenience. The quantity J is independent of the rotation angle $d\phi$.

Next, consider the rotation $R(\phi + d\phi)$, which can be evaluated in two ways:

(6.2-2) $$\begin{aligned} R(\phi + d\phi) &= R(\phi)R(d\phi) = R(\phi) - i\,d\phi\, R(\phi)J \\ R(\phi + d\phi) &= R(\phi) + d\phi \frac{dR(\phi)}{d\phi} \end{aligned}$$

Comparing the two equations, we obtain the differential equation,

(6.2-3) $$dR(\phi)/d\phi = -iR(\phi)J$$

We have, of course, also the boundary condition $R(0) = E$. The solution to Eq. (6.2-3) is therefore unique, we present it in the form of a theorem.

Theorem 6.3 (Generator of SO(2)): All 2-dimensional rotations can be expressed in terms of the operator J as:

$$R(\phi) = e^{-i\phi J} \quad . \tag{6.2-4}$$

J is called the *generator* of the group.

The significance of this result is that the general group structure and its representations are, to a large extent, determined by the single generator J which, in turn, is specified by the group operation near the identity. This gives the first indication of the power and beauty of the theory of Lie groups—the *local* behavior of the group near the identity determines most of the important properties of a continuous group. The group multiplication rule, Eq. (6.1-7), is explicitly satisfied when we express the group elements in terms of the generator as in Eq. (6.2-4). We can therefore focus our attention on one single object, the generator J, rather than the infinite number of group elements. Once J is known, the group elements can all be determined by Eq. (6.2-4).

It should be pointed out, nonetheless, that Eq. (6.2-4) does not contain all information about the rotation group. Certain *global* properties of the group, such as Eq. (6.1-8), cannot be deduced from it. These global properties, mostly topological in nature, also play a role in determining the irreducible representations of the group, as we shall see in the next section.

Let us turn from this abstract discussion to the explicit representation of $R(\phi)$ given by (6.1-3). We have, to first order in $d\phi$,

$$R(d\phi) = \begin{pmatrix} 1 & -d\phi \\ d\phi & 1 \end{pmatrix} \quad .$$

Comparing with Eq. (6.2-1), we deduce

$$J = \begin{pmatrix} 0 & -i \\ i & 0 \end{pmatrix} \quad . \tag{6.2-5}$$

Thus J is a traceless hermitian matrix. It is easy to show that $J^2 = 1, J^3 = J, \ldots$ etc. Therefore,

$$\begin{aligned} e^{-i\phi J} &= E - iJ\phi - E\phi^2/2! - iJ(-\phi^3/3!) + \cdots \\ &= E\cos\phi - iJ\sin\phi = \begin{pmatrix} \cos\phi & -\sin\phi \\ \sin\phi & \cos\phi \end{pmatrix} \end{aligned}$$

which reproduces Eq. (6.1-3).

6.3 Irreducible Representations of SO(2)

Consider any representation of SO(2) defined on a finite dimensional vector space V. Let $U(\phi)$ be the operator on V which corresponds to $R(\phi)$. Then, according to Eq. (6.1-7), we must have $U(\phi_2)U(\phi_1) = U(\phi_2 + \phi_1) = U(\phi_1)U(\phi_2)$ with the same understanding that $U(\phi) = U(\phi \pm 2\pi)$. For an infinitesimal transformation, we can again define an operator corresponding to the generator J in Eq. (6.2-1). In order to avoid a proliferation of symbols, we use the same letter J to denote this operator,

(6.3-1) $$U(d\phi) = E - id\phi J$$

Repeating the arguments of the last section, we obtain

(6.3-2) $$U(\phi) = e^{-i\phi J}$$

which is now an operator equation on V. If $U(\phi)$ is to be unitary for all ϕ, J must be hermitian.

Since SO(2) is an abelian group, all its irreducible representations are one-dimensional. This means that given any vector $|\alpha\rangle$ in a minimal invariant subspace under SO(2) we must have:

(6.3-3) $$J|\alpha\rangle = |\alpha\rangle\alpha$$

(6.3-4) $$U(\phi)|\alpha\rangle = |\alpha\rangle e^{-i\phi\alpha}$$

where the label α is a real number chosen to coincide with the eigenvalue of the hermitian operator J. It is easy to show that the form given by Eq. (6.3-4) automatically satisfies the group multiplication rule Eq. (6.1-7) for an arbitrary α. However, in order to satisfy the global constraint Eq. (6.1-8), a restriction must be placed on the eigenvalue α. Indeed, we must have $e^{\mp i2\pi\alpha} = 1$, which implies that α is an integer. We denote this integer by m, and the corresponding representation by U^m:

(6.3-5) $$J|m\rangle = |m\rangle m$$

(6.3-6) $$U^m(\phi)|m\rangle = |m\rangle e^{-im\phi} \quad .$$

Let us take a closer look at these representations:

(i) When $m = 0$, $R(\phi) \to U^0(\phi) = 1$. This is the identity representation;

(ii) When $m = 1$, $R(\phi) \to U^1(\phi) = e^{-i\phi}$. This is an isomorphism between SO(2) group elements and ordinary numbers on the unit circle in the complex number plane. As $R(\phi)$ ranges over the group space, $U^1(\phi)$ covers the unit circle once, in the clockwise sense;

(iii) When $m = -1$, $R(\phi) \to U^{-1}(\phi) = e^{i\phi}$. The situation is the same as above, except that the unit circle is covered once in the counter-clockwise direction;

(iv) When $m = \pm 2$, $R(\phi) \to U^{\mp 2}(\phi) = e^{\pm i2\phi}$. These are mappings of the group parameter space to the unit circle on the complex number plane covering the latter twice in opposite directions.

The general case follows in an obvious manner from these examples. We summarize these results in the form of a theorem.

Theorem 6.4 (Irreducible Representations of SO(2)): The single valued irreducible representations of SO(2) are given by $J = m$ where m is any integer, and

(6.3-7) $$U^m(\phi) = e^{-im\phi} \quad .$$

Of these, only the $m = \pm 1$ ones are faithful representations.

The defining equation for $R(\phi)$, Eq. (6.1-3), is a two-dimensional representation of the group. It has to be reducible. Indeed, it is equivalent to a direct sum of the

$m = \pm 1$ representations. To see this, we note that due to Eq. (6.3-2), it suffices to diagonalize the matrix corresponding to the generator,

$$J = \begin{pmatrix} 0 & -i \\ i & 0 \end{pmatrix}$$

It is obvious that J has two eigenvalues, ± 1; and the corresponding eigenvectors are: $\hat{\mathbf{e}}_\pm = (\mp\hat{\mathbf{e}}_1 - i\hat{\mathbf{e}}_2)/\sqrt{2}$. [Problem 6.2] Thus, with respect to the new basis,

$$\begin{aligned} J\,\hat{\mathbf{e}}_\pm &= \pm\hat{\mathbf{e}}_\pm \\ \mathrm{R}(\phi)\,\hat{\mathbf{e}}_\pm &= \hat{\mathbf{e}}_\pm\, e^{\mp i\phi} \end{aligned} \qquad (6.3\text{-}8)$$

6.4 Invariant Integration Measure, Orthonormality and Completeness Relations

We would like to formulate the orthonormality and completeness relations for the representation functions $U_m(\phi) = e^{-im\phi}$, in analogy to Theorem 3.7 for finite groups and Eqs. (1.4-1), (1.4-2) for the discrete translation group. [N.B. For one-dimensional representations, such as these, the representation "matrices" coincide with the characters thus Theorem 3.7 is the equivalent of Theorems 3.5 and 3.6 combined.] To this end, it appears only necessary to substitute ϕ for the group element label, m for the representation label, and $U_m(\phi)$ for the group representation or character function in the relevant formulas. However, because ϕ is a continuous variable, the summation over group elements must be replaced by an integration, and the integration measure must be well defined. To see that, indeed, care must be exercised, recall that the rotation angle ϕ is not the only parameter than can label the group elements. Any function $\xi(\phi)$, monotonic in $0 \le \phi < 2\pi$, can just as well serve as a satisfactory label. But for an arbitrary function f of the group elements,

$$\int d\xi\, f[\mathrm{R}(\xi)] = \int d\phi\, \xi'(\phi) f[\mathrm{R}(\phi)] \neq \int d\phi\, f[\mathrm{R}(\phi)] \quad .$$

Hence, "integration" of f over the group manifold is not well defined a priori. How can we find a natural and unambiguous definition of integral of f over the group?

The key to answering this question can be found by a careful examination of the underpinnings of the theoretical structure of Chaps. 3 and 4. A little reflection will reveal that it is not only necessary to integrate over all group elements, but that in addition it is crucial to preserve the Rearrangement Lemma—because this lemma lies at the heart of the proof of most important results of the representation theory. Therefore we seek to define an integration measure such that,

$$\int d\tau_{\mathrm{R}} f[\mathrm{R}] = \int d\tau_{\mathrm{R}} f[\mathrm{S}^{-1}\mathrm{R}] = \int d\tau_{\mathrm{SR}} f[\mathrm{R}] \qquad (6.4\text{-}1)$$

where $f[\mathrm{R}]$ is any function of the group elements and S is an arbitrary element of the group. If the group elements are labelled by the parameter ξ, then

$$d\tau_{\mathrm{R}} = \rho_{\mathrm{R}}(\xi) d\xi$$

where $\rho_{\mathrm{R}}(\xi)$ is some appropriately defined "weight function".

Definition 6.1 (Invariant Integration Measure): A parameterization $R(\xi)$ in group space with an associated weight function $\rho_R(\xi)$ is said to provide an *invariant integration measure* if Eq. (6.4-1) holds.

The validity of Eq. (6.4-1) requires

$$d\tau_R = d\tau_{SR}$$

which imposes the condition on the weight function,

$$\frac{\rho_R(\xi)}{\rho_{SR}(\xi)} = \frac{d\xi_{SR}}{d\xi_R} \quad . \tag{6.4-2}$$

This condition is automatically satisfied if we define

$$\rho_R(\xi) = \frac{d\xi_E}{d\xi_R} \tag{6.4-3}$$

where ξ_E is the group parameter around the identity element E and $\xi_R = \xi_{ER}$ is the corresponding parameter around R.[2] In evaluating the right-hand side of the above equation, R is to be regarded as fixed; the dependence of ξ_{ER} on ξ_E is determined by the group multiplication rule.

The situation is simplest when ξ_{SR} is linear in ξ_R. This is the case when $\xi = \phi$ is the rotation angle. The group multiplication rule, Eq. (6.1-7), requires

$$\phi_{ER} = \phi_E + \phi_R, \qquad \rho_R = \left(\frac{d\phi_E}{d\phi_{ER}}\right)_R = 1 \quad .$$

Theorem 6.5 (Invariant Integration Measure of SO(2)): The rotation angle ϕ, Fig. 6.1, and the volume measure $d\tau_R = d\phi$, provide the proper invariant integration measure over the SO(2) group space.

If ξ is a general parameterization of the group element, then

$$d\tau_R = \rho_R(\xi)d\xi = \rho_R(\phi)d\phi = d\phi \quad .$$

We must have, therefore,

$$\rho_R(\xi) = \frac{d\phi}{d\xi}; \quad .$$

The above discussion may appear to be rather long-winded just to arrive at a relatively obvious conclusion. The motivation for including so much detail is to set up a line of reasoning which can be applied to general continuous groups in later chapters.

Once an invariant measure is found, it is straightforward to write down the expected orthonormality and completeness relations.

[2] We note that $\rho_R = \frac{d\xi_E}{d\xi_{ER}} = \frac{d\xi_E}{d\xi_{SR}}\frac{d\xi_{SR}}{d\xi_R} = \rho_{SR}\frac{d\xi_{SR}}{d\xi_R}$.

Theorem 6.6: The SO(2) representation functions $U^n(\phi)$ of Theorem 6.4 satisfy the following orthonormality and completeness relations[3]:

(6.4-4)
$$\frac{1}{2\pi}\int_0^{2\pi} d\phi\, U_n^\dagger(\phi)\, U^m(\phi) = \delta_n^m \qquad \text{(orthogonality)}$$
$$\sum_n U^n(\phi)\, U_n^\dagger(\phi') = \delta(\phi - \phi') \qquad \text{(completeness).}$$

Three simple remarks of general importance are in order here:

(i) These relations are natural generalizations of Theorem 3.5 and 3.6 (for finite groups) to a continuous group; the only change is the replacement of the finite sum over group elements by the invariant integration over the continuous group parameter;

(ii) Theorem 6.6, with $U^n(\phi)$ given by Eq. (6.3-7), is equivalent to the classical Fourier Theorem for periodic functions, the continuous group parameter ϕ and the discrete representation label n are the "conjugate variables";

(iii) These relations are also identical to the results encountered in Chap. 1, Eqs. (1.4-1)–(1.4-2), in connection with the discrete translation group T^d. Note, however, the roles of the group element label (discrete) and the representation label (continuous) are exactly reversed in comparison to the present case.

6.5 Multi-Valued Representations

For later reference, we mention here a new feature of continuous groups—the possibility of having *multi-valued representations*. To introduce the idea, consider the mapping

(6.5-1)
$$R(\phi) \to U_{1/2}(\phi) = e^{-i\phi/2}$$

This is not a unique representation of the group, as

(6.5-2)
$$U_{1/2}(2\pi + \phi) = e^{-i\pi - i\phi/2} = -U_{1/2}(\phi)$$

whereas, we expect, on physical grounds, $R(2\pi + \phi) = R(\phi)$. However, since $U_{1/2}(4\pi + \phi) = U_{1/2}(\phi)$, Eq. (6.5-1) does define a one-to-two mapping where each $R(\phi)$ is assigned to two complex numbers $\mp e^{-i\phi/2}$ differing by a factor of -1. This is a *two-valued representation* in the sense that the group multiplication law for SO(2) is preserved if either one of the two numbers corresponding to $R(\phi)$ can be accepted.

Clearly, we can also consider general mappings,

(6.5-3)
$$R(\phi) \to U_{n/m}(\phi) = e^{-in\phi/m}$$

where n and m are integers with no common factors. For any pair (n, m) this mapping defines a "m-valued representation" of SO(2) in the same sense as described above.

The following questions naturally arise: (i) Do continuous groups always have multi-valued irreducible representation; (ii) How do we know whether (and for what values of m do) multi-valued representations exist; (iii) When multi-valued representations exist, are they realized in physical systems? In other words, does it make sense to restrict our attention to solutions of classical and/or quantum-

[3] Again, these relations can be put in a simple vector space notation — with the definitions $\langle\phi|m\rangle \equiv U^m(\phi)$ and $\sum_\phi \equiv \int d\phi/2\pi$, they become: $\sum_\phi \langle n|\phi\rangle\langle\phi|m\rangle = \delta^m{}_n$ and $\sum_n \langle\phi|n\rangle\langle n|\phi\rangle = \delta(\phi-\phi')$ respectively. (Cf. next section.)

mechanical systems only to those corresponding to single-valued representations of the appropriate symmetry groups?

It turns out that the existence of multi-valued representations is intimately tied to "connectedness"—a global topological property—of the group parameter space. In the case of SO(2), the group parameter space (the unit circle) is "multiply-connected"[4], which implies the existence of multi-valued representations. Thus, it is possible to determine the existence and the nature of multi-valued representations from an intrinsic property of the group.

In regard to the last question posed above, so far as we know, both single- and double-valued representations, but no others, are realized in quantum mechanical systems, and only single-valued representations appear in classical solutions to physical problems. The occurrence of double-valued representations can be traced to the connectedness of the group manifolds of symmetries associated with the physical 3- and 4-dimensional spaces. This observation will become clearer after we discuss the full rotation group and the Lorentz group in the next few chapters.

6.6 Continuous Translational Group in One Dimension

Rotations in the 2-dimensional plane (by the angle ϕ) can be interpreted as translations on the unit circle (by the arc length ϕ). This fact accounts for the similarity in the form of the irreducible representation function, $U^n(\phi) = e^{-in\phi}$, in comparison to the case of discrete translation, $t_k(n) = e^{-inkb}$, discussed in Chap. 1. The "complementary" nature of these results has been noted in Sec. 6.4. We now extend the investigation to the equally important and basic continuous *translation group in one dimension*, which we shall refer to as T_1.

Let the coordinate axis of the one-dimensional space be labelled x. An arbitrary element of the group T_1 corresponding to *translation* by the distance x will be denoted by $T(x)$. Consider "states" $|x_0\rangle$[5] of a "particle" localized at the position x_0,[6] the action of $T(x)$ on $|x\rangle$ is:

(6.6-1) $$T(x)|x_0\rangle \equiv |x + x_0\rangle$$

It is easy to see that $T(x)$ must have the following properties:

(6.6-2a) $$T(x_1)T(x_2) = T(x_1 + x_2)$$

(6.6-2b) $$T(0) = E$$

(6.6-2c) $$T(x)^{-1} = T(-x)$$

These are just the properties that are required for $\{T(x), -\infty < x < \infty\}$ to form a group [cf. Eqs. (1.2-1abc)].

For an infinitesimal displacement denoted by dx, we have

(6.6-3) $$T(dx) \equiv E - i\,dx\,P$$

[4] This means that there exist closed "paths" on the unit circle which wind around it m times (for all integers m) and which cannot be continuously deformed into each other.

[5] The "state" can be interpreted in the sense of either classical mechanics or quantum mechanics. We use the state-vector convention of quantum mechanics only for the sake of clarity in notation.

[6] By "particle" we simply mean an entity with no spatial extension, which can be represented by a mathematical point.

which defines the (displacement-independent) *generator* of translation P. Next, we write $\mathrm{T}(x + \mathrm{d}x)$ in two different ways:

(6.6-4a) $$\mathrm{T}(x + \mathrm{d}x) = \mathrm{T}(x) + \mathrm{d}x \frac{\mathrm{d}T(x)}{\mathrm{d}x}$$

and

(6.6-4b) $$\mathrm{T}(x + \mathrm{d}x) = \mathrm{T}(\mathrm{d}x)\,\mathrm{T}(x) \quad .$$

Substituting (6.6-3) in (6.6-4b), and comparing with (6.6-4a), we obtain

(6.6-5) $$\frac{\mathrm{dT}(x)}{\mathrm{d}x} = -iP\,\mathrm{T}(x) \quad .$$

Considering the boundary condition (6.6-2b), this differential equation yields the unique solution,

(6.6-6) $$\mathrm{T}(x) = e^{-iPx} \quad .$$

It is straightforward to see that with $\mathrm{T}(x)$ written in this form, all the required group properties, (6.6-2a,b,c), are satisfied. This derivation is identical to that given for the rotation group SO(2). [cf. Theorem 6.3] The only difference is that the parameter x in $\mathrm{T}(x)$ is no longer restricted to a finite range as for ϕ in $\mathrm{R}(\phi)$.

As before, all irreducible representations of the translation group are one-dimensional. For unitary representations, the generator P corresponds to a hermitian operator with real eigenvalues, which we shall denote by p. For the representation $\mathrm{T}(x) \to U^p(x)$, we obtain:

(6.6-7) $$P|p\rangle = |p\rangle p$$

(6.6-8) $$U^p(x)|p\rangle = |p\rangle e^{-ipx} \quad .$$

It is easy to see that all the group properties, Eqs. (6.6-2a,b,c), are satisfied by this representation function for any given real number p. Therefore the value of p is totally unrestricted.

Comparing these results with those obtained in Chap. 1 for the discrete translation group T^d and in Sections (6.1-6.5) for SO(2), we remark that:

(i) The representation functions in all these cases take the exponential form [cf. Eqs. (1.3-3), (6.3-6), (6.6-8)], reflecting the common group multiplication rule [cf. Eqs. (1.2-1a), (6.1-7), (6.6-2a)];

(ii) For T^d, the group parameter (n in Eq. (1.3-3)) is discrete and infinite, the representation label (k) is continuous and bounded. For SO(2), the former (ϕ in Eq. (6.3-6)) is continuous and bounded, the latter (m) is discrete and infinite. Finally, for T_1 the former (x in Eq. (6.6-8)) is continuous and unbounded, so is the latter (p).

The *conjugate* role of the group parameter and the representation label in the sense of Fourier analysis was discussed in Sec. 6.4. The case is strengthened more by applying the orthonormality and completeness relations of representation functions to the present case of full one-dimensional translation. For this purpose we must again define an appropriate invariant measure for integration over the group elements. Just as in the case of SO(2), one needs only to pick the natural Cartesian displacement x as the integration variable. Because the range of integration is now infinite, not all integrals are strictly convergent in the classical sense. But for our purposes, it suffices to say that all previous results hold in the sense of generalized functions. We obtain:

(6.6-9)
$$\int_{-\infty}^{\infty} dx\, U_p^\dagger(x)\, U^{p'}(x) = N\,\delta(p - p')$$

(6.6-10)
$$\int_{-\infty}^{\infty} dp\, U^p(x)\, U_p^\dagger(x') = N\,\delta(x - x')$$

where N is a yet unspecified normalization constant. Since $U^p(x) = e^{-ipx}$, these equations represent a statement of the Fourier theorem for arbitrary (generalized) functions. This correspondence also gives the correct value of N, i.e. $N = 2\pi$.

6.7 Conjugate Basis Vectors

In Chap. 1 we described two types of basis vectors: $\{|x\rangle\}$, defined by Eq. (1.1-6), and $|u(E, k)\rangle$, defined by Eq. (1.3-3). The first represents "localized states" at some position x; the second corresponds to normal modes which fill the entire lattice and have simple translational properties. Each one has its unique features and practical uses. State functions expressed in terms of these two bases are related by a Fourier expansion. Analogous procedures can be applied in the representation space of the rotation group SO(2) and the continuous translation group. We describe them in turn.

Consider a particle state localized at a position represented by polar coordinates (r, ϕ) on the 2-dimensional plane. The value of r will not be changed by any rotation; therefore we shall not be concerned about it in subsequent discussions. Intuitively,

(6.7-1)
$$U(\phi)\,|\phi_0\rangle = |\phi + \phi_0\rangle \quad ;$$

so that,

(6.7-2)
$$|\phi\rangle = U(\phi)\,|O\rangle \qquad 0 \le \phi < 2\pi$$

where $|O\rangle$ represents a "standard state" aligned with a pre-chosen x-axis. How are these states related to the eigenstates of J defined by Eqs. (6.3-5) and (6.3-6)?

If we expand $|\phi\rangle$ in terms of the vectors $\{|m\rangle;\ m = 0, \pm 1, \ldots\}$, $|\phi\rangle = \sum_m |m\rangle\langle m|\phi\rangle$, then $\langle m|\phi\rangle = \langle m|U(\phi)|O\rangle = \langle U^\dagger(\phi)m|O\rangle = \langle m|O\rangle e^{-im\phi}$. States $|m\rangle$ with different values of m are unrelated by rotation, and we can choose their phases (i.e. a multiplicative factor $e^{i\alpha m}$ for each m) such that $\langle m|O\rangle = 1$ for all m, thus obtaining

(6.7-3)
$$|\phi\rangle = \sum_m |m\rangle\, e^{-im\phi} \quad .$$

To invert this equation, multiply by $e^{in\phi}$ and integrate over ϕ. We obtain

(6.7-4)
$$|m\rangle = \int_0^{2\pi} |\phi\rangle\, e^{im\phi}\, \frac{d\phi}{2\pi} \quad .$$

We see that by this convention, the "transfer matrix elements" $\langle m|\phi\rangle$ between the two are just the group representation functions.

An arbitrary state $|\psi\rangle$ in the vector space can be expressed in either of the two bases:

$$|\psi\rangle = \sum_m |m\rangle \psi_m = \int_0^{2\pi} |\phi\rangle \psi(\phi) \frac{d\phi}{2\pi} \quad . \tag{6.7-5}$$

The "wave functions" ψ_m and $\psi(\phi)$ are related by

$$\psi(\phi) = \langle\phi|\psi\rangle = \sum_m \langle\phi|m\rangle\langle m|\psi\rangle = \sum_m e^{im\phi}\psi_m \tag{6.7-6}$$

and

$$\psi_m = \int_0^{2\pi} \psi(\phi) e^{-im\phi} d\phi/2\pi \quad . \tag{6.7-7}$$

Let us examine the action of the operator J on the states $|\phi\rangle$. From Eq. (6.7-3), we obtain

$$J|\phi\rangle = \sum_m J|m\rangle e^{-im\phi} = \sum_m |m\rangle m e^{-im\phi} = i\frac{d}{d\phi}|\phi\rangle \quad . \tag{6.7-8}$$

For an arbitrary state, we have:

$$\langle\phi|J|\psi\rangle = \langle J\phi|\psi\rangle = \frac{1}{i}\frac{d}{d\phi}\langle\phi|\psi\rangle = \frac{1}{i}\frac{d}{d\phi}\psi(\phi) \quad . \tag{6.7-9}$$

Readers who have had some quantum mechanics [Messiah, Schiff] will recognize that J is the *angular momentum operator* (measured in units of $\hbar$). The above purely group-theoretical derivation underlines the general, geometrical origin of these results.

The above discussion can be repeated for the continuous translation group. The "localized states" $|x\rangle$, Eq. (6.6-1), and the "translationally covariant" states $|p\rangle$, Eq. (6.6-7) are related by

$$|x\rangle = \int_{-\infty}^{\infty} |p\rangle e^{-ipx} \frac{dp}{2\pi} \tag{6.7-10}$$

and

$$|p\rangle = \int_{-\infty}^{\infty} |x\rangle e^{ipx} dx \tag{6.7-11}$$

where the normalization of the states is chosen, by convention, as $\langle x'|x\rangle = \delta(x - x')$, $\langle p'|p\rangle = 2\pi\delta(p - p')$. The transfer matrix elements are, again, the group representation functions [Eq. (6.6-8)],

$$\langle p|x\rangle = e^{-ipx} \quad . \tag{6.7-12}$$

As before, if

$$|\psi\rangle = \int |x\rangle \psi(x) dx = \int |p\rangle \psi(p) dp/2\pi, \tag{6.7-13}$$

then

$$\psi(x) = \int \psi(p)\, e^{ipx}\, \mathrm{d}p/2\pi, \tag{6.7-14}$$

$$\psi(p) = \int \psi(x)\, \mathrm{e}^{-ipx}\, \mathrm{d}x, \tag{6.7-15}$$

and

$$\langle x|P|\psi\rangle = \langle Px|\psi\rangle = -i\,\mathrm{d}\psi(x)/\mathrm{d}x. \tag{6.7-16}$$

Thus, the generator P can be identified with the *linear momentum operator* in quantum mechanical systems. [Messiah, Schiff]

Problems

6.1 Show that the rotation matrix $\mathrm{R}(\phi)$, Eq. (6.1-3), is an orthogonal matrix and prove that every SO(2) matrix represents a rotation in the plane.

6.2 Show that $\hat{\mathbf{e}}_{\pm} = (\mp \hat{\mathbf{e}}_1 - i\hat{\mathbf{e}}_2)/\sqrt{2}$ are eigenvectors of J with eigenvalues ± 1 respectively [cf. Eq. (6.3-8)].

CHAPTER 7

ROTATIONS IN 3-DIMENSIONAL SPACE—THE GROUP SO(3)

The three infinite groups discussed so far are all abelian. The group multiplication rules are very simple and the representation functions share universal features. We now study the best known and most useful non-abelian continuous group—SO(3), the group of rotations in 3 dimensions. A careful study of this first "non-trivial" group will also prove extremely useful in understanding general Lie group theory. The application of SO(3) itself extends far beyond rotational symmetry in ordinary 3-dimensional Euclidean space, as all simple and semi-simple Lie groups which are of interest in mathematics and physics contain SO(3) or its local equivalent SU(2) as a subgroup. This chapter covers the elementary theory of the rotation group. The next chapter establishes the connection to SU(2) and then goes on to treat some more advanced topics which have proved very useful both in physical applications and in the study of the general theory of Lie groups.

In Sec. 1 we define the SO(3) group, describe in detail the various parametrizations of the group elements, and characterize the group manifold. In Sec. 2 we specify the one parameter subgroups of SO(3), define the group generators, and derive the Lie algebra of the group. In Sec. 3 we construct the irreducible representations of the Lie algebra using the method of Cartan. Section 4 is devoted to useful properties of the representation matrices. Section 5 illustrates the use of the group theoretical method by studying a general physical problem—a particle in a central potential—from the group-theoretical point of view. Angular-momentum as well as plane-wave states are defined according to natural group-theoretical concepts, and the partial wave expansion of a general scattering amplitude is derived. In Sec. 6 we investigate the transformation properties of c-number and operator wave functions and fields under 3-dimensional rotations. In Sec. 7 we study direct product representations and their reduction by the use of Clebsch-Gordan coefficients. Finally, in Sec. 8 we introduce irreducible spherical tensor operators and consider the application of the Wigner-Eckart theorem for SO(3).

7.1 Description of the Group SO(3)

Definition 7.1 (The SO(3) group): The *SO(3) group* consists of all continuous linear transformations in 3-dimensional Euclidean space which leave the length of coordinate vectors invariant.

Consider a Cartesian coordinate frame specified by the orthonormal vectors $\hat{\mathbf{e}}_i$, $i = 1, 2, 3$. Under a rotation,

$$\hat{\mathbf{e}}_i \xrightarrow{\mathrm{R}} \hat{\mathbf{e}}_i' = \hat{\mathbf{e}}_j R^j{}_i \tag{7.1-1}$$

where $R^j{}_i$ are elements of 3×3 rotational matrices. Let $\mathbf{x}$ be an arbitrary vector, $\mathbf{x} = \hat{\mathbf{e}}_i x^i$, then $\mathbf{x} \to \mathbf{x}'$ under rotation R such that

$$x'^i = R^i{}_j x^j \quad . \tag{7.1-2}$$

The requirement that $|\mathbf{x}| = |\mathbf{x}'|$, or $x_i x^i = x'_i x'^i$, yields:

$$\mathrm{R}\,\mathrm{R}^{\mathrm{T}} = \mathrm{R}^{\mathrm{T}}\mathrm{R} = E \tag{7.1-3}$$

for all rotational matrices. Real matrices satisfying this condition have determinants equal to ± 1. Since all physical rotations can be reached continuously from the identity transformation (zero angle of rotation), and since the determinant for the latter is $+1$, it follows that all rotation matrices must have determinant $+1$. Thus, in addition to Eq. (7.1-3), the matrices R are restricted by the condition,

$$\det \mathrm{R} = 1 \quad . \tag{7.1-4}$$

Matrices satisfying Eq. (7.1-3) but with determinant equal to -1 correspond to rotations combined with discrete spatial reflection transformations such as:

$$I_s = \begin{pmatrix} -1 & & \\ & -1 & \\ & & -1 \end{pmatrix} \quad .$$

These will be discussed in Chap. 11.

We mention, for future reference, that both conditions on the rotational matrix R can be expressed as statements on *invariant tensors*. In particular, Eq. (7.1-3) can be written as

$$R^i{}_k R^j{}_l \delta^{kl} = \delta^{ij}, \tag{7.1-5}$$

which expresses the invariance of the 2nd rank tensor δ^{kl} under rotations. Similarly, Eq. (7.1-4) can be written as

$$R^i{}_l R^j{}_m R^k{}_n \varepsilon^{lmn} = \varepsilon^{ijk} \tag{7.1-6}$$

where ε^{ijk} is the *totally antisymmetric 3rd rank unit tensor*. When $(i, j, k) = (1, 2, 3)$, the left-hand side is just the determinant; this equation coincides with Eq. (7.1-4). For other values of (i, j, k), the identity follows from the totally anti-symmetrical nature of both sides of the equation. This identity states that ε^{lmn} is an invariant tensor under rotations.

Consider performing rotation R_1, followed by rotation R_2. The effect on the coordinate vectors can be expressed as follows:

$$\mathrm{R}_2(\mathrm{R}_1\hat{\mathbf{e}}_i) = \mathrm{R}_2\hat{\mathbf{e}}_j R_1{}^j{}_i = \hat{\mathbf{e}}_k R_2{}^k{}_j R_1{}^j{}_i = \hat{\mathbf{e}}_k (R_2 R_1)^k{}_i \quad .$$

Therefore, the net result is equivalent to a single rotation R_3,

$$\mathrm{R}_3 = \mathrm{R}_2\,\mathrm{R}_1 \tag{7.1-7}$$

where matrix multiplication on the right-hand side is understood. It is straightforward to verify that the product of two SO(3) matrices is again an SO(3) matrix, that the identity matrix is an SO(3) matrix, and that each SO(3) matrix has an inverse. Hence the rotation matrices form a group—the SO(3) group.

A general SO(3) group element depends on three continuous group parameters. There is an infinite number of possible ways to choose these parameters. The two most commonly used ways will be described here. A third one relating to the SU(2) group will be discussed in the next chapter.

7.1.1 The Angle-and-Axis Parameterization

Any rotation can be designated by $R_{\hat{n}}(\psi)$ where the unit vector $\hat{n}$ specifies the *direction of the axis of rotation* and ψ denotes the *angle of rotation* around that axis. Since the unit vector $\hat{n}$, in turn, is determined by the two angles—say the polar and the azmuthal angles (θ, ϕ) of its direction—we see that R is characterized by the three parameters (ψ, θ, ϕ) where $0 \le \psi \le \pi$, $0 \le \theta \le \pi$, and $0 \le \phi < 2\pi$. There is a redundancy in this parameterization:

$$R_{-\hat{n}}(\pi) = R_{\hat{n}}(\pi) \quad . \tag{7.1-8}$$

The structure of the group parameter space can be visualized by associating each rotation with a three dimensional vector $\mathbf{c} = \psi\hat{\mathbf{n}}$ pointing in the direction $\hat{\mathbf{n}}$ with magnitude equal to ψ. [see Fig. 7.1] The tips of these vectors fill a 3-dimensional sphere of radius π. Because of the redundancy expressed in Eq. (7.1-8), two points on the surface of the sphere on opposite ends of a diameter are equivalent to each other.

A sphere with this added feature is *compact* (i.e. closed and bounded) and *doubly connected.* The latter means that this *group manifold* allows two distinct classes of closed curves: those that can be continuously deformed into a point, and those that must wrap around the sphere once. Fig. 7.2 illustrates these two types of curves.

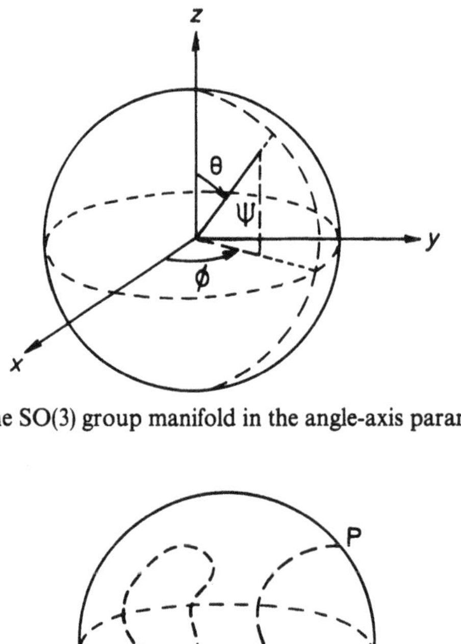

Fig. 7.1 The SO(3) group manifold in the angle-axis parametrization.

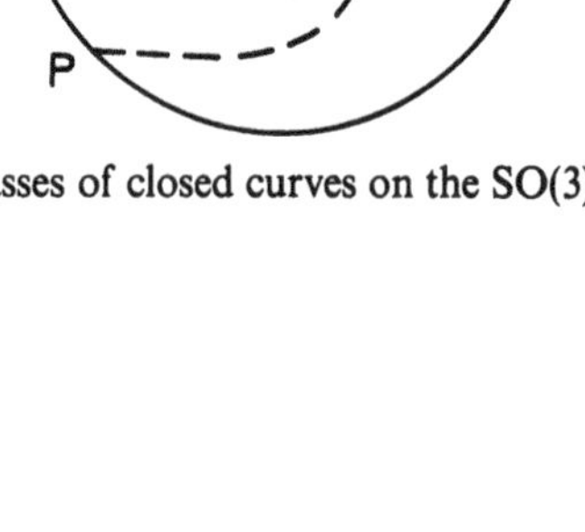

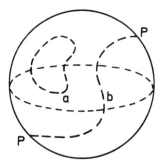

Fig. 7.2 Two classes of closed curves on the SO(3) group manifold.

Note that curve (b) is closed because the ends of the line correspond to *the same point* on the manifold. There is no way to deform this curve continuously to a shape like curve (a) because neither end of the line can move inside the sphere without breaking the curve, and when one end moves on the surface the other end must keep up with it by staying at the opposite end of the diameter (otherwise the curve breaks again). It is not hard to see that all curves which wind around the sphere an even number of times can be continuously deformed into curve (a) (hence into a point), and all curves which wind the sphere an odd number of times can be deformed into curve (b). As we learned from Chap. 6, these geometrical properties have a bearing on the nature of the group representations to be discussed later.

A very useful identity involving group multiplication [cf. Eq. (7.1-7)] in the angle-and-axis parameterization is:

$$R_{\hat{n}'}(\psi) = R\,R_{\hat{n}}(\psi)\,R^{-1} \tag{7.1-9}$$

where R is an arbitrary rotation and $\hat{\mathbf{n}}'$ is the unit vector obtained from $\hat{\mathbf{n}}$ by the rotation R, i.e. $\hat{\mathbf{n}}' = R\hat{\mathbf{n}}$. Thus the rotational matrix for $R_{\hat{n}'}(\psi)$ is obtained from that of $R_n(\psi)$ (N.B. the same angle of rotation) by a similarity transformation. An immediate consequence of this fact is the following theorem.

Theorem 7.1 (Classes of Rotations): All rotations by the same angle ψ belong to a single class of the group SO(3).

The content of Eq. (7.1-9) is basically geometrical in nature. Its validity (and hence that of Theorem 7.1) can be taken as empirically given.

7.1.2 The Euler Angles

A rotation can also be specified by the relative configuration of two Cartesian coordinate frames labelled by (1, 2, 3) and (1′, 2′, 3′) respectively. We refer to (1, 2, 3) as the "fixed frame" and (1′, 2′, 3′) as the "rotated frame". The effect of a given rotation R is to bring the axes of the fixed frame to those of the rotated frame. The three *Euler angles* (α, β, γ) which determine the orientation of the latter with respect to the former are depicted in Fig. 7.3. In addition to the coordinate axes, the definition makes use of an intermediate vector $\hat{\mathbf{N}}$ which lies along the nodal line where the (1, 2) and the (1′, 2′) planes intersect. Making use of the angle-and-axis notation of the previous section, we can write:[1]

$$R(\alpha, \beta, \gamma) = R_{3'}(\gamma)\,R_N(\beta)\,R_3(\alpha) \tag{7.1-10}$$

where the variables have the ranges $0 \le \alpha, \gamma < 2\pi$ and $0 \le \beta \le \pi$. It is straightforward to see how the fixed axes are brought to the rotated axes by successive application of the three rotations on the right-hand side of this equation. The three coordinate axes in the intermediate steps are labelled (x', y', z') and (x'', y'', z'') in Fig. 7.3.

For calculational purposes, it will be much more convenient to re-express $R(\alpha, \beta, \gamma)$ in terms of rotations around the fixed axes. This can be accomplished by

[1] Since the subscript on R and J always refers to a direction, we shall omit the caret sign on the subscript from now on. Thus, R_n stands for $R_{\hat{n}}$, and R_3 stands for $R_{\hat{e}_3}$.

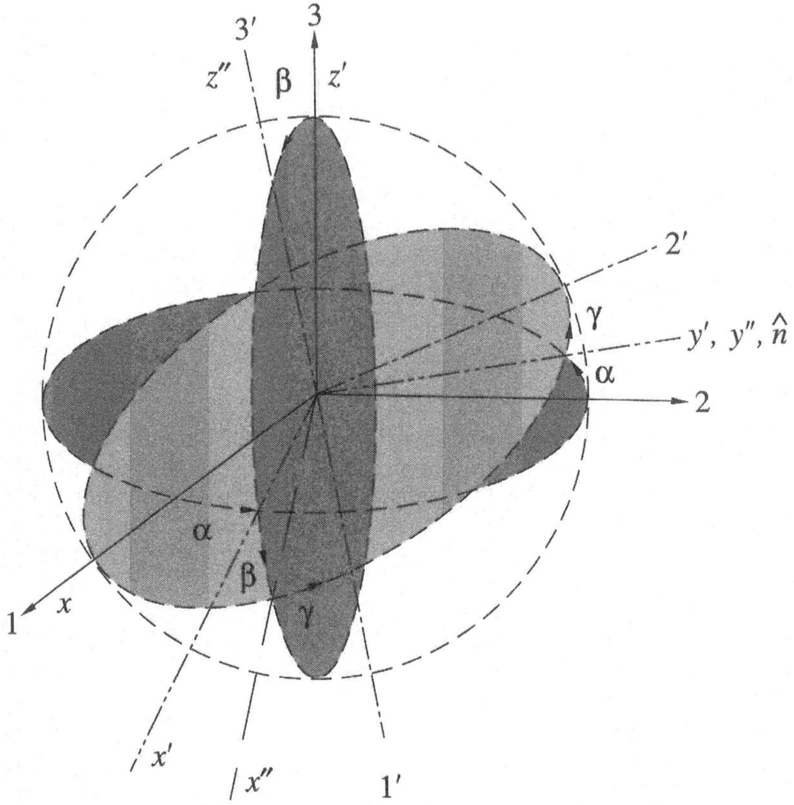

Fig. 7.3 The Euler Angles.

using Eq. (7.1-9) to show that:

(7.1-11) $$R_{3'}(\gamma) = R_N(\beta)\, R_3(\gamma)\, R_N^{-1}(\beta)$$

and $$R_N(\beta) = R_3(\alpha)\, R_2(\beta)\, R_3^{-1}(\alpha)$$

Substituting the first of these identities in Eq. (7.1-10) we obtain $R_N(\beta) \cdot R_3(\gamma + \alpha)$ for the right-hand side. Making use of the second identity, we obtain

(7.1-12) $$R(\alpha, \beta, \gamma) = R_3(\alpha)\, R_2(\beta)\, R_3(\gamma) \quad .$$

Thus, in terms of the Euler angles, every rotation can be decomposed into a product of simple rotations around the fixed axes $\hat{e}_2$ and $\hat{e}_3$. This decomposition makes it possible to combine rotations around arbitrary axes in a systematic way. This feature accounts for the great advantage of using the Euler angles in practical problems.

In view of Eq. (7.1-12), it is necessary to obtain expressions for $R_2(\psi)$ and $R_3(\psi)$. Using the original definition, Eq. (7.1-1), it is straightforward to show that:

(7.1-13a)
$$R_3(\psi) = \begin{pmatrix} \cos\psi & -\sin\psi & 0 \\ \sin\psi & \cos\psi & 0 \\ 0 & 0 & 1 \end{pmatrix}$$

(7.1-13b)
$$R_2(\psi) = \begin{pmatrix} \cos\psi & 0 & \sin\psi \\ 0 & 1 & 0 \\ -\sin\psi & 0 & \cos\psi \end{pmatrix}$$

and, for completeness,

(7.1-13c)
$$R_1(\psi) = \begin{pmatrix} 1 & 0 & 0 \\ 0 & \cos\psi & -\sin\psi \\ 0 & \sin\psi & \cos\psi \end{pmatrix} \quad .$$

These expressions are, of course, very similar to that of SO(2) discussed in the previous chapter. We shall come back to this point in the next section.

Substituting the above matrices in Eq. (7.1-12), one can obtain a formula for the 3×3 matrix representing a general SO(3) transformation (rotation) [cf. Problem 7.1]. One can also compare this expression with the angle-and-axis parametrization to derive the relations between the variables (α, β, γ) and (ψ, θ, ϕ) for a given rotation. The results are:

(7.1-14)
$$\begin{aligned} \phi &= (\pi + \alpha - \gamma)/2 \\ \tan\theta &= \frac{\tan(\beta/2)}{\sin(\gamma + \alpha)/2} \\ \cos\psi &= 2\cos^2\frac{\beta}{2}\cos^2\left(\frac{\alpha+\gamma}{2}\right) - 1 \quad . \end{aligned}$$

A way to prove these results is outlined in Problem 7.2.

7.2 One Parameter Subgroups, Generators, and the Lie Algebra

Given any fixed axis in the direction $\hat{\mathbf{n}}$, rotations about $\hat{\mathbf{n}}$ form a subgroup of SO(3). Each such subgroup is isomorphic to the group of rotations in a plane (the plane perpendicular to $\hat{\mathbf{n}}$)—SO(2)—studied in the previous chapter. Associated with each of these subgroups there is a *generator* which we shall denote by J_n. All elements of the given subgroup can be written as

(7.2-1)
$$R_n(\psi) = e^{-i\psi J_n} \quad .$$

They form an *one parameter subgroup* of SO(3).

Lemma: Given a unit vector $\hat{\mathbf{n}}$ and an arbitrary rotation R, the following identity holds,

(7.2-2)
$$R\, J_n R^{-1} = J_{n'} \qquad \text{where } \hat{\mathbf{n}}' = R\,\hat{\mathbf{n}} \quad .$$

Proof: This result is a direct consequence of Eq. (7.1-9) and the elementary matrix identity $R\, e^{-i\psi J} R^{-1} = e^{-i\psi(RJR^{-1})}$. QED

It follows that under rotations, J_n behaves as a "vector" in the direction of $\hat{\mathbf{n}}$. [N.B. Each J_n is a 3×3 matrix.] Let us consider the three basic matrices along the directions of the fixed axes. By using infinitesimal angles of rotation in Eqs. (7.1-13a) to (7.1-13c), we can deduce that

$$(7.2\text{-}3)\quad J_1 = \begin{pmatrix} 0 & 0 & 0 \\ 0 & 0 & -i \\ 0 & i & 0 \end{pmatrix} \qquad J_2 = \begin{pmatrix} 0 & 0 & i \\ 0 & 0 & 0 \\ -i & 0 & 0 \end{pmatrix} \qquad J_3 = \begin{pmatrix} 0 & -i & 0 \\ i & 0 & 0 \\ 0 & 0 & 0 \end{pmatrix} \quad .$$

These results can be summarized in one single equation,

$$(7.2\text{-}4)\qquad (J_k)^l{}_m = -i\,\varepsilon_{klm}$$

where ε_{klm} is the totally anti-symmetric unit tensor of rank 3 [cf. Eq. (7.1-6)].

Theorem 7.2 (Vector Generator **J**): (i) Under rotations, $\{J_k, k = 1, 2, 3\}$ behave in the same way as the coordinate vectors $\{\hat{\mathbf{e}}_k\}$, i.e.

$$(7.2\text{-}5)\qquad \mathrm{R}\, J_k \mathrm{R}^{-1} = J_l R^l{}_k \quad ;$$

(ii) the generator of rotations around an arbitrary direction $\hat{\mathbf{n}}$ can be written as

$$(7.2\text{-}6)\qquad J_n = J_k n^k, \qquad \text{where } \hat{\mathbf{n}} = \hat{\mathbf{e}}_k n^k \quad .$$

Proof: (i) In view of the decomposition, Eq. (7.1-12), it suffices to prove Eq. (7.2-5) for the special cases $\mathrm{R} = \mathrm{R}_2(\psi)$ and $\mathrm{R} = \mathrm{R}_3(\phi)$. This can be done by direct matrix multiplication, making use of Eqs. (7.1-13abc) and (7.2-3). Alternatively, we shall utilize the invariance relation Eq. (7.1-6). Multiplying both sides of the equation by $R^s{}_i$, summing over i, and using the orthogonality of R, we obtain:

$$(7.2\text{-}7)\qquad R^j{}_m R^k{}_n \varepsilon^{smn} = R^s{}_i \varepsilon^{ijk} \quad .$$

Identifying the anti-symmetric tensor ε components as elements of the J matrices as given in Eq. (7.2-4), we can establish that this relation is equivalent to Eq. (7.2-5).

(ii) The rotation $\mathrm{R}(\phi, \theta, 0)$ brings $\hat{\mathbf{e}}_3$ to $\hat{\mathbf{n}}(\theta, \phi)$ [cf. Fig. 7.4], hence

$$n^k = R(\phi, \theta, 0)^k{}_3 \quad .$$

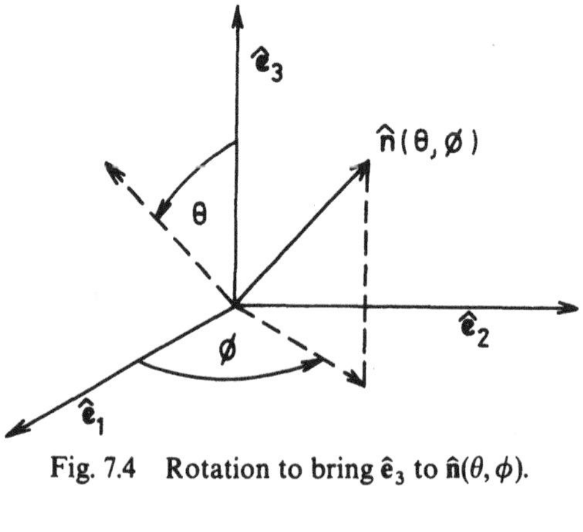

Fig. 7.4 Rotation to bring $\hat{\mathbf{e}}_3$ to $\hat{\mathbf{n}}(\theta, \phi)$.

It follows then from Eqs. (7.2-4) and (7.2-5) that

$$J_n = \mathrm{R}\, J_3\, \mathrm{R}^{-1} = J_k\, R(\phi, \theta, 0)^k{}_3 = J_k\, n^k \quad . \qquad \text{QED}$$

Eq. (7.2-6) shows that $\{J_1, J_2, J_3\}$ form a basis for the generators of all the one-parameter abelian subgroups of SO(3), and

(7.2-8) $$\mathrm{R}_n(\psi) = e^{-i\psi J_k n^k} \quad .$$

Similarly, we can write the Euler angle representation, Eq. (7.1-12), in terms of the generators:

(7.2-9) $$\mathrm{R}(\alpha, \beta, \gamma) = e^{-i\alpha J_3} e^{-i\beta J_2} e^{-i\gamma J_3} \quad .$$

Therefore, for all practical purposes, it suffices to work with the three *basis-generators* $\{J_k\}$ rather than the 3-fold infinity of group elements $\mathrm{R}(\alpha, \beta, \gamma)$.

Theorem 7.3 (Lie Algebra of SO(3)): The three basis generators $\{J_k\}$ satisfy the following *Lie algebra*:

(7.2-10) $$[J_k,\ J_l] = i\, \varepsilon_{klm} J^m$$

where the left-hand side is the *commutator* of J_k and J_l, i.e. $J_k J_l - J_l J_k$.

Proof: When $k = l$, both sides of the equation vanish, the identity obviously holds. Consider a typical case when $k \neq l$; say, $k = 1$ and $l = 2$. We apply an infinitesimal rotation around $\hat{\mathbf{e}}_2$ to J_1 and obtain from Eq. (7.2-5),

$$\mathrm{R}_2(\mathrm{d}\psi)\, J_1\, \mathrm{R}_2^{-1}(\mathrm{d}\psi) = J_k\, R_2(\mathrm{d}\psi)^k{}_1 \quad .$$

But $R_2(\mathrm{d}\psi) = E - i\,\mathrm{d}\psi\, J_2$. [$E$ is the unit matrix.] Thus, if only terms of first order in $\mathrm{d}\psi$ are retained, we obtain for the left-hand side of the equation

$$\mathrm{LHS} = J_1 - i\,\mathrm{d}\psi\,(J_2 J_1 - J_1 J_2) = J_1 + i\,\mathrm{d}\psi\,[J_1, J_2] \quad .$$

Substituting the same expression for $\mathrm{R}_2(\mathrm{d}\psi)$ in the right-hand side, and making use of the explicit form of J_2 given in Eq. (7.2-3), we obtain

$$\mathrm{RHS} = J_1 - \mathrm{d}\psi\, J_3 \quad .$$

[cf. Fig. 7.5] Comparing the two sides, we arrive at the result:

$$[J_1, J_2] = i\, J_3 \quad .$$

By cyclic permutation of the indices, we establish the validity of Eq. (7.2-10). QED

It is clear from the above derivation that the *commutation relation* Eq. (7.2-10) [i.e. the Lie algebra] is equivalent to the group multiplication rule, Eq. (7.1-9), in the vicinity of the identity transformation. Combined with Eq. (7.2-8) or (7.2-9), it determines most important properties of the group structure, and the group representations. However, there are certain "global" properties of the group which do not follow from the "local" commutation relations. Examples are: $\mathrm{R}_n(2\pi) = E$, $\mathrm{R}_n(\pi) = \mathrm{R}_{-n}(\pi), \ldots$ etc. Just as in the case of SO(2), these global properties place additional restrictions on the possible representations, as will be seen as we go along.

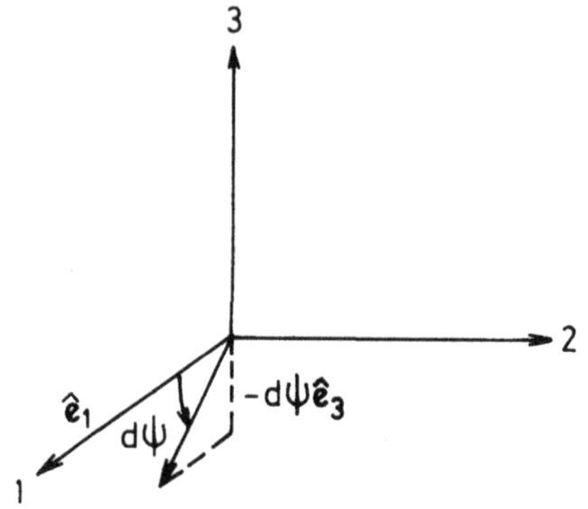

Fig. 7.5 Infinitesimal rotation around the $\hat{e}_3$ axis.

We finish this section with a few more remarks:

(i) It is fairly straightforward to verify that the matrices given in Eq. (7.2-3) satisfy the commutation relations specified by Eq. (7.2-10), as they should.

(ii) If on the space of the generators $\{J_k\}$ and all their linear combinations, one defines "multiplication" of two elements as taking their commutator, then the resulting mathematical system forms a linear algebra. This is the reason for using the terminology *Lie algebra* of the group under consideration.

(iii) In physics, the generators acquire even more significance, as they correspond to physically measurable quantities. Thus $\{J_k\}$ have the physical interpretation as components of the vector *angular momentum* operator (measured in units of $\hbar$). Eqs. (7.2-10) are, of course, recognized as the commutation relations of the quantum mechanical angular momentum operators, which are familiar to physicists. [Messiah, Schiff] It should be clear from the foregoing discussion that the origin of these commutation relations is really geometrical in nature.

We also note that if a physical system represented by a Hamiltonian H is invariant under rotations, then

(7.2-11) $$[H, R_n(\psi)] = 0, \qquad \text{for all } \hat{\mathbf{n}} \text{ and } \psi.$$

This is equivalent to the simpler condition

(7.2-12) $$[H, J_k] = 0 \qquad \text{for } k = 1, 2, 3.$$

This implies that the physical quantities corresponding to the generators of the symmetry group are, in addition, *conserved quantities.* We see here a prime example of the close connection between pure mathematics and physics.

7.3 Irreducible Representations of the SO(3) Lie Algebra

Since the basis elements of the Lie algebra are generators of infinitesimal rotations, it is quite obvious that every representation of the group is automatically a representation of the corresponding Lie algebra. Conversely, because of general expressions such as Eq. (7.2-8) and (7.2-9), a representation of the Lie algebra will also provide us with a representation of the group—provided certain appropriate global conditions, such as Eq. (7.1-8), are satisfied as well. In this section we construct the irreducible representations of the Lie algebra of SO(3), Eq. (7.2-10). Due to the fact that the group parameter space is compact, we expect that the irreducible representations are finite-dimensional, and that they are all equivalent to unitary representations. Correspondingly, the generators will be represented by hermitian operators. In the next chapter, we shall determine the invariant integration measure on the group parameter space which allows us to sum over group elements in a well-defined way and to prove that all the theorems governing irreducible representations of finite groups developed in Chaps. 3 and 4 are applicable to SO(3) as well.

Since the representation space for an irreducible representation is a proper (or minimal) invariant space under group transformations, the general strategy for constructing an irreducible representation is: (i) to pick one convenient "standard" vector as the starting point, and (ii) to generate the rest of the vectors in an irreducible basis by repeated application of selected generators.[2] This procedure represents the simplest case of the powerful general method of Cartan for analyzing Lie groups.

The basis vectors of the representation space V are naturally chosen to be eigenvectors of a set of mutually commuting generators. [Recall that only commuting operators can have complete sets of simultaneous eigenvectors.] The generators J_1, J_2, J_3 do not commute with each other. However, any single one does commute with the composite operator $J^2 = \mathbf{J}\cdot\mathbf{J} = (J_1)^2 + (J_2)^2 + (J_3)^2$, i.e.

$$[J_k, J^2] = 0, \qquad \text{for } k = 1,2,3 \tag{7.3-1}$$

[cf. Problem 7.5]. J^2 is an example of a Casimir operator.

Definition 7.2 (Casimir Operator): An operator which commutes with all elements of a Lie group is said to be a *Casimir Operator* of that group.

Eq. (7.3-1) implies that J^2 commutes with all SO(3) group transformations. By Schur's Lemma, J^2 is mapped to a multiple of the unit matrix in any irreducible representation. In other words, all vectors of the irreducible representation are eigenvectors of J^2 with the same eigenvalue. Since this value does not change throughout the subsequent discussion, we shall not explicitly display it, in order to focus attention on the variable index.

By convention, the basis vectors are chosen as eigenvectors of the commuting operators (J^2, J_3). The remaining generators also play an important role, in the form of *raising* and *lowering operators*:

$$J_\pm = J_1 \pm iJ_2 \quad . \tag{7.3-2}$$

[2] Alternatively, one can generate all the vectors of the irreducible vector space by repeated application of the operators corresponding to the group elements. This method will be used in later chapters on groups of motion.

They have the following useful properties:

(7.3-3) $$[J_3, J_+] = J_+$$

(7.3-4) $$[J_3, J_-] = -J_-$$

(7.3-5) $$[J_+, J_-] = 2J_3$$

(7.3-6) $$J^2 = J_3{}^2 - J_3 + J_+J_- = J_3{}^2 + J_3 + J_-J_+$$

(7.3-7) $$J_\pm{}^\dagger = J_\mp \quad .$$

Let $|m\rangle$ be any normalized eigenvector of J_3 in the representation space V,

(7.3-8) $$J_3|m\rangle = |m\rangle m$$

where the real eigenvalue m is unspecified for the moment. The new vector $J_+|m\rangle$ satisfies:

$$J_3J_+|m\rangle = [J_3, J_+]|m\rangle + J_+J_3|m\rangle = J_+|m\rangle(m+1) \quad .$$

Hence either $J_+|m\rangle$ is also an eigenstate of J_3 with the new eigenvalue $(m+1)$, or else it is the null vector. Likewise, we can show that the vector $J_-|m\rangle$ either vanishes, or it too is an eigenstate of J_3 with the eigenvalue $(m-1)$. The reason for the terminology "raising" and "lowering" operators is transparent from these results.

Let us assume that $J_+|m\rangle \neq 0$. We can normalize the state to unity and call it $|m+1\rangle$. Applying J_+ on this new vector, we obtain, again, either $|m+2\rangle$ or 0. This process can be repeated, generating a sequence of vectors $\{|m+k\rangle, k = 0, 1, 2, \ldots\}$. We require the sequence to terminate so that the representation space is finite dimensional. Suppose the last non-vanishing vector of this sequence is $|j\rangle$, we have:

(7.3-9a) $$J_3|j\rangle = |j\rangle j$$

(7.3-9b) $$J_+|j\rangle = 0 \quad ;$$

hence, by Eq. (7.3-6),

(7.3-9c) $$J^2|j\rangle = |j\rangle j(j+1) \quad .$$

Let us now reverse course and consider the sequence of vectors $\{(J_-)^n|j\rangle, n = 0, 1, 2, \ldots\}$. They are eigenvectors of J_3 corresponding to the eigenvalues $j, j-1, j-2, \ldots$ respectively; they are also eigenvectors of J^2 corresponding to the *same eigenvalue* $j(j+1)$ [cf. Eq. (7.3-9c)]. Again, we normalize these vectors to unity and denote them by $\{|m\rangle, m = j, j-1, j-2, \ldots\}$. For the same reason as mentioned earlier, this sequence is required to terminate after a finite number of steps. Let the last non-vanishing vector be $|l\rangle$, then:

(7.3-10) $$\begin{aligned} 0 &= \langle l|J_-{}^\dagger J_-|l\rangle = \langle l|J_+J_-|l\rangle = \langle l|(J^2 - J_3{}^2 + J_3)|l\rangle \\ &= j(j+1) - l(l-1) \quad . \end{aligned}$$

This condition requires $l = -j$. Since the vector $|l\rangle = |-j\rangle$ is obtained from $|j\rangle$ by applying the lowering operator an integer number of times, we must have $j - (-j) = 2j = n$, $n = 0, 1, 2, \ldots$, hence:

(7.3-11) $$j = 0, \frac{1}{2}, 1, \frac{3}{2}, 2, \ldots$$

The number of vectors in the basis so constructed, which gives the dimension of the representation, is $2j + 1$. We summarize these results in the form of a theorem.

Theorem 7.4 (Irreducible Representations of the SO(3) Lie Algebra): The irreducible representations of the Lie algebra of SO(3), Eq. (7.2-10), are each characterized by an *angular momentum* eigenvalue j from the set of positive integers and half-integers. The orthonormal basis vectors can be specified by the following equations:

(7.3-12) $$J^2 |jm\rangle = |jm\rangle j(j+1)$$

(7.3-13) $$J_3 |jm\rangle = |jm\rangle m$$

(7.3-14) $$J_\pm |jm\rangle = |jm \pm 1\rangle [j(j+1) - m(m \pm 1)]^{1/2} \quad .$$

The normalization factor which appears on the right-hand side of Eq. (7.3-14) arises from a simple calculation similar to Eq. (7.3-10). It should be pointed out that, in principle, we have the freedom to multiply the normalization constant in Eq. (7.3-14) by an additional arbitrary (m-dependent) *phase factor* (i.e. complex number of unit modulus). The resulting set of vectors is equally acceptable as a basis.[3] For definiteness, we comply with the almost universally adopted "Condon-Shortley convention" as written above. We also refer to a basis defined according to this convention as a *canonical basis.*

Knowing how the generators act on the basis vectors, we can immediately derive the matrix elements in the various irreducible representations. Let us write

(7.3-15) $$U(\alpha, \beta, \gamma) |jm\rangle = |jm'\rangle D^j(\alpha, \beta, \gamma)^{m'}{}_m$$

where U is the operator representing the group element $R(\alpha, \beta, \gamma)$. We can deduce from Eq. (7.2-9) that

(7.3-16) $$D^j(\alpha, \beta, \gamma)^{m'}{}_m = e^{-i\alpha m'} d^j(\beta)^{m'}{}_m e^{-i\gamma m}$$

(7.3-17) $$d^j(\beta)^{m'}{}_m = \langle jm' | e^{-i\beta J_2} | jm\rangle \quad .$$

In the Condon-Shortley convention, J_2 is always represented by an imaginary anti-symmetric matrix [recall from Eq. (7.3-14) that $J_\pm$ are real], hence the d^j-matrices are real orthogonal. To be specific, we shall examine the first two non-trivial cases.

Example 1: Angular momentum $\frac{1}{2}$ case. For $j = \frac{1}{2}$, Eqs. (7.3-12)–(7.3-14) imply,

(7.3-18) $$J_3 = \begin{pmatrix} 1/2 & 0 \\ 0 & -1/2 \end{pmatrix} \qquad J_+ = \begin{pmatrix} 0 & 1 \\ 0 & 0 \end{pmatrix} \qquad J_- = \begin{pmatrix} 0 & 0 \\ 1 & 0 \end{pmatrix}$$

[3] Two bases with different phase conventions give rise to group representation matrices which may differ by phase factors in off-diagonal elements. In applications to physical problems, no predictions on physically measurable quantities can depend on the phase convention adopted if the formalism is used consistently.

or $J_k = \sigma_k/2,\ k = 1,2,3$, where σ_k are the familiar Pauli matrices,

$$\sigma_1 = \begin{pmatrix} 0 & 1 \\ 1 & 0 \end{pmatrix} \quad \sigma_2 = \begin{pmatrix} 0 & -i \\ i & 0 \end{pmatrix} \quad \sigma_3 = \begin{pmatrix} 1 & 0 \\ 0 & -1 \end{pmatrix} \quad . \tag{7.3-19}$$

By making use of the property ${\sigma_k}^2 = E$ (valid only for $j = 1/2$), we can derive:

$$\begin{aligned} d^{1/2}(\beta) &= e^{-i\beta\sigma_2/2} = E\cos(\beta/2) - i\sigma_2\sin(\beta/2) \\ &= \begin{pmatrix} \cos(\beta/2) & -\sin(\beta/2) \\ \sin(\beta/2) & \cos(\beta/2) \end{pmatrix} \end{aligned} \tag{7.3-20}$$

hence,

$$D^{1/2}(\alpha,\beta,\gamma) = \begin{pmatrix} e^{-i\alpha/2}\cos(\beta/2)\,e^{-i\gamma/2} & -e^{-i\alpha/2}\sin(\beta/2)\,e^{i\gamma/2} \\ e^{i\alpha/2}\,\sin(\beta/2)\,e^{-i\gamma/2} & e^{i\alpha/2}\,\cos(\beta/2)\,e^{i\gamma/2} \end{pmatrix} \quad . \tag{7.3-21}$$

Applying Eq. (7.1-9), we can see that,

$$D(\mathrm{R}_n(2\pi)] = D[\mathrm{R}]e^{-i\pi\sigma_2}D[\mathrm{R}]^{-1} = D[\mathrm{R}](-E)D[\mathrm{R}]^{-1} = -E$$

where the second equality follows from Eq. (7.3-20). The result is independent of the direction of the rotation axis $\hat{\mathbf{n}}$. Thus, in this representation, rotations through one complete revolution are mapped to $-E$ rather than E. However, rotations through two revolutions, i.e. angle 4π, are mapped to E. Generalizing, we see that all odd numbered revolutions are represented by $-E$, and all even revolutions by E. Since, for the rotation group SO(3), $\mathrm{R}(2\pi) = \mathrm{R}(0)$, the $j = 1/2$ representation of the Lie algebra yields a *double-valued* representation of the group. We shall return to this point later.

Example 2: Consider the next simplest case, $j = 1$. Again, applying Eqs. (7.3-13), (7.3-14) we obtain:

$$J_3 = \begin{pmatrix} 1 & 0 & 0 \\ 0 & 0 & 0 \\ 0 & 0 & -1 \end{pmatrix} \quad J_+ = \begin{pmatrix} 0 & \sqrt{2} & 0 \\ 0 & 0 & \sqrt{2} \\ 0 & 0 & 0 \end{pmatrix} \quad J_- = \begin{pmatrix} 0 & 0 & 0 \\ \sqrt{2} & 0 & 0 \\ 0 & \sqrt{2} & 0 \end{pmatrix} \tag{7.3-22}$$

It is straightforward to verify that this representation is equivalent to the matrices defining the group SO(3). [cf. Eq. (7.2-3) and Problem 7.6] It is therefore a faithful, single-valued representation. The D-matrix is given by Eq. (7.3-16), with

$$d^1(\beta) = \begin{pmatrix} (1+\cos\beta)/2 & -\sin\beta/\sqrt{2} & (1-\cos\beta)/2 \\ \sin\beta/\sqrt{2} & \cos\beta & -\sin\beta/\sqrt{2} \\ (1-\cos\beta)/2 & \sin\beta/\sqrt{2} & (1+\cos\beta)/2 \end{pmatrix} \quad . \tag{7.3-23}$$

Theorem 7.5 (Irreducible Representations of the SO(3) Group): The irreducible representations of the Lie algebra, Theorem 7.4, when applied to the group SO(3), belong to two distinct categories: (i) for j a positive integer, the representations are all single-valued; (ii) for j a half-odd integer the representations are all double-valued.

Proof: We have seen one example in each category. In general, we have

$$D^j[R_3(2\pi)]^{m'}{}_m = D^j[e^{-i2\pi J_3}]^{m'}{}_m = \delta_{m'm} e^{-i2m\pi} = \delta_{m'm} e^{-i(2j\pi)} = (-1)^{2j}\delta_{m'm}$$

where in the third equality we have used the fact that $j - m$ is an integer. Since $R_n(2\pi) = RR_3(2\pi)R^{-1}$ for some R, the above result implies $D_j[R_n(2\pi)] = (-1)^{2j}E$ for all $\hat{\mathbf{n}}$. QED

The existence of double-valued representations (but no other multiple-valued ones) is intimately tied to the double-connectedness of the group manifold [cf. Sec. 7.1]. Since the irreducible representations were derived from the Lie algebra, which only involves the group structure in the vicinity of the identity, there is no control *a priori* on the global behavior of representation matrix elements. Whether the matrices $D[R(2\pi)]$, $D[R(4\pi)]$, ... etc. coincide with $D[R(0)] = E$ or not must be checked after all possible representations (of the Lie algebra) are found. [We may recall, in the case of SO(2), an infinitely-connected group space is tied to the existence of m-valued representations for all positive integers $m\ (= 1, 2, 3, \ldots)$.] In the next chapter, we shall show that there is one-to-two mapping between SO(3) and the group SU(2), and that the irreducible representations found above all correspond to single-valued representations of SU(2). SU(2) is said to be the *covering group* of the rotation group SO(3).

In applications to physical systems possessing rotational symmetry, there is no *a priori* reason to decide whether the double-valued representations occur in nature or not. In reality, we know that they do exist—all fermion (i.e. half-odd-integer spin) systems, such as electrons, protons, ... etc., are described by quantum mechanical wave functions that correspond to double-valued representations of SO(3). Of course, the single-valued representations are also realized in nature—they correspond to boson systems (with integer spin).

7.4 Properties of the Rotational Matrices $D^J(\alpha, \beta, \gamma)$

Unitarity

All the irreducible representations of SO(3) described in the previous section are constructed to be unitary; hence the D-matrices satisfy the relation

(7.4-1) $$D^\dagger(\alpha, \beta, \gamma) = D^{-1}(\alpha, \beta, \gamma) = D(-\gamma, -\beta, -\alpha)$$

where the representation label j is omitted.

Unit Determinant ("Special")

We can show that the determinant of every D-matrix is equal to 1. Indeed, using the axis-angle parameterization, we have

$$\det D[R_n(\psi)] = \det D[RR_3(\psi)R^{-1}] = \det D[R_3(\psi)]$$

But in the canonical basis $D[R_3(\psi)]$ is diagonal; hence

$$\det D[R_3(\psi)] = \prod_{m=-j}^{j} e^{-im\psi} = 1 \quad .$$

Therefore,

(7.4-2) $$\det D(\alpha, \beta, \gamma) = 1$$

for all rotations.

Reality of d(β)

In the Condon-Shortley convention, the matrices $d^j(\beta)$ are all real and orthogonal. This follows from the fact that $J_\pm$ have real matrix elements [cf. Eq. (7.3-14)] so that J_2 is imaginary [cf. Eq. (7.3-2)], which, in turn, implies that $\exp(-i\beta J_2)$ is real. We have, therefore,

(7.4-3) $$d^{-1}(\beta) = d(-\beta) = d^{\mathrm{T}}(\beta)$$

where the superscript T denotes the *transpose* of the matrix.

Complex Conjugation of D

Since J_3 is real in this convention, we can express the complex conjugate matrix of $\mathrm{D}[\mathrm{R}_3(\psi)]$ in terms of the original matrix by a similarity transformation,

$$\begin{aligned} D^*[\mathrm{R}_3(\psi)] &= D^*[\mathrm{e}^{-i\psi J_3}] = D[\mathrm{e}^{i\psi J_3}] = D[\mathrm{R}_3(-\psi)] \\ &= D[\mathrm{R}_2(\pi)\mathrm{R}_3(\psi)\mathrm{R}_2(-\pi)] \quad . \end{aligned}$$

For a different reason, we also have

$$D^*[\mathrm{R}_2(\psi)] = D[\mathrm{R}_2(\psi)] = D[\mathrm{R}_2(\pi)\mathrm{R}_2(\psi)\mathrm{R}_2(-\pi)] \quad .$$

Therefore, if we denote the special matrix $D[\mathrm{R}_2(\pi)]$ by Y, i.e.

(7.4-4) $$Y \equiv D[\mathrm{R}_2(\pi)] \qquad Y^{m'}{}_{m} = \delta^{m'}_{-m}(-1)^{j-m}$$

then the complex conjugate of the general rotation matrix is given by:

(7.4-5) $$D^*(\alpha, \beta, \gamma) = Y\, D(\alpha, \beta, \gamma)\, Y^{-1}$$

because $\mathrm{R}(\alpha, \beta, \gamma)$ can be written in the product form $\mathrm{R}_3(\alpha)\mathrm{R}_2(\beta)\mathrm{R}_3(\gamma)$.

Symmetry Relations

The real matrices $d^j(\beta)$ satisfy a number of symmetry relations, e.g.

(7.4-6) $$\begin{aligned} d^j(\beta)^{m'}{}_{m} &= d^j(-\beta)^{m}{}_{m'} \\ &= d^j(\pi - \beta)^{-m'}{}_{m}(-1)^{j-m'} \\ &= d^j(\beta)^{-m'}{}_{-m}(-1)^{m'-m} \quad . \end{aligned}$$

These relations can be derived quite easily from Eqs. (7.4-3) and (7.4-4).

Relation to Spherical Harmonics

In the next chapter, we shall derive the differential equations satisfied by $D(\alpha, \beta, \gamma)$, which will allow us to relate them to the classical "special functions" of mathematical physics. It is useful, at this point, to mention some of the important results.

(i) For integer values of j, which we shall denote by l, the D-functions are closely related to the spherical harmonics Y_{lm} and Legendre functions. Specifically,

$$Y_{lm}(\theta, \phi) = \left(\frac{2l+1}{4\pi}\right)^{1/2} [D^l(\phi, \theta, 0)^m{}_0]^* \tag{7.4-7}$$

$$P_{lm}(\cos\theta) = (-1)^m \left(\frac{(l+m)!}{(l-m)!}\right)^{1/2} d^l(\theta)^m{}_0 \tag{7.4-8}$$

$$P_l(\cos\theta) = P_{l0}(\cos\theta) = d^l(\theta)^0{}_0 \tag{7.4-9}$$

where $P_l(z)$ is the ordinary Legendre polynomial and $P_{lm}(z)$ is the associated Legendre function.

(ii) For arbitrary j, $d^j(\beta)^{m'}{}_m$ is proportional to the classical Jacobi Polynomial $P_l^{(a,b)}(\cos\beta)$ with $a = m' - m$, $b = m' + m$, and $l = j - m'$. Details will be given in Chap. 8.

(iii) The functions $D^j(\alpha, \beta, \gamma)^{m'}{}_m$ also satisfy orthonormality and completeness conditions which are generalizations of Theorems 3.5, 3.6, and 6.5. Details will be given after the appropriate invariant measure for integration over group parameters has been introduced.

Characters

The characters of the group SO(3) in an irreducible representation can be derived in a general way. As all rotations by the same angle (say, ψ) around any axis belong to the same class, it suffices to evaluate the group character for $R_3(\psi)$. With respect to the canonical basis, we have:

$$\chi^j(\psi) = \sum_m D^j[R_3(\psi)]^m{}_m = \sum_{m=-j}^{j} e^{-im\psi} = \frac{\sin(j+1/2)\psi}{\sin(\psi/2)} \quad . \tag{7.4-10}$$

Thus, for $j = 1/2$, we have $\chi^{1/2}(\psi) = \sin\psi/\sin(\psi/2) = 2\cos(\psi/2)$; and for $j = 1$, we obtain $\chi^1(\psi) = \sin(\psi + \psi/2)/\sin(\psi/2) = \cos\psi + \sin\psi\cos(\psi/2)/\sin(\psi/2) = \cos\psi + 2\cos^2(\psi/2) = 2\cos\psi + 1$. These results can be cross-checked by comparing with the traces of the d^j-matrices given by Eq. (7.3-21) and Eq. (7.3-23) respectively.

7.5 Application to a Particle in a Central Potential

We apply the group-theoretical notions developed so far to a familiar system in quantum mechanics—a single particle in a central potential (or, equivalently, two particles interacting with each other in their center-of-mass frame). The fact that the potential function $V(r)$ depends only on the magnitude r of the coordinate vector $\mathbf{x}$ is a manifestation of the *rotational symmetry* of the system. The mathematical statement of this symmetry principle is:

$$[H, U(R)] = 0 \qquad \text{for all } R \in SO(3) \tag{7.5-1}$$

where H is the Hamiltonian that governs the dynamics of the system, and $U(R)$ is the unitary operator on the state-vector space representing the rotation R. It follows from Eq. (7.5-1) that

$$[H, J_i] = 0 \qquad \text{for } i = 1, 2, 3 \quad . \tag{7.5-2}$$

We shall see that a number of important general results about such a system can be inferred from these symmetry considerations without having to solve the corresponding Schrödinger equation, as is normally done in texts on quantum mechanics. This example, on a familiar system, serves the purpose of introducing general group-theoretical techniques in physical applications.

7.5.1 Characterization of States

The quantum mechanical states of this system are most naturally chosen as eigenstates of the commuting operators $\{H, J^2, J_3\}$. These eigenstates will be denoted by $|E, l, m\rangle$. They satisfy:

$$H\,|E,l,m\rangle = |E,l,m\rangle\, E$$

(7.5-3) $$J^2\,|E,l,m\rangle = |E,l,m\rangle\, l(l+1) \qquad (l = \text{integer})$$

and $$J_3\,|E,l,m\rangle = |E,l,m\rangle\, m \qquad (m = -l,\ldots,l).$$

The Schrödinger wave-function of these states is:

(7.5-4) $$\psi_{Elm}(\mathbf{x}) = \langle \mathbf{x}|E,l,m\rangle$$

where $|\mathbf{x}\rangle$ is an eigenstate of the position operator $\mathbf{X}$. We shall use spherical coordinates (r,θ,ϕ) for the coordinate vector $\mathbf{x}$, and fix the relative phase of the vectors $|\mathbf{x}\rangle \equiv |r,\theta,\phi\rangle$ by

(7.5-5) $$\begin{aligned} |r,\theta,\phi\rangle &= U(\phi,\theta,0)\,|r\hat{\mathbf{z}}\rangle \\ &= e^{-i\phi J_3}e^{-i\theta J_2}\,|r,0,0\rangle \quad . \end{aligned}$$

Note, we have chosen to define all states in terms of a "standard reference state" $|r\hat{\mathbf{z}}\rangle = |r,0,0\rangle$; it represents a state localized on the z-axis at a distance r away from the origin. For a structureless particle, of the type that is tacitly assumed here, such a state must be invariant under a rotation around the z-axis; i.e.

(7.5-6) $$e^{-i\psi J_3}\,|r,0,0\rangle = |r,0,0\rangle$$

hence $$J_3\,|r,0,0\rangle = 0 \quad .$$

Combining Eqs. (7.5-4) and (7.5-5) we obtain

$$\begin{aligned} \psi_{Elm}(r,\theta,\phi) &= \langle r,0,0|U^{\dagger}(\phi,\theta,0)|E,l,m\rangle \\ &= \langle r,0,0|E,l,m'\rangle\,[D^l(\phi,\theta,0)^{\dagger}]^{m'}{}_{m} \quad . \end{aligned}$$

Because of Eq. (7.5-6), we must have

$$\langle r,0,0|E,l,m'\rangle = \delta_{m',0}\,\tilde{\psi}_{El}(r)$$

which implies

(7.5-7) $$\psi_{Elm}(r,\theta,\phi) = \tilde{\psi}_{El}(r)\,[D^l(\phi,\theta,0)^m{}_0]^* \quad .$$

Making use of Eq. (7.4-7), we arrive at the result:

(7.5-8) $$\psi_{Elm}(r,\theta,\phi) = \psi_{El}(r)\,Y_{lm}(\theta,\phi)$$

where $\psi_{El}(r) = \tilde{\psi}_{El}(r)\,(4\pi/2l+1)^{1/2}$. Eq. (7.5-8) gives the familiar decomposition of $\psi(\mathbf{x})$ into the general angular factor $Y_{lm}(\theta,\phi)$ and a "radial-wave-function" $\psi_{El}(r)$

which depends on the yet unspecified potential function $V(r)$. The occurrence of $Y_{lm}(\theta, \phi)$ in this decomposition is seen to be the direct consequence of spherical symmetry, which is independent of details of the dynamics of the system.

7.5.2 Asymptotic Plane Wave States

If the potential function $V(r)$ vanishes faster than r^{-1} at large distances, the asymptotic states far away from the origin are close to free-particle "plane-wave" states, these are eigenstates of the vector momentum operator **P**. If we denote the magnitude of the momentum by p and specify its direction by $\hat{\mathbf{p}}(\theta, \phi)$, then:

(7.5-9) $$E = p^2/2m$$

and $$|\mathbf{p}\rangle = |p, \theta, \phi\rangle = U(\phi, \theta, 0)\,|p\hat{\mathbf{z}}\rangle$$

where, again, we have picked the "standard reference state" to be along the z-axis. These plane-wave states can be related to the angular momentum states of the last paragraph by making use of the projection operation technique introduced in Chap. 4. Specifically, by applying Theorem 4.2 to the present case, one can show that

(7.5-10)
$$\begin{aligned} |p, l, m\rangle &= \left(\frac{2l+1}{4\pi}\right)^{1/2} \int_0^{2\pi} d\phi \int_{-1}^{1} d(\cos\theta)\,|p, \theta, \phi\rangle\, [D^l(\phi, \theta, 0)^m{}_0]^* \\ &= \int d\Omega\, |p, \theta, \phi\rangle\, Y_{lm}(\theta, \phi) \end{aligned}$$

where $d\Omega = d\phi\, d(\cos\theta)$. Detailed proof will be given in the next chapter. The inverse of Eq. (7.5-10) is:

(7.5-11) $$|p, \theta, \phi\rangle = \sum_{l,m} |p, l, m\rangle\, Y^*_{lm}(\theta, \phi)$$

7.5.3 Partial Wave Decomposition

Consider the scattering of a particle in the (central) potential field $V(r)$. Let the momentum of the initial asymptotic state be along the z-axis, i.e. $\mathbf{p}_i = (p, \theta_i = 0 = \phi_i)$; and that of the final state be along the direction (θ, ϕ), i.e. $\mathbf{p}_f = (p, \theta, \phi)$. Then the "scattering amplitude" can be written[4] as

(7.5-12) $$\langle \mathbf{p}_f | T | \mathbf{p}_i \rangle = \langle p, \theta, \phi | T | p, 0, 0\rangle$$

where the scattering operator T depends on the Hamiltonian. The only property of T which we shall use is that it be rotationally invariant. This means, when applied to a state of definite angular momentum, T will leave the quantum numbers (l, m) unchanged, i.e.

(7.5-13) $$\langle p, l, m | T | p, l', m'\rangle = \delta_{ll'}\,\delta_{mm'}\,T_l(p) \quad .$$

(The fact that the last factor is independent of m can be established by observing that $J_\pm$ commute with T.)

[4] Consult any standard introductory book on quantum mechanics on the definition of the scattering amplitude. For instance, see Chap. 19 of [Messiah].

Let us now apply Eq. (7.5-11) to Eq. (7.5-12), making use of Eq. (7.5-13), we obtain:

$$\begin{aligned}\langle \mathbf{p}_f|\mathrm{T}|\mathbf{p}_i\rangle &= \sum_{lm}\sum_{l'} Y_{lm}(\theta,\phi)\langle p,l,m|\mathrm{T}|p,l',0\rangle\, Y_{l'0}{}^*(0,0)\\ &= \sum_l \frac{2l+1}{4\pi}\mathrm{T}_l(E)\,P_l(\cos\theta)\end{aligned} \tag{7.5-14}$$

This is the famous *partial wave expansion* of the scattering amplitude. We see that its validity is intimately tied to the underlying spherical symmetry, being quite independent of the detailed interactions. All the "dynamics" resides in the yet unspecified "partial-wave amplitude" $\mathrm{T}_l(E)$.

7.5.4 Summary

This simple example illustrates the utility of group-theoretical technique applied to physical problems: it allows a clean separation of "kinematic" effects due to the underlying symmetry [e.g. Y_{lm} in Eq. (7.5-8), and P_l in Eq. (7.5-14), from "dynamic" effects which are specific to the system under study. This results in great simplification of the problem. For instance, to find the wave-function, Eq. (7.5-8) immediately reduces the original partial differential equation in 3 variables to an ordinary differential equation involving the radial variable r only. Similarly, the partial wave expansion, Eq. (7.5-14), reduces the scattering amplitude which originally depends on three variables (E,θ,ϕ) to a set of independent partial wave amplitudes, each one depending only on one variable E.

7.6 Transformation Properties of Wave Functions and Operators

So far, we have concentrated on transformation properties of state vectors under symmetry operations. In physical applications, it is useful to consider also transformation properties of wave functions and operators under symmetry operations. For concreteness, we shall start with the "coordinate representation" of quantum mechanics [Messiah, Schiff]. The results are general and can be applied to the "momentum representation" and to other areas of interest in classical physics and quantum field theory.

As our starting point, consider the basic relation

$$\begin{aligned} U[\mathrm{R}]\,|\mathbf{x}\rangle &= |\mathbf{x}'\rangle\\ \mathbf{x}' &= \mathrm{R}\mathbf{x} \qquad (x'^i = R^i{}_j x^j)\end{aligned} \tag{7.6-1}$$

where $\mathbf{x}$, $\mathbf{x}'$ are coordinate space 3-vectors, $|\mathbf{x}\rangle$ and $|\mathbf{x}'\rangle$ are localized states at $\mathbf{x}$, $\mathbf{x}'$ respectively, and $\mathrm{R}\in SO(3)$ is a rotation. Let $|\psi\rangle$ be an arbitrary state vector, then

$$|\psi\rangle = \int |\mathbf{x}\rangle\,\psi(\mathbf{x})\,d^3x \tag{7.6-2}$$

where $\psi(\mathbf{x})$ is the c-number wave function in the coordinate representation. We ask: how does $\psi(\mathbf{x})$ transform under a rotation R; or, more specifically, if

$$|\psi'\rangle = U[\mathrm{R}]\,|\psi\rangle = \int |\mathbf{x}\rangle\,\psi'(\mathbf{x})\,d^3x \tag{7.6-3}$$

then how is $\psi'(\mathbf{x})$ related to $\psi(\mathbf{x})$?

Theorem 7.6 (Transformation Formula for Wave Functions): The wave function of an arbitrary state transform under rotations as:

$$\psi(\mathbf{x}) \longrightarrow \psi'(\mathbf{x}) = \psi(\mathrm{R}^{-1}\mathbf{x}) \quad . \tag{7.6-4}$$

Proof: We apply the rotation operator to both sides of Eq. (7.6-2) and obtain:

$$U[\mathrm{R}]\,|\psi\rangle = \int U[\mathrm{R}]\,|\mathbf{x}\rangle\,\psi(\mathbf{x})\,d^3x = \int |\mathbf{x}'\rangle\,\psi(\mathbf{x})\,d^3x$$
$$= \int |\mathbf{x}'\rangle\,\psi(\mathrm{R}^{-1}\mathbf{x}')\,d^3x' = \int |\mathbf{x}\rangle\,\psi(\mathrm{R}^{-1}\mathbf{x})\,d^3x$$

where the second equality follows from Eq. (7.6-1), the third equality results from a change of integration variable $\mathbf{x} \rightarrow \mathbf{x}'$ (with unit Jacobian), and the last equality is a consequence of renaming the dummy integration variable. Comparing this result with Eq. (7.6-3), we conclude:

$$\psi'(\mathbf{x}) = \psi(\mathrm{R}^{-1}\mathbf{x}) \quad .$$

QED.

The appearance of the inverse of R on the right-hand side of Eq. (7.6-4) should not come as a surprise. Its presence is required in order that the mapping $\psi(\mathbf{x}) \rightarrow \psi'(\mathbf{x})$ be a representation of the symmetry group. This was pointed out earlier when we first introduced the idea of group representations on function space (Sec. 3.1, Example 7).

Example 1: Let $|\psi\rangle = |\mathbf{p}\rangle$ be a plane-wave state [cf. Eq. (7.5-9)]; then $\psi_p(\mathbf{x}) = e^{i\mathbf{p}\cdot\mathbf{x}}$ [cf. Eq. (6.7-12)]. Applying theorem 7.6, we obtain:

$$\psi'(\mathbf{x}) = \psi_p(\mathrm{R}^{-1}\mathbf{x}) = e^{i\mathbf{p}\cdot\mathrm{R}^{-1}\mathbf{x}} = e^{i\mathrm{R}\mathbf{p}\cdot\mathbf{x}} \quad .$$

This is just what we expect, as

$$\psi'(\mathbf{x}) = \langle\mathbf{x}|\,U[\mathrm{R}]\,|\mathbf{p}\rangle = \langle\mathbf{x}|\mathbf{p}'\rangle = \psi_{p'}(\mathbf{x})$$

where $\mathbf{p}' = \mathrm{R}\mathbf{p}$.

Example 2: Let $|\psi\rangle = |E,l,m\rangle$ of Sec. 7.5. According to Eq. (7.5-8), $\psi(x) = \psi_{El}(r)\,Y_{lm}(\hat{\mathbf{x}})$ where $\hat{\mathbf{x}}$ signifies the polar and azimuthal angles of the unit vector $\hat{\mathbf{x}}$. On the other hand, $|\psi'\rangle = U[\mathrm{R}]|\psi\rangle = U[\mathrm{R}]|E,l,m\rangle = |E,l,m'\rangle\,D^l[\mathrm{R}]^{m'}{}_m$, hence

$$\psi'(x) = \psi_{El}(r)\,Y_{lm'}(\hat{\mathbf{x}})\,D^l[\mathrm{R}]^{m'}{}_m \quad .$$

Applying Theorem 7.6, we obtain:

$$Y_{lm}(\mathrm{R}^{-1}\hat{\mathbf{x}}) = Y_{lm'}(\hat{\mathbf{x}})\,D^l[\mathrm{R}]^{m'}{}_m \quad . \tag{7.6-5}$$

This is a well known property of the spherical harmonics. [cf. Sec. 8.6, Eq. (8.6-2)].

Let us generalize the above consideration to wave functions which also carry a discrete index. Again, for concreteness, let us consider the case of coordinate space wave functions, this time spin 1/2 objects—these are the *Pauli spinor wave functions.* The basis vectors are $\{|\mathbf{x},\sigma\rangle, \sigma = \pm 1/2\}$, and they transform as:

$$U[\mathrm{R}]\,|\mathbf{x},\sigma\rangle = |\mathrm{R}\mathbf{x},\lambda\rangle\,\mathrm{D}^{1/2}[\mathrm{R}]^{\lambda}{}_{\sigma} \tag{7.6-6}$$

where $D^{1/2}[R]$ is the angular momentum 1/2 rotation matrix. An arbitrary state of such a spin 1/2 object can be written as,

$$|\psi\rangle = \sum_{\sigma} \int |\mathbf{x}, \sigma\rangle \, \psi^{\sigma}(\mathbf{x}) \, d^3x \tag{7.6-7}$$

where $\psi^{\sigma}(x)$ is the two-component *Pauli wave function* of $|\psi\rangle$. How does $\psi^{\sigma}(\mathbf{x})$ transform under rotations? We have

$$\begin{aligned} |\psi'\rangle = U[R]\,|\psi\rangle &= \int |R\mathbf{x}, \lambda\rangle \, D^{1/2}[R]^{\lambda}{}_{\sigma} \psi^{\sigma}(\mathbf{x}) \, d^3x \\ &= \int |\mathbf{x}, \lambda\rangle \, D^{1/2}[R]^{\lambda}{}_{\sigma} \psi^{\sigma}(R^{-1}\mathbf{x}) \, d^3x \\ &= \int |\mathbf{x}, \lambda\rangle \, \psi'^{\lambda}(\mathbf{x}) \, d^3x \end{aligned}$$

hence, $\psi \xrightarrow{R} \psi'$ such that:

$$\psi'^{\lambda}(\mathbf{x}) = D^{1/2}[R]^{\lambda}{}_{\sigma} \psi^{\sigma}(R^{-1}\mathbf{x}) \quad . \tag{7.6-8}$$

We leave the proof that the above mapping provides a representation of the rotation group SO(3) to the reader. [Problem 7.10]

There are numerous examples of *multi-component wave functions* or *fields* in addition to Pauli wave functions: the electromagnetic fields $E^i(\mathbf{x})$, $B^i(\mathbf{x})$; the stress and strain tensors; the energy-momentum density tensor, the velocity field of a fluid, the Dirac wave function for relativistic spin 1/2 particles, ... etc., just to name a few. The above result can be generalized to cover all these cases. In fact, we shall use the transformation property under SO(3) to categorize these objects.

Definition 7.3 (Irreducible Wave Functions and Fields): A set of multi-component functions $\{\phi^m(\mathbf{x}), m = -j, \ldots, j\}$ of the coordinate vector is said to form an *irreducible wave function* or *irreducible field* of spin j if they transform under rotations as:

$$\phi \xrightarrow{R} \phi'; \qquad \phi'^m(\mathbf{x}) = D^j[R]^m{}_n \phi^n(R^{-1}\mathbf{x}) \tag{7.6-9}$$

where $D^j[R]^m{}_n$ is the angular momentum j irreducible representation matrix of SO(3).

Among the physical quantities cited above, the electric field $E^i(\mathbf{x})$, magnetic field $B^i(\mathbf{x})$, and the velocity field $v^i(\mathbf{x})$ are spin one ($j = 1$) fields, the Pauli wave function $\psi^{\sigma}(x)$ is a spin 1/2 field, the Dirac wave function is a reducible field consisting of the direct sum of two spin 1/2 irreducible fields, and the stress tensor is a spin 2 field.

Next, we consider the transformation properties of operators on the state-vector space. Again we shall use, as our concrete example, the coordinate vector operators X^i defined by the eigenvalue equation:

$$X^i|\mathbf{x}\rangle = |\mathbf{x}\rangle \, x^i \quad . \tag{7.6-10}$$

Theorem 7.7 (Transformation Formula for Vector Operators): Components of the coordinate vector operator **X** (hence all "vector" operators, by definition) transform under rotations as:

(7.6-11) $$U[\mathrm{R}]\mathrm{X}_i U[\mathrm{R}]^{-1} = \mathrm{X}_j R^j{}_i$$

where $R^j{}_i$ is the 3×3 SO(3) matrix defining the rotation [Eqs. (7.1-1), (7.1-2)].

Proof: Applying the operator $U[\mathrm{R}]$ to Eq. (7.6-10), we obtain:

$$\mathrm{LHS} = U[\mathrm{R}]\mathrm{X}^i U[\mathrm{R}]^{-1} U[\mathrm{R}]|\mathbf{x}\rangle = U[\mathrm{R}]\mathrm{X}_i U[\mathrm{R}]^{-1}|\mathbf{x}'\rangle$$

and

$$\mathrm{RHS} = U[\mathrm{R}]|\mathbf{x}\rangle x^i = |\mathbf{x}'\rangle x^i = |\mathbf{x}'\rangle (R^{-1})^i{}_j x'^j \quad .$$

Hence,

$$U[\mathrm{R}]\mathrm{X}^i U[\mathrm{R}]^{-1}|\mathbf{x}\rangle = |\mathbf{x}\rangle x^j (R^{-1})^i{}_j$$

where we have renamed the free c-numbers $\mathbf{x}'$ by $\mathbf{x}$. Comparing with the defining formula, Eq. (7.6-10), we conclude that

(7.6-12) $$U[\mathrm{R}]\mathrm{X}^i U[\mathrm{R}]^{-1} = (R^{-1})^i{}_j \mathrm{X}^j \quad .$$

We can write this result in a more convenient form by noting that: (i) orthogonality of the matrices R implies $(R^{-1})^i{}_j = R^{\mathrm{T}i}{}_j = R_j{}^i$, and (ii) in 3-dimensional Euclidean space, there is no real distinction between upper and lower indices. The above equation can therefore be written in the alternative form:

$$U[\mathrm{R}]\mathrm{X}_i U[\mathrm{R}]^{-1} = \mathrm{X}_j R^j{}_i \quad .$$

This form is consistent with the notation of the general formula Eq. (4.3-1). QED.

[Apply two rotations in succession, and convince yourself that this transformation formula provides a representation of the group on the space of operators. cf. Problem 4.5.]

The momentum operators P_i are vector operators. We anticipate, therefore

(7.6-13) $$U[\mathrm{R}]\mathrm{P}_i U[\mathrm{R}]^{-1} = \mathrm{P}_j R^j{}_i \quad .$$

Notice that the right-hand sides of Eqs. (7.6-11) and (7.6-13) are analogous to that of Eq. (7.1-1) for unit coordinate vectors, rather than that of Eq. (7.1-2) for the coordinate components. It is also worthwhile to recall that Eq. (7.2-5), concerning **J**, which expresses the basic group structure of SO(3), has the same form as Eqs. (7.6-11) and (7.6-13). Thus, the angular momentum operator **J** also transforms as a vector operator. We shall return to Eqs. (7.2-5) and (7.6-13) and their generalizations in Chaps. 9 and 10 when we consider larger space-time symmetry groups including both rotations and translations.

Vector operators are not the only case of operators which transform among themselves in a definite way under rotations. They are special cases of the general notion of irreducible operators or irreducible tensors introduced in Chap. 4 [cf. Definition 4.3]. The simplest example of an irreducible operator under rotations is the Hamiltonian operator: it is invariant, hence corresponds to $s = 0$. Higher rank irreducible operators also play important roles in physics. In Sec. 7.8 we shall return to this subject for special discussion. In Sec. 8.7 we shall study in detail the multipole radiation operators—an important class of irreducible operators which we already encountered in the example at the end of Chap. 4.

To close this section, we consider transformation properties of operators which also depend on the space variables **x**. Such objects arise most explicitly, although not exclusively, in non-relativistic many-body theory ("second quantized" Schrödinger theory [Schiff]) and in relativistic quantum field theory. In these settings, the c-number wave functions and fields discussed earlier in this section become operators on the vector space of physical states. For concreteness, let us consider the second quantized Schrödinger theory of a spin 1/2 physical system. The operator in question is a *two-component operator-valued Pauli spinor* $\Psi^\sigma(\mathbf{x})$. We would like to find out how does Ψ transform under a general rotation R. To answer this question, we must know the basic relation between the operator Ψ and the c-number wave function discussed earlier. Suffice it to say that, if $|\psi\rangle$ is an arbitrary one-particle state in the theory, then

$$\langle 0|\Psi^\sigma(\mathbf{x})|\psi\rangle = \psi^\sigma(\mathbf{x}) \tag{7.6-14}$$

where $\psi^\sigma(\mathbf{x})$ is the c-number Pauli wave function for the state and $|0\rangle$ is the "vacuum" or 0-particle state. Under an arbitrary rotation, $U[\mathrm{R}]|\psi\rangle = |\psi'\rangle$ and $\psi'^\sigma(x)$ is related to $\psi^\sigma(x)$ by Eq. (7.6-8). Making use of the fact that the vacuum state is invariant under any rotation, we can write Eq. (7.6-14) as:

$$\langle 0|U[\mathrm{R}]\,\Psi^\sigma(\mathbf{x})\,U[\mathrm{R}]^{-1}|\psi'\rangle = \psi^\sigma(\mathbf{x}) = D^{1/2}[\mathrm{R}^{-1}]^\sigma{}_\lambda\,\psi'^\lambda(\mathrm{R}\mathbf{x}) \quad .$$

On the other hand, multiplying Eq. (7.6-14) on the left by $D^{1/2}[\mathrm{R}^{-1}]$ and substituting ψ' for ψ, and $\mathbf{x}' = \mathrm{R}\mathbf{x}$ for $\mathbf{x}$, we obtain

$$\langle 0|D^{1/2}[\mathrm{R}^{-1}]^\sigma{}_\lambda\,\Psi^\lambda(\mathrm{R}\mathbf{x})|\psi'\rangle = D^{1/2}[\mathrm{R}^{-1}]^\sigma{}_\lambda\,\psi'^\lambda(\mathrm{R}\mathbf{x}) \quad .$$

Comparison of the last two equations leads to the Ansatz:

$$U[\mathrm{R}]\,\Psi^\sigma(\mathbf{x})\,U[\mathrm{R}]^{-1} = D^{1/2}[\mathrm{R}^{-1}]^\sigma{}_\lambda\,\Psi^\lambda(\mathrm{R}\mathbf{x}) \quad . \tag{7.6-15}$$

This equation contrasts with Eq. (7.6-8) in that, on the right-hand side, R in one is replaced by R^{-1} in the other. The reason for this difference is exactly the same as that for the difference between the operators X^i, Eq. (7.8-12), and the components x^i, Eq. (7.1-2). One can readily prove that Eq. (7.6-15) provides a representation of the rotation group on the space of the operators $\{\Psi^\sigma(x)\}$.

Should we move the D matrix on the right-hand side of Eq. (7.6-15) to the right of Ψ as we did for the **X** operator in Theorem 7.7? Suppose we try. Since $D[\mathrm{R}]$ is unitary,

$$D[\mathrm{R}^{-1}]^\sigma{}_\lambda = D^\dagger[\mathrm{R}]^\sigma{}_\lambda = (D[\mathrm{R}]^\lambda{}_\sigma)^* \quad .$$

If this expression is substituted into the right-hand side of Eq. (7.6-15), the result would not look particularly attractive. However, if we take the hermitian conjugate of both sides, then we get:

$$U[\mathrm{R}]\,\Psi^\dagger_\sigma(\mathbf{x})\,U[\mathrm{R}] = \Psi^\dagger_\lambda(\mathbf{x})\,D^{1/2}[\mathrm{R}]^\lambda{}_\sigma \tag{7.6-16}$$

which is nice and simple. The last equation is the analog to Eqs. (7.6-11), (7.6-13), (7.2-5), and (4.3-1)—in all the previous cases, the operators have integer spin and are chosen to be hermitian. For half-integer spin operators they are not naturally hermitian, Eqs. (7.6-15) and (7.6-16) are distinct and we shall use them as they stand.

The above result can be generalized to fields of all kinds. Let $\{A^m(\mathbf{x});\ m = 1,2,\ldots,N\}$ be a set of field operators which transform among themselves under rotations, then we must have

$$U[\mathrm{R}]\,A^m(\mathbf{x})\,U[\mathrm{R}]^{-1} = D[\mathrm{R}^{-1}]^m{}_n\,A^n(\mathrm{R}\mathbf{x}) \tag{7.6-17}$$

where $\{D[\mathrm{R}]\}$ is some (N-dimensional) representation of SO(3). If the representation is irreducible and equivalent to $j = s$, $\{A\}$ is said to have spin s. The special example discussed above corresponds to the case $s = 1/2$. For vector fields such as the second-quantized electromagnetic fields $\mathbf{E}(\mathbf{x})$, $\mathbf{B}(\mathbf{x})$, and the vector potential $\mathbf{A}(\mathbf{x})$—$D[\mathrm{R}] = R$ and we have $s = 1$. For the relativistic Dirac field, we have the reducible representation $1/2 \oplus 1/2$.[5]

7.7 Direct Product Representations and their Reduction

In Sec. 3.8 we discussed in general the reduction of product representations to their irreducible parts. We can now apply that analysis to the representations of SO(3). The results are useful, as one encounters the reduction of product representations frequently in applications, and as forming direct products provides one with a convenient method to build higher dimensional irreducible representations from "fundamental" ones of lower dimension.

Let D^j and $D^{j'}$ be two irreducible representations of SO(3) defined on the vector spaces V and V′ respectively. The product representation $D^{j\times j'}$ is defined on the $(2j+1)(2j'+1)$ dimensional direct product vector space V × V′ [Definition 3.8]. It is natural to begin with the basis vectors $|m,m'\rangle$, which are "formal products" of the canonical basis vectors of V and V′:

$$|m,m'\rangle = |jm\rangle \times |j'm'\rangle \quad . \tag{7.7-1}$$

We have, by definition [cf. Eq. (3.8-1)],

$$U(\mathrm{R})\,|m,m'\rangle = |n,n'\rangle\,D^j(\mathrm{R})^n{}_m D^{j'}(\mathrm{R})^{n'}{}_{m'} \quad . \tag{7.7-2}$$

It is quite simple to show that: (i) Eq. (7.7-2) defines a representation of SO(3); (ii) the representation is single-valued if $j + j' =$ integer, and it is double-valued if $j + j' =$ half-odd-integer. Unless either j or j' is equal to zero, the product representation is reducible. Let us look at one simple example, $\mathrm{D}^{1/2\times1/2}$. The four basis vectors for the product space will be denoted by $|++\rangle$, $|+-\rangle$, $|-+\rangle$, and $|--\rangle$. We can show that the vector $|a\rangle = |+-\rangle - |-+\rangle$, which is anti-symmetric in the two indices, is invariant under rotations. Indeed,

$$\begin{aligned} U(\mathrm{R})\,|a\rangle &= |nn'\rangle\,[D^{1/2}(\mathrm{R})^n{}_+\,D^{1/2}(\mathrm{R})^{n'}{}_- - D^{1/2}(\mathrm{R})^n{}_-\,D^{1/2}(\mathrm{R})^{n'}{}_+] \\ &= (|+-\rangle - |-+\rangle)[D^{1/2}(\mathrm{R})^+{}_+\,D^{1/2}(\mathrm{R})^-{}_- - D^{1/2}(\mathrm{R})^+{}_-\,D^{1/2}(\mathrm{R})^-{}_+] \\ &= |a\rangle \det[D^{1/2}(\mathrm{R})] = |a\rangle \quad . \end{aligned} \tag{7.7-3}$$

Thus $|a\rangle$ spans a one-dimensional subspace invariant under SO(3), and $D^{1/2\times1/2}$ contains the irreducible representation D^0 at least once. It turns out that

[5] It will cease to be reducible when we include Lorentz symmetry and space inversion for consideration, as will be done in Chaps. 10 and 11.

$D^{1/2\times 1/2} = D^0 + D^1$ where D^1 is spanned by the three vectors $|++\rangle$, $(|+-\rangle + |-+\rangle)/2^{1/2}$, and $|--\rangle$. We shall prove this point shortly.

In order to investigate the reduction of product representations in general, it is useful to establish a connection between the generators on the product space V × V′ and those on the individual spaces V and V′. To this end, consider an infinitesimal rotation around an arbitrary axis $\hat{\mathbf{n}}$,

$$D^j[R_n(d\psi)]\cdot D^{j'}[R_n(d\psi)] = D^{j\times j'}[R_n(d\psi)] \quad .$$

Now, to first order in $d\psi$, the left-hand side is:

$$[E^j - i d\psi J_n^j]\cdot[E^{j'} - i d\psi J_n^{j'}] = E^j \times E^{j'} - i\, d\psi\, [J_n^j \times E^{j'} + E^j \times J_n^{j'}] \quad .$$

On the other hand, the right-hand side is, by definition,

$$E^{j\times j'} - i\, d\psi\, J_n^{j\times j'} \quad .$$

Equating the two expressions, we obtain:

(7.7-4) $$J_n^{j\times j'} = J_n^j \times E^{j'} + E^j \times J_n^{j'} \quad .$$

For simplicity, we shall write the right-hand side of this equation as $J_n^j + J_n^{j'}$, and refer to this combination as a simple sum. We shall also omit the representation label (i.e. the superscripts) whenever confusion does not arise.

Theorem 7.8: The generators of a direct product representation are the *sums* of the corresponding generators of its constituent representations.

We are now ready to tackle the reduction of the product representation $D^{j\times j'}$: starting from the set of vectors $|m, m'\rangle$, Eq. (7.7-1), we regroup them to form invariant subspaces by using generators of the product space—in very much the same way as we constructed the irreducible representations in Sec. 7.3. First, it is an immediate consequence of Theorem 7.8 [or Eq. (7.7-4)] that $|m, m'\rangle$ are eigenvectors of J_3,

(7.7-5) $$J_3\,|m, m'\rangle = |m, m'\rangle(m + m') \quad .$$

Since $-j \le m \le j$ and $-j' \le m' \le j'$, the highest eigenvalue of J_3 is $j + j'$. Indeed, there is only one vector corresponding to this eigenvalue—$|j, j'\rangle$. There are two vectors having the eigenvalue $J_3 = j + j' - 1$; they are $|j-1, j'\rangle$ and $|j, j'-1\rangle$. The general situation is depicted in Fig. 7.6 where each point represents one basis state. Those states with the same eigenvalue of J_3 (denoted by M) are connected by dashed lines.

We shall construct eigenvectors of $\{J^2, J_3\}$ with eigenvalues $\{J(J+1), M\}$ as defined in Eqs. (7.3-12)–(7.3-14). Since the state with $M = j + j'$ is unique, and there is no state with a higher eigenvalue of J_3, it must be the highest member of an irreducible basis with $J = j + j'$, i.e.

(7.7-6) $$|J = j+j',\ M = j+j'\rangle = |j,\ j'\rangle \quad .$$

This can be verified by applying the operator J^2 [i.e. $(J^j + J^{j'})^2$] to the vector on the right-hand side, and confirming that it is an eigenvector with eigenvalue $(j+j')(j+j'+1)$. [cf. Problem 7.8] We can now generate the $|J, M\rangle$ states

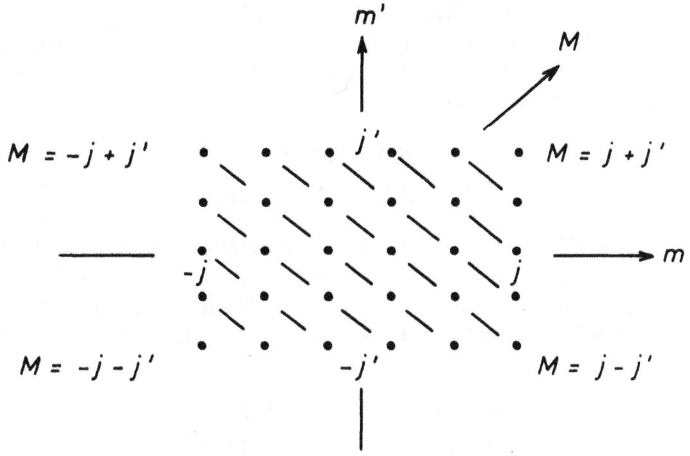

Fig. 7.6 Vector addition of angular momenta.

with $M = j+j'-1, \ldots, -j-j'$ by repeated application of J_-, e.g.

$$\begin{aligned} |J = j+j', M = j+j'-1\rangle\,[2(j+j')]^{1/2} &\\ = J_-\,|J = j+j', M = j+j'\rangle &\\ = J_-\,|j, j'\rangle &\\ = |j-1, j'\rangle(2j)^{1/2} + |j, j'-1\rangle(2j')^{1/2}. & \end{aligned} \tag{7.7-7}$$

where the vectors on the first two lines belong to the new basis $|J, M\rangle$ while those of the last two lines refer to the original basis $|m, m'\rangle$. The $2(j+j')+1$ states derived this way span an invariant subspace corresponding to $J = j+j'$.

Since there are two linearly independent states with $M = j+j'-1$, and one of them is already included in the $J = j+j'$ invariant subspace [Eq. (7.7-7)], we are left with a unique state, orthogonal to the former, which must have $J = j+j'-1$ (by the same reasoning as before). [N.B. Even if we agree that this vector must be normalized to 1, there is still the freedom to choose an arbitrary "phase factor" $e^{i\alpha}$ where α is any real number. This phase factor must be fixed by an arbitrary convention. The commonly used Condon-Shortley convention will be explained in a moment.] Denoting this vector by $|J = j+j'-1, M = j+j'-1\rangle$, we can generate another invariant subspace corresponding to $J = j+j'-1$ by the repeated application of the lowering operator J_-; its basis has $2(j+j'-1)+1 = 2(j+j')-1$ vectors.

This process can be repeated, yielding an invariant subspace with J smaller by one at each stage, until we are left with $2|j-j'|+1$ vectors which span an invariant subspace corresponding to $J = |j-j'|$. The counting of independent basis states will work out correctly as is evident from Fig. 7.6, and it can also be checked by noting that,

$$[2(j+j')+1] + [2(j+j'-1)+1] + \cdots + [2|j-j'|+1] = (2j+1)(2j'+1).$$

By construction, the new basis vectors $\{|J,M\rangle; M = -J,\ldots,J; J = |j-j'|,\ldots,(j+j')\}$ are orthonormal, just as the original ones. The transformation matrix between the two sets, the elements of which are called Clebsch-Gordan coefficients [cf. Sec. 3.8], is unitary:

$$|J,M\rangle = |m,m'\rangle\langle m\,m'(jj')JM\rangle \tag{7.7-8}$$

$$|m,m'\rangle = |J,M\rangle\langle JM(jj')m\,m'\rangle \tag{7.7-9}$$

where $\langle JM(jj')m\,m'\rangle = \langle m\,m'(jj')JM\rangle^*$ and repeated indices are summed over. The constructive process described in the previous paragraph determines the Clebsch-Gordan coefficients up to a common phase factor for each invariant subspace with label J, as mentioned earlier. The Condon-Shortley convention specifies that:

$$\begin{aligned} &\langle m\,m'(jj')JM\rangle \quad \text{are real; and} \\ &\langle j, J-j(jj')JJ\rangle \quad \text{are positive for all } j, j', J. \end{aligned} \tag{7.7-10}$$

In this convention the unitary condition appears as

$$\langle JM(jj')m\,m'\rangle = \langle m\,m'(jj')JM\rangle \quad . \tag{7.7-11}$$

Unlike the phase convention, there is no universally accepted notation for the Clebsch-Gordan coefficient. Some of the often encountered symbols for the same coefficients are $\langle JM|jj',m\,m'\rangle$, or $\langle JM|jm,j'm'\rangle$, or $C(JM;jm,j'm')$, or $C(Jjj';Mm\,m')$ or ... etc. Our notation is chosen for its symmetry and for the clear distinction between unsummed labels $[jj']$ and the summation indices $[JM$ and $m\,m']$.

Let us return to the example of $D^{1/2\times 1/2}$ encountered earlier. According to our general discussion, the state $|+,+\rangle$ corresponds to $J = 1$ and $M = 1$, i.e.

$$|1,1\rangle = |++\rangle \quad .$$

Eq. (7.7-7) implies

$$|1,0\rangle = (|+-\rangle + |-+\rangle)/2^{1/2} \quad ;$$

and, applying J_- to $|1,0\rangle$, we obtain $|1,-1\rangle 2^{1/2} = |--\rangle 2^{1/2}$, hence

$$|1,-1\rangle = |--\rangle \quad .$$

This substantiates the statement made below Eq. (7.7-3). All three states obtained here are symmetric in the $(+,-)$ indices. The anti-symmetric state $|a\rangle$, which was shown to be invariant under SO(3), is the only vector orthogonal to $|1,0\rangle$ in the $J_3 = 0$ sector.

As mentioned earlier, the reduction of product representations, Eqs. (7.7-8), (7.7-9), are very frequently used in physical applications of group theory. Hence, commonly encountered Clebsch-Gordan coefficients are tabulated in most books on the rotation group. We reproduce some of these tables in Appendix V. General methods to calculate Clebsch-Gordan coefficients (other than through the constructive process described here) are discussed in various books [Edmond, Hammermesh, Rose]. Incidentally, we have calculated three such coefficients along the way in Eqs. (7.7-6) and (7.7-7):

$$\langle jj'(jj')j+j', j+j'\rangle = 1$$
$$\langle j-1, j'(jj')j+j', j+j'-1\rangle = [j/(j+j')]^{1/2}$$
$$\langle j, j'-1(jj')j+j', j+j'-1\rangle = [j'/(j+j')]^{1/2} \quad .$$

We list below some useful general properties of the Clebsch-Gordan coefficients.

Angular Momentum Selection Rule:

(7.7-12) $$\langle m m'(jj')JM\rangle = 0$$

unless $m + m' = M$, and $|j - j'| \le J \le j + j'$.

Orthogonality and Completeness:

(7.7-13)
$$\sum_{mm'} \langle JM(jj')mm'\rangle\langle mm'(jj')J'M'\rangle = \delta^J_{J'}\,\delta^M_{M'}$$
$$\sum_{JM} \langle mm'(jj')JM\rangle\langle JM(jj')nn'\rangle = \delta^m_n\,\delta^{m'}_{n'} \quad .$$

Symmetry Relations:

(7.7-14)
$$\begin{aligned}\langle mm'(jj')JM\rangle &= (-1)^{j+j'-J}\langle m'm(j'j)JM\rangle \\ &= (-1)^{j+j'-J}\langle -m, -m'(jj')J, -M\rangle \\ &= (-1)^{j-J+m'}\langle M, -m'(Jj')jm\rangle[(2J+1)/(2j+1)]^{1/2} \quad .\end{aligned}$$

These symmetry relations are most conveniently expressed in terms of the Wigner *three-j symbols*:

(7.7-15) $$\begin{pmatrix} j & j' & J \\ m & m' & -M\end{pmatrix} = (-1)^{j-j'+M}\langle mm'(jj')JM\rangle/(2J+1)^{1/2} \quad .$$

Eq. (7.7-14) is equivalent to the statement that the 3-j symbols are invariant under the following changes:

(a) cyclic permutation of the three columns;

(b) simultaneous change of sign of the three elements of the bottom row and multiplication of the coefficient by $(-1)^{j+j'+J}$;

(c) transposition of any two columns and multiplication by $(-1)^{j+j'+J}$.

We refer the reader to more specialized books for the proof of these results and for more detailed properties of these coefficients. [Edmond, Hammermesh, Messiah]

To conclude this section, we write down the equations which display the reduction of the product representation explicitly into its irreducible parts,

(7.7-16) $$D^j(\mathrm{R})^m{}_n D^{j'}(\mathrm{R})^{m'}{}_{n'} = \sum_{J,M,N} \langle mm'(jj')JM\rangle D^J(\mathrm{R})^M{}_N\langle JN(jj')nn'\rangle \quad .$$

This can be derived by applying $U(\mathrm{R})$ to Eq. (7.7-9) and using Eqs. (7.7-2), (7.7-8) and the transformation properties of the states $|J, M\rangle$. Of course, Eq. (7.7-16) is just the specialization of the general result, Eq. (3.8-9), applied to the group SO(3). The inverse of this relation is:

(7.7-17) $$\delta^J_{J'} D^J(\mathrm{R})^M{}_{M'} = \sum_{mm'nn'} \langle JM(jj')mm'\rangle D^j(\mathrm{R})^m{}_n D^{j'}(\mathrm{R})^{m'}{}_{n'} \langle nn'(jj')J'M'\rangle \quad .$$

This relation allows us to build representation matrices of higher dimensions from those of lower ones.

7.8 Irreducible Tensors and the Wigner-Eckart Theorem

Definition 7.4 (Irreducible Spherical Tensor): Following Sec. 4.3, we shall call any set of operators $\{\mathrm{O}^s_\lambda, \lambda = -s, \ldots, s\}$ which transforms under rotation as

(7.8-1) $$U(\mathrm{R})\,\mathrm{O}^s_\lambda U(\mathrm{R})^{-1} = \sum_{\lambda'} \mathrm{O}^s_{\lambda'} D^s(\mathrm{R})^{\lambda'}{}_\lambda$$

an *irreducible spherical tensor* of angular momentum s with respect to SO(3); individual operators in this set are called *spherical components* of the tensor.

Theorem 7.9 (Differential Characterization of Irreducible Spherical Tensor): If O^s_λ are components of a spherical tensor as defined above, then:

(7.8-2) $$\begin{aligned} [J^2, \mathrm{O}^s_\lambda] &= s(s+1)\,\mathrm{O}^s_\lambda \\ [J_3, \mathrm{O}^s_\lambda] &= \lambda\,\mathrm{O}^s_\lambda \\ [J_\pm, \mathrm{O}^s_\lambda] &= [s(s+1) - \lambda(\lambda \pm 1)]^{1/2}\,\mathrm{O}^s_{\lambda\pm1} \quad . \end{aligned}$$

Proof: Consider an infinitesimal rotation around the l-th axis. Applying Eq. (7.8-1) we obtain from the left-hand side

$$\mathrm{LHS} = \mathrm{O}^s_\lambda - i\,d\psi\,[J_l, \mathrm{O}^s_\lambda] \quad .$$

However, the right-hand side is

$$\mathrm{RHS} = \mathrm{O}^s_\lambda - i d\psi\,\mathrm{O}^s_{\lambda'} (J^s_l)^{\lambda'}{}_\lambda$$

where J^s_l is the matrix to which the generator J_l is mapped in the s-representation, as can be inferred from Eq. (7.3-13). Comparing the two expressions, the theorem follows. QED

Examples: (i) An operator invariant under rotations, such as the Hamiltonian, commutes with all generators of rotations, hence corresponds to $s = 0$; (ii) $J_\pm/2^{1/2}$ together with J_3 form spherical components of a vector (i.e. $s = 1$).

Obviously, it is often convenient also to express vector and tensor operators in terms of their Cartesian components.

Definition 7.5 (Vector Operator—Cartesian Components): (i) Three operators $\{A_l, l = 1,2,3\}$ are *Cartesian components of a Vector* if they satisfy the following commutation relations with the generators of rotations:

(7.8-3) $$[J_k, A_l] = i\,\varepsilon^{klm} A_m \quad ;$$

(ii) A set of operators $\{T_{l_1 \cdots l_n}; l_i = 1,2,3\}$ are components of a n-th rank tensor if they satisfy the following commutation relations with J_k,

(7.8-4) $$[J_k, T_{l_1 \cdots l_n}] = i\,\{\varepsilon^{kl_1m}\,T_{ml_2\cdots l_n} + \cdots + \varepsilon^{kl_nm}\,T_{l_1\cdots l_{n-1}m}\}$$

Thus $\{J_l\}$ themselves transform as a vector, as do the momentum operators $\{P_i, i = 1, 2, 3\}$. An example of a second-rank tensor under rotation is the stress tensor, T_{ij}. A general second-rank tensor transforms under rotation as the $D^{1\times 1}$ representation; it is, therefore, reducible. According to the analysis of last section, $D^{1\times 1} = D^0 + D^1 + D^2$. It can be shown that: (i) the trace of the tensor is invariant under SO(3), it transforms as D^0; (ii) the three independent components of the anti-symmetric part of the tensor behave like a vector under rotation, they transform as D^1; and (iii) the five independent components of the traceless symmetric part of the tensor transform into each other, they form the D^2 representation. [cf. Problem 7.9] Higher rank tensors can similarly be decomposed into irreducible parts by separating the components with different symmetry patterns. A systematic method to accomplish this, making use of the symmetric group, will be discussed in Chap. 8.

If a physical system admits a symmetry group such as SO(3), symmetry operations imply relations between physical observables (operators) which belong to the same irreducible representation. Hence meaningful physical quantities correspond to irreducible tensors. If a set of operators $\{O^s_\lambda\}$ transform according to the s-representation, their matrix elements in between irreducible physical states satisfy the Wigner-Eckart theorem of Sec. 4.3. We have,

$$\langle j' m' | O^s_\lambda | j m \rangle = \langle j' m' (s, j) \lambda m \rangle \langle j' \| O^s \| j \rangle \tag{7.8-5}$$

where the first factor on the right-hand side is a Clebsch-Gordan coefficient (which is determined by group theory, independent of the specific operator O), and $\langle j' \| O^s \| j \rangle$ is the "reduced matrix element" (which depends on O, but is independent of m, m', and λ). Without any specific knowledge of the physical system, we can derive the following general, physically important consequences of Eq. (7.8-5):

(i) *Selection rules*: the matrix elements vanish unless
 (a) $|j - s| \le j' \le j + s$, and
 (b) $m' = \lambda + m$;

(ii) *Branching ratios*:

$$\frac{\langle j' m' | O^s_\lambda | j m \rangle}{\langle j' n' | O^s_\sigma | j n \rangle} = \frac{\langle j' m' (s, j) \lambda m \rangle}{\langle j' n' (s, j) \sigma n \rangle} \tag{7.8-6}$$

where the right-hand side only involves known Clebsch-Gordan coefficients.

In the concrete example given in Sec. 4.3 concerning electromagnetic transition of atomic or nuclear systems, we saw that this theorem leads to predictions on the number of spectral lines and their relative intensities.

Problems

7.1 Derive the general expression for the 3×3 matrix $R(\alpha, \beta, \gamma)$.

7.2 Derive the relation between the Euler angle variables (α, β, γ) and the angle-and-axis parameters (ψ, θ, ϕ) for a general rotation. [Hint: use (*i*) the trace condition, and (*ii*) the fact that $\hat{\mathbf{n}}$ is left invariant by the rotation $R(\alpha, \beta, \gamma)$.]

7.3 From geometrical considerations, derive the following result which describes the effect of the rotation $R_{\hat{n}}(\psi)$ on an arbitrary vector $\hat{r}$:

$$R_{\hat{n}}(\psi)\hat{r} = \hat{r}\cos\psi + \hat{n}(1 - \cos\psi)(\hat{r}\cdot\hat{n}) + (\hat{n} \times \hat{r})\sin\psi \quad .$$

7.4 An alternative way of writing the Lie Algebra for SO(3), Eq. (7.2-10), can be obtained by defining $J^{kl} = \varepsilon^{klm} J_m$ (i.e. $J^{12} = J_3, \ldots$ etc.) as the generator for rotations in the $k-l$ plane. Show that

$$[J^{kl}, J^{mn}] = i(\delta^{km} J^{ln} - \delta^{kn} J^{lm} - \delta^{lm} J^{kn} + \delta^{ln} J^{km}).$$

Although this form may appear a little less compact than Eq. (7.2-10), it is more readily generalized to higher dimensions.

7.5 Using the group algebra of SO(3), verify that $[J^2, J_l] = 0$ for $l = 1, 2, 3$.

7.6 Show that the three matrices of Eq. (7.3-22) are related to those of Eq. (7.2-3) by a similarity transformation. Express the "canonical" basis vectors (on which the first set of matrices are based) in terms of the "Cartesian" basis vectors $\hat{e}_i, i = 1, 2, 3$ on which the second set of matrices are defined.

7.7 (i) From the definition of the canonical basis vectors and the Lie Algebra of SO(3) show that

$$U[R_2(\pi)]\,|j\,m\rangle = |j - m\rangle\, \eta^j{}_m$$

where $|\eta^j{}_m|^2 = 1$, and $\eta^j{}_{m\pm 1} = -\eta^j{}_m$; (ii) Using $\eta^{1/2}{}_{1/2} = 1$ which follows from Eq. (7.3-20), prove that $\eta^j{}_j = 1$ for all j by mathematical induction;

(iii) Combine the above results to derive the useful formula:

$$D^j[R_2(\pi)]^{m'}{}_m = (-1)^{j-m}\, \delta^{m'}{}_{-m} \qquad ;$$

(iv) Use this formula to derive the explicit expression for $D^j[R_1(\pi)]$.

7.8 Verify that the vector in Eq. (7.7-6) is an eigenvector of J^2 with eigenvalue $(j + j')(j + j' + 1)$.

7.9 If $\{T_{ij}; i,j = 1, 2, 3\}$ are components of a second-rank tensor, show that: (i) tr $T = \delta^{ij} T_{ij}$ is invariant under SO(3); (ii) $\hat{T}_{ij} = (T_{ij} - T_{ji})/2$ remains anti-symmetric after an SO(3) transformation, and $\hat{T}_k = \varepsilon^{kij} T_{ij}/2$ transform as a vector; and (iii) $\tilde{T}_{ij} = (T_{ij} + T_{ji})/2$ remains symmetric under an SO(3) transformation, and the 5 independent components of $\tilde{T}$ transform as D^2 under rotations.

7.10 Prove that on the space of multi-component functions $\{\psi^m(x); m = -j, \ldots, j\}$ the mapping given by Eq. (7.6-9) (in definition 7.3) forms a representation of the symmetry group SO(3). [Hint: pattern the proof after that given in Example 7, Sec. 3.1.]

CHAPTER 8

THE GROUP SU(2) AND MORE ABOUT SO(3)

In many ways, the simplest non-abelian continuous group is SU(2)—the group of two-dimensional unitary matrices with unit determinant. This group is locally equivalent to SO(3) (as will be shown in Sec. 8.1), hence it has the same Lie algebra as the latter. On the global level, it is compact and simply connected. Therefore all irreducible representations for the Lie algebra are single-valued representations of SU(2), in contrast to the case of SO(3). The study of more advanced topics on the representations of SO(3) proceeds most directly from its "universal-covering group" SU(2).

In Sec. 1 we establish the relation between SO(3) and SU(2) in several ways (which are useful for later development) and derive general expressions for the representation matrices of these groups using the tensor method of Chap. 5. In Sec. 2, we introduce the appropriate invariant measure for integration over group elements. In Sec. 3, we formulate the orthonormality and completeness relations for the D^j functions. In Sec. 4 we show how scalars, vectors, or tensor operators defined on the group manifold can be decomposed into irreducible components under rotations with the general projection technique introduced in Chap. 4. The power of this approach is illustrated by the development of the Jacob-Wick helicity formalism for describing quantum mechanical states involving arbitrary spin and for analyzing general scattering amplitudes. In Sec. 5, we derive the differential equations satisfied by the D^j-functions from group theoretical considerations. These results make it possible to identify the D^j-functions with the appropriate classical "special functions of mathematical physics". In Sec. 6 we describe the properties of the spherical harmonics systematically from this geometrical point of view. The last section concerns the application of the group theoretical technique to the analysis of multipole expansions in electromagnetic radiation processes.

8.1 The Relationship Between SO(3) and SU(2)

We have seen, in Sec. 7.3, that every element of SO(3) can be mapped to a 2×2 unitary matrix with unit determinant $D^{1/2}(\alpha, \beta, \gamma)$, given by Eq. (7.3-20). It is not hard to prove, conversely, that all SU(2) matrices can be parametrized in that form. Indeed, an arbitrary 2×2 matrix

$$A = \begin{pmatrix} a & b \\ c & d \end{pmatrix}$$

contains 8 real constants. The unitarity condition,

$$A A^\dagger = \begin{pmatrix} a & b \\ c & d \end{pmatrix} \begin{pmatrix} a^* & c^* \\ b^* & d^* \end{pmatrix} = \begin{pmatrix} aa^* + bb^* & ac^* + bd^* \\ ca^* + db^* & cc^* + dd^* \end{pmatrix} = E$$

implies

$$(8.1\text{-}1)\qquad |a|^2 + |b|^2 = 1$$

$$(8.1\text{-}2)\qquad |c|^2 + |d|^2 = 1$$

$$(8.1\text{-}3)\qquad ac^* + bd^* = 0 \quad .$$

Eq. (8.1-1) has the solution:

$$(8.1\text{-}4)\qquad a = \cos\theta\, e^{i\xi_a} \qquad b = -\sin\theta\, e^{i\xi_b}$$

where $0 \le \theta \le \pi/2$, and $0 \le \xi_a, \xi_b < 2\pi$. Similarly, Eq. (8.1-2) implies

$$(8.1\text{-}5)\qquad c = \sin\phi\, e^{i\xi_c} \qquad d = \cos\phi\, e^{i\xi_d} \quad .$$

Substituting Eqs. (8.1-4), (8.1-5) into Eq. (8.1-3), we obtain

$$(8.1\text{-}6)\qquad \cos\theta \sin\phi\, e^{i(\xi_a - \xi_c)} = \sin\theta \cos\phi\, e^{i(\xi_b - \xi_d)} \quad .$$

Equating the magnitudes of the two sides, we obtain

$$\sin(\theta - \phi) = 0 \quad .$$

For the allowed ranges of θ and ϕ, there is only one solution, $\theta = \phi$. Equating the phases of the two sides of the same equation, we obtain

$$\xi_a - \xi_c = \xi_b - \xi_d, \qquad \text{(modulo } 2\pi)$$

or,

$$\xi_a + \xi_d = \xi_b + \xi_c \equiv 2\lambda \quad .$$

The general solution to this equation is

$$\begin{aligned} \xi_a &= \lambda + \zeta & \xi_d &= \lambda - \zeta \\ \xi_b &= \lambda + \eta & \xi_c &= \lambda - \eta \end{aligned} \qquad \text{(modulo } 2\pi)$$

where λ, η, and ζ are arbitrary real phases.

Theorem 8.1: An arbitrary 2×2 unitary matrix U can be written in the form

$$(8.1\text{-}7)\qquad U = e^{i\lambda} \begin{pmatrix} \cos\theta\, e^{i\zeta} & -\sin\theta\, e^{i\eta} \\ \sin\theta\, e^{-i\eta} & \cos\theta\, e^{-i\zeta} \end{pmatrix}$$

where $0 \le \theta \le \pi$, $0 \le \lambda < \pi$, and $0 \le \eta, \zeta < 2\pi$.

Proof: The form of the matrix and the range of θ have already been obtained. The ranges of η, ζ are self-evident. The range of λ is restricted because any additional overall phase factor $e^{i\pi}\,(= -1)$ can always be absorbed into the second factor on the right-hand side. QED

Corollary: An arbitrary 2×2 SU(2) matrix A can be parametrized in terms of three real parameters (θ, η, ζ) as in Eq. (8.1-7) without the overall phase factor in front.

This follows from the fact that the determinant of U is equal to 1 (within the allowed range of λ) if and only if $\lambda = 0$. The general SU(2) matrix can be cast in the form of

$D^{1/2}(\alpha, \beta, \gamma)$, Eq. (7.3-21), with the correspondence:

$$\theta = \beta/2$$
(8.1-8) $$\zeta = (-\alpha - \gamma)/2$$
$$\eta = (-\alpha + \gamma)/2 \quad .$$

The ranges of the new variables then become:

$$0 \leq \beta \leq \pi$$
(8.1-9) $$0 \leq \alpha < 2\pi$$
$$0 \leq \gamma < 4\pi \quad .$$

Notice that the range of γ is twice that of the physical Euler angle γ, reflecting the fact that the SU(2) matrices form a double-valued representation of SO(3).

The same SU(2) matrix can also be written in the form

(8.1-10) $$A = \begin{pmatrix} r_0 - ir_3 & -r_2 - ir_1 \\ r_2 - ir_1 & r_0 + ir_3 \end{pmatrix}$$

subject to the condition

(8.1-11) $$\det A = r_0{}^2 + r_1{}^2 + r_2{}^2 + r_3{}^2 = 1$$

where r_i are real numbers. This particular parametrization offers the most convenient way to show the structure of the group manifold. If we regard (r_i; $i = 0, \ldots, 3$) as the Cartesian coordinates in a 4-dimensional Euclidean space, the group parameter space is simply the surface of the unit sphere. Thus, the group manifold is both *compact* and *simply connected.* These features make the SU(2) group particularly well behaved.

The fact that every SU(2) matrix is associated with a rotation can be seen in another way. Let us associate every coordinate vector $\mathbf{x} = (x^1, x^2, x^3)$, with a 2×2 hermitian traceless matrix,

(8.1-12) $$\mathrm{X} = \sigma_i x^i \qquad \text{where}$$

(8.1-13) $$\sigma_1 = \begin{pmatrix} 0 & 1 \\ 1 & 0 \end{pmatrix} \quad \sigma_2 = \begin{pmatrix} 0 & -i \\ i & 0 \end{pmatrix} \quad \text{and} \quad \sigma_3 = \begin{pmatrix} 1 & 0 \\ 0 & -1 \end{pmatrix}$$

are the *Pauli matrices* [cf. Eq. (7.3-19)]. It is easy to see that

$$-\det \mathrm{X} = -\begin{vmatrix} x^3 & x^1 - ix^2 \\ x^1 + ix^2 & -x^3 \end{vmatrix} = |\mathbf{x}|^2 \quad .$$

Now, let A be an arbitrary SU(2) matrix, which induces a linear transformation on X

(8.1-14) $$\mathrm{X} \rightarrow \mathrm{X}' = A\,\mathrm{X}\,A^{-1} \quad .$$

It is obvious that X′ is also hermitian and traceless. Hence it can be associated with a coordinate vector $\mathbf{x}'$ as in Eq. (8.1-1). Furthermore, $\det \mathrm{X}' = \det \mathrm{X}$, so that $|\mathbf{x}'|^2 = |\mathbf{x}|^2$. Therefore, the SU(2) transformation (8.1-14) induces an SO(3) transformation in the three dimensional Euclidean space. The mapping from

$A \in SU(2)$ to $R \in SO(3)$ is two-to-one, since the two SU(2) matrices $\pm A$ correspond to the same rotation (as is evident from Eq. (8.1-14)).

In the $(r_i, i = 0, \ldots, 3)$ parametrization of SU(2) matrices, we can regard (r_1, r_2, r_3) as the independent variables, with

$$r_0 = [1 - (r_1{}^2 + r_2{}^2 + r_3{}^2)]^{1/2} \quad .$$

The identity element of the group, E, corresponds to $r_1 = r_2 = r_3 = 0$. Let us consider an infinitesimal transformation around the identity element. We will have $r_k = \mathrm{d}r^k$, $i = 1, 2, 3$, $r_0 = 1 +$ (second order terms in $\mathrm{d}r^k$), hence Eq. (8.1-10) can be written in the form:

$$A = E - i\,\mathrm{d}r^k \sigma_k \tag{8.1-15}$$

where σ_k are the Pauli matrices. We see that $\{\sigma_k\}$ is a basis for the Lie algebra of SU(2). One may show from Eq. (8.1-13) that the following commutation relations are satisfied by σ_k

$$[\sigma_k, \sigma_l] = 2i\,\varepsilon^{klm}\sigma_m \quad . \tag{8.1-16}$$

Comparing with Eq. (7.2-10), we see that SU(2) and SO(3) have the same Lie algebra if we make the identification

$$J_k \rightarrow \sigma_k/2 \quad . \tag{8.1-17}$$

In Sec. 7.3, we constructed all the irreducible representations of this Lie algebra. By virtue of the fact that SU(2) is a simply connected group, all the irreducible representations of its Lie algebra are also single-valued irreducible representations of the group.

SU(2) is, of course, a subgroup of the general linear group GL(2, C). Consequently, we can apply the tensor method of Chap. 5 (Sec. 5.5) to construct higher dimensional representations of this group. It turns out that for this special case: (i) the irreducible tensors belonging to symmetry classes of the permutation group generate irreducible representations of SU(2) as they do for GL(2, C); and (ii) the totally symmetric tensors of rank n form an $(n + 1)$-dimensional space, generating the $j = n/2$ irreducible representation of SU(2). Thus, all irreducible representations of SU(2) and SO(3) can be generated by the tensor method. We take advantage of this result to construct the functions $d^j(\beta)^m{}_{m'}$ explicitly.

For convenience, let us denote the basic matrix by

$$r(\beta) \equiv d_{1/2}(\beta) = \begin{pmatrix} c & -s \\ s & c \end{pmatrix} \tag{8.1-18}$$

where $c = \cos\beta/2$ and $s = \sin\beta/2$. Let $\{\xi^i, i = +, -\}$ be the components of an arbitrary vector $\boldsymbol{\xi}$ (henceforth referred to as *spinor* by convention), in the basic two-dimensional space V_2. Then, as usual,

$$\xi^i \rightarrow \xi'^i = r(\beta)^i{}_j\,\xi^j \tag{8.1-19}$$

hence,

$$\begin{aligned} \xi'^+ &= c\,\xi^+ - s\,\xi^- \\ \xi'^- &= s\,\xi^+ + c\,\xi^- \quad . \end{aligned} \tag{8.1-20}$$

In the tensor space $V_2{}^n$ [cf. notation of Sec. 5.5], define the following tensor $\xi^{\{i\}}$ with components:

$$\xi^{\{i\}} = \xi^{i_1}\xi^{i_2}\ldots\xi^{i_n} \quad . \tag{8.1-21}$$

This tensor is totally symmetric by construction, and irreducible. Since each i_j can only take two values, + or −, all components of the tensor can be written as

$$\xi^{\{i\}} = (\xi^+)^k(\xi^-)^{n-k} \qquad 0 \le k \le n \quad . \tag{8.1-22}$$

There are $n + 1$ independent components characterized by the $n + 1$ possible values of k. It is convenient to label these components by $m = k - j$ and normalize them as follows:

$$\xi^{(m)} = (2j!)\frac{(\xi^+)^{j+m}(\xi^-)^{j-m}}{[(j+m)!\,(j-m)!]^{1/2}} \tag{8.1-23}$$

where $j = n/2$ and $m = -j, -j+1, \ldots, j$. Then $\{\xi^{(m)}\}$ transform as the canonical components of the $j = n/2$ irreducible representation of the SU(2) Lie algebra. [cf. Problem 8.5] Explicitly,

$$\xi^{(m)} \xrightarrow{r(\beta)} \xi'^{(m)} = d^j(\beta)^m{}_{m'}\,\xi^{(m')} \tag{8.1-24}$$

Applying Eq. (8.1-23) to $\xi'^{(m)}$ and $\xi^{(m')}$ and Eq. (8.1-20) to $\xi'^{\pm}$, we can deduce a closed expression for the general matrix element,

$$\begin{aligned} \mathrm{d}^j(\beta)^m{}_{m'} &= \sum_k (-1)^k \frac{[(j+m)!\,(j-m)!\,(j+m')!\,(j-m')!]^{1/2}}{k!\,(j+m-k)!\,(k-m+m')!\,(j-m'-k)!} \\ &\quad \times (\cos\beta/2)^{2j+m-m'-2k}(\sin\beta/2)^{2k-m+m'} \quad . \end{aligned} \tag{8.1-25}$$

Combining this result with Eq. (7.3-16), we have the complete expression for all representation matrices of the SU(2) and SO(3) groups.

8.2 Invariant Integration

We have emphasized the crucial role of the Rearrangement Lemma in the general theory of representations for finite groups in Chapters 3 and 4, as well as its generalization to one-parameter continuous groups in Chap. 6. We need to find the appropriate definition of integration over group elements for SU(2) (and SO(3)) in the present Chapter. Following the considerations of Sec. 6.4, we seek to find an infinitesimal volume measure $d\tau_A$ around each group element A, such that

$$\int f(A)\,d\tau_A = \int f(B^{-1}A)\,d\tau_A = \int f(A)\,d\tau_{BA} \tag{8.2-1}$$

for an arbitrary function of the group element $f(A)$. Let (ξ, η, ζ) be a set of parameters characterizing the group element A, and

$$d\tau_A = \rho(\xi,\eta,\zeta)\,d\xi\,d\eta\,d\zeta \tag{8.2-2}$$

where ρ is the "weight function" for the invariant measure. It is clear that the validity of Eq. (8.2-1) requires $d\tau_A = d\tau_{BA}$, or

$$\frac{\rho(\xi,\eta,\zeta)}{\rho(\xi',\eta',\zeta')} = \frac{\partial(\xi',\eta',\zeta')}{\partial(\xi,\eta,\zeta)} \tag{8.2-3}$$

where (ξ',η',ζ') are the parameters for $A' = BA$ and the right-hand side is the Jabobian determinant for the change of variables $(\xi,\eta,\zeta) \to (\xi',\eta',\zeta')$. We note that the same equation must hold if (ξ,η,ζ) and (ξ',η',ζ') are two different sets of parameters for the same group element with their corresponding weight functions appearing on the left-hand side of Eq. (8.2-3).

There are many ways to find the correct weight function ρ. We shall describe a specific approach for SU(2), and then re-derive the result using a general method. Clearly, the weight function is simplest when the right-hand side of Eq. (8.2-3) is a constant. This happens if (ξ',η',ζ') are linear functions of (ξ,η,ζ). Of the several parametrizations of SU(2) and SO(3) group elements that we have described, there is one set which has this property, namely (r_0, r_1, r_2, r_3) with the constraint $\sum r_i^2 = 1$. If $\{r_i\}$, $\{r'_i\}$ and $\{s_i\}$ correspond to A, A' and B respectively [as given in Eq. (8.1-11)], and $A' = BA$, then $\{r'_i\}$ are linear functions of $\{r_i\}$. Let us, for the moment, overlook the constraint on the four components $\{r_i\}$ and $\{r'_i\}$. Since

$$\det A' = \sum_{i=0}^{3} (r'_i)^2 = \det B \det A = \sum_i r_i^2$$

the linear transformation $\{r_i\} \to \{r'_i\}$ is an orthogonal transformation. The Jacobian for this linear transformation is $\det B = 1$. Since the right-hand side of Eq. (8.2-3) is equal to 1, the simplest choice $\rho = 1$ will suffice. Taking into consideration the constraints on $\{r_i\}$, we have

(8.2-4) $$d\tau_A = \delta\left(1 - \sum_i r_i^2\right) dr_0\, dr_1\, dr_2\, dr_3 \quad .$$

If we regard (r_1, r_2, r_3) as the independent variables, Eq. (8.2-4) implies

(8.2-5) $$d\tau_A = \left[2\left(1 - \sum_{k=1}^{3} r_k^2\right)^{1/2}\right]^{-1} dr_1\, dr_2\, dr_3 \quad .$$

The first factor on the right-hand side is the appropriate weight function for this set of parameters. It is not simple because, after eliminating r'_0 and r_0 (r'_1, r'_2, r'_3) are no longer linear functions of (r_1, r_2, r_3).

To obtain the invariant measure for other parametrizations such as (θ,ζ,η), given by Eq. (8.1-8), or the Euler angles (α,β,γ), we make use of the above result for $\{r_i\}$ and derive the new weight function by means of Eq. (8.2-3). For convenience, we again relax the constraint on $\{r_i\}$ in Eq. (8.1-10). To compensate for this, we multiply the matrix elements in the other parametrization, Eq. (8.1-7), by $r = \left(\sum_i r_i^2\right)^{1/2}$. Comparing the two equations, we obtain

$$\begin{aligned} r_0 &= r\cos\theta\cos\zeta \\ r_3 &= -r\cos\theta\sin\zeta \\ r_2 &= r\sin\theta\cos\eta \\ r_1 &= r\sin\theta\sin\eta \quad . \end{aligned}$$

The Jacobian determinant can be calculated in a straightforward manner. The result is

(8.2-6) $$\frac{\partial(r_0,r_1,r_2,r_3)}{\partial(r,\theta,\zeta,\eta)} = r^3\cos\theta\sin\theta = \frac{1}{2}r^3\sin 2\theta \quad .$$

We obtain, therefore

(8.2-7) $$\begin{aligned} d\tau_A &= \delta(1-r^2)\frac{1}{2}r^3\sin 2\theta\, dr\, d\theta\, d\zeta\, d\eta \\ &= \frac{1}{8}d(\cos 2\theta)\, d\zeta\, d\eta \quad . \end{aligned}$$

Passing to the Euler angle variables (α,β,γ) is trivial, in view of Eq. (8.1-8),

(8.2-8) $$d\tau_A = d\alpha\, d\cos\beta\, d\gamma/16 \quad .$$

In practice, one can choose the overall constant factor arbitrarily.

The above procedure relies on starting with the "linear parametrization", Eq. (8.1-10). Can we derive the invariant measure for any given parametrization, say (θ,ζ,η) of Eq. (8.1-7), directly without referring to (r_0,r_1,r_2,r_3)? The answer is yes. We shall now present a general method to do this, patterned after the consideration of Sec. 6.4 for the simpler group SO(2).

Theorem 8.2 (Invariant Integration Measure): The following procedure defines an invariant integration measure on the SU(2) or SO(3) group manifold:

(i) for a given parametrization $A(\xi)$, calculate $\partial A/\partial\xi_i$,

(ii) form the product $A^{-1}(\xi)(\partial A/\partial\xi_i)$, and express them as linear combinations of basis elements $\{J_\alpha\}$ of the Lie algebra (i.e. generators), defining the matrix $\tilde{A}$,

(8.2-9) $$A^{-1}\frac{\partial A}{\partial\xi_i} = \sum_\alpha J_\alpha \tilde{A}(\xi)^\alpha{}_i$$

(iii) the weight function is

(8.2-10) $$\rho_A(\xi) = \det\tilde{A}(\xi)^\alpha{}_i$$

and the invariant measure is

$$d\tau_A = \rho_A(\xi)\prod_i d\xi_i \quad .$$

Proof: First, this definition is independent of the local coordinates at A. Let $\{\eta_i\}$ be another set of parameters, then

$$A^{-1}\frac{\partial A}{\partial\eta_i} = A^{-1}\frac{\partial A}{\partial\xi_j}\frac{\partial\xi_j}{\partial\eta_i} = \sum_\alpha J_\alpha\tilde{A}(\xi)^\alpha{}_j\frac{\partial\xi_j}{\partial\eta_i};$$

therefore

$$\det\tilde{A}(\eta) = \det\left[\tilde{A}(\xi)\frac{\partial\xi}{\partial\eta}\right] = [\det\tilde{A}(\xi)]\left[\det\frac{\partial\xi}{\partial\eta}\right],$$

and

$$\frac{\rho_A(\eta)}{\rho_A(\xi)} = \det \frac{\partial \xi}{\partial \eta}$$

as required by (8.2-3). Now, let $\{\xi_i\}$ be local coordinates at A. For a fixed group element B, we choose local coordinates at BA as

$$(BA)(\xi) = B \cdot A(\xi) \quad .$$

Then,

$$(BA)^{-1} \frac{\partial}{\partial \xi_i}(BA) = A^{-1} B^{-1} B \frac{\partial A}{\partial \xi_i} = A^{-1} \frac{\partial A}{\partial \xi_i}$$

therefore,

$$\rho_{BA} = \rho_A(\xi) \quad .$$

For arbitrary local coordinates $\{\eta_i\}$ at BA, we obtain:

$$\rho_{BA}(\eta) = \rho_{BA}(\xi) \cdot \det \frac{\partial \xi}{\partial \eta} = \rho_A(\xi) \frac{\partial(\xi_i)}{\partial(\eta_i)} \quad .$$

Therefore, Eq. (8.2-3) is satisfied in general, and Eq. (8.2-10) indeed defines an invariant measure on group parameter space. QED

We note that this definition for the invariant measure is essentially independent of the choice of generators $\{J_\alpha\}$ in Eq. (8.2-9): a change of basis for the Lie algebra will modify the weight function by an overall constant (equal to the determinant of the transformation matrix) which is arbitrary in the first place. It should also be obvious that the procedure for evaluation the invariant measure given by Theorem 8.2 is applicable to all compact Lie groups—the proof does not in any way depend on the specific group under consideration.[1]

We now apply this method to the SU(2) group at hand. Using the Euler angle parametrization, Eq. (7.3-21), we obtain:

$$(2/i)\, A^{-1}\partial A/\partial \alpha = \sigma_1 \sin\beta \cos\gamma - \sigma_2 \sin\beta \sin\gamma - \sigma_3 \cos\beta$$
$$(2/i)\, A^{-1}\partial A/\partial \beta = -\sigma_1 \sin\gamma - \sigma_2 \cos\gamma$$
$$(2/i)\, A^{-1}\partial A/\partial \gamma = -\sigma_3 \quad .$$

Therefore,

$$\rho_A = \begin{vmatrix} \sin\beta\cos\gamma & -\sin\beta\sin\gamma & -\cos\beta \\ -\sin\gamma & -\cos\gamma & 0 \\ 0 & 0 & -1 \end{vmatrix} = \sin\beta \begin{vmatrix} \cos\gamma & -\sin\gamma \\ \sin\gamma & \cos\gamma \end{vmatrix} = \sin\beta$$

and $d\tau_A = d\alpha\, d(\cos\beta)\, d\gamma$ which reproduces Eq. (8.2-8). In the following, we shall normalize the invariant measure to the "group volume", $V_G = \int d\alpha\, d(\cos\beta)\, d\gamma$, obtaining the *normalized invariant measure*,

(8.2-11) $$d\tau_A = d\alpha\, d(\cos\beta)\, d\gamma / V_G$$

[1] The reason for restricting to compact groups is to ensure that the group volume [see Eq. (8.2-11) below] is finite and that all integrals over the group manifold exist.

where

$$V_{SO(3)} = 8\pi^2$$

$$V_{SU(2)} = 16\pi^2$$

The rearrangement lemma now reads for, say, SU(2):

$$\begin{aligned}(8.2\text{-}12)\quad &\frac{1}{16\pi^2}\int_0^{2\pi} d\alpha \int_{-1}^{1} d(\cos\beta) \int_{-2\pi}^{2\pi} d\gamma\, f[A(\alpha,\beta,\gamma)] \\ &= \frac{1}{16\pi^2}\int_0^{2\pi} d\alpha \int_{-1}^{1} d(\cos\beta) \int_{-2\pi}^{2\pi} d\gamma\, f[BA(\alpha,\beta,\gamma)]\end{aligned}$$

We mention that, so far, we have only discussed the "left-invariant integration", as written above. A corresponding "right-invariant integration" where B appears to the right of A, perhaps with its own weight function, should, in principle, also be investigated. It can be proved, however, that for compact groups, such as SU(2) and SO(3), the two weight functions coincide. [Gilmore, Miller]

8.3 Orthonormality and Completeness Relations of D^j

Armed with a valid normalized invariant integration measure for the group SU(2), we can define quantities similar to Eqs. (3.3-1), (3.5-3) which were essential in establishing the central theorems of Chap. 3. With the help of these integrated quantities over the group manifold, we can prove that all the important results of the representation theory for finite groups also hold for SU(2) and SO(3) (indeed, for all compact Lie groups). Thus, every irreducible representation of the SU(2) group is finite dimensional and is equivalent to some unitary representation. Also, if a representation is reducible, then it is fully decomposible. We have, of course, already constructed all the unitary irreducible representations of the group in Chap. 7. Let us now write out in detail the orthonormality relations satisfied by the representation functions.

Theorem 8.3 (Orthonormality of $D[R]$): The irreducible representation matrices $D^j(A)$ for the SU(2) group satisfy the following orthonormality condition:

$$(8.3\text{-}1)\qquad (2j+1)\int d\tau_A\, D_j^{\dagger}(A)^m{}_n\, D^{j'}(A)^{n'}{}_{m'} = \delta_j^{j'}\, \delta_n^{n'}\, \delta_{m'}^{m}$$

where $D_j^{\dagger}(A)^m{}_n = [D^j(A)^n{}_m]^*$, and $d\tau_A$ is the normalized invariant measure.

The interpretation of this relation as an orthonormality relation is based on treating (j, m, n) as indices for "vectors" D which have "components" labelled by the group elements A. If we use the Euler-angle parametrization of A and exploit the fact that the α- and γ- dependence of $D^j(\alpha,\beta,\gamma)$ is known [cf. Eq. (7.3-15)], the above relation can be simplied to:

$$(8.3\text{-}2)\qquad \frac{2j+1}{2}\int d\cos\beta\; d^j(\beta)^m{}_n\, d^{j'}(\beta)^m{}_n = \delta_j^{j'}$$

where the labels (m, n) are fixed (no summation implied).

We also expect the functions $D^j(\alpha,\beta,\gamma)^m{}_n$ to form a basis in the space of functions defined on the group manifold, as is true with previous cases. Since here we are surely dealing with an infinite dimensional space, a rigorous formulation of the problem must invoke the theory of Hilbert space, which we are not prepared to go into in any detail. The result is, however, analogous to Theorem 3.6 for the case of finite groups, and to the Fourier theorem encountered in Sec. 6.4. This is the celebrated Peter-Weyl Theorem.

Theorem 8.4 (Completeness of $D[R]$, Peter-Weyl): The irreducible representation functions $D^j(A)^m{}_n$ form a complete basis in the space of (Lebesgue) square-integrable functions defined on the group manifold.

Let $f(A)$ be any one of these functions, then:

$$f(A) = \sum_{jmn} f_{jm}^{\ n} D^j(A)^m{}_n \quad . \tag{8.3-3}$$

Using Eq. (8.3-1), we obtain

$$f_{jm}^{\ n} = (2j+1)\int d\tau_A\, D_j^{\dagger}(A)^n{}_m f(A) \quad . \tag{8.3-4}$$

The two equations (8.3-3), (8.3-4) can be combined in one formal equation

$$\sum_{jmn} (2j+1)\, D^j(A)^m{}_n D_j^{\dagger}(A')^n{}_m = \delta(A-A') \quad . \tag{8.3-5}$$

Since the group elements A, A' depend on continuous variables, the right-hand side of Eq. (8.3-5) must be a suitably defined generalized function. In particular, in the Euler-angle parameterization,

$$\delta(A-A') = 16\pi^2\, \delta(\alpha-\alpha')\,\delta(\cos\beta-\cos\beta')\,\delta(\gamma-\gamma') \quad . \tag{8.3-6}$$

The Peter-Weyl Theorem is important on at least two accounts: (i) it is valid not only for the group SU(2) as stated explicitly, but it holds for all compact Lie groups. As such, it represents a very significant generalization of the classical Fourier Theorem; (ii) the "function" $f(A)$ does not have to be a c-number (complex-number-valued) function, it can also be a vector-valued or an operator-valued function on the group. We shall see many applications of this theorem in the remainder of this book.

For physical systems, the functions $f(A)$ usually belong to one of two categories:

(i) Bose-Einstein case: $f(\alpha,\beta,\gamma+2\pi) = f(\alpha,\beta,\gamma)$ or

(ii) Fermi-Dirac case: $f(\alpha,\beta,\gamma+2\pi) = -f(\alpha,\beta,\gamma)$.

It is simple to show that, in the Bose-Einstein case,

$$f_{jm}^{m'} = 0 \qquad \text{for all } j = n + \tfrac{1}{2} \tag{8.3-7}$$

and in the Fermi-Dirac case,

$$f_{jm}^{m'} = 0 \qquad \text{for all } j = n \tag{8.3-8}$$

where n is any non-negative integer. In both these cases, the non-vanishing coefficient functions have the following explicit expression in terms of the Euler angles

(8.3-9) $$f_{jm}^{m'} = \frac{2j+1}{8\pi^2}\int_0^{2\pi} d\alpha \int_{-1}^{1} d\cos\beta \int_0^{2\pi} d\gamma\, D_j{}^{\dagger}(\alpha,\beta,\gamma)^{m'}{}_m f(\alpha,\beta,\gamma) \quad .$$

In most applications, the function f has the form

(8.3-10) $$f(\alpha,\beta,\gamma) = \tilde{f}(\alpha,\beta)\, e^{-i\lambda\gamma}$$

where λ is either an integer or a half-odd-integer. In this case,

(8.3-11) $$f_{jm}^{m'} = 0 \qquad \text{if } m' \neq \lambda, \quad \text{and}$$

(8.3-12) $$f_{jm}^{\lambda} = \frac{2j+1}{4\pi}\int_0^{2\pi} d\alpha \int_{-1}^{1} d\cos\beta\, D_j{}^{\dagger}(\alpha,\beta,0)^{\lambda}{}_m \tilde{f}(\alpha,\beta) \quad .$$

[For an example, see discussion concerning Eq. (8.4-9) which is to follow.] A particular case of this situation is when $\lambda = 0$, then f depends only on two angles. If we (i) change the name of the angles (α, β) to the more familiar (ϕ, θ), (ii) call the j-label l, as is usually associated with integer angular momenta, (iii) modify the normalization of the coefficient f_{lm} by a factor of $(4\pi)^{1/2}$, and (iv) define

(8.3-13) $$\left(\frac{2l+1}{4\pi}\right)^{1/2} D^l(\phi,\theta,0)^m{}_0 \equiv Y_{lm}^*(\theta,\phi)$$

then the Peter-Weyl Theorem becomes:

(8.3-14) $$f(\theta,\phi) = \sum_{lm} f_{lm}\, Y_{lm}(\theta,\phi)$$

and

(8.3-15) $$f_{lm} = \int d\cos\theta\, d\phi\; Y_{lm}^*(\theta,\phi)\, f(\theta,\phi) \quad .$$

Hence the functions $\{Y_{lm}(\theta,\phi)\}$ form an orthonormal basis in the space of square integrable functions defined on the unit sphere. They are just the classical functions of mathematical physics called *spherical harmonics*. The above derivation reveals the group-theoretical significance of these familiar functions.

8.4 Projection Operators and their Physical Applications

The application of the Peter-Weyl Theorem to vectors and operators can be formulated most conveniently in terms of the projection operators introduced in Chap. 4,

(8.4-1) $$\mathrm{P}_{jm}^{n} = (2j+1)\int d\tau_A\, D_j{}^{\dagger}(A)^n{}_m\, U(A) \quad .$$

According to Theorem 4.2, given any vector $|x\rangle$ in the representation space, $\{\mathrm{P}_{jm}^{n}|x\rangle, m = -j,\ldots,j\}$ transform irreducibly under SU(2) [or SO(3)] as the canonical basis vectors $\{|jm\rangle\}$. In addition, we know from Theorem 4.3 that

(8.4-2) $$\mathrm{P}_{jm}^{n}\,|j'm'\rangle = |j'm'\rangle\, \delta_j{}^{j'}\, \delta_{m'}{}^{n} \quad .$$

We shall apply these projection operators to the description of quantum mechanical states of particles with "spin". By contrasting this treatment with "old-fashioned" treatment of systems with spin, one can appreciate both the generality and the power of this technique.

8.4.1 Single Particle State with Spin

A particle is said to possess *intrinsic spin s* if the quantum mechanical states of that particle in its own rest frame are eigenstates of J^2 with the eigenvalue $s(s+1)$. We shall denote these states by $|\mathbf{p}=0, \lambda\rangle$ where $\lambda = -s, \ldots, s$ is the eigenvalue of the operator J_3 in the rest frame (the subscript 3 refers to an appropriately chosen z-direction). The question to be addressed is the following: What is the most natural and convenient way of characterizing the states of such a system when the particle is not at rest? Because of the important role played by conserved quantities, we know by experience that we are interested in states with either definite linear momentum $\mathbf{p}$ or definite energy and angular momentum (E, J, M), depending on the nature of the problem. [cf. Sec. 7.5] For a particle with spin s, however, there are $(2s+1)$ "spin-states" for each $\mathbf{p}$ or (E, J, M); our problem concerns the proper characterization of these spin states.

In order to define unambiguously a particle state with linear momentum of magnitude p and direction $\hat{\mathbf{n}}(\theta, \phi)$, let us follow the general procedure used in Sec. 7.5: (i) specify a "standard state" in a fixed direction (usually chosen to be along the z-axis); and (ii) define all other states relative to the standard state by means of a specific rotational operation.[2] The standard state is an eigenstate of momentum with components $p_1 = p_2 = 0$, and $p_3 = p$:

$$P_1 |p\hat{z}, \lambda\rangle = 0 = P_2 |p\hat{z}, \lambda\rangle \tag{8.4-3}$$

and

$$P_3 |p\hat{z}, \lambda\rangle = |p\hat{z}, \lambda\rangle p \quad . \tag{8.4-4}$$

Since along the direction of motion (z-axis) there can be no "orbital angular momentum", the spin index λ can be interpreted as the eigenvalue of the total angular momentum $\mathbf{J}$ along that direction. More formally, we observe that, since $\mathbf{J}\cdot\mathbf{P}$ commutes with $\mathbf{P}$, the standard state can be chosen as simultaneous eigenstates of these operators; thus, in conjunction with Eqs. (8.4-3) and (8.4-4), we have

$$\frac{\mathbf{J}\cdot\mathbf{P}}{p} |p\hat{z}, \lambda\rangle = J_3 |p\hat{z}, \lambda\rangle = |pz, \lambda\rangle \lambda \quad . \tag{8.4-5}$$

Now, we can define a general single particle state with momentum in the $\hat{\mathbf{n}}(\theta, \phi)$ direction by

$$|\mathbf{p}, \lambda\rangle \equiv |p, \theta, \phi, \lambda\rangle = U(\phi, \theta, 0) |p\hat{z}, \lambda\rangle \tag{8.4-6}$$

(verify that $|\mathbf{p}, \lambda\rangle$ is an eigenstate of $\mathbf{P}$ with eigenvalue $\mathbf{p}$. [cf. Problem 8.1]). By construction, the label λ represents the *helicity* of the particle. We can see that

[2] The idea behind this procedure is the same as that used in defining the angular momentum states, i.e. all the $|j, m\rangle$ states in a given multiplet are obtained from the "standard state" $|j, j\rangle$ by the lowering operator.

this interpretation is preserved by Eq. (8.4-6), as $\mathbf{J}\cdot\mathbf{P}$ is invariant under all rotations. [Prove that $\mathbf{J}\cdot\mathbf{P}$ commutes with J_k!] Explicitly, we have

$$\begin{aligned}\frac{\mathbf{J}\cdot\mathbf{P}}{p}|\mathbf{p},\lambda\rangle &= \mathbf{J}\cdot\mathbf{P}\,U[\mathrm{R}(\phi,\theta,0)]\,|p\hat{z},\lambda\rangle/p \\ &= U[\mathrm{R}]\,U[\mathrm{R}]^{-1}\,\mathbf{J}\cdot\mathbf{P}\,U[\mathrm{R}]\,|p\hat{z},\lambda\rangle/p \\ &= U[\mathrm{R}]\,\mathbf{J}\cdot\mathbf{P}\,|p\hat{z},\lambda\rangle/p \\ &= U[\mathrm{R}]\,|p\hat{z},\lambda\rangle\,\lambda = |p,\theta,\phi,\lambda\rangle\,\lambda \quad .\end{aligned} \tag{8.4-7}$$

Next, let us turn attention to states with definite angular momentum (J, M). These can be obtained from the same standard state $|p\hat{z},\lambda\rangle$ by applying the projection operators P^n_{jm}. Bearing in mind Eqs. (8.4-2) and (8.4-5), we can write:

$$|p\,J\,M\,\lambda\rangle = \mathrm{P}^{\lambda}_{JM}\,|p\hat{z},\lambda\rangle \tag{8.4-8}$$

where $\mathrm{P}^{\lambda}_{JM}$ is given in Eq. (8.4-1). The right-hand side is non-vanishing according to Eq. (8.4-2), and the vectors defined this way automatically transform as the canonical basis $\{|JM\rangle\}$ under rotations [cf. Theorem 4.2]. Let us write this equation explicitly in terms of physical variables:

$$\begin{aligned}|p\,J\,M\,\lambda\rangle &= \frac{2J+1}{8\pi^2}\int \mathrm{d}\phi\,\mathrm{d}\cos\theta\,\mathrm{d}\psi\;U(\phi,\theta,\psi)\,|p\hat{z},\lambda\rangle\,D_J{}^{\dagger}(\phi,\theta,\psi)^{\lambda}{}_{M} \\ &= \frac{2J+1}{4\pi}\int \mathrm{d}\phi\,\mathrm{d}\cos\theta\;U(\phi,\theta,0)\,|p\hat{z},\lambda\rangle\,D_J{}^{\dagger}(\phi,\theta,0)^{\lambda}{}_{M} \\ &= \frac{2J+1}{4\pi}\int \mathrm{d}\phi\,\mathrm{d}\cos\theta\,|p,\theta,\phi,\lambda\rangle\,D_J{}^{\dagger}(\phi,\theta,0)^{\lambda}{}_{M} \quad .\end{aligned} \tag{8.4-9}$$

This is the exact vectorial analog of the scalar formula Eq. (8.3-12). We see that these angular momentum states are linear combinations of the linear momentum states with the transfer matrix being given by $(2J+1)D_J{}^{\dagger}(\phi,\theta,0)^{\lambda}{}_{M}$. In the special case when the particle is spinless, we can set the index λ on the D-matrices equal to 0 and omit λ as a label for the states. We then obtain the familiar connection between orbital angular momentum and linear momentum states via the spherical harmonics, Eq. (7.5-10), discussed in the previous chapter. Equation (8.4-9) generalizes that result to states with arbitrary intrinsic angular momentum s. It is worthwhile to note that Eq. (8.4-9) is an example of the Peter-Weyl Theorem applied to vector-valued functions (rather than scalars); it also corresponds to the special case of the theorem expressed by Eqs. (8.3-10)–(8.3-12).

The angular momentum states $\{|p\,J\,M\,\lambda\rangle\}$ also form a basis in the space of single particle states. Hence we can invert Eq. (8.4-9) to obtain

$$|p,\theta,\phi,\lambda\rangle = \sum_{JM}|p\,J\,M\,\lambda\rangle\,D^J(\phi,\theta,0)^M{}_{\lambda} \quad . \tag{8.4-10}$$

In particular, the "standard state" is given by

$$|p\hat{z},\lambda\rangle = \sum_{J}|p\,J\,\lambda\,\lambda\rangle \quad . \tag{8.4-11}$$

We see that it is composed of states with all values of total angular momentum J.

The above characterization of quantum mechanical particle states is not necessarily unique. Historically, spin states were defined as eigenstates of *spin angular momentum* operators $\{S_i\}$ in conjunction with linear momentum $\{P_i\}$ or *orbital angular momentum* $\{L_i\}$. Thus, instead of the states given by Eq. (8.4-6), one deals with $|p,\theta,\phi,\sigma\rangle$ which are eigenstates of $\{P_i\}$ and S_3, with σ as the eigenvalue of S_3. One also constructs orbital angular momentum states $|p,l,m,\sigma\rangle$ which are eigenstates of P^2, L^2, L_3 and S_3. The relation between these two types of states is:

$$|p,l,m,\sigma\rangle = \int d\Omega\, |p,\theta,\phi,\sigma\rangle\, Y_{lm}(\theta,\phi) \quad . \tag{8.4-12}$$

The problem with these characterizations of states is that $\{S_i\}$ and $\{L_i\}$ are not conserved quantities like $\{P_i\}$ and $\{J_i\}$. They can be defined only for restricted systems (e.g. non-relativistic) under specific dynamical assumptions. There is no unambiguous general method to measure the quantum numbers (l,m,σ). In order to form states of definite total angular momentum (which is conserved in physical processes) from those given by Eq. (8.4-12), one must combine the "orbital" and the "static spin" degrees of freedom by the rules of addition of angular momentum,

$$|p\,J\,M\,l\rangle = \sum_{m\sigma} |p,l,m,\sigma\rangle\, \langle m\,\sigma\,(l,s)\,J\,M\rangle \quad . \tag{8.4-13}$$

These states differ from those defined by Eq. (8.4-9) in the last quantum number. Each vector in the set is a linear combination of those in the other set. [Prove that l takes on the same number of values as λ!] Although this points to the mathematical equivalence of the two sets of states, we emphasize that the label λ in Eq. (8.4-9) has a well-defined physical meaning (i.e. helicity) while the label l is model-dependent unless it happens to correspond to another conserved quantum number (such as parity, for spin 1/2 systems).

Finally, we mention that the helicity characterization of states applies equally well for zero-mass states (e.g. photon and neutrino states) as for non-zero ones. In contrast, the static spin has no meaning for zero-mass states. The two cases then have to be treated very differently in the old formalism. A full discussion of particle states will be given in Chap. 10 in connection with the representations of the Poincaré group.

8.4.2 Two Particle States with Spin

Two particle states are important in physics both in bound state and in scattering problems. If one or both of the particles involved have non-zero spin, the characterization of possible quantum mechanical states can become quite complicated if one does not employ general group theoretical methods. For instance, if the spin and orbital angular momentum language is used, one must couple the spins of the two particles with the (relative) orbital angular momentum in various ways (e.g. *L-S* coupling, *j-j* coupling,... etc. [Schiff]) using a string of Clebsch-Gordan coefficients in order to form a state with definite total angular momentum. Thus, in describing a physical process, one needs to go through one of these coupling schemes for the initial state (to form states with definite total angular momentum which is conserved), consider the transition to some final state (with the same total angular momentum), then decouple to the original characterization of states. This is often a very complicated exercise. Most of this complication can be avoided if the initial characterization of physical states is chosen properly.

The natural group theoretical description of two particle states with spin follows exactly the same line of reasoning as for the case of a single particle. One starts with a physical "standard state" in the center-of-mass frame of the two particles involving particle 1 moving (in the $\hat{\mathbf{z}}$-direction) with momentum $p\hat{\mathbf{z}}$, helicity λ_1, and particle 2 moving in the opposite direction with momentum $-p\hat{\mathbf{z}}$ and helicity λ_2,

(8.4-14) $$|p\hat{\mathbf{z}}, \lambda_1\lambda_2\rangle = |p\hat{\mathbf{z}}, \lambda_1\rangle \times U(0,\pi,0)\,|p\hat{\mathbf{z}}, \lambda_2\rangle \quad .$$

This state has a net angular momentum $(\lambda_1 - \lambda_2)$ along the $\hat{\mathbf{z}}$-direction, i.e.

(8.4-15) $$J_3\,|p\hat{\mathbf{z}}, \lambda_1\lambda_2\rangle = |p\hat{\mathbf{z}}, \lambda_1\lambda_2\rangle(\lambda_1 - \lambda_2) \quad .$$

The general "plane-wave states" are defined, as in Eq. (8.4-6),

(8.4-16) $$|p,\theta,\phi,\lambda_1\lambda_2\rangle = U(\phi,\theta,0)\,|p\hat{\mathbf{z}}, \lambda_1\lambda_2\rangle \quad .$$

Applying the projection operator $\mathrm{P}_{JM}^{\lambda_1-\lambda_2}$, one obtains directly the total angular momentum states

(8.4-17) $$|p\,J\,M\,\lambda_1\lambda_2\rangle = \frac{2J+1}{4\pi}\int d\Omega\,|p,\theta,\phi,\lambda_1\lambda_2\rangle\, D_J{}^{\dagger}(\phi,\theta,0)^{\lambda_1-\lambda_2}{}_M \quad .$$

Just as in the case of single particles, this equation can be inverted:

(8.4-18) $$|p,\theta,\phi,\lambda_1\lambda_2\rangle = \sum_{JM} |p\,J\,M\,\lambda_1\lambda_2\rangle\, D^J(\phi,\theta,0)^M{}_{\lambda_1-\lambda_2} \quad .$$

The two-particle helicity plane-wave and total angular momentum states were first formulated by Jacob and Wick [Jacob], thirty years after the first systematic application of group theory to quantum mechanics [Wigner (2), Weyl (1)].

The advantages of the *helicity states* of Jacob and Wick are manifold:

(i) All quantum numbers labelling the states are physical and measurable, being independent of dynamical assumptions;

(ii) The relationship between the "plane-wave" states, Eq. (8.4-16), and the "angular-momentum" states, Eq. (8.4-17), is direct, being free from arbitrary "coupling schemes" (such as *L-S*, *j-j*, ..., etc.);

(iii) The behavior of the helicity states under discrete physical symmetry transformations such as space-inversion, time-reversal [cf. Chap. 11], charge conjugation, and identical particle interchange [Sakurai] are in general simple and definite;

(iv) The same formalism is applicable to massless particle states as well as to massive ones [cf. Chap. 10]. This is not the case in other coupling schemes for spins;

(v) The description of scattering and decay processes in atomic, nuclear, and elementary particle physics in this framework is simple, elegant, and practical, as will be illustrated in the next paragraph.

8.4.3 Partial Wave Expansion for Two Particle Scattering with Spin

Consider the scattering of two arbitrary particles with spin labelled (a, b), creating two particles labelled (c, d) in the final state. In the center-of-mass frame, the initial and final momenta in the scattering plane are as depicted in Fig. 8.1. According to our previous discussion, the initial two-particle state can be characterized as

$$|\mathbf{p}_i, \lambda_a\lambda_b\rangle = \sum_J |p_i\, J\, M = \lambda_a - \lambda_b, \lambda_a\lambda_b\rangle \tag{8.4-19}$$

and the final two-particle state as

$$|\mathbf{p}_f, \lambda_c\lambda_d\rangle = \sum_{JM} |p_f\, J\, M\, \lambda_c\lambda_d\rangle\, D^J(\phi, \theta, 0)^M{}_{\lambda_c - \lambda_d} \quad . \tag{8.4-20}$$

Since all known interactions are invariant under spatial rotations, the scattering matrix conserves total angular momentum. According to the Wigner-Eckart theorem, Eq. (7.8-5), we must have

$$\langle p_f\, J_f\, M_f\, \lambda_c\lambda_d|\,\mathrm{T}\,|p_i\, J_i\, M_i\, \lambda_a\lambda_b\rangle = \langle \lambda_c\lambda_d\, \|\mathrm{T}_J(E)\|\, \lambda_a\lambda_b\rangle\, \delta_J{}^{J_f}\, \delta_{M_i}{}^{M_f}\, \delta_{J_i}{}^J \tag{8.4-21}$$

where E denotes the total energy of the system and the first factor on the right-hand side is the "reduced matrix element" depending only on the variables explicitly displayed. Combining Eqs. (8.4-19)–(8.4-21), we obtain

$$\langle \mathbf{p}_f\, \lambda_c\lambda_d|\,\mathrm{T}\,|\mathbf{p}_i\, \lambda_a\lambda_b\rangle = \sum_J \langle \lambda_c\lambda_d\|\mathrm{T}_J(E)\|\lambda_a\lambda_b\rangle\, d^J(\theta)^{\lambda_a - \lambda_b}_{\lambda_c - \lambda_d} \cdot e^{i(\lambda_a - \lambda_b)\phi} \quad . \tag{8.4-22}$$

This is the general *partial wave expansion* applicable to any two particle scattering or reaction. Comparing the above development with that of Subsection 7.5.3, it is seen that, in the helicity formalism, the spin degrees of freedom for the participating particles do not introduce any real complication over that for spinless particles. Had one used conventional static spin labels for the particles, the relationship between "plane-wave" and "angular momentum" states would have involved multiple Clebsch-Gordan coupling coefficients for both the initial and the final states. The resulting partial wave expansion would accordingly have been much more complicated than that for the spinless case.

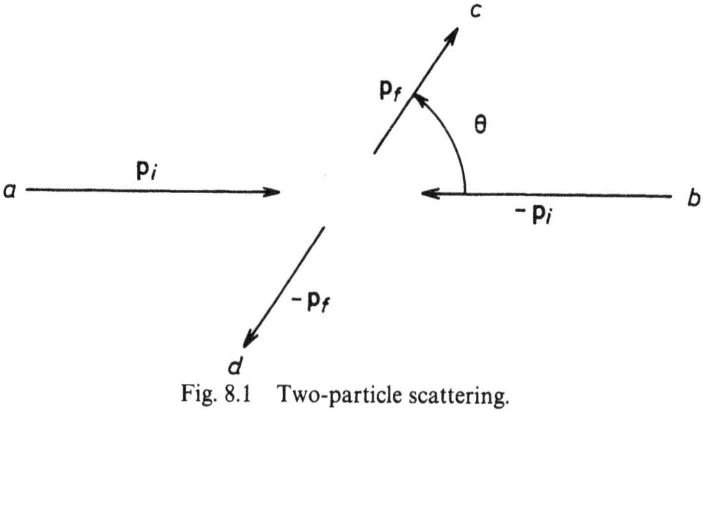

Fig. 8.1 Two-particle scattering.

We shall further develop the general theory of partial wave expansion, concerning consequences of spatial inversion, time reversal, and their applications, in Sec. 11.4 and Sec. 12.7.

8.5 Differential Equations Satisfied by the D^j-Functions

In classical analysis, the various special functions of mathematical physics are most commonly defined by the differential equations they satisfy. In order to establish the general relationship between our D^j-functions with these classical functions, we derive the differential equations satisfied by the representation functions. In the group-theoretical approach, the relevant differential operators are naturally associated with generators of the group which determine the infinitesimal transformations. In this way, the well-known analytic results of classical analysis are given geometrical significance; hence they are rendered much easier to understand and to categorize.

A prototype of the following analysis has already been discussed in Chap. 6 in the context of the simple group SO(2), Eq. (6.2-3), and the one-dimensional translation group T_1, Eq. (6.6-5). We need only to generalize the procedure to all the one-parameter subgroups of SU(2) and SO(3). Starting with

$$R(\alpha,\beta,\gamma) = e^{-i\alpha J_3} e^{-i\beta J_2} e^{-i\gamma J_3} \tag{8.5-1}$$

it is straightforward to compute the effects due to infinitesimal changes in the three group parameters (α,β,γ):

$$i\frac{\partial}{\partial\alpha} R(\alpha,\beta,\gamma) = J_3\, R(\alpha,\beta,\gamma) = R\,[R^{-1} J_3\, R]$$

$$i\frac{\partial}{\partial\beta} R(\alpha,\beta,\gamma) = R\,[e^{i\gamma J_3} J_2\, e^{-i\gamma J_3}]$$

$$i\frac{\partial}{\partial\gamma} R(\alpha,\beta,\gamma) = R\, J_3$$

The entities inside the square brackets on the right-hand sides of the first two equations can be written as linear combinations of the generators J_3, J_+, and J_-:

$$R^{-1} J_3\, R = -\sin\beta\,(J_+ e^{i\gamma} + J_- e^{-i\gamma})/2 + J_3\cos\beta$$

$$e^{i\gamma J_3} J_2\, e^{-i\gamma J_3} = i[-J_+ e^{i\gamma} + J_- e^{-i\gamma}]/2$$

By forming the appropriate linear combinations of the resulting equations, we can isolate the three generators on the right-hand side and obtain:

$$e^{-i\gamma}\left[-\frac{\partial}{\partial\beta} - \frac{i}{\sin\beta}\left(\frac{\partial}{\partial\alpha} - \cos\beta\frac{\partial}{\partial\gamma}\right)\right] R = R\, J_+ \tag{8.5-2}$$

$$e^{i\gamma}\left[\frac{\partial}{\partial\beta} - \frac{i}{\sin\beta}\left(\frac{\partial}{\partial\alpha} - \cos\beta\frac{\partial}{\partial\gamma}\right)\right] R = R\, J_- \tag{8.5-3}$$

$$i\frac{\partial}{\partial\gamma} R = R\, J_3 \tag{8.5-4}$$

Exactly the same equations apply to the operators $U(\alpha, \beta, \gamma)$ on the representation space. By sandwiching both sides of these equations between canonical states $|jm\rangle$ and $\langle jm'|$, and cancelling out common factors, we obtain

$$\left[-\frac{\mathrm{d}}{\mathrm{d}\beta}-\frac{1}{\sin\beta}(m'-m\cos\beta)\right]d^j(\beta)^{m'}{}_m = d^j(\beta)^{m'}{}_{m+1}\,[j(j+1)-m(m+1)]^{1/2}$$

(8.5-5)

$$\left[\frac{\mathrm{d}}{\mathrm{d}\beta}-\frac{1}{\sin\beta}(m'-m\cos\beta)\right]d^j(\beta)^{m'}{}_m = d^j(\beta)^{m'}{}_{m-1}\,[j(j+1)-m(m-1)]^{1/2} \tag{8.5-6}$$

from Eqs. (8.5-2), (8.5-3) respectively and an identity from Eq. (8.5-4).

Eqs. (8.5-5) and (8.5-6) are *recurrence relations* in the column index of $\mathrm{d}^j(\beta)^{m'}{}_m$ induced by the raising and lowering operators $J_\pm$. In order to derive differential equations for D^j and d^j which do not involve any change in the indices, we need to combine the actions of J_+ and J_-. The required relation is:

$$\begin{aligned} \mathrm{R}\,J^2 &= \mathrm{R}\,[J_+J_- + J_3{}^2 - J_3] \\ &= \left\{e^{-i\gamma}\left[-\frac{\partial}{\partial\beta}-\frac{i}{\sin\beta}\left(\frac{\partial}{\partial\alpha}-\cos\beta\frac{\partial}{\partial\gamma}\right)\right]\right. \\ &\quad \left.\times\, e^{i\gamma}\left[\frac{\partial}{\partial\beta}-\frac{i}{\sin\beta}\left(\frac{\partial}{\partial\alpha}-\cos\beta\frac{\partial}{\partial\gamma}\right)\right]-\frac{\partial^2}{\partial\gamma^2}-i\frac{\partial}{\partial\gamma}\right\}\mathrm{R} \quad . \end{aligned}$$

Sandwiching this equation between canonical states, we obtain

$$\left\{\frac{1}{\sin\beta}\frac{\partial}{\partial\beta}\sin\beta\frac{\partial}{\partial\beta}+\frac{1}{\sin^2\beta}\left[\frac{\partial^2}{\partial\alpha^2}+\frac{\partial^2}{\partial\gamma^2}-2\cos\beta\frac{\partial^2}{\partial\alpha\partial\gamma}\right]+j(j+1)\right\}D^j(\alpha,\beta,\gamma)^{m'}{}_m = 0.$$

(8.5-7)

By writing out the α- and γ-dependence of $D^j(\alpha, \beta, \gamma)$, we derive the differential equation for $d^j(\beta)$,

$$\left\{\frac{1}{\sin\beta}\frac{\mathrm{d}}{\mathrm{d}\beta}\sin\beta\frac{\mathrm{d}}{\mathrm{d}\beta}-\frac{1}{\sin^2\beta}(m^2+m'^2-2mm'\cos\beta)+j(j+1)\right\}d^j(\beta)^{m'}{}_m = 0. \tag{8.5-8}$$

To make contact with known functions, let us first specialize to the case $m = 0$. This forces j to be an integer. To render the result more familiar, we also make the notational substitutions $(j, m') \to (l, m)$ and $(\beta, \alpha) \to (\theta, \phi)$ to obtain from Eq. (8.5-7):

$$\left[\frac{1}{\sin\theta}\frac{\partial}{\partial\theta}\sin\theta\frac{\partial}{\partial\theta}+\frac{1}{\sin^2\theta}\frac{\partial^2}{\partial\phi^2}+l(l+1)\right]D^l(\phi,\theta,0)^m{}_0 = 0 \quad . \tag{8.5-9}$$

The reader will, no doubt, recognize this as the well-known differential equation for the Spherical Harmonics. Taking into account the correct normalization, the proper identification is (as has already been used in Chap. 7)

$$\left[\frac{2l+1}{4\pi}\right]^{1/2}[D^l(\phi,\theta,0)^m{}_0]^* = Y_{lm}(\theta,\phi) \quad . \tag{8.5-10}$$

By using the familiar relationship between Y_{lm} and the associated Legendre function $P_{lm}(\theta)$, the above equation can be rewritten as,

$$d^l(\theta)^m{}_0 = \left[\frac{(l-m)!}{(l+m)!}\right]^{1/2} (-1)^m P_{lm}(\theta) \quad . \tag{8.5-11}$$

For general values of (j, m, m'), $d^j(\beta)^{m'}{}_m$ is related to the classical Jacobi Polynomials $P_l^{\alpha,\beta}$. This can be seen by recalling the differential equation for the latter:

$$\left\{(1-z^2)\frac{d^2}{dz^2} + [\beta - \alpha - (2+\alpha+\beta)z]\frac{d}{dz} + l(l+\alpha+\beta+1)\right\} P_l^{\alpha,\beta}(z) = 0 \quad . \tag{8.5-12}$$

It is straightforward but tedious to verify that Eq. (8.5-8) can be transformed into Eq. (8.5-12) with the following identification:

$$d^j(\beta)^{m'}_m = \left[\frac{(j+m')!\,(j-m')!}{(j+m)!\,(j-m)!}\right]^{1/2} \left(\cos\frac{\beta}{2}\right)^{m+m'} \left(\sin\frac{\beta}{2}\right)^{m-m'} P_{j-m'}^{m'-m,m'+m}(\cos\beta) \quad . \tag{8.5-13}$$

Eq. (8.5-11) can be reproduced from Eq. (8.5-13) by noting that associated Legendre polynomials are special cases of the Jacobi polynomial:

$$P_{l-m}^{m,m}(z) = (-2)^m \frac{l!}{(l-m)!}(1-z^2)^{-m/2} P_{lm}(z) \quad . \tag{8.5-14}$$

For completeness, we note that the most familiar Legendre polynomials are given by

$$P_l(\cos\theta) = P_{l0}(\cos\theta) = P_l^{0,0}(\cos\theta) = d^l(\theta)^0{}_0 \quad . \tag{8.5-15}$$

8.6 Group Theoretical Interpretation of Spherical Harmonics

The identification of special functions of mathematical physics with group representation functions provides us with new insight of these classical functions. We shall illustrate this important gain by reviewing the various general properties of the spherical harmonics from the group-theoretical point of view. [Talman]

We start with the definition of Y_{lm} in terms of group representation matrix elements:

$$Y_{lm}(\theta,\phi) = \left(\frac{2l+1}{4\pi}\right)^{1/2} [D^l(\phi,\theta,0)^m{}_0]^* = \langle\theta,\phi|l\,m\rangle \tag{8.6-1}$$

where[3]

$$|\theta,\phi\rangle = \sum_{lm} |l\,m\rangle\, D^l(\phi,\theta,0)^m{}_0 \left[\frac{2l+1}{4\pi}\right]^{1/2} .$$

[3] Note that there is an extra normalization factor here on the right-hand side, as compared to Eq. (8.4-10) in order to conform to the conventional definition of Y_{lm}.

This definition reveals two important roles played by $\{Y_{lm}\}$: (i) they are special irreducible representation matrix elements [first equality in Eq. (8.6-1]; (ii) they are elements of the "transformation matrix" from the (θ, ϕ) basis to the (l, m) basis [second equality in (8.6-1)]. All the following properties follow from one or the other of these interpretations.

8.6.1 Transformation under Rotation

Consider a coordinate system denoted by $(\hat{\mathbf{x}}, \hat{\mathbf{y}}, \hat{\mathbf{z}})$, and a unit vector $\hat{\mathbf{u}}$ which is specified by the polar and azimuthal angles (θ, ϕ). Let $R(\alpha, \beta, \gamma)$ be a rotation under which the $(\hat{\mathbf{x}}, \hat{\mathbf{y}}, \hat{\mathbf{z}})$ axes go into new $(\hat{\mathbf{X}}, \hat{\mathbf{Y}}, \hat{\mathbf{Z}})$ axes and the vector $\hat{\mathbf{u}}$ goes into a new vector $\hat{\mathbf{v}}$. Clearly, $\hat{\mathbf{v}}$ is specified by the same angles (θ, ϕ) with respect to the new axes $(\hat{\mathbf{X}}, \hat{\mathbf{Y}}, \hat{\mathbf{Z}})$. We denote the polar and azimuthal angles of $\hat{\mathbf{v}}$ with respect to the original axes $(\hat{\mathbf{x}}, \hat{\mathbf{y}}, \hat{\mathbf{z}})$ by (ξ, ψ). [See Fig. 8.2] By definition we have:

$$|\xi,\psi\rangle = U(\alpha, \beta, \gamma)\,|\theta,\phi\rangle$$

which implies

$$\langle\theta, \phi|l\,m\rangle = \langle\xi, \psi|U(\alpha, \beta, \gamma)|l\,m\rangle = \langle\xi, \psi|l\,m'\rangle\, D^l(\alpha, \beta, \gamma)^{m'}{}_m \quad .$$

In other words, we obtain *the transformation law of the spherical harmonics,*

$$Y_{lm}(\theta, \phi) = Y_{lm'}(\xi, \psi)\, D^l(\alpha, \beta, \gamma)^{m'}{}_m \quad . \tag{8.6-2}$$

Basically, this relation is a manifestation of group multiplication law. [Recall that we have previously used this result in Sec. 7.6, Eq. (7.6-5).]

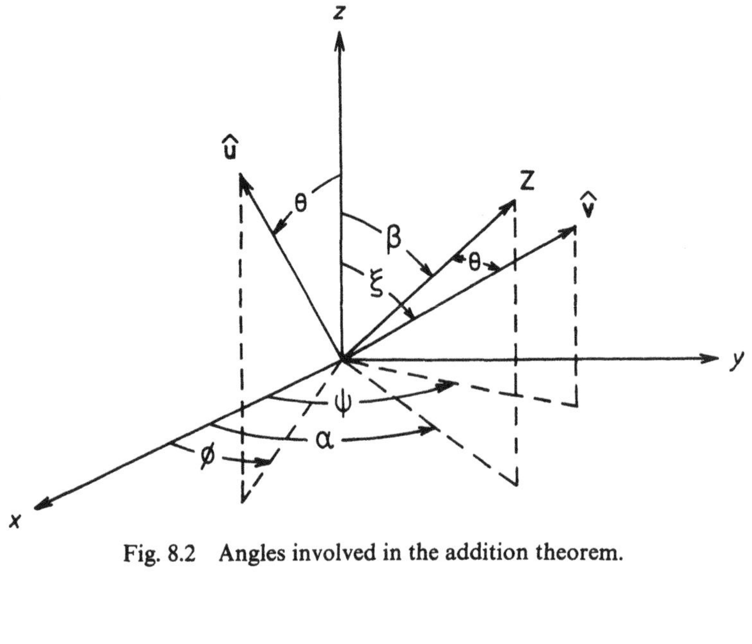

Fig. 8.2 Angles involved in the addition theorem.

8.6.2 Addition Theorem

Consider a special case of the above formula with $m = 0$. On the left-hand side, we obtain

$$Y_{l0}(\theta, \phi) = P_l(\cos\theta)\left[\frac{2l+1}{4\pi}\right]^{1/2}$$

and on the right-hand side,

$$Y_{lm'}(\xi, \psi)\, D^l(\alpha, \beta, \gamma)^{m'}{}_0 = \sum_{m'} Y_{lm'}(\xi, \psi)\, Y^*_{lm'}(\beta, \alpha)\left[\frac{4\pi}{2l+1}\right]^{1/2} .$$

Equating these two, we obtain

$$\frac{2l+1}{4\pi} P_l(\cos\theta) = \sum_{m'} Y_{lm'}(\xi, \psi)\, Y^*_{lm'}(\beta, \alpha) \quad . \tag{8.6-3}$$

This is the familiar *addition theorem for spherical harmonics*: (ξ, ψ) and (β, α) specify the direction of the two vectors $\hat{\mathbf{v}}$ and $\hat{\mathbf{Z}}$ [with respect to the $(\hat{\mathbf{x}}, \hat{\mathbf{y}}, \hat{\mathbf{z}})$ coordinate system], and θ is the angle between them. In usual applications, this relation is used to *decouple* the dependence of $P_l(\cos\theta)$ on the direction of the individual vectors [$\hat{\mathbf{v}}(\xi, \psi)$ and $\hat{\mathbf{Z}}(\beta, \alpha)$] which span the angle θ.

8.6.3 Decomposition of Products of Y_{lm} with the Same Arguments

If we have a product of spherical harmonics with the same arguments but of different order l, we can interpret it as the product representation matrix of a given group element. We know how to decompose this product into its irreducible parts, obtaining a linear combination of single spherical harmonics of the same arguments. To wit, by applying Eq. (7.7-16) to the present situation, we obtain

$$\begin{aligned} Y_{lm}(\theta, \phi)\, Y_{l'm'}(\theta, \phi) = \sum_L \langle m\, m'(ll')\, L\; m+m'\rangle\, Y_{L,m+m'}(\theta, \phi) \langle L0(ll')00\rangle \\ \times\, [(2l+1)(2l'+1)/4\pi(2L+1)]^{1/2} \end{aligned} \tag{8.6-4}$$

where the first factor of the right-hand side is the Clebsch-Gordan coefficient.

8.6.4 Recursion Formulas

The simplest kind of recursion formula is induced by the raising and lowering operators in group representation space, as has already been mentioned in the last section. From Eqs. (8.5-2) and (8.5-3) one can immediately derive:

$$[l(l+1) - m(m+1)]^{1/2}\, Y_{l,m+1}(\theta, \phi) = e^{i\phi}\left(\frac{d}{d\theta} - m\cot\theta\right) Y_{lm}(\theta, \phi) \tag{8.6-5}$$

$$[l(l+1) - m(m-1)]^{1/2}\, Y_{l,m-1}(\theta, \phi) = e^{-i\phi}\left(-\frac{d}{d\theta} - m\cot\theta\right) Y_{lm}(\theta, \phi) \quad . \tag{8.6-6}$$

Since the action by $J_\pm$ does not affect the eigenvalue l, the value of l remains unchanged in these relations.

In order to increase the value of l, we need to enlarge the group representation space. This is done by taking direct products of representations as done in the previous paragraph. A variety of recursion formulas can be derived this way. The simplest example is obtained by setting $l' = 1$ and $m' = 0$ in Eq. (8.6-4), making use of $Y_{10} = \cos\theta\,(3/4\pi)^{1/2}$, and looking up the Clebsch-Gordan coefficients $\langle m0(l1)Lm\rangle$ [Appendix V]. The result is:

(8.6-7)
$$(2l+1)^{1/2}\cos\theta\, Y_{lm}(\theta,\phi) = \left[\frac{(l+m)(l-m)}{2l-1}\right]^{1/2} Y_{l-1,m}(\theta,\phi) + \left[\frac{(l+m+1)(l-m+1)}{2l+3}\right]^{1/2} \cdot Y_{l+1,m}(\theta,\phi) \quad .$$

8.6.5 Symmetry in *m*

It follows readily from the definition Eq. (8.6-1) and previously discussed properties of the *D*-functions [e.g. (7.4-6)] that,

(8.6-8)
$$Y_{l,-m}(\theta,\phi) = (-1)^m\, Y^*_{lm}(\theta,\phi) \quad .$$

8.6.6 Orthonormality and Completeness

As a special case of Theorem 8.3, we obtain the well-known *orthonormality* relation for the spherical harmonics:

(8.6-9)
$$\int \mathrm{d}(\cos\theta)\,\mathrm{d}\phi\; Y^*_{lm}(\theta,\phi)\, Y_{l'm'}(\theta,\phi) = \delta_{ll'}\,\delta_{mm'} \quad .$$

Similarly, as we have discussed at the end of Sec. 8.3, Theorem 8.4 (Peter-Weyl) leads to the *completeness* of $\{Y_{lm}\}$ over the space of square-integrable functions defined on the unit sphere. The corresponding formulas have previously been cited as an example of the general theorem, Eqs. (8.3-14)–(8.3-15). They can be cast in the following more compact form:

(8.6-10)
$$\sum_{l,m} Y_{lm}(\theta,\phi)\, Y^*_{lm}(\theta',\phi') = \delta(\cos\theta - \cos\theta')\,\delta(\phi-\phi') \quad .$$

8.6.7 Summary Remarks

The intimate relationship between classical analysis and group theoretical considerations (associated with symmetries) which we have highlighted—from almost trivial cases involving abelian groups in Chap. 1 and Chap. 6—becomes truly fruitful in SU(2) and SO(3). The geometric interpretation given to the differential equations, recursion formulas, addition theorems, orthonormality and completeness relations, ... etc. provides a much deeper understanding of classical special functions such as the spherical harmonics. This approach also makes it very clear how classical Fourier analysis can be generalized, in an open-ended way, to functions defined on all group manifolds for which the Peter-Weyl theorem holds (i.e. compact Lie groups).

We also remind the reader that the *D*-functions in general, and $\{Y_{lm}\}$ in particular, provide natural bases on the group manifold not only for c-number functions, but also for Hilbert space vectors and operators. We have illustrated this important point in the extensive discussion of the characterization of one- and two-particle quantum mechanical Hilbert space given in Sec. 7.5 and 8.4. We now turn to an example of group-theoretical analysis of tensor operators which is physically useful and mathematically interesting.

8.7 Multipole Radiation of the Electromagnetic Field

As the last example of this chapter, we shall describe the multipole expansion of the electromagnetic field which forms the basis for the theory of electromagnetic transitions (i.e. emission and absorption of photons) in atomic, nuclear, and elementary particle physics.

Plane-wave photon states can be characterized in the same way as described in Sec. 8.4 for general single particle states,

$$|\mathbf{k},\lambda\rangle = |k,\theta,\phi,\lambda\rangle = U(\phi,\theta,0)\,|k\hat{\mathbf{z}},\lambda\rangle \quad . \tag{8.7-1}$$

Here we use the "wave vector" **k** (rather than the momentum **p**), and the helicity λ $(=\pm)$ to characterize the states. According to our earlier discussion, photon states which carry definite angular momentum can be defined according to the general rule:

$$|k\,J\,M\,\lambda\rangle = \int |k,\theta,\phi,\lambda\rangle\,[D^J(\phi,\theta,0)^M{}_\lambda]^*\,d\cos\theta\,d\phi\,(2J+1)/4\pi \quad . \tag{8.7-2}$$

If we define *creation operators* $a^\dagger(\mathbf{k},\lambda)$ and $a^\dagger(k,J,M,\lambda)$ by:

$$\begin{aligned} |\mathbf{k},\lambda\rangle &= a^\dagger(\mathbf{k},\lambda)\,|0\rangle \\ |k\,J\,M\,\lambda\rangle &= a^\dagger(k,J,M,\lambda)\,|0\rangle \end{aligned} \tag{8.7-3}$$

where $|0\rangle$ is the "vacuum state" with no photon in it, then these operators are related by

$$a^\dagger(k,J,\mathrm{M},\lambda) = \int a^\dagger(k,\theta,\phi,\lambda)\,[D^J(\phi,\theta,0)^M{}_\lambda]^*\,d\cos\theta\,d\phi\,(2J+1)/4\pi \quad . \tag{8.7-4a}$$

The inverse of this formula is

$$a^\dagger(k,\theta,\phi,\lambda) = \sum_{JM} a^\dagger(k,J,M,\lambda)\,D^J(\phi,\theta,0)^M{}_\lambda \quad . \tag{8.7-4b}$$

Taking the hermitian conjugate of both sides, we obtain the relation between the corresponding *annihilation operators*:

$$a(k,\theta,\phi,\lambda) = \sum_{JM} a(k,J,M,\lambda)\,[D^J(\phi,\theta,0)^M{}_\lambda]^* \quad . \tag{8.7-5}$$

The (quantized) electromagnetic vector potential functions in free space $\mathbf{A}(\mathbf{x},t)$ are related to the plane wave creation and annihilation operators by the familiar *plane-wave expansion*[4]

$$\mathbf{A}(\mathbf{x},t) = \sum_\lambda \int d^3k\,[a(\mathbf{k},\lambda)\,\mathbf{A}_{\mathbf{k}\lambda}(\mathbf{x})\,e^{-i\omega t} + a^\dagger(\mathbf{k},\lambda)\,\mathbf{A}^*_{\mathbf{k}\lambda}(\mathbf{x})\,e^{+i\omega t}] \tag{8.7-6}$$

[4] We are using the "Coulomb-gauge" which requires $A^0 = 0$ and $\nabla\cdot\mathbf{A} = 0$. [For reference, see Chapter XXI of Messiah.]

where $$\mathbf{A}_{\mathbf{k}\lambda}(\mathbf{x}) = \hat{\mathbf{e}}(\mathbf{k},\lambda)\, e^{i\mathbf{k}\cdot\mathbf{x}}$$

are the *plane-wave* elementary *solutions* for given *wave-vector* **k** to Maxwell's equations, $\omega = kc$ is the frequency (c = velocity of light), and $\hat{\mathbf{e}}(\mathbf{k},\lambda)$ is the *polarization vector* which is transverse to the wave vector **k**,

$$\mathbf{k}\cdot\hat{\mathbf{e}}(\mathbf{k},\lambda) = 0 \quad . \tag{8.7-7}$$

The electromagnetic fields associated with the plane-wave solutions are

$$\begin{aligned} \mathbf{E}_{\mathbf{k}\lambda}(\mathbf{x}) &= i\,k\,\mathbf{A}_{\mathbf{k}\lambda}(\mathbf{x}) \quad , \\ \mathbf{B}_{\mathbf{k}\lambda}(\mathbf{x}) &= i\,\mathbf{k}\times\mathbf{A}_{\mathbf{k}\lambda}(\mathbf{x}) \quad . \end{aligned} \tag{8.7-8}$$

Since in physical processes the initial and final states are often eigenstates of angular momentum, it is convenient to expand $\mathbf{A}(\mathbf{x},t)$ in terms of the operators $a(k,J,M,\lambda)$ and $a^\dagger(k,J,M,\lambda)$. This is done conveniently with the aid of Eqs. (8.7-4b) and (8.7-5). We shall concentrate on the first term of the right-hand side of Eq. (8.7-6), noting that the second is just the hermitian conjugate. Separating the $\int d^3k$ integral into $\int k^2 dk \int d\cos\theta_k d\phi_k$ we obtain

$$\mathbf{A}(\mathbf{x},t) = \sum_{J,M,\lambda} \int k^2\, dk\, [a(k,J,M,\lambda)\, \hat{\mathbf{A}}^{k\lambda}_{JM}(\mathbf{x})\, e^{-i\omega t} + h.c.] \tag{8.7-9}$$

where *h.c.* stands for "hermitian conjugate of the first term", and the *multipole wave function* is

$$\hat{\mathbf{A}}^{k\lambda}_{JM}(\mathbf{x}) \equiv \int d\cos\theta_k\, d\phi_k\, [D^J(\phi_k,\theta_k,0)^M{}_\lambda]^*\, \mathbf{A}_{\mathbf{k}\lambda}(\mathbf{x}) \quad . \tag{8.7-10}$$

Note we have introduced the subscript k on the angles to indicate explicitly that it is the direction of **k** which is to be integrated over, with the vector **x** fixed. We recognize the right-hand side of this equation as simply the projection of the (JM) component of the "plane-wave state wave function" $\mathbf{A}_{\mathbf{k}\lambda}(\mathbf{x})$ [cf. Eq. (8.3-12)].

The easiest way to evaluate $\hat{\mathbf{A}}^{k\lambda}_{JM}(\mathbf{x})$ is to examine the (θ_k,ϕ_k)-dependence of the plane-wave state wave function. We know, for instance,

$$\hat{\mathbf{e}}(\mathbf{k},\lambda) = R(\phi,\theta,0)\,\hat{\mathbf{e}}(\hat{\mathbf{z}},\sigma) = \mathbf{e}(\mathbf{z},\sigma)\, D^1(\phi,\theta,0)^\sigma{}_\lambda \tag{8.7-11}$$

where $\hat{\mathbf{e}}(\hat{\mathbf{z}},\pm 1) = (\mp\hat{\mathbf{e}}_x - i\hat{\mathbf{e}}_y)/\sqrt{2}$, and $\hat{\mathbf{e}}(\hat{\mathbf{z}},0) = \hat{\mathbf{z}}$.

It is also known that

$$e^{i\mathbf{k}\cdot\mathbf{x}} = e^{ikx\cos\theta_{kx}} = \sum_l i^l (2l+1)\, j_l(kx)\, P_l(\cos\theta_{kx}) \tag{8.7-12}$$

where $\{j_l(kx)\}$ are spherical Bessel functions and θ_{kx} is the angle between **k** and **x**. Applying the addition theorem of spherical harmonics, Eq. (8.6-3), we obtain:

$$e^{i\mathbf{k}\cdot\mathbf{x}} = 4\pi \sum_l i^l j_l(kx) \sum_m Y^*_{lm}(\theta_k\phi_k)\, Y_{lm}(\theta_x\phi_x) \quad . \tag{8.7-13}$$

Combining Eqs. (8.7-11), (8.7-13), and separating **x**-dependent and **k**-dependent factors, we arrive at

$$A_{k\lambda}(\mathbf{x}) = 4\pi \sum_{lm\sigma} \left(\frac{2l+1}{4\pi}\right)^{1/2} i^l j_l(kx)\hat{\mathbf{e}}(\hat{\mathbf{z}},\sigma)\, Y_{lm}(\theta_x,\phi_x)$$
$$\times\, D^l(\phi_k,\theta_k,0)^m{}_0\, D^l(\phi_k,\theta_k,0)^\sigma{}_\lambda$$

The second line of the right-hand side is in the form of a product representation which can be reduced [using Eq. (7.7-16)] to yield

$$\sum_{JM} \langle m\sigma(l1)JM\rangle\, D^J(\phi_k,\theta_k,0)^M{}_\lambda \langle J\lambda(l1)\lambda 0\rangle \quad .$$

Substituting into the previous equation and collecting terms again, we obtain:

$$A_{k\lambda}(\mathbf{x}) = \sum_{JM} \frac{2J+1}{4\pi} D^J(\phi_k,\theta_k,0)^M{}_\lambda\, \mathbf{A}^{k\lambda}_{JM}(\mathbf{x}) \tag{8.7-14}$$

with

$$\mathbf{A}^{k\lambda}_{JM}(\mathbf{x}) = \frac{16\pi^2}{2J+1}\sum_l \left(\frac{2l+1}{4\pi}\right)^{1/2} i^l j_l(kx)\,\langle J\lambda(l1)\lambda 0\rangle\, \mathbf{T}^l_{JM}(\mathbf{x}) \tag{8.7-15}$$

$$\mathbf{T}^l_{JM}(\mathbf{x}) = \sum_{m\sigma} \hat{\mathbf{e}}(\hat{\mathbf{z}},\sigma)\, Y_{lm}(\theta_x,\phi_x)\langle m\sigma(l1)JM\rangle \quad . \tag{8.7-16}$$

These are the desired results. $\mathbf{T}^l_{JM}(\mathbf{x})$ are 3-vector-valued *multipole wave functions* with definite "orbital angular momentum" (l) (they are often called *vector spherical harmonics* [cf. Problem 8.10]); whereas $\mathbf{A}^{k\lambda}_{JM}(\mathbf{x})$ are the same with definite helicity for the physical photon. The sum over l in Eq. (8.7-15) extends over the values $J-1$, $J, J+1$. It is natural to separate the $l = J$ from the $l = J \pm 1$ terms because they have opposite *parity* under space inversion. This can be done by forming the combinations $\mathbf{A}^{k+}_{JM} \pm \mathbf{A}^{k-}_{JM}$ which are the *electric* and *magnetic* multipoles respectively. We shall pick up this subject in Chap. 11 on space inversion.

In most books on the multipole expansion, the above result is derived by solving the Maxwell's equations for $\mathbf{A}(\mathbf{x}, t)$ in spherical coordinates. We have taken the "constructive" approach, building from the physical photon states. In this way, the physics behind the expansion, Eq. (8.7-9), and the formulas for the multipole wave functions, Eqs. (8.7-15) and (8.7-16), become more transparent.

We conclude by indicating how the multipole expansion is used in actual applications to the electromagnetic transition processes in physics. For definiteness, let us consider photo-absorption in which a physical system (atom, nucleus, elementary particle...etc.) in an initial state $|i\rangle = |E_i j_i m_i \alpha_i\rangle$ absorbs a photon with quantum numbers (k, J, M, λ) and ends in a final state $|f\rangle = |E_f j_f m_f \alpha_f\rangle$ where E_i (E_f) is the energy of the initial (final) state and α_i (α_f) denotes additional quantum numbers needed to specify the state. The electromagnetic interaction which is responsible for this process to take place is specified by an interacting Hamiltonian

$$H_I = -e\int d^3x\, \mathbf{J}(x)\cdot \mathbf{A}(x) \tag{8.7-17}$$

where e is the unit of electric charge, $\mathbf{J}(x)$ is the electromagnetic current operator for the physical system and $\mathbf{A}(x)$ is the vector potential function discussed above. In first order perturbation theory, the transition amplitude for this process is given by

(8.7-18) $$T_{if} = -e\langle f|H^{k\lambda}_{JM}|i\rangle\, 2\pi\,\delta(E_i + \hbar\omega - E_f)$$

where

(8.7-19) $$H^{k\lambda}_{JM} = \int d^3x\, \mathbf{J}(\mathbf{x})\cdot \mathbf{A}^{k\lambda}_{JM}(\mathbf{x})$$

are multipole moment operators in the state vector space of the system. Since, by construction, these operators are irreducible tensors under rotations, we can apply the Wigner-Eckart theorem to evaluate the matrix element in Eq. (8.7-18):

(8.7-20) $$\begin{aligned}\langle f|H^{JM}|i\rangle &= \langle E_f\, j_f\, m_f\, \alpha_f|H^{k\lambda}_{JM}|E_i\, j_i\, m_i\, \alpha_i\rangle \\ &= \langle j_f m_f (J\, j_i)\, M\, m_i\rangle \langle j_f\, \alpha_f \| H^{\lambda}_{J}(E) \| j_i\, \alpha_i\rangle \quad .\end{aligned}$$

This result was invoked in an earlier example on the use of the Wigner-Eckart theorem. [cf. Sec. 4.3]

Problems

8.1 Verify that $U(\phi,\theta,0)|p\mathbf{z},\sigma\rangle$ is an eigenstate of the linear momentum operators $\mathbf{P} = (P_1, P_2, P_3)$ with eigenvalues $\mathbf{p}$ which, when converted into spherical coordinates, give (p,θ,ϕ).

8.2 Identify the conventionally defined properties of the spherical harmonics which lead to the precise relation between $Y_{lm}(\theta,\phi)$ and $D^l(\phi,\theta,0)$ given by Eq. (8.5-10).

8.3 (i) Prove Eq. (8.6-4) explicitly. (ii) Can this equation be "inverted" to yield a formula which expresses $Y_{LM}(\theta,\phi)$ as a linear combination of terms such as $Y_{lm}(\theta,\phi)\, Y_{l'm'}(\theta,\phi)$? Why?

8.4 Derive recursion formula for the spherical harmonics Y_{lm} which increments both l and m by ± 1.

8.5 Define the action of $J_\pm$ on the symmetric tensors of $V_2{}^n$, and verify that $\{\xi^{(m)}\}$ as defined by Eq. (8.1-23) do transform as canonical components of the $j = n/2$ irreducible representation of SU(2).

8.6 Evaluate the integral

$$\int d(\cos\theta) \int d\phi\; Y^*_{LM}(\theta,\phi)\, Y_{lm}(\theta,\phi)\, Y_{l'm'}(\theta,\phi) \quad .$$

8.7 Derive the invariant integration measure in the angle-and-axis parametrization of the SO(3) group.

8.8 Derive the orthonormality and completeness relations for group characters of SO(3) and SU(2).

8.9 Consider the inelastic scattering of electron (e) on proton (p) yielding a final state consisting of an electron (e') and a "nuclear resonance" of spin 3/2 called Δ',

$$e + p \rightarrow e' + \Delta \quad .$$

Taking into account the fact that both the electron and the proton have spin 1/2, count the number of independent initial, final states, and scattering amplitudes for given values of total angular momentum quantum numbers (J, M) using both the helicity and the $L-S$ coupling schemes.

8.10 On the space V of vector-valued functions $\{\mathbf{A}(\mathbf{x})\}$, prove that the angular momentum operators $\{J_k, k = 1, 2, 3\}$ have the following action:

$$J_k A^n(\mathbf{x}) = -i\,\varepsilon^{klm}\,x_l\,\partial_m A^n(\mathbf{x}) + i\,\varepsilon_{kmn}\,A^m(\mathbf{x}).$$

Show that the vector spherical harmonics $\mathbf{T}^l_{JM}(\mathbf{x})$ defined by Eq. (8.7-16) form an orthonormal angular momentum basis on V, satisfying

$$J^2\,\mathbf{T}^l_{JM} = \mathbf{T}^l_{JM}\,J(J+1)$$

$$J_3\,\mathbf{T}^l_{JM} = \mathbf{T}^l_{JM}\,M$$

$$\int d\Omega_x\,[\mathbf{T}^l_{JM}(\mathbf{x})]^*\cdot\mathbf{T}^{l'}_{J'M'}(\mathbf{x}) = \delta^l_{l'}\,\delta^{J'}_J\,\delta^{M'}_M \quad .$$

CHAPTER 9

EUCLIDEAN GROUPS IN TWO- AND THREE-DIMENSIONAL SPACE

All evidence indicates that the 3-dimensional physical space is homogeneous and isotropic, so that results of scientific experiments performed on isolated systems should not depend on the specific location or orientation of the experimental setup (or "reference frame") used. This basic fact is incorporated in the mathematical framework by assuming the underlying space to be an *Euclidean space.* The symmetry group of a n-dimensional Euclidean space is the *Euclidean group* E_n. It consists of two types of transformations: uniform translations (along a certain direction $\hat{\mathbf{b}}$ by a distance b) $T(\mathbf{b})$, and uniform rotations (around a unit vector $\hat{\mathbf{n}}$ by some angle θ) $R_{\hat{n}}(\theta)$. These transformations have been studied in Chapters 6 and 7 separately. Since $T(\mathbf{b})$ and $R_{\hat{n}}(\theta)$ in general do not commute, E_n combines them in non-trivial ways, which leads to many new and interesting results.

In addition to their intrinsic importance, we study E_2 and E_3 with the following objectives in mind: (i) to introduce new techniques for analyzing the irreducible unitary representations of non-compact, non-abelian symmetry groups; (ii) to pave the way for a full discussion of Lorentz and Poincaré groups which underlie the space-time symmetry of the physical world according to Einstein's (special) relativity; and (iii) to extend our understanding of the special functions associated with the representation functions—in this case, Bessel functions—which are encountered in physical applications, as a consequence of the underlying symmetry.

Definition 9.1 (Euclidean Groups): The *Euclidean group* E_n consists of all continuous linear transformations on the n-dimensional Euclidean space R_n which leave the length of all vectors invariant.

Points in R_n are characterized by their coordinates $\{x^i; i = 1, 2, \ldots, n\}$. A general linear transformation takes the form:

$$\mathbf{x} \to \mathbf{x}' \quad \text{with} \quad x'^i = R^i{}_j x^j + b^i \quad . \tag{9.1-1}$$

The *length of a vector*, with end points at $\mathbf{x}$ and $\mathbf{y}$ respectively, is given by

$$l = \left[\sum_i (x^i - y^i)^2\right]^{1/2} \quad . \tag{9.1-2}$$

The condition for the transformation (9.1-1) to be length-preserving is that $(R^i{}_j)$ be an orthogonal matrix. Thus the "homogeneous" part of Eq. (9.1-1) corresponds to a *rotation* [cf. Chapters 6 and 7]. The "inhomogeneous" part (parameterized by b^i) corresponds to a uniform *translation* of all points.

The Euclidean group E_n is also called the *group of motion* in the space R_n. In classical and quantum physics, we can understand that E_n is the symmetry group of general motion in the physical space by considering the *Hamiltonian* which governs the motion of the system. The Hamiltonian function (or operator) is the sum of a kinetic energy term T and a potential energy term V. In classical physics, we have

$$T = \sum_r \frac{1}{2} m_r \mathbf{v}_r^2$$

where r labels the "particles" of the system, m_r is the mass and $\mathbf{v}_r$ is the velocity of particle r; i.e. $\mathbf{v}_r = d\mathbf{x}_r/dt$. Since $d\mathbf{x}_r$ is the difference of two coordinates, $\mathbf{v}_r$ is invariant under translations, hence so is T. Furthermore, since the square of the velocity $\mathbf{v}_r^2$ is invariant under rotations as well, T is invariant under the full Euclidean group. We can reach the same conclusion in quantum mechanics since, in this case,

$$T = \sum_r \frac{1}{2m_r} \mathbf{p}_r^2 = -\sum_r \frac{\hbar^2}{2m_r} \partial_r^2$$

where $\partial_r = \partial/\partial x_r$. The potential energy V is a function of the coordinate vector $\{\mathbf{x}_r\}$. The homogeneity of space implies that the laws of motion derived from V should not vary with the (arbitrary) choice of coordinate origin. Therefore, V can only depend on relative coordinates $\mathbf{x}_{rs} = \mathbf{x}_r - \mathbf{x}_s$. Likewise, the isotropy of space requires that the laws of motions be independent of the (a priori unspecified) orientation of coordinate axes. Consequently, the variables $\{\mathbf{x}_{rs}\}$ can only enter V in rotationally invariant scalar combinations. For a two-particle system, these considerations restrict the inter-particle potential to be a function of the magnitude of the relative coordinate $r = |\mathbf{x}_1 - \mathbf{x}_2|$ only: $V(\mathbf{x}_1, \mathbf{x}_2) = V(r)$. In the terminology of elementary physics, this general class of potential functions is called "central potential". [Goldstein] We know, of course, that well-known two-particle systems such as planetary motion around the sun and electron motion around the hydrogen nucleus do conform to this expectation. The validity of the basic assumptions as applied to more complex systems is established in somewhat more indirect ways. For instance, the homogeneity of space is in general tied to the conservation of momenta, and the isotropy of space to the conservation of angular momenta. [Goldstein, Messiah] Both of those conservation laws are very well established for arbitrarily complex systems.

Classical mechanics and electromagnetic theory as well as the new quantum theory are consistent with symmetry under the Euclidean group in 2- and 3-dimensions. The symmetry group is extended to include the time-dimension in Einstein's theory of special relativity, as we shall study in Chap. 10. In the exploration of frontier areas of physics where the basic laws are not yet completely established, symmetry considerations such as those discussed above play an extremely important role as they can suggest promising forms of interaction and provide powerful restrictions which limit the range of possibilities to be studied.

In Sec. 1 we describe general features of the group E_2 and its Lie algebra. In Sec. 2 we construct the angular momentum bases of unitary irreducible representations of E_2 by the *Lie algebra* method of Chap. 7. In Sec. 3 we introduce the method of *induced representation*, working with the group elements and emphasizing the role of the *invariant subgroup* of translations. In this way, the same irreducible representations are derived in terms of a different set of bases—the linear momentum basis. Section 4 is devoted to the group-theoretical investigation of the properties of the representation functions of E_2—Bessel functions. Section 5 presents a third method of deriving the irreducible representations—group contraction—which also helps to establish the connection between Legendre functions and Bessel functions. The Euclidean group in 3-dimensions E_3 is studied in Sec. 6. Its unitary irreducible representations are derived in Sec. 7 by the induced representation method. The final section (Sec. 8) discusses the relation between the angular momentum and the linear momentum bases for representations of E_3 and provides the group theoretical introduction of the spherical Bessel functions.

9.1 The Euclidean Group in Two Dimensional Space E_2

In 2-dimensional space, rotations (in the plane) are characterized by one angle θ, and translations are specified by two parameters (b^1, b^2). Eq. (9.1-1) takes the specific form:

$$x'^1 = x^1 \cos\theta - x^2 \sin\theta + b^1 \qquad (9.1\text{-}3)$$
$$x'^2 = x^1 \sin\theta + x^2 \cos\theta + b^2 \quad .$$

We shall denote this element of the E_2 group by $g(\mathbf{b}, \theta)$. It is straightforward to derive the group multiplication rule for E_2. One obtains

$$g(\mathbf{b}_2, \theta_2)\, g(\mathbf{b}_1, \theta_1) = g(\mathbf{b}_3, \theta_3) \qquad (9.1\text{-}4)$$

where $\theta_3 = \theta_1 + \theta_2$, and $\mathbf{b}_3 = \mathrm{R}(\theta_2)\mathbf{b}_1 + \mathbf{b}_2$.

We see that the inverse to $g(\mathbf{b}, \theta)$ is $g(-\mathrm{R}(-\theta)\mathbf{b}, -\theta)$.

The transformation rule embodied in Eqs. (9.1-3) and (9.1-4) can be expressed in matrix form if we represent each point $\mathbf{x}$ by a 3-component vector $(x^1, x^2, 1)$ and the group element by

$$g(\mathbf{b}, \theta) = \begin{pmatrix} \cos\theta & -\sin\theta & b^1 \\ \sin\theta & \cos\theta & b^2 \\ 0 & 0 & 1 \end{pmatrix} \quad . \qquad (9.1\text{-}5)$$

We leave as an exercise for the reader to confirm the validity of this representation. [Problem 9.1]

The subset of elements $\{g(0, \theta) = R(\theta)\}$ forms the *subgroup of rotations* which is just the SO(2) of Chap. 6. The generator of this one-parameter subgroup is, in the above representation,

$$J = \begin{pmatrix} 0 & -i & 0 \\ i & 0 & 0 \\ 0 & 0 & 0 \end{pmatrix} \quad . \qquad (9.1\text{-}6)$$

A general element of the rotation subgroup is $\mathrm{R}(\theta) = e^{-i\theta J}$.

The subset of elements $\{g(\mathbf{b}, 0) = \mathrm{T}(\mathbf{b})\}$ forms the *subgroup of translations* T_2. It has two independent one-parameter subgroups with generators:

$$P_1 = \begin{pmatrix} 0 & 0 & i \\ 0 & 0 & 0 \\ 0 & 0 & 0 \end{pmatrix} \quad \text{and} \quad P_2 = \begin{pmatrix} 0 & 0 & 0 \\ 0 & 0 & i \\ 0 & 0 & 0 \end{pmatrix} \quad . \qquad (9.1\text{-}7)$$

It is clear that P_1 and P_2 commute with each other, as all translations do. Hence, a general translation can be written

$$T(\mathbf{b}) = e^{-i\mathbf{b}\cdot\mathbf{P}} = e^{-ib^1P_1}e^{-ib^2P_2} \tag{9.1-8}$$

where **P** is the *momentum operator* [cf. end of Sec. 6.7].

Theorem 9.1 (Decomposition of Elements of E_2): The general group element of E_2 can be written as

$$g(\mathbf{b}, \theta) = T(\mathbf{b})\, R(\theta) \quad . \tag{9.1-9}$$

Proof: Applying Eq. (9.1-4), we have:

$$g(\mathbf{b}, \theta)\, R(\theta)^{-1} = g(\mathbf{b}, \theta)\, g(\mathbf{0}, -\theta) = g(\mathbf{b}, \theta - \theta) = T(\mathbf{b})$$

i.e. the product on the left-hand side is a pure translation. Multiplying both sides by $R(\theta)$ on the right, we obtain (9.1-9). QED

How do translations and rotations "interact" with each other? To pursue this question systematically, we start with the Lie algebra.

Theorem 9.2 (Lie Algebra of E_2): The generators of E_2 satisfy the following commutation relations (Lie algebra):

$$[P_1, P_2] = 0 \tag{9.1-10}$$

$$[J, P_k] = i\varepsilon^{km}P_m, \qquad k = 1, 2 \tag{9.1-11}$$

where ε^{km} is the 2-dimensional unit anti-symmetric tensor.

These relations can be easily established using the explicit matrix representation for J [Eq. (9.1-6)] and P_k [Eq. (9.1-7)].

Equation (9.1-11) has the interpretation that under rotations, $\{P_k\}$ transform as components of a vector operator. This can be expressed in more explicit terms as

$$e^{-i\theta J}\, P_k\, e^{i\theta J} = P_m\, R(\theta)^m{}_k \tag{9.1-12}$$

which can be readily verified starting from infinitesimal rotations. [cf. Theorem 7.7 and Eq. (7.6-13)] Eqs. (9.1-11) and (9.1-12) are similar to Eqs. (7.2-10) and (7.2-5) respectively, which express the rotational properties of the operator J_k. It follows from Eq. (9.1-12) that

$$e^{-i\theta J}\, \mathbf{P}\cdot\mathbf{b}\, e^{i\theta J} = P_m\, R(\theta)^m{}_k\, b^k = \mathbf{P}\cdot\mathbf{b}'$$

where $b'^m = R(\theta)^m{}_k\, b^k$; hence

$$e^{-i\theta J}\, T(\mathbf{b})\, e^{i\theta J} = T[R(\theta)\mathbf{b}] \quad . \tag{9.1-13}$$

This is an equivalent statement to the group multiplication rule, Eq. (9.1-4), since the above equation, together with Eq. (9.1-9), implies

$$\begin{aligned} g(\mathbf{a}, \theta)\, g(\mathbf{b}, \phi) &= T(\mathbf{a})\, R(\theta)\, T(\mathbf{b})\, R(\phi) \\ &= T(\mathbf{a})\, [R(\theta)\, T(\mathbf{b})\, R(-\theta)]\, R(\theta)\, R(\phi) \\ &= T(\mathbf{a})\, T[R(\theta)\mathbf{b}]\, R(\theta + \phi) = T[R(\theta)\mathbf{b} + \mathbf{a}]\, R(\theta + \phi) \\ &= g[R(\theta)\mathbf{b} + \mathbf{a}, \theta + \phi] \quad . \end{aligned}$$

Theorem 9.3 (Invariant Subgroup of E_2): The translations $\{T(\mathbf{b})\}$ form an *invariant subgroup* T_2 of E_2. The factor group E_2/T_2 is isomorphic to SO(2).

Proof: (i) Making use of (9.1-9) and (9.1-13), we obtain

$$\begin{aligned} g(\mathbf{b},\theta)\,T(\mathbf{a})\,g(\mathbf{b},\theta)^{-1} &= T(\mathbf{b})\,R(\theta)\,T(\mathbf{a})\,R(-\theta)\,T(-\mathbf{b}) \\ &= T(\mathbf{b})\,T[R(\theta)\mathbf{a}]\,T(-\mathbf{b}) = T[(R(\theta)\mathbf{a})] \quad . \end{aligned}$$

Hence T_2 is an invariant subgroup.

(ii) Elements of the factor group E_2/T_2 are cosets consisting of $\{T \cdot g(\mathbf{b},\theta)\}$ where the argument of T is omitted because each coset contains all possible elements of T. For convenience, we have picked right cosets (which are identical to left cosets for invariant subgroups). As cosets, the following equation holds,

$$T\,g(\mathbf{b},\theta) = T\,g(\mathbf{0},\theta) = T\,R(\theta) \quad .$$

This follows from the decomposition Eq. (9.1-9) and the fact that the product of two translations is another translation. Since distinct cosets are labelled by one parameter θ; they are in one-to-one correspondence with elements of the group $SO(2) = \{R(\theta)\}$. The proof of isomorphism is quite trivial, and will be omitted. QED

Since E_2 has an invariant subgroup, it is not a simple group; since that invariant subgroup is abelian, it is not semi-simple either. Furthermore, since the parameters characterizing translations (b^1, b^2) have an infinite range, the group manifold is not compact. As a consequence of these facts, the representation theory for E_2 (hence E_n, in general) is considerably more complicated than for the groups studied so far. We shall not be concerned with the complete representation theory; rather, we shall concentrate on the physically interesting *unitary representations.* As we shall see, these representations are typically infinite dimensional, and they are amenable to methods of analysis similar to those introduced in Chaps. 6–8.

9.2 Unitary Irreducible Representations of E_2— The Angular-Momentum Basis

The basic procedure for constructing irreducible representations of Lie groups involves starting with an initial "standard (reference) vector" $|v_0\rangle$ in the representation space V, then operating on this vector repeatedly with either the group elements or the generators until a closed (irreducible) invariant subspace or a basis for such a subspace is generated. In this section, the method of Lie algebra (involving generators) will be used to derive unitary irreducible representations of E_2. The procedure bears close resemblance to that used in Chap. 7 for the group SO(3). The only major difference is that in the present case all faithful representations will be infinite dimensional.

Before embarking on a study of the general theory, let us first consider degenerate representations induced by that of its factor group $E_2/T_2 \sim SO(2)$. According to Chap. 6, the irreducible representations of SO(2) are labelled by an integer $m = 0, \pm 1, \pm 2, \ldots$, they are all one-dimensional, and the homomorphism is simply

$R(\theta) \rightarrow e^{-im\theta}$. We obtain from these one-dimensional representations of E_2,

$$g(\mathbf{b}, \theta) \in E_2 \qquad U_m(\mathbf{b}, \theta) = e^{-im\theta} \qquad \text{for all } \mathbf{b} \quad . \tag{9.2-1}$$

To verify that this is indeed a representation, note that $U(\mathbf{a}, 0) = 1$, and

$$U_m(\mathbf{b}, \theta)\, U_m(\mathbf{a}, \phi) = e^{-im\theta} e^{-im\phi} = e^{-im(\theta+\phi)}$$

in agreement with $U_m[R(\theta)\mathbf{a} + \mathbf{b},\ \theta + \phi] = e^{-im(\theta+\phi)}$. These are the only finite dimensional unitary representations of E_2.

We now follow the procedure of Chap. 7 to construct the general unitary representation of E_2. For this purpose, define raising and lowering operators consisting of generators of translations,

$$P_\pm = P_1 \pm i P_2 \quad . \tag{9.2-2}$$

It is easy to verify that they commute with each other and satisfy the following commutation relations with the generator of rotations J:

$$[J, P_\pm] = \pm P_\pm \quad . \tag{9.2-3}$$

If we define the "squared momentum" operator as

$$\mathbf{P}^2 = (P_1)^2 + (P_2)^2 = P_+ P_- = P_- P_+ \tag{9.2-4}$$

then it is easy to show that it commutes with all the generators of the group, i.e.

$$[\mathbf{P}^2, J] = [\mathbf{P}^2, P_\pm] = 0 \quad . \tag{9.2-5}$$

Hence, $\mathbf{P}^2$ is a Casimir operator and has a unique eigenvalue for each irreducible representation. For *unitary representations*, the generators (J, P_1, P_2) are mapped into *hermitian operators* which we shall denote by the same symbols. It follows from Eq. (9.2-2) that $P^{\pm\dagger} = P^{\mp}$; and from Eq. (9.2-4) that the eigenvalues of $\mathbf{P}^2$ are positive definite. We shall denote the eigenvalue by p^2 (≥ 0).

Any unitary irreducible representation of E_2 is also a unitary (in general, reducible) representation of the subgroup SO(2). The representation space is therefore a direct sum of one-dimensional subspaces labelled by the eigenvalue m of J ($m = 0, \pm 1, \pm 2, \ldots$). [cf. Chap. 6] Let us consider basis vectors which are simultaneous eigenvectors of $\mathbf{P}^2$ and J,

$$\mathbf{P}^2 |p\, m\rangle = |p\, m\rangle\, p^2 \qquad p^2 \geq 0 \tag{9.2-6}$$

$$J\, |p\, m\rangle = |p\, m\rangle\, m \qquad m = 0, \pm 1, \ldots \tag{9.2-7}$$

Eq. (9.2-3) requires $P_\pm |p, m\rangle$ to be eigenstates of J, with eigenvalue $(m \pm 1)$ and normalization

$$\begin{aligned} \langle p\, m | P_\pm{}^\dagger P_\pm | p\, m\rangle &= \langle p\, m | P_\mp P_\pm | p\, m\rangle = \langle p\, m | \mathbf{P}^2 | p\, m\rangle \\ &= p^2 \langle p\, m | p\, m\rangle = p^2 \end{aligned}$$

where in the last step we assumed that the original vector $|p\, m\rangle$ is normalized to one. We must consider two distinct cases:

(i) For $p^2 = 0$, the above equation implies

$$P_\pm |0\, m\rangle = 0 \quad . \tag{9.2-8}$$

The representation is one-dimensional,

$$J|0\,m\rangle = |0\,m\rangle\, m$$

$$R(\theta)\,|0\,m\rangle = |0\,m\rangle\, e^{-im\theta}$$

and
$$T(\mathbf{b})\,|0\,m\rangle = |0\,m\rangle \quad .$$

Thus we rediscover the "degenerate" irreducible representation induced by the factor group [Eq. (9.2-1)].

In the above equations, we used the same symbols $R(\theta)$ and $T(\mathbf{b})$ for the group elements to denote their realization as unitary operators on the representation space. The convention used in earlier chapters of explicitly distinguishing the latter—by the symbols, say, $U[R(\theta)]$ and $U[T(\mathbf{b})]$—is deemed unnecessary by now, as the reader should already be familiar with the concepts involved. The compact notation will simplify future formulas, and thus contribute to the clarity of some subsequent discussions. We shall restore the explicit notation only if there is a reason to emphasize the difference between the group elements and their realizations on a vector space.

(ii) For $p^2 > 0$, we shall define

(9.2-9)
$$|p\,m\pm 1\rangle \equiv P_{\pm}|p\,m\rangle(\pm i/p)$$

where the phase factor $\pm i$ is introduced for later convenience. Given any initial reference vector $|p\,m_0\rangle$, repeated application of $P^{\pm}$ as in Eq. (9.2-9) leads to the sequence of basis vectors $\{|p\,m\rangle, m = 0, \pm 1, \pm 2, \ldots\}$. The representation space is clearly infinite dimensional. In this space, the matrix elements of the generators are:

(9.2-10)
$$\langle p\,m'|J|p\,m\rangle = m\,\delta^{m'}{}_{m},$$

(9.2-11)
$$\langle p\,m'|P_{\pm}|p\,m\rangle = \mp i\,p\,\delta^{m'}{}_{m\pm 1}$$

Theorem 9.4 (Unitary Irreducible Representations of E_2): The faithful unitary irreducible representations of E_2 are characterized by a non-zero positive number p; the matrix elements of the generators are given by Eqs. (9.2-10) and (9.2-11), and the representation matrices for finite transformations are given by

(9.2-12)
$$D^{p}(\mathbf{b},\theta)^{m'}{}_{m} = e^{i(m-m')\phi}\, J_{m-m'}(pb)\, e^{-im\theta}$$

where (b, ϕ) are the polar coordinates of the 2-vector $\mathbf{b}$, and J_n is the *Bessel function of the first kind.*

Proof: In view of the general decomposition, Eq. (9.1-9), it suffices to examine rotations and translations separately. The first is easy, since from Eq. (9.2-10) it follows

$$\langle p\,m'|\,e^{-i\theta J}\,|p\,m\rangle = e^{-im\theta}\,\delta^{m'}{}_{m} \quad .$$

Turning to translations, we note that

$$T(b,\phi) = R(\phi)\,T(b,0)\,R(\phi)^{-1}$$

leads to the simplification

$$\langle p\,m'|\,T(\mathbf{b})\,|p\,m\rangle = e^{i(m-m')\phi}\,\langle p\,m'|\,T(b,0)\,|p\,m\rangle \quad .$$

Hence, it is sufficient to consider only translations along the x-direction.

$$\mathrm{T}(b,0) = e^{-ibP_1} = e^{-ib(P_+ + P_-)/2}$$
$$= \sum_{k,l} (iP_+)^k(-iP_-)^l(-1)^k(b/2)^{k+l}/(k!\,l!) \quad .$$

When we take the matrix element of the operator $P_+{}^kP_-{}^l$ between the states $|pm\rangle$ and $\langle pm'|$, the non-vanishing terms must satisfy the condition $k - l = m' - m$ due to the raising and lowering properties of $P_\pm$. With $k - l$ fixed, we can shift the summation index to $n = k + l$, and obtain:

$$\langle pm'|\mathrm{T}(b,0)|pm\rangle$$
$$= \sum_n (-1)^{(n+m'-m)/2}(pb/2)^n/[(n+m'-m)/2]!\,[(n-m'+m)/2]!$$

where the summation is taken from $n = |m' - m|$ to infinity over *every other integer* [cf. Fig. 9.1]. For definiteness, let us assume $m' \leq m$; then shifting the summation index to $q = (n + m' - m)/2$, we obtain

(9.2-13) $$\langle pm'|\mathrm{T}(b,0)|pm\rangle = (pb/2)^{m-m'} \sum_{q=0}^{\infty} (-1)^q(pb/2)^{2q}/(q!\,(q + m - m')!).$$

We recognize the right-hand side as the standard series representation for the Bessel function of the first kind $\mathrm{J}_{m-m'}(pb)$. [Watson]

When $m < m'$, we shift the summation index to $q = (n - m' + n)/2$ and obtain

$$\langle pm'|\mathrm{T}(b,0)|pm\rangle = (-pb/2)^{m'-m}\sum_q(-1)^q(pb/2)^{2q}/(q!\,(q + m' - m)!)$$
$$= (-1)^{m'-m}\mathrm{J}_{m'-m}(pb) = \mathrm{J}_{m-m'}(pb)$$

where the last equality follows from the usual definition of Bessel functions of negative integer indices. Therefore, for the general translation matrix element, we have

(9.2-14) $$\langle pm'|\mathrm{T}(b,\phi)|pm\rangle = e^{i(m-m')\phi}\mathrm{J}_{m-m'}(pb). \quad \text{QED}$$

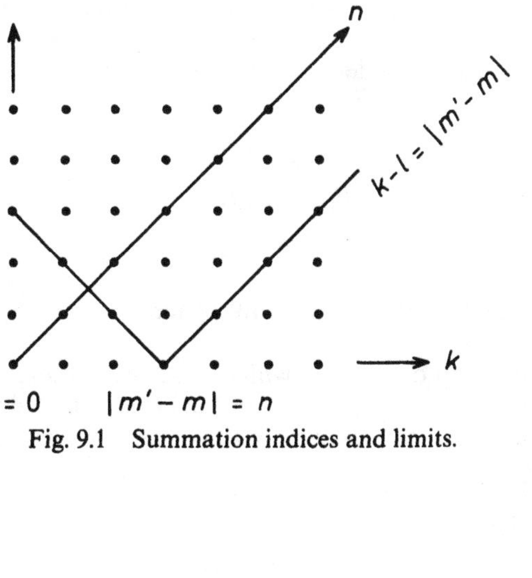

Fig. 9.1 Summation indices and limits.

The basis $\{|pm\rangle, m = 0, \pm 1, \ldots\}$ just described will be referred to as the *angular momentum basis* in the rest of this chapter. The terminology follows from the fact that these basis vectors are eigenvectors of J, the "angular momentum operator" [cf. Sec. 6.7].

We should not be surprised to find Bessel functions emerging as representation functions of the group E_2. In both classical and quantum physics, we encounter Bessel functions routinely for systems which are effectively two-dimensional in nature, e.g. systems possessing cylindrical symmetry. The group-theoretical study underlines the basic geometrical origin of all such systems, independently of specifics. In Sec. 4 we shall study the properties of the Bessel function from the group theory point of view.

9.3 The Induced Representation Method and the Plane-Wave Basis

The induced representation method provides an alternative method to generate the irreducible representations of continuous groups which contain an abelian invariant subgroup. (For the Euclidean group E_n, the abelian invariant subgroup is the group of translations T_n.) One seeks to construct a basis for the irreducible vector space consisting of eigenvectors of the generators of the invariant subgroup and other appropriately defined operators. We first introduce this method by way of the relatively simple group E_2. In subsequent applications to E_3 and the Poincaré group (to be discussed in Chap. 10), we shall describe precisely the ideas behind this approach and the concept of the "little group".

The abelian invariant subgroup of E_2 is the 2-dimensional translation group T_2. The two generators (P_1, P_2) are components of a vector operator $\mathbf{P}$. Possible eigenvalues of $\mathbf{P}$ are two dimensional vectors $\mathbf{p}$ with components of arbitrary real values. We shall proceed by the following steps:

(i) Selecting a "standard vector" and the associated subspace:

Consider the subspace corresponding to a conveniently chosen "standard momentum vector", say $\mathbf{p}_0 \equiv (p, 0)$. What is the dimensionality of this subspace? The answer depends on whether there are any group operations in the factor group (rotations, in this case) which leave this eigenvector invariant. Equivalently, one can ask for the maximum set of generators of this group that commute with P_1. In the present case, there is only one such generator (J), and it does not commute with P_1; hence there is only one independent eigenstate of $\mathbf{P}$ corresponding to the standard momentum vector $\mathbf{p}_0$. We have

$$P_1 |\mathbf{p}_0\rangle = |\mathbf{p}_0\rangle p$$

$$P_2 |\mathbf{p}_0\rangle = 0 \tag{9.3-1}$$

and

$$P^2 |\mathbf{p}_0\rangle = |\mathbf{p}_0\rangle p^2 \quad .$$

(ii) Generating the full irreducible invariant space:

This is done with group operations which produce new eigenvalues of $\mathbf{P}$. These operations are associated with generators of the group which do not commute with $\mathbf{P}$. In the current case, they can only be $R(\theta) = e^{-i\theta J}$. We examine the momentum content of $R(\theta)|p_0\rangle$,

$$P_k R(\theta)|\mathbf{p}_0\rangle = R(\theta)[R(\theta)^{-1}P_k R(\theta)]|\mathbf{p}_0\rangle = R(\theta)P_l|\mathbf{p}_0\rangle R(-\theta)^l{}_k = R(\theta)|\mathbf{p}_0\rangle p_k \tag{9.3-2}$$

where the second step follows from Eq. (9.1-12) and the third step from (9.3-1) and[1]

$$p_k = p_{0l} R(-\theta)^l{}_k \quad \text{or} \quad p^k = R(\theta)^k{}_l p_0{}^l \quad .$$

Hence, $R(\theta)|\mathbf{p}_0\rangle$ is a new eigenvector of $\mathbf{P}$ corresponding to the momentum vector $\mathbf{p} = R(\theta)\mathbf{p}_0$. This suggests that we define

$$|\mathbf{p}\rangle \equiv R(\theta)|\mathbf{p}_0\rangle \quad . \tag{9.3-3}$$

This definition also fixes the relative phase of the general basis vector $|\mathbf{p}\rangle$ with respect to the standard, or reference, vector $|\mathbf{p}_0\rangle$. The polar coordinates of the new eigenvector $\mathbf{p}$ are (p, θ). Also, since $R(\theta) = e^{-i\theta J}$ is unitary, $|\mathbf{p}\rangle$ has the same normalization (not yet specified) as $|\mathbf{p}_0\rangle$.

The set of vectors $\{|\mathbf{p}\rangle\}$ so generated is closed under all group operations:

$$T(\mathbf{b})|\mathbf{p}\rangle = |\mathbf{p}\rangle e^{-i\mathbf{b}\cdot\mathbf{p}} \tag{9.3-4}$$

$$R(\phi)|\mathbf{p}\rangle = |\mathbf{p}'\rangle \qquad \mathbf{p}' = R(\phi)\mathbf{p} = (p, \theta+\phi) \quad . \tag{9.3-5}$$

Eq. (9.3-4) follows from the fact that $|\mathbf{p}\rangle$ are eigenstates of $\mathbf{P}$; Eq. (9.3-5) is proved as follows:

$$R(\phi)|\mathbf{p}\rangle \equiv R(\phi)R(\theta)|\mathbf{p}_0\rangle = R(\theta+\phi)|\mathbf{p}_0\rangle \equiv |\mathbf{p}'\rangle$$

with $\mathbf{p}'$ given as above. We conclude that $\{|\mathbf{p}\rangle\}$ form the basis of an *irreducible vector space* which is invariant under E_2.

(iii) Fixing the normalization of the basis vectors:

If $\mathbf{p} \neq \mathbf{p}'$, the two vectors $|\mathbf{p}\rangle$ and $|\mathbf{p}'\rangle$ must be orthogonal to each other, i.e. $\langle\mathbf{p}'|\mathbf{p}\rangle = 0$, since they are eigenvectors of the hermitian operator $\mathbf{P}$ corresponding to different eigenvalues. But what is the proper normalization when $\mathbf{p} = \mathbf{p}'$? Since p^2, the eigenvalue of the Casimir operator $\mathbf{P}^2$, is invariant under all group operations, we need only consider the continuous label θ in $|p, \theta\rangle \equiv |\mathbf{p}\rangle$. The definition Eq. (9.3-3) indicates a one-to-one correspondence between these basis vectors and elements of the subgroup of rotations SO(2), $\{R(\theta)\}$. It is therefore natural to adopt the invariant measure (say, $d\theta/2\pi$) of the subgroup as the measure for the basis vectors. Consequently, the *orthonormality condition* of the basis vectors is:

$$\langle\mathbf{p}'|\mathbf{p}\rangle = \langle p, \theta'|p, \theta\rangle = 2\pi\,\delta(\theta' - \theta) \quad . \tag{9.3-6}$$

It is worth noting that the key to the induced representation approach resides in the existence of the abelian invariant subgroup T_2. The abelian nature allows the labelling of the basis vectors by $\mathbf{p}$, and the invariant property [cf. Theorem 9.3] is essential in the procedure of generating all $|\mathbf{p}\rangle$ from $|\mathbf{p}_0\rangle$. [The second equality in Eq. (9.3-2) relies on Eq. (9.1-12), or, equivalently, Theorem 9.3.] In the following, we

[1] In this step, we have used the orthogonality property of R, i.e. $R(-\theta)^l{}_k = R(\theta)^k{}_l$. Also, there is no distinction between upper and lower case indices for a vector such as $\mathbf{p}$.

shall refer to the linear momentum basis vectors $\{|\mathbf{p}\rangle\}$ so constructed as the *plane wave basis*, using a terminology familiar in physics.

It is of interest to establish the relationship of these plane wave basis vectors $\{|p,\theta\rangle\}$ to the angular momentum basis vectors $\{|p\,m\rangle\}$ of the last section. Each vector in one basis can be written as a linear combination of vectors in the other basis. We shall first try to obtain $|pm\rangle$ in terms of $|p,\theta\rangle$. Since the parameter p is an invariant label, we shall suppress it in the following discussion.

$|m\rangle$ is an eigenvector of J, the generator of the compact SO(2) subgroup of rotations. It can be obtained from any vector of the representation space by the *projection method* of Chap. 4 [cf. also Sec. 6.7]. Consider a state defined by

$$|\tilde{m}\rangle \equiv \int_0^{2\pi} \mathrm{R}(\phi)|\mathbf{p}_0\rangle e^{im\phi}\frac{\mathrm{d}\phi}{2\pi} = \int |\phi\rangle e^{im\phi}\frac{\mathrm{d}\phi}{2\pi} \quad . \tag{9.3-7}$$

This is an eigenstate of J with eigenvalue m, since

$$\mathrm{R}(\theta)|\tilde{m}\rangle = \int |\theta+\phi\rangle e^{im\phi}\,\mathrm{d}\phi/2\pi = \int |\phi'\rangle e^{im\phi'}(\mathrm{d}\phi'/2\pi)e^{-im\theta}$$
$$= |\tilde{m}\rangle e^{-im\theta} \quad .$$

It follows that $|\tilde{m}\rangle$ must be proportional to $|m\rangle$. In order to identify the appropriate proportionality constant, one must check the normalization and the relative phases of $|\tilde{m}\rangle$ for different m. We leave it to the reader to verify that [cf. Problem 9.2]:

$$|m\rangle = |\tilde{m}\rangle i^m = \int |\phi\rangle e^{im(\phi+\pi/2)}\,\mathrm{d}\phi/2\pi \quad . \tag{9.3-8}$$

The "transfer matrix" between the two sets of basis is

$$\langle\phi|m\rangle = e^{im(\phi+\pi/2)} \quad ; \tag{9.3-9}$$

and the inverse to Eq. (9.3-8) is

$$|\phi\rangle = \sum_m |m\rangle e^{-im(\phi+\pi/2)} \quad . \tag{9.3-10}$$

In particular, when $\phi = 0$, we have

$$|\mathbf{p}_0\rangle = \sum_m |m\rangle(-i)^m \quad . \tag{9.3-11}$$

Let us apply a translation to the two sides of Eq. (9.3-8),

$$\mathrm{T}(\mathbf{b})|m\rangle = \int |\phi\rangle e^{im(\phi+\pi/2)-ipb\cos(\theta-\phi)}\,\mathrm{d}\phi/2\pi \quad ; \tag{9.3-12}$$

then form the matrix element, using Eq. (9.3-9),

$$\langle m'|\mathrm{T}(\mathbf{b})|m\rangle = \int e^{i(m-m')(\phi+\pi/2)-ipb\cos(\theta-\phi)}\,\mathrm{d}\phi/2\pi \tag{9.3-13}$$
$$= e^{i(m-m')\theta}\int e^{i(m-m')\psi-ipb\sin\psi}\,\mathrm{d}\psi/2\pi$$

where we shifted to a new integration variable $\psi = \pi/2 + \phi - \theta$. Comparing with Eq. (9.2-14), we obtain the familiar integral representation of the Bessel function [Watson]

(9.3-14)
$$J_n(z) = \int_0^{2\pi} e^{in\psi - iz\sin\psi}\, d\psi/2\pi \quad .$$

9.4 Differential Equations, Recursion Formulas, and Addition Theorem of the Bessel Function

We further illustrate the connection between group representations and the classical theory of special functions by exploring the properties of the Bessel function as representation function of the E_2 group. It suffices to focus on the subgroup of translations. From

(9.4-1)
$$T(\mathbf{b}) = \exp[-i\mathbf{b}\cdot\mathbf{P}] = \exp[-i(b^- P_+ + b^+ P_-)]$$

where $b^\pm = (b^1 \pm ib^2)/2$, we obtain first:

(9.4-2)
$$i\frac{\partial}{\partial b^\mp} T(\mathbf{b}) = T(\mathbf{b})\, P_\pm \quad .$$

We now switch to polar coordinates, $\mathbf{b} = (b, \phi)$, so that

(9.4-3)
$$b^\pm = (b/2)\, e^{\pm i\phi}$$

(9.4-4)
$$b^2 = 4b^+ b^-$$

(9.4-5)
$$\phi = (i/2)\ln(b^-/b^+) \quad .$$

Eq. (9.4-2) can then be written as

(9.4-6)
$$i\, e^{\pm i\phi}\left[\frac{\partial}{\partial b} \pm \frac{i}{b}\frac{\partial}{\partial \phi}\right] T(\mathbf{b}) = T(\mathbf{b})\, P_\pm \quad .$$

We can sandwich both sides of the above question between states $|m\rangle$ and $\langle m'|$ to obtain

(9.4-7)
$$e^{\pm i\phi}\left[\frac{\partial}{\partial b} \pm \frac{i}{b}\frac{\partial}{\partial \phi}\right]\langle m'|T(\mathbf{b})|m\rangle = \mp p\,\langle m'|T(\mathbf{b})|m+1\rangle \quad .$$

Making use of Eq. (9.2-14), setting $n = m - m'$ and $p = 1$, we obtain

(9.4-8)
$$\left(\frac{d}{db} \mp \frac{n}{b}\right) J_n(b) = \mp J_{n\pm 1}(b) \quad .$$

Theorem 9.5 (Recursion Formulas of Bessel Functions): The Bessel Functions $J_n(b)$ satisfy the following *recursion formulas*:

(9.4-9)
$$2\,J_n'(b) = J_{n-1}(b) - J_{n+1}(b)$$
$$\frac{2n}{b} J_n(b) = J_{n-1}(b) + J_{n+1}(b) \quad .$$

We see that these well known recurrence relations have the geometrical interpretation as coming from raising and lowering operations.

The differential equation satisfied by a single Bessel function can be derived from the group theoretical identity, $T(\mathbf{b})P^2 = T(\mathbf{b})P_+P_-$. We obtain, in analogy to Eq. (9.4-7),

$$-\left[\frac{\partial^2}{\partial b^2} + \frac{1}{b}\frac{\partial}{\partial b} + \frac{1}{b^2}\frac{\partial^2}{\partial \phi^2}\right]\langle m'|T(\mathbf{b})|m\rangle = p^2\langle m'|T(\mathbf{b})|m\rangle \quad . \tag{9.4-10}$$

Theorem 9.6 (Differential Equation for Bessel Functions): The Bessel functions satisfy the following *differential equation*:

$$\left[\frac{d^2}{db^2} + \frac{1}{b}\frac{d}{db} + \left(1 - \frac{n^2}{b^2}\right)\right]J_n(b) = 0 \quad . \tag{9.4-11}$$

This equation, which follows trivially from Eq. (9.4-10) on account of Eq. (9.2-14), is the traditional defining differential equation for Bessel functions.

We can also derive an addition theorem for Bessel functions from the group multiplication rule—along the same line as for the spherical harmonics [cf. Sec. 8.6]. Consider the simple group identity

$$T(\mathbf{r})T(\mathbf{r}') = T(\mathbf{R}) \tag{9.4-12}$$

where, in terms of polar coordinates, $\mathbf{r} = (r, \phi)$, $\mathbf{r}' = (r', 0)$ and $\mathbf{R} = (R, \theta)$. [See Fig. 9.2] It leads to the following theorem on Bessel functions.

Theorem 9.7 (Addition Theorem): The Bessel functions satisfy

$$e^{in\theta} J_n(R) = \sum_k e^{ik\phi} J_k(r) J_{n-k}(r') \tag{9.4-13}$$

where the summation is over all integers.

Proof: Taking the matrix element of both sides of Eq. (9.4-12), we obtain

$$\sum_k \langle m'|T(\mathbf{r})|k\rangle\langle k|T(\mathbf{r}')|m\rangle = \langle m'|T(\mathbf{R})|m\rangle \quad .$$

Applying Eq. (9.2-14), we obtain

$$e^{i(m-m')\theta} J_{m-m'}(R) = \sum_k e^{i(k-m')\phi} J_{k-m'}(r) J_{m-k}(r') \quad .$$

Making the substitution, $m - m' \to n$ and $k - m' \to k$, we arrive at (9.4-13).

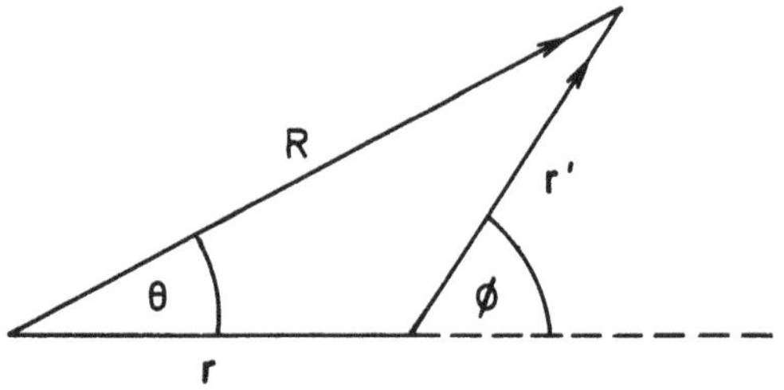

Fig. 9.2 Arguments in the addition theorem for Bessel functions.

9.5 Group Contraction—SO(3) and E_2

To complete our exploration of the group E_2, we consider an interesting relation between it and the group SO(3). As groups of transformations, SO(3) is the symmetry group of the surface of a sphere, and E_2 is the symmetry group of a plane. It is possible to establish a correspondence between elements of these groups by the stereographic projection of points on the sphere onto the plane. This correspondence becomes simpler when the radius of the sphere becomes larger. In the limit of infinite radius, as we shall see, the group SO(3) "contracts" to E_2.

Let us take the plane in question to be tangent to the sphere at its north pole, and set up coordinate axes as shown in Fig. 9.3. It should be clear that, subject to corrections which vanish in the limit of infinite R, rotations around the x- (y-) axis on the sphere correspond to translations in the $-\hat{\mathbf{e}}_y$ $(\hat{\mathbf{e}}_x)$ direction on the plane, whereas rotations around the z-axis retain the same interpretation in the two cases. Thus, from the correspondences

(9.5-1)
$$
\begin{aligned}
e^{-\theta_x J_x} = e^{-ib_y J_x/R} &\longleftrightarrow e^{ib_y P_y} \\
e^{-i\theta_y J_y} = e^{-ib_x J_y/R} &\longleftrightarrow e^{-ib_x P_x} \\
e^{-i\phi J_z} &\longrightarrow e^{-i\phi J_z}
\end{aligned}
$$

we identify the mapping:

(9.5-2)
$$J_y/R \longleftrightarrow P_x \qquad -J_x/R \longleftrightarrow P_y \quad \text{and} \quad J_z \longleftrightarrow J_z \quad .$$

Let us check the Lie algebra resulting from this correspondence:

$$
\begin{aligned}
[P_x, P_y] &\longrightarrow [J_y/R, -J_x/R] = [J_x, J_y]/R^2 = i\,J_z/R^2 \longrightarrow 0 \\
[P_x, J_z] &\longrightarrow [J_y/R, J_z] = [J_y, J_z]/\mathrm{R} = i\,J_x/R \longrightarrow -iP_y \\
[P_y, J_z] &\longrightarrow [-J_x/R, J_z] = -[J_x, J_z]/R = i\,J_y/R \longrightarrow iP_x \quad .
\end{aligned}
$$

Thus we arrive at the following theorem.

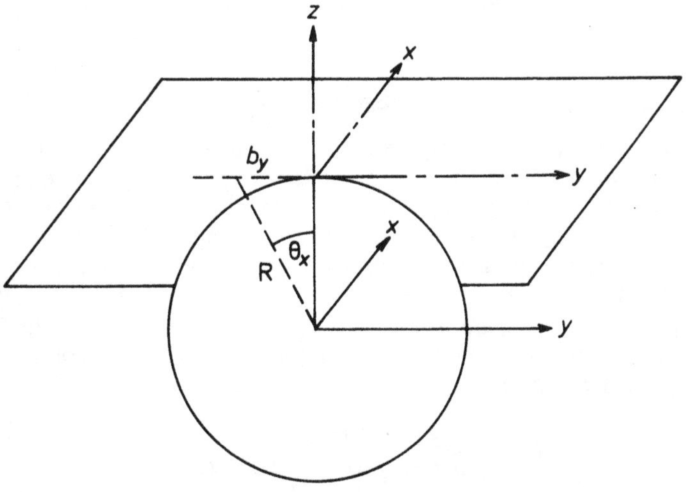

Fig. 9.3 Stereographic projection underlying the group-contraction SO(3) → E_2.

Theorem 9.8 (Contraction of SO(3) to E_2): In the limit of infinite R, the group SO(3) *contracts* to the group E_2 according to the correspondence Eq. (9.5-2).

Let us turn to the relation between the irreducible representations of the two groups. We shall derive the representations of E_2 in the $\{|p\, m\rangle\}$ basis from the more familiar representations of the rotation group SO(3). To begin with, the matrix element of the generator J_z certainly remains unchanged. We consider that of the raising and lowering operators,

$$\langle m'|\, J_x \pm i\, J_y\, |m\rangle = \delta^{m'}{}_{m\pm 1}\, [j(j+1) - m(m\pm 1)]^{1/2}$$

which, according to Eq. (9.5-2), translate to:

$$\langle m'|\, P_x \pm i\, P_y\, |m\rangle = \mp i\, \delta^{m'}{}_{m+1} [j(j+1) - m(m\pm 1)]^{1/2}/R \quad . \tag{9.5-3}$$

To keep the right-hand side of this equation non-vanishing as R increases without limit, we must use values of j proportional to R.

Theorem 9.9 (Irreducible Representations of E_2 by Contraction from SO(3)): Non-trivial irreducible representations of E_2 can be obtained from those of SO(3) if $j = pR$ as $R \to \infty$.

Proof: If $j = pR$, then according to Eq. (9.5-3),

$$\langle m'|\, P_\pm\, |m\rangle = \mp i\, p\, \delta^{m'}{}_{m\pm 1}$$

and
$$\langle m'|\, P_\pm P_\mp\, |m\rangle = \langle m'|\, \mathbf{P}^2\, |m\rangle = p^2\, \delta^{m'}{}_m \quad .$$

We recover the irreducible representations of Sec. 9.2 [cf. Eq. (9.2-11)]. QED

This result allows us to express Bessel functions as limits of the d-functions of Chap. 7. Consider a rotation around the y-axis at finite R. The representation function is:

$$d^j(\theta)^{m'}{}_m = d^j(b/R)^{m'}{}_m = d^j(pb/j)^{m'}{}_m \quad .$$

Taking the $j \to \infty$ limit, this function should converge to the representation function of a translation along the x-direction by the displacement b. We obtain, therefore,

$$J_n(z) = \langle -n|\, T(z, 0)\, |0\rangle_{p=1} = \lim_{j\to\infty} d^j(z/j)^{-n}{}_0 \quad . \tag{9.5-4}$$

9.6 The Euclidean Group in Three Dimensions: E_3

The symmetry group of the 3-dimensional Euclidean group, E_3, can be analyzed by the same methods introduced in the previous sections for E_2. Therefore, we shall be relatively brief in the discussion here. We shall first consider the linear momentum basis, using the induced representation method and emphasizing the concept of the little group. Then, in discussing the angular momentum basis, we shall look into the group-theoretical significance of the spherical Bessel functions.

The group E_3 consists of translations $\{T_3\colon T(\mathbf{b})\}$, rotations $\{SO(3)\colon R(\alpha, \beta, \gamma)\}$, and all their products in 3-dimensional Euclidean space. The generators of the group are $\{\mathbf{P}\colon P_1, P_2, P_3\}$ for translations, and $\{\mathbf{J}\colon J_1, J_2, J_3\}$ for rotations. We have, as usual,

$$T(\mathbf{b}) = e^{-i\mathbf{b}\cdot\mathbf{P}} \tag{9.6-1}$$

$$R(\alpha, \beta, \gamma) = e^{-i\alpha J_3}\, e^{-i\beta J_2}\, e^{-i\gamma J_3} \quad . \tag{9.6-2}$$

We regard it as self-evident, from previous studies of SO(3) and E_2, that the following theorems hold:

Theorem 9.10 (Lie Algebra of E_3): The Lie algebra of the group E_3 is specified by the following set of commutation relations:

(9.6-3) $$[P_k, P_l] = 0$$

(9.6-4) $$[J_k, J_l] = i\,\varepsilon_{klm} J^m$$

(9.6-5) $$[P_k, J_l] = i\,\varepsilon_{klm} P^m$$

where ε_{klm} is the 3-dimensional totally anti-symmetric unit tensor.

Theorem 9.11 (Invariant Subgroup of E_3): The group of translations T_3 forms an invariant subgroup of E_3, and the following identities hold:

(9.6-6) $$\mathrm{R}\, P_i \mathrm{R}^{-1} = P_j R^j{}_i,$$

(9.6-7) $$\mathrm{R}\,\mathrm{T}(\mathbf{b})\,\mathrm{R}^{-1} = \mathrm{T}(\mathbf{b}')$$

where $b'^i = R^i{}_j b^j$ for all rotations $\mathrm{R}(\alpha, \beta, \gamma)$.

Corollary: The general group element $g \in E_3$ can always be written as

(9.6-8) $$g = \mathrm{T}(\mathbf{b})\,\mathrm{R}(\alpha, \beta, \gamma)$$

or as

(9.6-9) $$g = \mathrm{R}(\phi, \theta, 0)\,\mathrm{T}(\mathbf{b}_3)\,\mathrm{R}(\alpha, \beta, \gamma)$$

where $\mathbf{b}_3 = b\,\hat{\mathbf{e}}_3$.

Proof: Since products of translations (rotations) are translations (rotations), a general group element is of the form

$$g = \mathrm{R}_1 \mathrm{T}_1 \mathrm{R}_2 \mathrm{T}_2 \cdots \mathrm{R}_n \mathrm{T}_n \quad .$$

Making use of Eq. (9.6-7), we can rewrite the above expression as

$$g = \mathrm{T}_1' \mathrm{T}_2' \cdots \mathrm{T}_n' \mathrm{R} = \mathrm{T}\,\mathrm{R}$$

where $\mathrm{T}_1' = \mathrm{R}_1 \mathrm{T}_1 \mathrm{R}_1^{-1}$, $\mathrm{T}_2' = \mathrm{R}_1 \mathrm{R}_2 \mathrm{T}_2 \mathrm{R}_2^{-1} \mathrm{R}_1^{-1}, \cdots$ etc. and $\mathrm{R} = \mathrm{R}_1\ \mathrm{R}_2 \cdots \mathrm{R}_n$. Hence Eq. (9.6-8) is established. If the spherical coordinates of $\mathbf{b}$ are (b, θ, ϕ), then $\mathrm{T}(\mathbf{b}) = \mathrm{R}(\phi, \theta, 0)\ \mathrm{T}(\mathbf{b}_3)\ \mathrm{R}(\phi, \theta, 0)^{-1}$. Substituting this expression in Eq. (9.6-8), we obtain Eq. (9.6-9). QED

Theorem 9.12 (Casimir Operator of E_3): The Casimir operators of the group E_3 are $\mathbf{P}^2$ and $\mathbf{J} \cdot \mathbf{P}$.

Proof: (i) $\mathbf{P}^2 = \mathbf{P} \cdot \mathbf{P}$ commutes with $\{P_k\}$ due to the abelian nature of the translational subgroup; it commutes with $\{J_k\}$ since, being the scalar product of two vectors, it is rotationally invariant.
(ii) $\mathbf{J} \cdot \mathbf{P}$ commutes with $\{J_k\}$ since it is rotationally invariant; it also commutes with $\{P_k\}$, since

$$[J_l P^l, P_k] = [J_l, P_k]\, P^l = -i\,\varepsilon_{lkm} P^m P^l = 0 \quad .$$

QED

In the following discussion, we shall need maximal sets of commuting operators. Two natural sets are: the angular momentum set $\{\mathbf{P}^2, \mathbf{J}\cdot\mathbf{P}; J^2, J_3\}$, and the linear momentum set $\{\mathbf{P}^2, \mathbf{J}\cdot\mathbf{P}; P_1, P_2\}$. It is also possible to have a "mixed set" such as $\{\mathbf{P}^2, \mathbf{J}\cdot\mathbf{P}; P_3, J_3\}$.

9.7 Unitary Irreducible Representations of E_3 by the Induced Representation Method

Since T_3 is an invariant subgroup of E_3, and the factor group E_3/T_3 is isomorphic to the group of rotations SO(3), degenerate irreducible representations of E_3 are induced by the known representations of SO(3). Thus we obtain for any positive integer or half-integer j,

$$g = \mathrm{T}\,\mathrm{R} \longrightarrow D^j(\mathrm{R}) \tag{9.7-1}$$

where $D^j(\mathrm{R})$ is the $(2j+1)\times(2j+1)$ rotation matrix of Chap. 7. In this representation, all pure translations are mapped to the identity operator. Hence, the generators of translations correspond to null operators, and both the regular Casimir operators $\mathbf{P}^2$ and $\mathbf{J}\cdot\mathbf{P}$ have zero eigenvalues.

Now, consider a vector space with non-zero eigenvalue for the operator $\mathbf{P}^2$. We shall generate the *plane wave basis* consisting of eigenvectors of the linear momentum operator set $\{\mathbf{P}^2, \mathbf{J}\cdot\mathbf{P}; \mathbf{P}\}$. The eigenvalues will be denoted by $\{p^2, \lambda p; \mathbf{p}\}$ where $\mathbf{p}$ is referred to as the *momentum vector* and λ as the *helicity*. It suffices to label the eigenvectors $|p, \lambda; \hat{\mathbf{p}}\rangle$ where $\hat{\mathbf{p}} = \mathbf{p}/p$ is the unit vector along the direction of $\mathbf{p}$ characterized by two angles; say (θ, ϕ). Up to a phase factor to be determined in the next paragraph, these eigenvectors are defined by:

$$\mathbf{P}^2|p,\lambda;\hat{\mathbf{p}}\rangle = |p,\lambda;\hat{\mathbf{p}}\rangle\, p^2 \tag{9.7-2}$$

$$\mathbf{J}\cdot\mathbf{P}|p,\lambda;\hat{\mathbf{p}}\rangle = |p,\lambda;\hat{\mathbf{p}}\rangle\, \lambda p \tag{9.7-3}$$

$$\mathbf{P}|p,\lambda;\hat{\mathbf{p}}\rangle = |p,\lambda;\hat{\mathbf{p}}\rangle\, \mathbf{p} \quad . \tag{9.7-4}$$

To construct this basis precisely, we follow the procedure formulated in Sec. 9.3.

(i) Consider the subspace characterized by a *standard vector* $\hat{\mathbf{p}} = \hat{\mathbf{p}}_0 \equiv \hat{\mathbf{e}}_z$.

Definition 9.2 (Little Group): All group elements in the factor group (in the current case, rotations) which leave the subspace corresponding to the standard vector $\hat{\mathbf{p}}_0$ invariant form a subgroup [cf. Problem 9.3], called the *little group* of $\hat{\mathbf{p}}_0$.

Since $\hat{\mathbf{p}}_0$ is along the z-axis, the only rotations which do not change its value are rotations around the z-axis, $\mathrm{R}_3(\phi) = e^{-i\phi J_3}$. The little group of $\hat{p}_0$ is therefore isomorphic to SO(2). We shall show that every irreducible representation of the little group induces an irreducible representation of the full group.

The irreducible representations of SO(2) are all one-dimensional; they are labelled by one index λ, which is the eigenvalue of the generator J_3. We know that $\lambda = 0, \pm 1, \pm 2, \ldots$ from Chap. 6. In the present case, these states are also eigenstates of $\mathbf{P}$ with eigenvalue $\mathbf{p}_0$. When acting on vectors of this subspace, the Casimir operator $\mathbf{J}\cdot\mathbf{P}$ has the following effect:

$$\mathbf{J}\cdot\mathbf{P} = \mathbf{J}\cdot\mathbf{p}_0 = pJ_3 = \lambda p \quad . \tag{9.7-5}$$

Thus the λ parameter of Eq. (9.7-3) can be identified with the SO(2) representation label, and it can only be an integer. It follows that the basis vectors of the subspace corresponding to the standard vector $\hat{\mathbf{p}}_0$ behave under the little group transformations [cf. Eq. (6.3-6)] as

(9.7-6) $$R_3(\psi)|p,\lambda;\hat{\mathbf{p}}_0\rangle = |p,\lambda;\hat{\mathbf{p}}_0\rangle e^{-i\lambda\psi} \quad ;$$

and under translations [cf. Eq. (9.7-4)] as

(9.7-7) $$T(\mathbf{b})|p,\lambda;\hat{\mathbf{p}}_0\rangle = |p,\lambda;\hat{\mathbf{p}}_0\rangle e^{-i\mathbf{b}\cdot\mathbf{p}_0} \quad .$$

(ii) The full vector space for the irreducible representation of E_3 labelled by (p, λ) can be constructed by generating new basis vectors from $|p,\lambda;\hat{\mathbf{p}}_0\rangle$ with the help of rotations which are not in the little group. To be specific, we shall define:

(9.7-8) $$|p,\lambda;\hat{\mathbf{p}}\rangle \equiv R(\phi,\theta,0)|p,\lambda;\hat{\mathbf{p}}_0\rangle,$$

where $\hat{\mathbf{p}} = R(\phi,\theta,0)\,\hat{\mathbf{p}}_0$. To simplify the notation, we again omit the labels (p,λ) (which remain unchanged) in subsequent formulas.

Theorem 9.13 (Irreducible Representation Matrices of E_3): The basis vectors defined by Eq. (9.7-8) have the required properties specified by Eqs. (9.7-2)-(9.7-4). The effect of group operations on these vectors is:

(9.7-9) $$T(\mathbf{b})|\hat{\mathbf{p}}\rangle = |\hat{\mathbf{p}}\rangle e^{-i\mathbf{b}\cdot\mathbf{p}} \qquad \hat{\mathbf{p}} = (\theta,\phi)$$

(9.7-10) $$R(\alpha,\beta,\gamma)|\hat{\mathbf{p}}\rangle = |\hat{\mathbf{p}}'\rangle e^{-i\lambda\psi} \qquad \hat{\mathbf{p}}' = (\theta',\phi')$$

where $p'^k = R(\alpha,\beta,\gamma)^k{}_j\, p^j$ and ψ is an angle to be determined from the equation

(9.7-11) $$R(0,0,\psi) = R(\phi',\theta',0)^{-1}R(\alpha,\beta,\gamma)R(\phi,\theta,0) \quad .$$

Proof: Eq. (9.7-9) follows immediately from Eq. (9.7-4). To prove Eq. (9.7-10), one makes strict use of the definition, Eq. (9.7-8), as follows:

(9.7-12) $$\begin{aligned} R(\alpha,\beta,\gamma)|\hat{\mathbf{p}}\rangle &\equiv R(\alpha,\beta,\gamma)R(\phi,\theta,0)|\hat{\mathbf{p}}_0\rangle \\ &= R(\phi',\theta',0)R(0,0,\psi)|\hat{\mathbf{p}}_0\rangle \\ &= R(\phi',\theta',0)|\hat{\mathbf{p}}_0\rangle e^{-i\lambda\psi} \equiv |\hat{\mathbf{p}}'\rangle e^{-i\lambda\psi} \end{aligned}$$

where $R(0,0,\psi)$ is given by Eq. (9.7-11). The fact that the product of the three rotations on the right-hand side of Eq. (9.7-11) is a rotation around the z-axis follows from the observation that, by definition, it leaves the standard vector $\hat{\mathbf{p}}_0$ invariant; hence it must be a member of the little group. QED

Theorem 9.13 confirms that the vector space with $\{|p,\lambda;\hat{\mathbf{p}}\rangle\}$ as its basis is invariant under the E_3 group, and Eqs. (9.7-9), (9.7-10) define a unitary representation of E_3. This representation is irreducible since all basis vectors are generated from one single vector ($|\hat{\mathbf{p}}_0\rangle$) by group operations, and no smaller invariant subspace exists. So far, we have not been concerned with the normalization of the basis vectors. The proper normalization condition is

(9.7-13) $$\langle\hat{\mathbf{p}}'|\hat{\mathbf{p}}\rangle \equiv \delta(\Omega_{p'}-\Omega_p) \equiv 4\pi\delta(\cos\theta'-\cos\theta)\,\delta(\phi'-\phi) \quad .$$

This follows from the fact that $\{|\hat{\mathbf{p}}\rangle\}$ are generated from $|\hat{\mathbf{p}}_0\rangle$ by elements of the factor group (rotations), and the δ-function of Eq. (9.7-13) is the appropriate δ-function associated with the invariant measure on the group (i.e. $\sin\theta d\theta\, d\phi/4\pi$).

9.8 Angular Momentum Basis and the Spherical Bessel Function

On the vector space of the (p, λ) irreducible representation, it is often convenient to work with the angular momentum basis, rather than the plane-wave basis discussed above. The angular momentum basis $\{|p, \lambda; jm\rangle\}$ consists of vectors which are eigenvectors of the operators $\{\mathbf{P}^2, \mathbf{J}\cdot\mathbf{P}; \mathbf{J}^2, \mathbf{J}_3\}$. For given (p, λ), j takes all possible positive integer values, hence the representation is infinite dimensional. As before, we shall suppress the labels (p, λ) whenever possible. For each value of j, the basis vectors $\{|jm\rangle\}$ are most conveniently chosen in the same way as the "canonical basis" vectors of the SO(3) group (Sec. 7.3):

(9.8-1) $$\mathbf{P}^2 |jm\rangle = |jm\rangle p^2$$

(9.8-2) $$\mathbf{J}\cdot\mathbf{P} |jm\rangle = |jm\rangle \lambda p$$

(9.8-3) $$\mathbf{J}^2 |jm\rangle = |jm\rangle j(j+1)$$

(9.8-4) $$J_3 |jm\rangle = |jm\rangle m$$

(9.8-5) $$J_\pm |jm\rangle = |jm\rangle [j(j+1) - m(m\pm 1)]^{1/2} \quad .$$

The relation between the angular-momentum and plane-wave bases can be derived by the *projection method.* The results are essentially the same as contained in the example of Sec. 8.4 [cf. Eqs. (8.4-9), (8.4-10)],

(9.8-6) $$|jm\rangle = \int d\Omega_p |\hat{\mathbf{p}}\rangle D_j^\dagger(\phi, \theta, 0)^\lambda{}_m \frac{2j+1}{4\pi}$$

(9.8-7) $$|\hat{\mathbf{p}}\rangle = \sum_{jm} |jm\rangle D^j(\phi, \theta, 0)^m{}_\lambda \quad .$$

These formulas are also to be compared to Eqs. (9.3-8), (9.3-10) for the E_2 case.

Theorem 9.14 (Angular Momentum Basis of Unitary Irreducible Representations of E_3): Let $R_{p\lambda}(\alpha, \beta, \gamma)$ and $T_{p\lambda}(\mathbf{b})$ be the rotation- and translation-operators on the vector space for the (p, λ) irreducible representation. Then, with respect to the angular momentum basis, we have:

(9.8-8) $$\langle l'm'| R_{p\lambda}(\alpha, \beta, \gamma) |lm\rangle = \delta^{l'}{}_l D^l(R)^{m'}{}_m$$

(9.8-9) $$\langle l'm'| T_{p\lambda}(\mathbf{b}) |lm\rangle = \sum_n \langle l'n| T_{p\lambda}(b\hat{\mathbf{z}}) |ln\rangle D^{l'}(\hat{\mathbf{b}})^{m'}{}_n D^l(\hat{\mathbf{b}})^m{}_n{}^*$$

(9.8-10) $$\langle l'n| T_{p\lambda}(b\hat{\mathbf{z}}) |ln\rangle = \sum_L (2L+1)(-i)^L j_L(pb) \langle n0(l'L)ln\rangle \langle l\lambda(l'L)\lambda 0\rangle$$

where $j_l(z)$ is the spherical Bessel function of order l.

Proof: Eq. (9.8-8) is a direct consequence of the fact that the basis vectors are chosen to be a "canonical basis" in the sense of Sec. 7.3. To verify Eq. (9.8-9), we start from Eq. (9.6-7),

(9.8-11) $$\begin{aligned} \langle l'm'| T(\mathbf{b}) |lm\rangle &= \langle l'm'| R(\hat{\mathbf{b}}) T(b\hat{\mathbf{z}}) R(\hat{\mathbf{b}})^{-1} |lm\rangle \\ &= \sum_{nn'} D^{l'}(\hat{\mathbf{b}})^{m'}{}_{n'} \langle l'n'| T(b\hat{\mathbf{z}}) |ln\rangle D^l(\hat{\mathbf{b}})^m{}_n{}^* \end{aligned}$$

where we have adopted the abbreviation $R(\hat{\mathbf{b}}) = R(\phi_b, \theta_b, 0)$, and likewise for $D(\hat{\mathbf{b}})$.

To evaluate the matrix element of a translation along the z-axis, we use the definition, Eq. (9.8-6),

$$T(b\hat{\mathbf{z}})|lm\rangle = N_l^2 \int d\Omega_p |\hat{\mathbf{p}}\rangle e^{-ipb\cos\theta_p} D_l^\dagger(\hat{\mathbf{p}})^\lambda{}_m$$

where $N_l = [(2l+1)/4\pi]^{1/2}$. Taking the scalar product with $\langle l'm'|$, we obtain

$$(9.8\text{-}12) \qquad \langle l'm'|T_{p\lambda}(b\hat{\mathbf{z}})|lm\rangle = N_l^2 \int d\Omega_p D^{l'}(\hat{\mathbf{p}})^{m'}{}_\lambda e^{-ipb\cos\theta_p} D_l^\dagger(\hat{\mathbf{p}})^\lambda{}_m \quad .$$

The exponential factor can be decomposed by a well-known formula,

$$\begin{aligned} e^{-ipb\cos\theta_p} &= \sum_L (2L+1)(-i)^L j_L(pb)\, P_L(\cos\theta_p) \\ &= \sum_L (2L+1)(-i)^L j_L(pb)\, D^L(\hat{\mathbf{p}})^0{}_0, \end{aligned}$$

where $j_L(x)$ is the *spherical Bessel function* of order L. We can combine the two D-functions using Clebsch-Gordan coefficients,

$$D^{l'}(\hat{\mathbf{p}})^{m'}{}_\lambda D^L(\hat{\mathbf{p}})^0{}_0 = \sum_J \langle m'0(l'L)Jm'\rangle D^J(\hat{\mathbf{p}})^{m'}{}_\lambda \langle J\lambda(l'L)\lambda 0\rangle \quad .$$

The remaining $\hat{\mathbf{p}}$-dependent factors can be integrated over, utilizing the orthonormality condition of the D-functions,

$$N_j^2 \int d\Omega_p D^J(\hat{\mathbf{p}})^{m'}{}_\lambda D_l^\dagger(\hat{\mathbf{p}})^\lambda{}_m = \delta^J{}_l \delta^{m'}{}_m \quad .$$

Collecting these results, we obtain for Eq. (9.8-12),

$$\langle l'm'|T_{p\lambda}(b\hat{\mathbf{z}})|lm\rangle = \delta^{m'}{}_m \sum_L (2L+1)(-i)^L j_L(pb) \langle m0(l'L)lm\rangle \langle l\lambda(l'L)\lambda 0\rangle \quad .$$

This proves Eq. (9.8-10). Substituting into Eq. (9.8-11), we obtain (9.8-9). QED

Eq. (9.8-10) is the E_3 counterpart of Eq. (9.2-14) for the simpler group E_2. If we choose $l' = 0$ in Eq. (9.8-10), the sum on the right-hand side reduces to one single term, and we obtain

$$(9.8\text{-}12) \qquad \langle 00|T_{p0}(b\hat{\mathbf{z}})|l0\rangle = (-i)^l (2l+1)\, j_l(pb)$$

which gives the group-theoretical definition of j_l. We also note that Eq. (9.8-10) implies that $\langle l'n|T_{p\lambda}(b\hat{\mathbf{z}})|ln\rangle$ vanishes unless $\lambda \le l$ and $\lambda \le l'$. Many well-known properties of the spherical Bessel functions can be given a group theoretical interpretation, just as in the case of spherical harmonics (Sec. 8.6) and Bessel function of the first kind (Sec. 9.4). We shall not carry out this investigation explicitly here. [cf. Problem 9.5] [Talman]

Problems

9.1 Verify that the space of 3-component vectors $(x^1, x^2, 1)$ is invariant under the transformation $g(\hat{\mathbf{a}}, \theta)$ given by Eq. (9.1-5), and that the latter reproduces Eqs. (9.1-3) and (9.1-4).

9.2 Verify Eq. (9.3-8) by considering the action of $P_{\pm}$ on the state and by evaluating the norm of the vector.

9.3 Prove that, in the induced representation method, all group elements of the factor group which leave the subspace associated with the standard vector $\hat{\mathbf{p}}_0$ invariant form a subgroup.

9.4 Combine Eqs. (9.8-9) and (9.8-10) to show that

$$\langle j'm' | \mathrm{T}_{p\lambda}(\mathbf{b}) | jm \rangle = (-1)^{m-m'} \sum_l (2l+1)(-i)^l \, \mathrm{j}_l(pb) \, D^l(\hat{\mathbf{b}})^{m-m'}_0$$

$$\times \langle m', m-m' (j'l) jm \rangle \langle j\lambda (j'l) \lambda 0 \rangle \quad .$$

[Hint: Orthonormality and symmetry relations of Clebsch-Gordan coefficients are needed.]

9.5 Derive the recursion formulas for spherical Bessel functions

$$\frac{2l+1}{x} \mathrm{j}_l(x) = \mathrm{j}_{l-1}(x) + \mathrm{j}_{l+1}(x)$$

$$\frac{\mathrm{d}}{\mathrm{d}x} \mathrm{j}_l(x) = \frac{1}{2l+1} [l \mathrm{j}_{l-1}(x) - (l+1) \mathrm{j}_{l+1}(x)]$$

using group theoretical methods.

CHAPTER 10

THE LORENTZ AND POINCARÉ GROUPS, AND SPACE-TIME SYMMETRIES

In the far-reaching theory of *Special Relativity* of Einstein, the homogeneity and isotropy of the 3-dimensional space are generalized to include the time dimension as well. The space-time structure embodied in this theory provides the foundation on which all branches of modern physics are formulated.[1] In Sec. 1 we shall introduce the symmetry groups of 4-dimensional *space-time*—the proper Lorentz group and Poincaré group. These are, respectively, generalizations of the rotation groups and Euclidean groups in 2- and 3-dimensional spaces discussed in Chaps. 6-9. In Sec. 2, we examine the generators of the two groups and study the associated Lie algebras. Due to the different way the time dimension enters, we shall show in Sec. 3 that, in contrast to our experience with rotation groups, the finite dimensional irreducible representations of the Lorentz group cannot be unitary. Nonetheless, we shall derive these representations, as well as the infinite-dimensional unitary representations, using techniques established in earlier chapters. In Sec. 4, we analyze the unitary representations of the Poincaré group using the induced representation method [Wigner (1)]. The results of this analysis correspond so naturally to physical elementary quantum mechanical systems, that we obtain a powerful framework to formulate basic laws of physics and, at the same time, witness the deep unity between mathematics and physics. The last section consists of a discussion of transformation properties of classical and quantum mechanical wave functions, field operators, and relativistic wave equations. This topic illustrates the complementary roles played by the finite dimensional (non-unitary) representations of the Lorentz group and by the (infinite dimensional) unitary representations of the Poincaré group in physical applications.

10.1 The Lorentz and Poincaré Groups

The basic tenet of the theory of relativity is that there is a fundamental symmetry between the three space dimensions and the time dimension, as manifested most directly in the constancy of the velocity of light in all coordinate frames. In order to

[1] Only in the theory of gravitation, involving large masses of the cosmic scale, is it necessary to generalize the concepts of space-time beyond the special theory of relativity. The resulting theory of General Relativity is intimately related to the group of general coordinate transformations. We shall not venture into that theory in this book.

formulate this symmetry mathematically, it is useful to introduce a set of convenient definitions and notations.

Definition 10.1 (Event): An *event*, characterized by the spatial coordinates (x^i; $i = 1, 2, 3$) and the time t, will be denoted by $\{x^\mu; \mu = 0, 1, 2, 3\}$ where

$$x^{\mu=0} = ct \qquad x^{\mu=i} = x^i$$

and c is the velocity of light in vacuum.[2] The convention is that Greek indices refer to space-time in general (hence range over 0 to 3), and Roman indices refer to 3-space only (hence range over 1 to 3). We shall continue to use the notation $\mathbf{x}$ to indicate a 3-vector.

Definition 10.2 (Coordinate Four-vector, Length of Vectors): Let x_1^μ and x_2^μ represent two events. The difference between the two events defines a *coordinate four-vector* $x^\mu = x_1^\mu - x_2^\mu$. The *length* $|x|$ of a 4-vector x is defined by

$$|x|^2 \equiv (\mathbf{x})^2 - (x^0)^2 = (\mathbf{x})^2 - c^2t^2 \quad . \tag{10.1-1}$$

The coordinates x^μ of an event can be considered as a 4-vector if we understand it to mean the difference between that event and the event represented by the origin $(0, \mathbf{0})$. In this notation, the wave-front of a light signal sent out from the origin at $t = 0$ will be specified by the simple equation, $|x| = 0$.

In terms of a *metric tensor* $g^{\mu\nu}$, the definition of the length of a vector x can be written as

$$|x|^2 = g_{\mu\nu} x^\mu x^\nu \tag{10.1-2}$$

where the implicit summations extend over all 4 components, $g_{\mu\nu} = 0$ if $\mu \neq \nu$, and $-g_{00} = g_{11} = g_{22} = g_{33} = 1$. This metric is called the *Minkowski metric*; it is said to have the *signature* $(-1, 1, 1, 1)$. More explicitly,

$$(g_{\mu\nu}) = \begin{pmatrix} -1 & & & \\ & 1 & & \\ & & 1 & \\ & & & 1 \end{pmatrix}.$$

In contrast to the Euclidean metric $\delta_{\mu\nu}$, the Minkowski metric is not positive definite. This fact leads to important differences in the representations of the associated symmetry groups. We shall point out these differences as they arise.

The principle of special relativity stipulates that basic laws of physics are invariant with respect to translations in all 4 coordinates (homogeneity of space-time) and to all homogeneous linear transformations on the space-time coordinates which leave the length of 4-vectors invariant (isotropy of space-time).

10.1.1 Homogeneous Lorentz Transformations

Definition 10.3 (Homogeneous Lorentz Transformation): *Homogeneous Lorentz transformations* are continuous linear transformations Λ on the unit coordinate

[2] In this notation, all four coordinates carry the same scale dimension—the dimension of length.

vectors and coordinate components given by

(10.1-3)
$$\begin{aligned} \hat{e}_\mu &\to \hat{e}'_\mu = \hat{e}_\nu \Lambda^\nu{}_\mu \\ x^\mu &\to x'^\mu = \Lambda^\mu{}_\nu x^\nu \end{aligned}$$

which preserve the length of 4-vectors, i.e.

(10.1-4)
$$|x|^2 = |x'|^2 \quad .$$

Combining Eqs. (10.1-2)-(10.1-4), one can reformulate the condition on Lorentz transformations Λ without referring to any specific 4-vector as either

(10.1-5)
$$g_{\mu\nu} \Lambda^\mu{}_\lambda \Lambda^\nu{}_\sigma = g_{\lambda\sigma}$$

or
$$\Lambda^\mu{}_\lambda \Lambda^\nu{}_\sigma g^{\lambda\sigma} = g^{\mu\nu}$$

where $g^{\mu\nu} = g_{\mu\nu}$. This result is an apparent generalization of Eq. (7.1-5) for rotations in 3-dimensional Euclidean space.[3] If we suppress the indices in Eq. (10.1-5), it can be written as

(10.1-5a)
$$\Lambda^{-1} = g \Lambda^{\mathrm{T}} g^{-1} \quad .$$

[Prove!] This is to be compared with Eq. (7.1-3), which implies $\mathrm{R}^{-1} = \mathrm{R}^{\mathrm{T}}$.

Taking the determinant on both sides of Eq. (10.1-5a), we obtain $(\det \Lambda)^2 = 1$, hence $\det \Lambda = \pm 1$. In this chapter we restrict ourselves to those transformations which are continuously connected to the identity transformation. Since the latter has unit determinant, we must have

$$\det \Lambda = \Lambda^0{}_\mu \Lambda^1{}_\nu \Lambda^2{}_\lambda \Lambda^3{}_\sigma \varepsilon^{\mu\nu\lambda\sigma} = 1$$

where $\varepsilon^{\mu\nu\lambda\sigma}$ is the 4-dimensional totally anti-symmetric unit tensor (with $\varepsilon^{0123} = 1$). As in Eq. (7.1-6), this condition can be rewritten as

(10.1-6)
$$\Lambda^\alpha{}_\mu \Lambda^\beta{}_\nu \Lambda^\gamma{}_\lambda \Lambda^\delta{}_\sigma \varepsilon^{\mu\nu\lambda\sigma} = \varepsilon^{\alpha\beta\gamma\delta} \quad .$$

We also note that, setting $\lambda = \sigma = 0$ in the first equation in (10.1-5), we obtain the condition

$$(\Lambda^0{}_0)^2 - \sum_i (\Lambda^i{}_0)^2 = 1 \quad .$$

This implies $(\Lambda^0{}_0)^2 \geq 1$, hence $\Lambda^0{}_0 \geq 1$ or $\Lambda^0{}_0 \leq -1$. The two solutions represent disjoint regions of the real axis for $\Lambda^0{}_0$. Since $\Lambda^0{}_0 = 1$ for the identity transformation, continuity requires that all *proper* Lorentz transformations have

(10.1-7)
$$\Lambda^0{}_0 \geq 1 \quad .$$

In the next chapter, it will be shown that the other branch, $\Lambda^0{}_0 \leq -1$, corresponds to transformations associated with time-reversal. From all these discussions, we conclude:

Theorem 10.1 (Characterization of Homogeneous Lorentz Transformations): Homogeneous Lorentz transformations are linear transformations of 4×4 matrices with $\Lambda^0{}_0 \geq 1$ that leave two special tensors $g^{\mu\nu}$ and $\varepsilon^{\mu\nu\lambda\sigma}$ invariant.

[3] If we restrict the indices $(\mu, \nu, \lambda, \sigma)$ to the three spatial dimensions, Eq. (10.1-5) reduces to Eq. (7.1-5).

A general homogeneous proper Lorentz transformation depends on 6 real parameters as can be seen as follows: the 4×4 real matrix Λ has 16 arbitrary elements; Eq. (10.1-5) contains 10 independent constraints—as both sides of the equation are manifestly symmetric in the $(\mu\nu)$ indices. Since Eq. (10.1-7) follows from (10.1-5), it does not lead to an additional relational constraint. (It only imposes restrictions on the range of solutions to Eq. (10.1-5), such as the exclusion of spatial and time inversions and related transformations.)

Rotations in the 3 spatial dimensions are examples of Lorentz transformations in this generalized sense. They are of the form

$$(R)^{\mu}{}_{\nu} = \begin{pmatrix} 1 & 0 & 0 & 0 \\ 0 & & & \\ 0 & & (R)^{i}{}_{j} & \\ 0 & & & \end{pmatrix} \tag{10.1-8}$$

where $(R)^{i}{}_{j}$ denotes ordinary 3×3 rotation matrices. It is straightforward to verify that this form satisfies Eqs. (10.1-5) and (10.1-7).

Of more interest are *special Lorentz transformations* which mix spatial coordinates with the time coordinate. The simplest of these is a *Lorentz boost* along a given coordinate axis, say the x-axis:

$$(L_1)^{\mu}{}_{\nu} = \begin{pmatrix} \cosh\xi & \sinh\xi & 0 & 0 \\ \sinh\xi & \cosh\xi & 0 & 0 \\ 0 & 0 & 1 & 0 \\ 0 & 0 & 0 & 1 \end{pmatrix} \quad . \tag{10.1-9}$$

This corresponds physically to the transformation between two coordinate frames moving with respect to each other along the x-direction at the speed $v = c \tanh \xi$. [cf. Fig. 10.1]

The relation between the parameter ξ and the physical variable v can be conveniently established through the dimensionless quantities $\beta = v/c$, and $\gamma = (1 - \beta^2)^{-1/2}$. The hyperbolic sine and cosine functions in Eq. (10.1-9) become

$$\begin{aligned} \sinh\xi &= \beta\gamma \\ \cosh\xi &= \gamma \quad . \end{aligned} \tag{10.1-10}$$

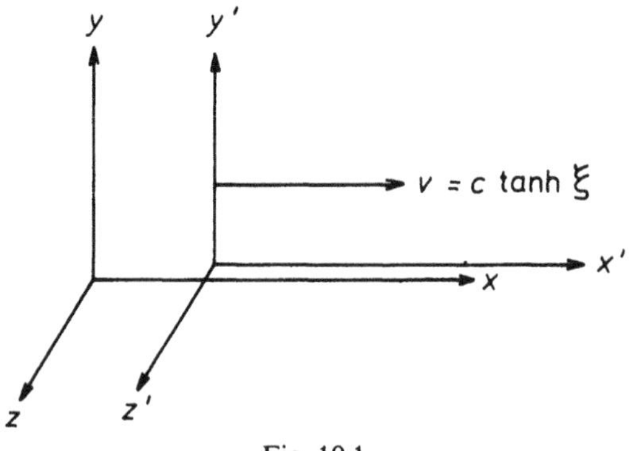

Fig. 10.1

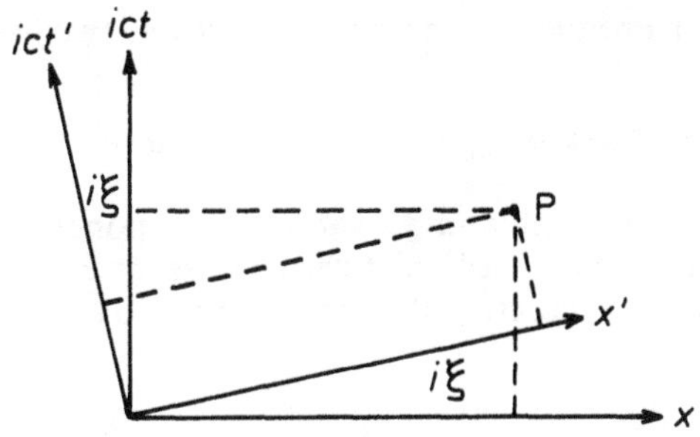

Fig. 10.2

Substituting these expressions in Eq. (10.1-9) will result in more familiar formulas for the Lorentz transformation seen in elementary physics texts. The parametrization in terms of hyperbolic functions is, however, useful in emphasizing the similarity between rotations and special Lorentz transformations. Thus a Lorentz boost along the x-axis by the velocity v can be interpreted as a "rotation" in the $(x^0 - x^1)$ plane by the hyperbolic angle $\xi = \tanh^{-1}(v/c)$. [cf. Fig. 10.2]

10.1.2 The Proper Lorentz Group

A general Lorentz transformation can be written as the product of rotations and Lorentz boosts.

Definition 10.4 (Proper Lorentz Group): The set of all proper Lorentz transformations $\{\Lambda\}$ satisfying the conditions of Eqs. (10.1-5)–(10.1-7) forms the *Proper Lorentz Group* or, in short, the *Lorentz Group*. It will be denoted by the symbol $\tilde{L}_+$.

The group consists of all *special "orthogonal"* 4×4 matrices—the quotation marks here call attention to the non-Euclidean signature of the invariant metric $g^{\mu\nu}$, $(-1, 1, 1, 1)$. Thus, Λ-matrices for Lorentz boosts (such as given by Eq. (10.1-9)) are not unitary like the rotation matrices. The mathematical designation of this group is SO(3, 1) where the arguments refer to the fact that the *signature* of the metric tensor $g^{\mu\nu}$ involve 3 positive signs and 1 negative sign. In the next chapter, we will enlarge this group to include reflections of the coordinate axes, and thereby be concerned with the group O(3, 1).

The law of multiplication for the group $\tilde{L}_+$ is, of course, given by matrix multiplication of the corresponding Λ-matrices. We shall describe the rules for combining rotations and Lorentz boosts in more physical terms after the generators are introduced in the next section. The explicit formula, Eq. (10.1-9), for the Lorentz boost $L_1(\xi)$ reveals that, unlike the group SO(3), elements of the Lorentz group can be *unbounded*, as the range of ξ is $(-\infty, \infty)$. Therefore, the Lorentz group is *non-compact*.

Definition 10.5 (Minkowski Space): The 4-dimensional space-time endowed with the Minkowski metric, Eq. (10.1-2), is called the *Minkowski space*. Any 4-component object v^μ, transforming under Lorentz transformations as the coordinate vector in Eq. (10.1-3) is said to be a *four-vector*, or a *Lorentz vector*.

Definition 10.6 (Scalar Product): The *scalar product* of two four-vectors u^μ and v^μ is defined as

(10.1-11) $$u \cdot v \equiv g_{\mu\nu} u^\mu v^\nu = -u^0 v^0 + \mathbf{u} \cdot \mathbf{v}.$$

Definition 10.7 (Contravariant and Covariant Components): The ordinary 4 components of a Lorentz vector $\{v^\mu\}$ are referred to as the *contravariant components* of v. An alternative way to represent the same vector is by its *covariant components* $\{v_\mu\}$ defined as

(10.1-12) $$v_\mu \equiv g_{\mu\nu} v^\nu .$$

It is obvious that $v_0 = -v^0$ and $v_i = v^i$, $i = 1, 2, 3$. With these definitions, we can simplify the definition of the scalar product, Eq. (10.1-11) to

(10.1-13) $$u \cdot v = u_\mu v^\mu = u^\mu v_\mu .$$

Theorem 10.2 (Transformation Law of Covariant Components): The covariant components of a 4-vector v transform under proper Lorentz transformations as

(10.1-14) $$v_\mu \longrightarrow v'_\mu = v_\nu (\Lambda^{-1})^\nu{}_\mu .$$

Proof: Making use of Eqs. (10.1-3) and (10.1-12), we have

$$v'_\mu = g_{\mu\lambda} v'^\lambda = g_{\mu\lambda} \Lambda^\lambda{}_\sigma v^\sigma = g_{\mu\lambda} \Lambda^\lambda{}_\sigma g^{\sigma\nu} v_\nu = v_\nu (\Lambda^{-1})^\nu{}_\mu$$

where the last step follows from Eq. (10.1-5). QED

This result displays the transformation property of v_μ in the form which most explicitly indicates why $v_\mu u^\mu$ is an invariant. There is a natural covariant four-vector, the 4-gradient ∂_μ. We can verify that

$$\partial_\mu \longrightarrow \partial'_\mu = \frac{\partial}{\partial x'^\mu} = \frac{\partial x^\lambda}{\partial x'^\mu} \frac{\partial}{\partial x^\lambda} = (\Lambda^{-1})^\lambda{}_\mu \frac{\partial}{\partial x^\lambda}$$

in agreement with Eq. (10.1-14).

With respect to an arbitrarily chosen coordinate origin, space-time is divided into three distinct regions separated by the *light-cone* which is defined by the equation

$$|\mathbf{x}|^2 - c^2 t^2 = 0 .$$

This is illustrated in Fig. 10.3. The *future cone* consists of all points with $|x|^2 < 0$ and $x^0 > 0$. These points can be reached from the origin by the "world-line" of an evolving event. The *past cone* consists of all points with $|x|^2 < 0$ and $x^0 < 0$. They represent events on world-lines which can, in principle, evolve through the origin. By a suitable Lorentz transformation, the coordinates of any point in these two regions can be transformed into the form $(ct', 0)$; hence these coordinate vectors are said to be *time-like*. The region outside the light-cone are characterized by $|x|^2 > 0$. For any given point in this region, there exists some Lorentz transformation which transforms the components of the coordinate vector into the form $(0, \mathbf{x}')$. Hence these coordinate vectors are said to be *space-like* and the entire region is called the space-like region (with respect to the origin). By analogy to the coordinates, an arbitrary 4-vector v is said to be time-like or space-like depending on whether $|v|^2$ is

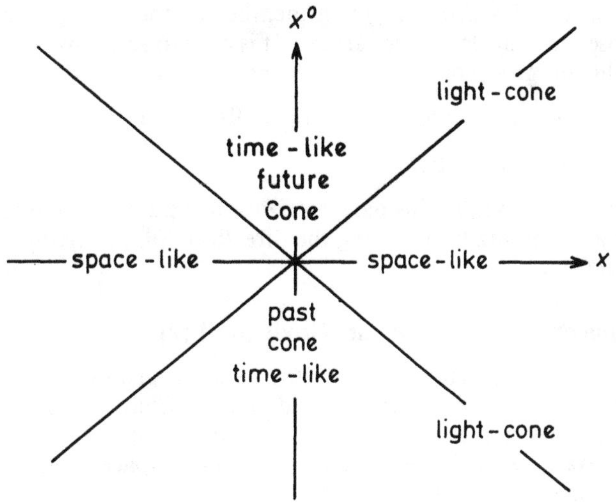

Fig. 10.3

less or greater than 0, respectively. When $|v|^2 = 0$, it is said to be *light-like*—as the coordinate vectors for light propagation satisfy this condition.

10.1.3 Decomposition of Lorentz Transformations

Theorem 10.3 (Decomposition of Lorentz Transformations): A general element of the proper Lorentz group $\tilde{L}_+$ can be uniquely written in the factorized form

$$\Lambda = R(\alpha, \beta, 0)\, L_3(\xi)\, R(\phi, \theta, \psi)^{-1} \tag{10.1-15}$$

where $L_3(\xi)$ is a Lorentz boost along the positive z-axis by the velocity $v = c \tanh \xi$, $0 \le \xi < \infty$, and the Euler angles for the rotations have their usual ranges.

Proof: If Λ is a proper Lorentz transformation, then it satisfies the constraint equation Eq. (10.1-5). Choosing $\lambda = \sigma = 0$ in the first identity in that equation, and writing $\Lambda^\mu{}_0 = A^\mu$, we obtain:

$$(A^0)^2 - \mathbf{A}^2 = 1$$

where $\mathbf{A}$ is the 3-dimensional spatial vector with components (A^1, A^2, A^3). This relation suggests the following parameterization for A^μ:

$$A^0 = \cosh \xi \qquad A^1 = \sinh \xi \sin\beta \cos\alpha$$

$$A^3 = \sinh \xi \cos\theta \qquad A^2 = \sinh \xi \cos\beta \sin\alpha$$

where $0 \le \xi$, $0 \le \beta < \pi$, and $0 \le \alpha \le 2\pi$. Let $\hat{t}$ denote a unit 4-vector along the time-axis, $t^\nu = (1, 0, 0, 0)$. Clearly $(\Lambda\hat{t})^\mu = \Lambda^\mu{}_\nu t^\nu = \Lambda^\mu{}_0 = A^\mu$. On the other hand, $L_3(\xi)\, \hat{t} = (\cosh \xi, 0, 0, \sinh \xi)$ and $[R(\alpha, \beta, 0)\, L_3(\xi)\hat{t}]^\mu = A^\mu$. Since $R(\alpha, \beta, 0)\, L_3(\xi)$ and Λ have the same effect on the vector $\hat{t}$, we obtain

$$\Lambda^{-1} R(\alpha, \beta, 0)\, L_3(\xi)\hat{t} = \hat{t} \quad .$$

In other words, $\Lambda^{-1} R(\alpha, \beta, 0)\, L_3(\xi)$ is a member of the little group of $\hat{t}$ (i.e. the subgroup whose elements leave $\hat{t}$ invariant). It is easy to see, however, that the little group of $\hat{t}$ is the full group of 3-rotations; hence,

$$\Lambda^{-1} R(\alpha, \beta, 0)\, L_3(\xi) = R(\phi, \theta, \psi) \quad .$$

This is just Eq. (10.1-15). QED

It is not hard to see that, in this parametrization, a pure rotation corresponds to $\xi = 0$, and a pure Lorentz boost along the direction $\hat{\mathbf{n}}(\theta, \phi)$ corresponds to $\psi = 0$, $\alpha = \phi$, and $\beta = \theta$.

10.1.4 Relation of the Proper Lorentz Group to SL(2)

In analogy to the connection between the rotation group SO(3) to the special unitary group SU(2), as we studied in detail in Chap. 8, there is a natural correspondence between the Lorentz group $\tilde{L}_+$ and the special linear group SL(2). Following the example of Sec. 8.1, we associate each space-time point x^μ with a 2×2 hermitian matrix X by the relation

$$x^\mu \rightarrow X = \sigma_\mu \cdot x^\mu \qquad (10.1\text{-}16)$$

where σ_i, $i = 1, 2, 3$, are the Pauli matrices and σ_0 is the identity matrix. Explicitly, we have

$$X = \begin{pmatrix} x^0 + x^3 & -x^1 - ix^2 \\ -x^1 + ix^2 & x^0 - x^3 \end{pmatrix} \quad . \qquad (10.1\text{-}17)$$

The length of the 4-vector corresponds to the negative of the determinant of X,

$$-\det X = |\mathbf{x}|^2 - |x^0|^2 \quad . \qquad (10.1\text{-}18)$$

A Lorentz transformation Λ on the 4-vector x^μ induces a linear transformation on the matrix X which preserves its hermiticity [Eqs. (10.1-16) and (10.1-17)] and the value of its determinant [Eq. (10.1-18)]. This can be accomplished by the mapping

$$X \xrightarrow{\Lambda} X' = A\, X\, A^\dagger \qquad (10.1\text{-}19)$$

where A is a 2×2 matrix (dependent on Λ, obviously) which satisfies

$$\det A \cdot \det A^\dagger = |\det A|^2 = 1 \quad . \qquad (10.1\text{-}20)$$

The matrix A is determined up to an overall phase factor. It is natural to fix this phase by choosing

$$\det A = 1 \quad . \qquad (10.1\text{-}21)$$

Hence we establish a natural correspondence between elements of the Lorentz group $\tilde{L}_+$ and the special linear group SL(2). Note that a general SL(2) matrix contains 6 arbitrary real parameters—precisely the same number as a general proper Lorentz transformation should have. The right-hand side of Eq. (10.1-19), as well as det(A), are quadratic in the matrix elements of A. It follows that the above conditions specify the matrix A only up to a sign. Therefore, to each $\Lambda \in \tilde{L}_+$

[SO(3, 1)] is associated two SL(2) matrices $\pm A(\Lambda)$, just as in the case of SO(3) and SU(2).

The group SL(2) is useful in many ways in an in-depth study of the Lorentz group, as one can surmise from our experience with SU(2) and the rotation group in Chap. 8. In fact, SL(2) is the *universal covering group* of SO(3, 1) in the same way that SU(2) is of SO(3). The scope of this book dictates, however, that we shall only make limited use of this useful connection—mainly in the discussion of the finite dimensional representations of the Lorentz group in this Chapter, and as a concrete example of linear groups in Chap. 13. For this reason, we relegate further discussion of the SL(2) group to Appendix VI. More detailed discussion of the association of the two groups and its applications can be found in [Berestetskii, Naimark, Miller].

10.1.5 Four-Dimensional Translations and the Poincaré Group

Lorentz transformations are homogeneous transformations on the 4-dimensional coordinates. The assumption of homogeneity of space-time requires the invariance of laws of physics under *4-dimensional translations* T(b) which are inhomogeneous transformations,

$$x^\mu \longrightarrow x'^\mu = x^\mu + b^\mu \quad . \tag{10.1-22}$$

This is entirely similar to the 2- and 3-dimensional translations discussed in previous chapters. Thus, the 4-dimensional translation group is abelian and, by itself, the group structure is very simple. We shall not dwell on the translation group for its own sake.

When we combine all the continuous space-time symmetries of 4-dimensional space-time into one general symmetry group, we obtain the generalization of the Euclidean groups discussed in Chap. 9 for 2- and 3-dimensional space. Many interesting and significant results will then emerge.

Definition 10.8 (Poincaré Group): The set of transformations in Minkowski space consisting of all translations and proper Lorentz transformations and their products form a group $\tilde{P}$, called the *Poincaré Group*, or the *inhomogeneous Lorentz group*.

A general element of the Poincaré group is denoted by $g(b, \Lambda)$, it induces the coordinate transformation

$$x^\mu \xrightarrow{g} x'^\mu = \Lambda^\mu{}_\nu x^\nu + b^\mu \quad . \tag{10.1-23}$$

A transformation $g(b, \Lambda)$ followed by another, $g(b', \Lambda')$, is equivalent to a single transformation given by the group multiplication rule

$$g(b', \Lambda')\, g(b, \Lambda) = g(\Lambda' b + b', \Lambda'\Lambda) \quad . \tag{10.1-24}$$

This can be seen by applying Eq. (10.1-23) a second time,

$$x' \xrightarrow{g'} x'' = \Lambda' x' + b' = \Lambda'(\Lambda x + b) + b' = (\Lambda'\Lambda)x + (\Lambda' b + b')$$

where we have suppressed the Lorentz indices. As in the case of the E_3 group, the (inhomogeneous) Poincaré group action, Eq. (10.1-23), can be cast in the form of (homogeneous) matrix multiplication by the following device:

$$(10.1\text{-}25) \qquad g(b,\Lambda) \to \begin{pmatrix} & & & & b^0 \\ & & & & b^1 \\ & (\Lambda)^\mu{}_\nu & & & b^2 \\ & & & & b^3 \\ 0 & 0 & 0 & 0 & 1 \end{pmatrix} \qquad x^\mu \to \begin{pmatrix} x^0 \\ x^1 \\ x^2 \\ x^3 \\ 1 \end{pmatrix} \quad .$$

The verification of this scheme will be left to the reader.

Theorem 10.4 (Decomposition of Poincaré Transformations): A general element of the Poincaré group can be written in the factorized form:

$$(10.1-26) \qquad g(b,\Lambda) = \mathrm{T}(b)\,\Lambda$$

where $\mathrm{T}(b) = g(b, E)$ (E is the unit matrix) is a translation, and $\Lambda = g(0, \Lambda)$ is a proper Lorentz transformation.

This useful decomposition is a trivial consequence of the group multiplication rule given above.

Theorem 10.5 (Invariant Subgroup of Translations): Let Λ be an arbitrary proper Lorentz transformation and $\mathrm{T}(b)$ a 4-dimensional translation. Then (i) the Lorentz transformed translation is another translation, i.e.

$$(10.1\text{-}27) \qquad \Lambda\,\mathrm{T}(b)\,\Lambda^{-1} = \mathrm{T}(\Lambda b) \quad ;$$

(ii) the group of translations forms an invariant subgroup of the Poincaré group.

Proof: (i) Eq. (10.1-27) is a direct consequence of the general group multiplication rule if in Eq. (10.1-24) we set $g = (b, E)$ and $g' = g(0, \Lambda)$; (ii) Using (10.1-26) and (10.1-27) we have

$$(10.1\text{-}28) \qquad \begin{aligned} g(b,\Lambda)\,\mathrm{T}(a)\,g(b,\Lambda)^{-1} &= \mathrm{T}(b)\,\Lambda\,\mathrm{T}(a)\,\Lambda^{-1}\,\mathrm{T}(b)^{-1} \\ &= \mathrm{T}(b)\,\mathrm{T}(\Lambda a)\,\mathrm{T}(b)^{-1} = \mathrm{T}(\Lambda a) \quad . \end{aligned}$$

Hence the set of all translations is invariant under operations of the full group $\{g(b,\Lambda)\}$. QED

10.2 Generators and the Lie Algebra

The Poincaré group has ten generators—one for each of its independent one-parameter subgroups. We consider first those associated with infinitesimal translations.

Definition 10.9 (Generators of Translations P_μ): The covariant *generators for translations* $\{P_\mu\}$ are defined by the following expression for infinitesimal translations:

$$(10.2\text{-}1) \qquad \mathrm{T}(\delta b) = E - i\,\delta b^\mu\,P_\mu$$

where E is the unit matrix and $\{\delta b^\mu\}$ are components of an arbitrarily small 4-dimensional displacement vector. The corresponding *contravariant generators*

$\{P^\mu\}$ are defined by $P^\mu = g^{\mu\nu} P_\nu$; hence

(10.2-2) $$P^0 = -P_0 \qquad P^i = P_i \quad .$$

As discussed in Chaps. 6 and 9, the generators for spatial translations $\{P_i\}$ are realized as momentum operators in physical applications of the translation group. Correspondingly, the generator for time translations P^0 will be shown to relate to the energy operator—or *Hamiltonian*—in physics. In that context, we shall refer to $P = \{P^\mu\}$ collectively as the *four-momentum operator*.

As usual, finite translations can be expressed in terms of the generators by exponentiation,

(10.2-3) $$\mathrm{T}(b) = \exp(-ib^\mu P_\mu) \quad .$$

The group multiplication rule discussed earlier can be used to infer the transformation properties of the generators.

Theorem 10.6 (Lorentz Transformation Property of P): Under the Lorentz group, the generators $\{P_\mu\}$ transform as 4-coordinate unit vectors,

(10.2-4) $$\Lambda P_\mu \Lambda^{-1} = P_\nu \Lambda^\nu{}_\mu \qquad \text{for all } \Lambda \in \tilde{L}_+ \quad .$$

Correspondingly, the contravariant generators $\{P^\mu\}$ transform as

(10.2-5) $$\Lambda P^\mu \Lambda^{-1} = (\Lambda^{-1})^\mu{}_\nu P^\nu \quad .$$

Proof: (i) Eq. (10.2-4) follows readily from Theorem 10.3, which requires $\Lambda(P_\mu b^\mu)\Lambda^{-1} = P_\nu(\Lambda b)^\nu$ for arbitrary b^μ. The left-hand side of this equation is equal to $(\Lambda P_\mu \Lambda^{-1})\, b^\mu$; the right-hand side to $P_\nu \Lambda^\nu{}_\mu b^\mu$.
(ii) Eq. (10.2-5) follows from the SO(3, 1) nature of Λ, Eq. (10.1-5), which implies $g^{\mu\lambda}\Lambda^\nu{}_\lambda = g^{\nu\lambda}(\Lambda^{-1})^\mu{}_\lambda$; hence $\Lambda P^\mu \Lambda^{-1} = g^{\mu\lambda}\Lambda P_\lambda \Lambda^{-1} = g^{\mu\lambda} P_\nu \Lambda^\nu{}_\lambda = g^{\nu\lambda} P_\nu (\Lambda^{-1})^\mu{}_\lambda = (\Lambda^{-1})^\mu{}_\lambda P^\lambda$. QED

Next, we turn to the generators for Lorentz transformations. As indicated in Sec. 10.1, the independent one-parameter subgroups can be chosen to correspond to "rotations" in the (μ, ν) plane by a trigonometric or hyperbolic angle. There are six distinct pairings of the indices (μ, ν)—three involving 3-dimensional rotations (1, 2), (2, 3), (3, 1); and three corresponding to Lorentz boosts (0, 1), (0, 2), (0, 3).

Definition 10.10 (Generators of Lorentz Transformations $J_{\mu\nu}$): The covariant *generators for Lorentz transformations* $\{J_{\mu\nu}\}$ are anti-symmetric tensors defined by the following expression for infinitesimal "rotations" in Minkowski space:

(10.2-6) $$\Lambda(\delta\omega) = E - \frac{i}{2}\delta\omega^{\mu\nu} J_{\mu\nu}$$

where $\delta\omega^{\mu\nu} = -\delta\omega_{\mu\nu}$ are anti-symmetrical infinitesimal parameters. The corresponding *contravariant generators* are

$$J^{\mu\nu} = g^{\mu\lambda} J_{\lambda\sigma} g^{\sigma\nu}$$

hence, with $m = 1, 2, 3$,

(10.2-7) $$J^{mn} = J_{mn} \qquad J^{0m} = -J_{0m} = J_{m0} \quad .$$

A spatial rotation in the (m, n) plane can be interpreted as rotation around the k-axis where (k, m, n) is some permutation of $(1, 2, 3)$. In previous chapters we have used the notation

$$\mathrm{R}(\delta\theta) = E - i\,\delta\theta^k\,J_k \quad .$$

Comparing with Eq. (10.2-6), we can make the identification

(10.2-8) $$\delta\theta^1 = \delta\omega^{23} \qquad J_1 = J_{23} \qquad \text{plus cyclic permutations} \quad .$$

In a more compact notation, we can write

(10.2-9) $$J_k = \frac{1}{2}\varepsilon^{kmn}\,J_{mn} \qquad J_{mn} = \varepsilon^{mnk}\,J_k \quad .$$

These generators can be expressed as 4 × 4 matrices by combining Eqs. (10.1-8), (10.2-6), to yield the previously obtained result, Eq. (7.2-3), trivially extended to 4-dimensions. The matrix for J_{mn} has non-vanishing elements only at the (m, n) and (n, m) positions. The association of rotations in the (m-n) plane with a unique "axis" ($\hat{k}$) perpendicular to that plane is a special property of 3-dimensions. In the 4-dimensional Minkowski space, as well as in other higher dimensional spaces, the subspace perpendicular to a plane is multi-dimensional, there is no unique "axis" associated with a set of one-parameter rotations. It is most natural to use the second-rank tensor notation $J_{\mu\nu}$ for generators of "rotations" in the (μ-ν) plane as in Eq. (10.2-6).

The three generators of special Lorentz transformations (or Lorentz boosts) mix the time axis with one of the spatial dimensions. When focusing on this class of transformations, we shall use the notation

(10.2-10) $$\delta\xi^m = \delta\omega^{m0} \qquad K_m \equiv J_{m0}$$

hence

$$\Lambda(\delta\xi) = E - i\,\delta\xi^m\,K_m \quad .$$

The 4 × 4 matrices for K_m can be derived in the same way as for J_m, making use of expressions of Lorentz boosts such as Eq. (10.1-9), specialized to infinitesimal transformations. As an example, we obtain

(10.2-11) $$(K_1) = \begin{pmatrix} 0 & i & 0 & 0 \\ i & 0 & 0 & 0 \\ 0 & 0 & 0 & 0 \\ 0 & 0 & 0 & 0 \end{pmatrix}$$

likewise for the other generators. Finite Lorentz boosts assume the familiar form

(10.2-12) $$\Lambda(\xi) = \exp(-i\xi^m K_m) \quad .$$

Similarly, the general proper Lorentz transformations can be written as

(10.2-13) $$\Lambda(\omega) = \exp(-\frac{i}{2}\omega^{\mu\nu} J_{\mu\nu})$$

where $\omega^{\mu\nu}$ is a six-parameter anti-symmetric second-rank tensor. This parametrization is useful for proving theorems on general Lorentz transformations. In contrast, the decomposition of Λ provided by Theorem 10.3 is more useful in solving practical problems.

Theorem 10.7 (Transformation Law of Lorentz Generators): (i) Let $\Lambda(\omega)$ be a proper Lorentz transformation parametrized as in Eq. (10.2-13), and Ω be another arbitrary Lorentz transformation, then

(10.2-14) $$\Omega\,\Lambda(\omega)\,\Omega^{-1} = \Lambda(\omega') \quad \text{where} \quad \omega'^{\mu\nu} = \Omega^{\mu}{}_{\lambda}\Omega^{\nu}{}_{\sigma}\omega^{\lambda\sigma} \quad .$$

(ii) The generators $\{J_{\mu\nu}\}$ transform under Ω as

(10.2-15) $$\Omega\, J_{\mu\nu}\,\Omega^{-1} = J_{\lambda\sigma}\,\Omega^{\lambda}{}_{\mu}\,\Omega^{\sigma}{}_{\nu} \quad .$$

Eq. (10.2-14) is the generalization of Eq. (7.1-9) for 3-dimensional rotations. [Also compare with Eq. (10.2-4)] Eq. (10.2-15) states that, under proper Lorentz transformations, $J_{\mu\nu}$ transform as components of a second rank tensor. It can be derived from the previous equation in the same way that Eq. (10.2-4) was derived from Theorem 10.3.

Theorem 10.8 (Lie Algebra of the Poincaré Group): The Lie algebra of the Poincaré group is given by

(10.2-16) $$[P_\mu, P_\lambda] = 0$$

(10.2-17) $$[P_\mu, J_{\lambda\sigma}] = i(P_\lambda g_{\mu\sigma} - P_\sigma g_{\mu\lambda})$$

(10.2-18) $$[J_{\mu\nu}, J_{\lambda\sigma}] = i(J_{\lambda\nu} g_{\mu\sigma} - J_{\sigma\nu} g_{\mu\lambda} + J_{\mu\lambda} g_{\nu\sigma} - J_{\mu\sigma} g_{\nu\lambda}) \quad .$$

These relations are identical in form to those of the subgroup E_3 [cf. Problem 10.2]. The only difference lies in the fact that the indices here go over four space-time dimensions and that the Minkowski metric $g_{\mu\nu}$ replaces the Euclidean one, δ_{kl}.

Proof: Eq. (10.2-16) is an obvious consequence of the abelian nature of the translational subgroup. Eqs. (10.2-17) and (10.2-18) can be established in at least two ways:

We first note that the 4×4 matrix form of the generator $J_{\lambda\sigma}$ is[4]

(10.2-19) $$(J_{\lambda\sigma})^{\nu}{}_{\mu} = -i(\delta^{\nu}{}_{\lambda} g_{\sigma\mu} - \delta^{\nu}{}_{\sigma} g_{\lambda\mu}) \quad .$$

Correspondingly, the 5×5 matrix form of the generator P_μ is, according to Eq. (10.1-25),

(10.2-20) $$(P_\mu)^{4}{}_{\lambda} = i\,\delta_{\mu\lambda}$$

and $(P_\mu)^{\sigma}{}_{\lambda} = 0 = (P_\mu)^{\sigma}{}_{4} = (P_\mu)^{4}{}_{4}$; where (as usual) the Greek indices range from 0 to 3. The brute force method to prove the Lie algebra is to calculate the commutators of the generators from these explicit expressions for their matrices.

The alternative method is to use Theorems 10.6 and 10.7. We shall illustrate this method by proving Eq. (10.2-17) from Theorem 10.6. Applying the infinitesimal

[4] For 3-dimensional rotations, verify that this expression agrees with Eq. (7.2-3). For Lorentz transformations, check this result against Eq. (10.2-11) and related expressions for K_2 and K_3.

form of Λ from Eq. (10.2-6), the left-hand side of Eq. (10.2-4) is

$$\Lambda P_\mu \Lambda^{-1} = \left(E - \frac{i}{2}\delta\omega^{\lambda\sigma} J_{\lambda\sigma}\right) P_\mu \left(E + \frac{i}{2}\delta\omega^{\lambda\sigma} J_{\lambda\sigma}\right)$$

$$= P_\mu + \frac{i}{2}\delta\omega^{\lambda\sigma}[P_\mu, J_{\lambda\sigma}] + 0(\delta\omega^2)$$

while the right-hand side is

$$P_\nu\left[E - \frac{i}{2}\delta\omega^{\lambda\sigma} J_{\lambda\sigma}\right]^\nu_{\ \mu} = P_\mu - \frac{i}{2}\delta\omega^{\lambda\sigma}(J_{\lambda\sigma})^\nu_{\ \mu} P_\nu$$

$$= P_\mu - \frac{1}{2}\delta\omega^{\lambda\sigma}(\delta^\nu_\lambda g_{\sigma\mu} - \delta^\nu_\sigma g_{\lambda\mu}) P_\nu \quad .$$

Comparing these two expressions, we obtain Eq. (10.2-17). This proof underscores that Eq. (10.2-17) is the differential expression of the 4-vector nature of $\{P_\mu\}$ with respect to Lorentz transformations. The proof of Eq. (10.2-18) from Theorem 10.7 follows the same line of reasoning: each of the two tensor indices independently behaves in the same way as that of the P-vector. QED

To gain some further insight on these commutation relations, we can separate the spatial and time components and rewrite the Lie algebra in terms of the more familiar quantities $\{P^0, P_m, J_m, K_m\}$. Eq. (10.2-16) remains simple:

(10.2-21) $$[P^0, P_m] = [P_n, P_m] = 0$$

Eq. (10.2-17) is decomposed into:

(10.2-22a) $$[P^0, J_n] = 0$$

(10.2-22b) $$[P_m, J_n] = i\varepsilon^{mnl} P_l$$

(10.2-22c) $$[P_m, K_n] = i\delta_{mn} P^0$$

(10.2-22d) $$[P^0, K_n] = i P_n$$

and Eq. (10.2-18) into:

(10.2-23a) $$[J_m, J_n] = i\varepsilon^{mnl} J_l$$

(10.2-23b) $$[K_m, J_n] = i\varepsilon^{mnl} K_l$$

(10.2-23c) $$[K_m, K_n] = -i\varepsilon^{mnl} J_l$$

Many of these equations are familiar from the discussion of E_3. Among new ones, Eq. (10.2-22a) indicates that P^0 is a scalar under 3-dimensional rotations, and J_n is invariant under time translations. Eqs. (10.2-22c) and (10.2-22d) state that translations and Lorentz boosts in different spatial directions commute; but they mix if both involve the same direction in space.

Eqs. (10.2-23abc) specify the Lie algebra of the proper Lorentz group. The negative sign on the right-hand side of the last equation is noteworthy. It is another manifestation of the non-compactness of the group pointed out earlier in connection with unbounded group elements. As a consequence, the irreducible representations of the Lorentz group are radically different in nature from those of the rotation group. This is significant, as physical systems involve realizations of these representations. The negative sign originates, of course, from that of the Minkowski metric associated with the time dimension.

Immediate consequences of Eq. (10.2-23b) are

(10.2-24) $$\mathrm{R}\, K_m\, \mathrm{R}^{-1} = K_{m'}\, R^{m'}_{\ m}$$

and

(10.2-25) $$\mathrm{R}\, \mathrm{L}_{\hat{n}}(\xi)\, \mathrm{R}^{-1} = \mathrm{L}_{\mathrm{R}\hat{n}}(\xi)$$

where R is any 3-rotation, and $\mathrm{L}_{\hat{n}}(\xi)$ a special Lorentz transformation (boost) along the $\hat{n}$-direction. In words, the generators of Lorentz boosts transform under rotations as components of a 3-vector; a Lorentz boost in the direction $\hat{\mathrm{n}}$ is transformed into a boost in the direction $\mathrm{R}\hat{\mathrm{n}}$ by the rotation R. The argument for establishing these intuitively obvious results should be familiar by now, hence it won't be repeated here.

10.3 Irreducible Representations of the Proper Lorentz Group

The Lie algebra of the proper Lorentz group is given by Eq. (10.2-18) or, equivalently, by the three equations of (10.2-23). We shall derive the irreducible representations of the Lorentz group from the Lie algebra, beginning with the finite-dimensional ones. Because the group is non-compact, these representations will not be unitary. In the second part of this section, we shall study the (infinite-dimensional) unitary irreducible representations.

10.3.1 Equivalence of the Lie Algebra to SU(2) × SU(2)

The Lie algebra of the Lorentz group can be reduced to the direct product of two subalgebras by transforming to a new basis,

(10.3-1) $$\begin{aligned} M_m &= (J_m + i\,K_m)/2 \\ N_m &= (J_m - i\,K_m)/2 \end{aligned} \qquad (m = 1, 2, 3)\ .$$

It is then a straightforward calculation to show that

(10.3-2) $$\begin{aligned} [M_m,\ M_n] &= i\,\varepsilon^{mnk}\, M_k \\ [N_m,\ N_n] &= i\,\varepsilon^{mnk}\, N_k \qquad (m, n = 1, 2, 3) \\ [M_m,\ N_n] &= 0 \ . \end{aligned}$$

This algebra is identical to the Lie algebra of the group $SU(2)_M \times SU(2)_N$, where the subscripts M and N refer to the symbols given to the generators above. Finite dimensional irreducible representations of the SU(2) × SU(2) Lie algebra are easily obtained from those of SU(2) [Chaps. 7 and 8]. Every such representation provides a finite dimensional irreducible representation of the proper Lorentz group SO(3, 1).

Note that the group SU(2) × SU(2) is compact but the Lorentz group is not. Even though the two groups share the same Lie algebra, one corresponds to the exponentiation of $\{iM_m, iN_m\}$, whereas the other to the exponentiation of

$\{iJ_m, iK_m\}$—in each case with real coefficients in the exponent. Although irreducible representations of one group are also irreducible representations of the other, some important properties of the representation, such as unitarity, are not preserved. We note that, for any unitary representation, the generators must be hermitian. Because of the factors of i in Eq. (10.3-1), the two sets of generators (M_m, N_m) and (J_m, K_m) cannot be simultaneously hermitian. The non-unitary nature of finite dimensional representations of the Lorentz group is an important consideration for physical applications. In particular, these representations cannot correspond to *physical states*, since all symmetry operations must be realized as unitary operators on the space of physical states. We shall address this problem immediately after we derive an explicit form for the representations.

10.3.2 Finite Dimensional Representations

The finite dimensional irreducible representations of the Lie algebra, Eq. (10.3-2), are direct products of those for the sub-algebras $SU(2)_M$ and $SU(2)_N$. These have been studied exhaustively in Chaps. 7 and 8. We know, therefore, the representations of the direct product algebra are labelled by two numbers $(u, v;\ 2u, 2v = 0, 1, 2, \ldots)$ such that $u(u+1)$ and $v(v+1)$ are eigenvalues of the two Casimir operators $\mathbf{M}^2$ and $\mathbf{N}^2$. The natural choice of a basis in the representation space is $\{|k\,l\rangle;\ k = -u, \ldots, u;\ l = -v, \ldots, v\}$ which consists of direct products of vectors from the canonical bases $\{|u, k\rangle\}$, $\{|v, l\rangle\}$ of the two SU(2) sub-algebras. (The labels u, v on the basis vectors of the product space are suppressed for simplicity.) On such a basis, the generators of the Lorentz group act as follows,

$$\begin{aligned} J_3\,|k\,l\rangle &= (M_3 + N_3)\,|k\,l\rangle = |k\,l\rangle\,(l+k) \\ J_\pm\,|k\,l\rangle &= (M_\pm + N_\pm)\,|k\,l\rangle = |k\pm 1\ l\rangle\,[u(u+1) - k(k\pm 1)]^{1/2} \\ &\qquad + |k\ l\pm 1\rangle\,[v(v+1) - l(l\pm 1)]^{1/2} \end{aligned} \tag{10.3-3}$$

$$\begin{aligned} K_3\,|k\,l\rangle &= i(N_3 - M_3)|kl\rangle = |k\,l\rangle\, i(l-k) \\ K_\pm\,|k\,l\rangle &= i(N_\pm - M_\pm)\,|k\,l\rangle = |k\ l\pm 1\rangle\, i[v(v+1) - l(l\pm 1)]^{1/2} \\ &\qquad - |k\pm 1\ l\rangle\, i[u(u+1) - k(k\pm 1)]^{1/2}. \end{aligned} \tag{10.3-4}$$

It follows from Eq. (10.3-3) that, when restricted to the subgroup of 3-dimensional rotations, the representation space is equivalent to that of a direct product of angular momentum u and angular momentum v. [cf. Sec. 7.7] If we diagonalize with respect to J^2 and J_3, this space becomes a direct sum of invariant subspaces (with respect to rotations) with $j = |u-v|, |u-v+1|, \ldots, (u+v)$. A new basis $\{|j, m\rangle\}$ associated with this decomposition can be formed according to the procedure of Sec. 7.7. [In particular, cf. Eqs. (7.7-8) and (7.7-9)] Notice that each irreducible representation can also be labelled by (j_0, j_1) where $j_0 = |u-v|$ and $j_1 = u+v$ are the lowest and highest value of angular momentum contained in the representation. We shall return to this basis in the next sub-section.

We see from Eq. (10.3-4) that in the (u, v) representation, the generators $\{K_m;\ m = 1, 2, 3\}$ are non-hermitian. In particular, the matrix representing K_3 is diagonal and imaginary; it is therefore anti-hermitian. We conclude that the finite dimensional representations of the Lorentz group are non-unitary. This is expected, since non-compact groups do not have non-trivial finite dimensional unitary representations. As mentioned earlier, these representations cannot be directly realized as physical states. Do they have any relevance to physical applications, then? The answer is definitely "yes", because all *physical variables* (such as position, momentum, angular momentum, energy-momentum tensor,...) anc classical and quantum *wave functions* and *fields* (such as the electromagnetic 4-potential and fields, the Dirac spinor field,...) transform as finite dimensional representations of the Lorentz group. The wave functions and fields are, of course, related to the physical states—solutions to the wave equations correspond to basis states in the space of physical states. The last section of this chapter will be devoted to the elucidation of the connection between the wave functions and fields (which transform as finite dimensional representations of the Lorentz group) on the one hand, and physical particle states (which transform as unitary representations of the Poincaré group) on the other.

The simplest non-trivial irreducible representations generated the above way are, of course, the two-dimensional ones labelled by $(0, 1/2)$ and $(1/2, 0)$. The representation matrices of the former are just the SL(2) matrices $\{A\}$ determined by Eq. (10.1-19); those of the latter are, correspondingly, $\{A^*\}$. These two representations are equivalent when applied to the subgroup of rotations, but they are inequivalent over the full proper Lorentz group. Basic properties of these two *fundamental representations* are discussed in some detail in Appendix VI. It is shown there and in Chap. 13 that all finite dimensional representations of the group can be obtained by the decomposition of repeated direct products of the fundamental representations.

It is easy to see that 4-vectors a^μ transform as the $(1/2, 1/2)$ representation under Lorentz transformations—since under 3-dimensional rotations, the time component a^0 is invariant (corresponding to $j_0 = 0$), and the spatial components $\mathbf{a}$ transform as a 3-vector (corresponding to $j_1 = 1$), it follows that $u = (j_0 + j_1)/2 = 1/2 = (j_1 - j_0)/2 = v$. [An alternative and complementary proof, demonstrating that a "mixed spinor" of the $(1/2, 1/2)$ genre is equivalent to a 4-vector, is given in Appendix VI.] This means that the *coordinate vector* X^μ, the *4-momentum operator* P_μ, the *electromagnetic 4-potential* A^μ,... etc. all transform as the $(1/2, 1/2)$ representation of the proper Lorentz group.

Now, consider a second-rank tensor $t^{\mu\nu}$ in Minkowski space. The 6 independent anti-symmetric components $t^{[\mu,\nu]}$ are invariant under Lorentz transformations. One can show that these components transform as the $(1, 0) \oplus (0, 1)$ representation of the group. [cf. Problem 10.5]. The *electromagnetic field* tensor $F^{\mu\nu}$ (with $F^{0i} = -F^{i0} = E^i$ and $F^{ij} = \varepsilon^{ijk} B_k$) is an example. The 10 symmetric components $t^{\{\mu,\nu\}}$ can be separated into 9 independent traceless components plus the trace $t^\mu{}_\mu$, each being irreducible under all proper Lorentz transformations. The traceless, symmetric second-rank tensor components transform as the $(1, 1)$ representation while the trace $t^\mu{}_\mu$ transforms as the $(0, 0)$ representation. [cf. Problem 10.6] A physical example of symmetric second-rank tensor is the *energy-momentum tensor* $T^{\mu\nu}$.

10.3.3 Unitary Representations

Because the Lorentz group is non-compact, all its unitary representations are infinite dimensional. They are of interest in the mathematical theory of group representations as well as being of potential relevance to physical applications. We shall outline the procedure for constructing these representations.

(i) The methods for labelling the basis states are the same as those described in the previous subsection. The only difference lies in the allowed eigenvalues for $(u, v; l, k)$, or equivalently $(j_0, j_1; j, m)$,—as the previous values for these parameters were obtained by requiring finite-dimensionality (cf. Sec. 7.3 where the values of the parameters for the representations of SU(2) were determined) rather than by demanding unitarity. For compact Lie groups, unitarity follows from finite dimensionality. But for the non-compact Lorentz group, we must give up one or the other. We shall investigate the constraints imposed by unitarity using the "canonical" basis $\{|j_0, j_1; j, m\rangle\}$.

(ii) The action of the generators of rotations $\{J_m\}$ on the basis vectors $\{|j, m\rangle\}$ follows the canonical prescription of Sec. 7.3. The value of j does not change upon such action. To find the effect of the generators or Lorentz boosts $\{K_m\}$, we note that they transform as components of a 3-vector under rotations [cf. Eq. (10.2-23b)]. We can therefore apply the Wigner-Eckart theorem [Sections 4.3 and 7.8] to obtain

$$\begin{aligned} \langle j' m' | K_3 | j m \rangle &= A^{j'}{}_j \langle j' m' (1, j) 0 m \rangle, \\ \langle j' m' | K_\pm | j m \rangle &= \mp \sqrt{2} A^{j'}{}_j \langle j' m' (1, j) \pm 1 m \rangle \quad . \end{aligned} \tag{10.3-5}$$

The coefficient $A^{j'}{}_j$ corresponds to the "reduced matrix element" of Eq. (7.8-5). The Clebsch-Gordan coefficients $\langle j' m' (1, j) n m \rangle$ vanish unless $j' = j-1,\ j,\ j+1$ and $m' = n + m$. The non-vanishing ones can be obtained from information provided in Appendix V or from any standard text on angular momentum. [Edmond, Rose] The factor $\mp\sqrt{2}$ arises from the fact that $\mp K_\pm 2^{-1/2}$, together with K_3, form a normalized set of irreducible spherical tensor operators [Definition 7.4].

(iii) We can obtain constraints on the coefficients $A^{j'}{}_j$ by requiring that the group algebra be satisfied, i.e. $[K_\pm, K_3] = \pm J_\pm$ and $[K_+, K_-] = -2J_3$. The derivation of these constraints is straightforward but somewhat tedious. As the details are not of any special interest, we leave the complete derivation to Appendix VII. [cf. also Problem 10.7] The solution of this set of constraints is:

$$\begin{aligned} A^{j}{}_j &= i \frac{\nu j_0}{[j(j+1)]^{1/2}} \\ A^{j}{}_{j-1} &= -[j(2j-1)]^{1/2}\, B_j\, \xi_j \\ A^{j-1}{}_j &= [j(2j+1)]^{1/2}\, B_j\, \xi_j^{-1} \\ B_j^2 &= \frac{(j^2 - j_0^2)(j^2 - \nu^2)}{j^2(4j^2 - 1)} \end{aligned} \tag{10.3-6}$$

where ν and ξ_j are arbitrary complex numbers and $j_0 = 0, 1/2, 1, \ldots$ is the lowest value that j may take. The parameter ν can be identified with j_1 of the previous subsection. We choose to use a different symbol to avoid any possible implication that it would take integer or half-integer values.

(iv) The allowed values for ν and ζ_j are constrained by the requirements of unitarity of the representation and by the orthonormality of the canonical basis. Unitarity dictates that the matrix for K_3 be hermitian and the matrix for K_+ be the hermitian conjugate of K_-. Leaving details to Appendix VII, we obtain two distinct classes of solutions to the coefficients $\{A^k{}_j\}$, hence two types of irreducible, unitary representations as summarized in the following theorem.

Theorem 10.9 (Irreducible Unitary Representations of the Lorentz Group): There are two classes of irreducible unitary representations of the proper Lorentz group: (a) the *principal series* is characterized by the parameters ($\nu = -iw$, w real; $j_0 = 0$, 1/2, 1,...); and (b) the *complementary series* is characterized by the parameters ($-1 \le \nu \le 1; j_0 = 0$). The matrix elements of the generators $\{J_m\}$ are given by the canonical form of Sec. 7.3; those of $\{K_m\}$ are given by Eq. (10.3-5) where the coefficients $A^k{}_j(k = j, j \pm 1)$ are specified by Eqs. (10.3-6) with ζ_j set equal to 1.

The details of the proof of this theorem are given in Appendix VII. The two parameters (j_0, ν) which label the irreducible representations are, of course, related to eigenvalues of the two Casimir operators $\mathbf{M}^2$ and $\mathbf{N}^2$ [cf. Sec. 10.3.1]. Recalling the isomorphism of the Lie algebra to that of the group SO(3) × SO(3), it is easy to see that $j_0 = |u - v|$ and $\nu = u + v$ where $u(u + 1)$ and $v(v + 1)$ are eigenvalues of $\mathbf{M}^2$ and $\mathbf{N}^2$. Of course, the allowed values of j_0 and ν are such that u and v are quite different from those encountered in Sec. 10.3.2 for finite dimensional representations.

The requirement that the representations be unitary, hence that the generators $\{J_m, K_m; m = 1,2,3\}$ be hermitian, is responsible for determining, in particular, the value of ν. If, instead of requiring unitarity, step (iv) in the above derivation is replaced by the condition of finite dimensionality, we will recover the results of the previous subsection. [cf. Problem 10.8]

10.4 Unitary Irreducible Representations of the Poincaré Group

The unitary irreducible representations of the Poincaré group $\tilde{\mathrm{P}}$ can be derived by the same methods introduced in Chap. 9 for analyzing the Euclidean groups. We shall use exclusively the method of induced representation, as it brings out features of the representations which are manifestly related to physical applications. In fact the natural correspondence between the basis vectors of unitary irreducible representations of $\tilde{\mathrm{P}}$ and quantum mechanical states of elementary physical systems stands out as one of the remarkable monuments to unity between mathematics and physics.

The induced representation method is based on the use of the abelian invariant subgroup of translations $\{T_4 \colon T(b)\}$. The basis vectors will be chosen as eigenvectors of the generators of translations P^μ, along with commuting operators chosen from the Lie algebra of the relevant little group. The eigenvalues of P^μ will be denoted by p^μ. Our experience with the Euclidean groups suggests that the square of the 4-momentum is a Casimir operator which commutes with all generators, hence all group transformations. We define this operator as

$$C_1 \equiv -P_\mu P^\mu = P_0{}^2 - \mathbf{P}^2 \qquad (10.4\text{-}1)$$

It has the stated property because: (i) as the scalar product of the 4-vector P_μ with itself, C_1 is invariant under homogeneous Lorentz transformations; and (ii) C_1 is also invariant under translations, as a consequence of the abelian nature of T_4. Unlike the case of Euclidean groups, however, the eigenvalue of C_1, which we shall denote by c_1, is not positive definite.

The irreducible representations of $\tilde{P}$ are labelled, among other indices, by c_1. We shall consider basis vectors with a definite linear momentum vector p^μ which is related to c_1 by $-p_\mu p^\mu = c_1$. We must distinguish between the following four cases:

(i) Null vector p: $c_1 = 0$ and $p^0 = \mathbf{p} = 0$

(ii) Time-like p: $c_1 > 0$

(iii) Light-like p: $c_1 = 0$ and $\mathbf{p} \neq 0$

(iv) Space-like p: $c_1 < 0$.

We shall study these cases in turn, emphasizing those results most directly related to known applications in physics.

The Poincaré group has a second Casimir operator C_2. Because its nature is a little more complicated than C_1, we shall defer its introduction until after we have gained some experience with the representation space.

10.4.1 Null Vector Case ($P^\mu = 0$)

The *null vector* $p_n{}^\mu = 0$ is invariant under all homogeneous Lorentz transformations. (The subscript n reminds us about the null character of this case.) In the terminology of the induced-representation method, the "little group" of p_n is the full Lorentz group $\tilde{L}_+$. Each irreducible unitary representation of the group $\tilde{L}_+$ (characterized by j_0, ν; cf. Sec. 10.3) induces an irreducible unitary representation of the Poincaré group. Basis vectors of such a representation are eigenvectors of $(P^\mu, \mathbf{J}^2, J_3)$ with eigenvalues $(p_n{}^\mu = 0, j, m)$. (They are, of course, also eigenvectors of the Casimir operators as well. To avoid cluttering the vectors with too many indices, however, we suppress the invariant parameters.) They satisfy the defining equations:[5]

$$\begin{aligned} T(b)\,|0jm\rangle &= |0jm\rangle \\ \Lambda\,|0jm\rangle &= |0j'm'\rangle\, D^{j_0\nu}[\Lambda]^{j'm'}{}_{jm} \end{aligned} \tag{10.4-2}$$

where $D^{j_0\nu}[\Lambda]$ are the unitary representation matrices of the homogeneous Lorentz group discussed in the previous section.

10.4.2 Time-Like Vector Case ($c_1 > 0$)

For a given positive $c_1 = -p_\mu p^\mu = M^2$, we pick a "standard vector" $p_t{}^\mu \equiv (p^0, \mathbf{p}) = (M, \mathbf{0})$. (Obviously, the subscript t stands for "time-like".) Physically, this corresponds to a state at rest ($\mathbf{p} = 0$) with *mass* or "rest energy" equal to M. The factor group of the Poincaré group with respect to the full invariant subgroup T_4 is

[5] Recall that the $T(b)$ and Λ to the left of $|\ \rangle$ stand for unitary operators on the space of physical states representing the Poincaré transformations which are denoted by the same symbols.

the homogeneous Lorentz group. The maximum subgroup of $\tilde{L}_+$ which leaves p_t invariant is the group of 3-dimensional rotations. Therefore, the little group of $\tilde{L}_+$ is SO(3). We shall demonstrate that every unitary irreducible representation of SO(3) (labelled by $j = s$) induces a unitary irreducible representation of the Poincaré group.

The basis vectors of the subspace corresponding to the eigenvalues p_t^{μ} of P^{μ} will be denoted by $\{|\mathbf{0}, \lambda\rangle\}$ where $\mathbf{0}$ refers to $\mathbf{p} = 0$. Two implicit indices $p^0 = M$ and $\mathbf{J}^2 = s(s+1)$ are suppressed. The defining equations for these vectors are:

$$\begin{aligned} P^{\mu}|\mathbf{0}\,\lambda\rangle &= |\mathbf{0}\,\lambda\rangle\, p_t^{\mu} \qquad p_t^{\mu} = (M, \mathbf{0}) \\ \mathbf{J}^2|\mathbf{0}\,\lambda\rangle &= |\mathbf{0}\,\lambda\rangle\, s(s+1) \\ J_3|\mathbf{0}\,\lambda\rangle &= |\mathbf{0}\,\lambda\rangle\, \lambda \quad . \end{aligned} \tag{10.4-3}$$

The relative phase of these vectors (with respect to a reference vector, say $|\mathbf{0}\,s\rangle$) and their normalization can be chosen according to the canonical rules of Sec. 7.3. This subspace is invariant under the action of the little group—the group of rotations.

To generate a complete basis consisting of general eigenvectors of P^{μ}, we operate on $|\mathbf{0}\,\lambda\rangle$ by the remaining transformations of the factor group. Recalling the decomposition of a general Lorentz transformation given by Theorem 10.3, and realizing that the first rotation factor on the right-hand side of Eq. (10.1-15) leaves the subspace associated with the standard vector invariant (since it is a member of the little group), one need only consider the Lorentz boost $L_3(\xi)$ followed by a rotation $R(\alpha, \beta, 0)$. We define first

$$|p\hat{\mathbf{z}}\,\lambda\rangle \equiv L_3(\xi)|\mathbf{0}\,\lambda\rangle \tag{10.4-4}$$

where $p = M \sinh\xi$ is the magnitude of the 3-momentum of the state; and then

$$|\mathbf{p}\,\lambda\rangle \equiv R(\alpha, \beta, 0)|p\hat{\mathbf{z}}\,\lambda\rangle \equiv H(p)|\mathbf{0}\,\lambda\rangle \tag{10.4-5}$$

where (β, α) are the polar and azimuthal angles of the momentum vector $\mathbf{p}$. The Lorentz transformation $H(p)$ introduced in (10.4-5),

$$H(p) = R(\alpha, \beta, 0)\, L_3(\xi) \tag{10.4-6}$$

will be referred to frequently in what follows. It transforms the rest frame vector p_t^{μ} to a general p^{μ}. We should note that, for a given p^{μ}, $H(p)$ is not the only Lorentz transformation which has this property—adding an arbitrary factor of rotation (i.e. member of the little group) to the right side of the above equation will give an equally acceptable definition. The convention adopted in Eq. (10.4-6) has proved by experience to be among the most convenient.

Theorem 10.10 (Time-like Unitary Irreducible Representations of the Poincaré Group): (i) The basis vectors $\{|\mathbf{p}\,\lambda\rangle\}$ described above span a vector space which is invariant under Poincaré group transformations. The action of group transformations on these basis vectors is given by

$$T(b)|\mathbf{p}\,\lambda\rangle = |\mathbf{p}\,\lambda\rangle\, e^{-ib^{\mu}p_{\mu}} \tag{10.4-7}$$

and

$$\Lambda|\mathbf{p}\,\lambda\rangle = |\mathbf{p}'\,\lambda'\rangle\, D^s[R(\Lambda, p)]^{\lambda'}{}_{\lambda} \tag{10.4-8a}$$

where $p'^{\mu} = \Lambda^{\mu}{}_{\nu} p^{\nu}$,

$$\mathrm{R}(\Lambda, p) \equiv H^{-1}(p')\Lambda H(p) \tag{10.4-8b}$$

and $D^s[\mathbf{R}]$ is the representation matrix of the SO(3) group corresponding to "angular momentum" s.

(ii) The resulting representation, labelled by (M, s), is unitary and irreducible.

Proof: The first step is to show that $|\mathbf{p}\,\lambda\rangle$, as defined by Eq. (10.4-5), is an eigenstate of P^{μ} with eigenvalues $p^{\mu} = (p^0, \mathbf{p})$ where p is given above and $p^0 = M\cosh\xi$ (so that $-p_{\mu}p^{\mu} = M^2$). This follows since the translations, with $\{P^{\mu}\}$ as generators, form an invariant subgroup (Theorem 10.5). The proof is identical to that for the group E_2 [Eq. (9.3-2)] and E_3 [Theorem 9.13],

$$\begin{aligned} P^{\mu}|\mathbf{p}\,\lambda\rangle &= P^{\mu} H(p)|\mathbf{0}\,\lambda\rangle = H(p)H(p)^{-1}P^{\mu}H(p)|\mathbf{0}\,\lambda\rangle \\ &= H(p)P^{\nu}|\mathbf{0}\,\lambda\rangle H(p)^{\mu}{}_{\nu} = H(p)|\mathbf{0}\,\lambda\rangle H(p)^{\mu}{}_{\nu}\,p_t{}^{\nu} \\ &= |\mathbf{p}\,\lambda\rangle\,p^{\mu} \quad . \end{aligned}$$

Eq. (10.4-7) is a direct consequence of this result. Now, consider a homogeneous Lorentz transformation. The derivation of Eq. (10.4-8) can be patterned exactly after that of Eq. (9.7-10) for the Euclidean group E_3. We have:

$$\begin{aligned} \Lambda|\mathbf{p}\,\lambda\rangle &= \Lambda H(p)|\mathbf{0}\,\lambda\rangle = H(p')[H(p')^{-1}\Lambda H(p)]|\mathbf{0}\,\lambda\rangle \\ &= |\mathbf{p}'\,\lambda'\rangle D^s[\mathrm{R}(\Lambda, p)]^{\lambda'}{}_{\lambda} \end{aligned}$$

where p' and $\mathrm{R}(\Lambda, p)$ are given by Eq. (10.4-8). The fact that $\mathrm{R}(\Lambda, p)$ is a 3-dimensional rotation follows from the fact that the combined Lorentz transformation on the right-hand side of Eq. (10.4-8b) leaves the standard vector $p_t{}^{\mu}$ invariant:

$$p_t \xrightarrow{H(p)} p \xrightarrow{\Lambda} p' \xrightarrow{H^{-1}(p')} p_t$$

hence it is a member of the little group.

Eqs. (10.4-7) and (10.4-8) show that the space spanned by $\{|\mathbf{p}\,\lambda\rangle\}$ is invariant under Poincaré group transformations. The space is irreducible because all the basis vectors are generated from one single vector (say, $|\mathbf{0}, \lambda = s\rangle$) by action of the generators $\{J_{\pm}\}$ and group operators $\{H(p)\}$; there cannot be a nontrivial invariant subspace. The representation is unitary because the generators are realized as hermitian operators and the representation matrices on the right-hand sides of Eqs. (10.4-7) and (10.4-8a) are unitary. QED

Let us turn to the physical interpretation of the basis vectors $|M,s;\mathbf{p}\,\lambda\rangle$. We know that M corresponds to the *mass* and $\mathbf{p}$ represents the 3-*momentum* of the system. What are the significance of s and λ? This question has already been answered in Sec. 8.4! [cf. also Sec. 9.7] In fact, we showed that s corresponds to the *intrinsic spin*; and that λ is the eigenvalue of the operator $\mathbf{J}\cdot\mathbf{P}/|\mathbf{p}|$, hence it corresponds to the angular momentum along the direction of the motion, or *helicity* of the state. [cf. Eq. (8.4-7)]

10.4.3 The Second Casimir Operator

The irreducible representations of the last section carry invariant labels (M, s). The "mass" parameter M is the square root of the eigenvalue of the Casimir operator $C_1 = -P_\mu P^\mu$. It is natural to ask: how is the "spin" parameter s related to a second, as yet unspecified, Casimir operator? We shall answer this question here. The result will be used in subsequent study of other unitary irreducible representations of the group.

In the subspace corresponding to $\mathbf{p} = 0$, the parameter s is, of course, directly related to the eigenvalue of the operator $\mathbf{J}^2$. $\mathbf{J}^2$ commutes only with the generators of the little group of $\mathbf{p} = 0$; it is certainly not invariant in general. The Casimir operator we are looking for must fulfill the following requirements: (i) it is translationally invariant, (ii) it is a Lorentz scalar, and (iii) it reduces to $\mathbf{J}^2$ when $c_1{}^2 = M^2 > 0$.

Condition (iii) indicates that this operator is a compound object quadratic in $J_{\mu\nu}$. Condition (ii) might then suggest the Lorentz scalar $J_{\mu\nu} J^{\mu\nu}$. This is, however, not a viable choice because it satisfies neither requirement (i) nor (iii). We must look for an expression somewhat less obvious in order to proceed. There is only one independent non-trivial choice.

Theorem 10.11 (The Pauli-Lubanski Vector W_μ): The *Pauli-Lubanski vector* defined by:

(10.4-9) $$W^\lambda \equiv \varepsilon^{\lambda\mu\nu\sigma} J_{\mu\nu} P_\sigma / 2$$

has the following properties:

(10.4-10) $$W^\lambda P_\lambda = 0$$

(10.4-11) $$[W^\lambda, P^\mu] = 0$$

(10.4-12) $$[W^\lambda, J^{\mu\nu}] = i(W^\mu g^{\lambda\nu} - W^\nu g^{\mu\lambda})$$

(10.4-13) $$[W^\lambda, W^\sigma] = i\,\varepsilon^{\lambda\sigma\mu\nu} W_\mu P_\nu \quad .$$

Proof: (i) Eq. (10.4-10) states that the 4-vectors P and W [cf. (iii) below] are perpendicular to each other. Its validity can be established by noting that

$$W^\lambda P_\lambda = \varepsilon^{\mu\nu\lambda\sigma} J_{\mu\nu} P_\lambda P_\sigma / 2$$

and that the right-hand side vanishes, as the ε-tensor is antisymmetric in the summation indices $(\lambda\sigma)$ whereas the product of the two momentum factors is symmetric in the same indices.

(ii) Eq. (10.4-11) expresses the translational invariance of W^λ. It is straightforward to see that

$$\begin{aligned} [W^\lambda, P^\mu] &= \varepsilon^{\lambda\alpha\beta\sigma} [J_{\alpha\beta}, P^\mu] P_\sigma / 2 \\ &= i\,\varepsilon^{\lambda\alpha\beta\sigma} [\delta^\mu_\alpha P_\beta - \delta^\mu_\beta P_\alpha] P_\sigma / 2 \quad . \end{aligned}$$

Both terms on the right-hand side vanish for the same reason as above.

(iii) Eq. (10.4-12) is equivalent to the statement that $\{W^\lambda\}$ transform as components of a 4-vector under homogeneous Lorentz transformations. This is a direct consequence of the definition, Eq. (10.4-9), as the contraction of known vectors and tensors. The commutation relation can, of course, also be verified by direct calculation, making use of the group algebra.

(iv) Eq. (10.4-13) is the only non-trivial relation. The proof is, nonetheless, straightforward and shall be left as an exercise [Problem 10.10]. QED

Theorem 10.12 (Second Casimir Operator of the Poincaré Group): The operator $C_2 \equiv W^\lambda W_\lambda$ commutes with all generators of the Poincaré group. It is, therefore, a Casimir operator.

The proof is simple, given the previous theorem: C_2 is invariant under translations since each component of W has that property [Eq. (10.4-11)]; W^2 is invariant under homogeneous Lorentz transformations because it is the square of the "length" of a 4-vector. QED

To gain some physical feeling about $\{W^\lambda\}$, consider the vector space corresponding to the (M, s) representation discussed in the previous section. When operating on the basis vectors—which are eigenstates of $\{P^\mu\}$—we can replace $\{P^\mu\}$ with their eigenvalues. Thus,

(10.4-14)
$$W^\lambda = \varepsilon^{\lambda\mu\nu\sigma} J_{\mu\nu} p_\sigma/2 \quad .$$

In the subspace corresponding to the "standard vector" of the physical system with $p^0 = M$ and $\mathbf{p} = 0$, we have:

(10.4-15)
$$W^0 = 0 \quad \text{and} \quad W^i = \frac{M}{2}\varepsilon^{ijk} J_{jk} = M J^i \quad .$$

In other words, the independent components of the 4-vector W are proportional to the generators $\{J^i\}$ of the little group SO(3).

Theorem 10.13 (Little Group, Induced Representation): (i) On the subspace corresponding to a given 4-vector $\{p^\mu\}$, the independent components of $\{W^\mu\}$ form a Lie algebra—the Lie algebra of the *little group* of p^μ. (ii) For every irreducible unitary representation of the little group, one can derive a corresponding *induced representation* of the full Poincaré group by successive application of homogeneous Lorentz transformations. (iii) The irreducible unitarity representations of the Poincaré group are characterized by the eigenvalues of the two Casimir operators $-P^2$ and $-W^2/p^2$.

The Lie algebra referred to above is given by Eq. (10.4-13) with the operators P^μ replaced by their eigenvalues p^μ. The precise form of this algebra is, therefore, determined by the nature of the vector $\{p^\mu\}$. For time-like p^μ, the little group is identified with the rotation group SO(3), as already developed in the previous subsection, and verified above in the context of the $\{W^\mu\}$ algebra. We now turn to the other cases.

10.4.4 Light-Like Case ($c_1 = 0$)

When $p_\mu p^\mu = 0$, the magnitudes of the time component p^0 and the spatial 3-vector $|\mathbf{p}|$ are equal. This is typified by the 4-momenta of photons, or equivalently the 4-wavevector of light propagation. Hence this case is termed "light-like". Light-like 4-vectors do not have a "rest-frame". The velocity of physical states with light-like momenta remains constant at the value $v = |\mathbf{p}|/p^0 = 1$ (in units of c, the velocity of light) in all Lorentz frames.

Since a "standard" light-like vector must have equal time and spatial components, it is customary to pick it as

(10.4-16) $$p_l^{\mu} = (\omega_0, 0, 0, \omega_0)$$

where ω_0 is an arbitrarily fixed scale and l is the label for "light-like". To obtain a general state of momentum $p^{\mu} = (\omega, \mathbf{p})$ where $\mathbf{p} = \omega\hat{\mathbf{p}}$ and the unit vector $\hat{\mathbf{p}}$ is characterized by the angles (θ, ϕ), we first apply a Lorentz boost $\mathrm{L}_3(\xi)$ to transform the "energy" from ω_0 to ω, then apply a rotation $\mathrm{R}(\phi, \theta, 0)$ to bring the z-axis into the $\hat{\mathbf{p}}$-direction. As in the last subsection, we shall denote the transformation from $p_1{}^{\mu}$ to p^{μ} by $H(p)$,

(10.4-17) $$p^{\mu} = H(p)^{\mu}{}_{\nu}\, p_l{}^{\nu} = [\mathrm{R}(\phi, \theta, 0)\mathrm{L}_3(\xi)]^{\mu}{}_{\nu}\, p_l{}^{\nu} \quad .$$

According to Theorem 10.13, the generators of the little group of the standard vector $p_1{}^{\mu}$ are independent components of the corresponding Pauli-Lubinski vector

$$W^{\lambda} = \frac{1}{2}\varepsilon^{\lambda\mu\nu\sigma} J_{\mu\nu}\, p_{l\sigma} \quad .$$

We obtain:

(10.4-18) $$\begin{aligned} W^0 &= W^3 = \omega_0 J_{12} = \omega_0 J_3 \\ W_1 &= \omega_0(J_{23} + J_{20}) = \omega_0(J_1 + K_2) \\ W_2 &= \omega_0(J_{31} - J_{10}) = \omega_0(J_2 - K_1) \quad . \end{aligned}$$

The second Casimir operator is given by

(10.4-19) $$\mathrm{C}_2 = W_{\mu}W^{\mu} = (W_1)^2 + (W_2)^2 \quad .$$

The Lie algebra is

(10.4-20) $$\begin{aligned} [W^1, W^2] &= 0 \\ [W^2, J_3] &= iW^1 \\ [W^1, J_3] &= -iW^2 \quad . \end{aligned}$$

We recognize this algebra being the same as that of the Euclidean group in 2-dimensions, E_2 (with $W^{1,2}$ replacing $P^{1,2}$). We know, from Chap. 9, the irreducible unitary representations of this group: the degenerate representations correspond to $w = 0$, they are one-dimensional, and the basis vectors $|\lambda\rangle$ are labelled by λ, the eigenvalue of J_3. The non-degenerate representations correspond to $w > 0$, they are all infinite-dimensional and the basis vectors can be chosen as $\{|w\,\lambda\rangle, \lambda = 0, \pm 1, \ldots\}$. Starting from any of these representations, we can generate a basis for a corresponding representation of the full Poincaré group, labelled by M $(=0)$ and w, by applying the homogeneous Lorentz transformations $H(p)$ [cf. Eq. (10.4-17)] to the basis vectors of the subspace.

In the physical world, no states corresponding to the ($M = 0$, $w > 0$) representations are known. On the other hand, the ($M = 0 = w$, λ) representations are realized as photon ($\lambda = \pm 1$), neutrino ($\lambda = -1/2$), and anti-neutrino ($\lambda = 1/2$) states. Hence, in the subsequent study, we shall confine ourselves to the degenerate case. Extension to the general situation is quite straightforward as briefly indicated at the end of the above paragraph.

According to the above discussion, the subspace corresponding to the standard vector p_l is one dimensional and the basis vector $|\mathbf{p}_l\,\lambda\rangle$ has the following defining properties:

$$\begin{aligned} P^\mu|\mathbf{p}_l\,\lambda\rangle &= |\mathbf{p}_l\,\lambda\rangle\, p_l^{\,\mu} \qquad & p_l^{\,\mu} &= (\omega_0, 0, 0, \omega_0) \\ J_3|\mathbf{p}_l\,\lambda\rangle &= |\mathbf{p}_l\,\lambda\rangle\, \lambda & & \\ W_i|\mathbf{p}_l\,\lambda\rangle &= 0 & i &= 1,2 \quad . \end{aligned} \tag{10.4-21}$$

When λ is an integer, we obtain a single-valued representation; when λ is an odd-half-integer, we obtain a double-valued representation. The reader may wonder what is the reason for including the double-valued representations along with the single-valued representations of the little group SO(2). There are two (related) answers to this question. (i) the choice is based on the occurrence in nature of these representations (and only these), as mentioned earlier [cf. also Chaps. 6-8]; and (ii) if we consider the $c_1 = 0$ representations as limiting cases of the $c_1 = M^2$ representations when $M \to 0$, then the original little group SO(3) selects out the single- and double-valued representations of the restricted little group SO(2) from all its possible multi-valued representations.

The general basis vector is defined as:

$$\begin{aligned} |\mathbf{p}\,\lambda\rangle &= \mathrm{R}(\phi,\theta,0)\,|p\hat{\mathbf{z}}\,\lambda\rangle = H(p)\,|\mathbf{p}_l\,\lambda\rangle \\ |p\hat{\mathbf{z}}\,\lambda\rangle &= \mathrm{L}_3(\xi)\,|\mathbf{p}_l\,\lambda\rangle \end{aligned} \tag{10.4-22}$$

where $p = \omega_0 e^{\xi}$ is the magnitude of $\mathbf{p}$. These definitions are very similar to those adopted for the time-like case, Eqs. (10.4-4), (10.4-5). As in the previous case, one can establish the following basic result, expressed as a theorem.

Theorem 10.14 (Light-like Unitary Irreducible Representations of the Poincaré Group): The basis vectors $\{|\mathbf{p}\lambda\rangle\}$ described above span a vector space which is invariant under Poincaré group transformations. The resulting representation, labelled by ($M=0$, λ), is unitary and irreducible. The effect of the group transformations on these basis vectors is:

$$\mathrm{T}(b)\,|\mathbf{p}\,\lambda\rangle = |\mathbf{p}\,\lambda\rangle\, e^{-ib^\mu p_\mu}, \tag{10.4-23}$$

$$\Lambda\,|\mathbf{p}\,\lambda\rangle = |\Lambda\mathbf{p}\,\lambda\rangle\, e^{-i\lambda\theta(\Lambda,p)} \tag{10.4-24}$$

where $\theta(\Lambda, p)$ is an angle depending on Λ and p which can be determined from the equation

$$e^{-i\lambda\theta(\Lambda,p)} = \langle \mathbf{p}_l\,\lambda|H^{-1}(\Lambda p)\,\Lambda\, H(p)\,|\,\mathbf{p}_l\lambda\rangle. \tag{10.4-25}$$

This theorem can be proved in exactly the same way as Theorem 10.10. We shall not repeat the arguments here.

As pointed out previously, $|\mathbf{p}\,\lambda\rangle$ represents a state with *momentum* p and *helicity* λ. Although there is a lot of similarity between these states with those of the time-like case, one essential difference must be kept in mind: The helicity index λ is invariant under Lorentz transformations for massless (light-like) states, whereas it is transformed among all $2s + 1$ possible values for massive (time-like) states. In the literature, massless particles corresponding to the ($M = 0, \pm\lambda$) representations are often said to have "spin λ" (e.g. *photon* ("spin" 1), *neutrino* ("spin" 1/2),...). Those statements can be very misleading, as they may suggest a transformation law such as Eq. (10.4-7) (which mixes the helicity index λ) rather than Eq. (10.4-24) (which leaves λ invariant). Only the latter is appropriate for massless states. (Although, if a very careful $M \to 0$ limit is taken of equations for the time-like representations, we can arrive at the correct massless results, as already alluded to once before.) It is preferable to use the term "helicity" rather than "spin" when discussing massless states; Eqs. (10.4-23) and (10.4-24) clearly indicate that λ is invariant under all continuous space-time symmetry transformations.

10.4.5 Space-like Case ($c_1 < 0$)

When $C_1 = -p_\mu p^\mu < 0$, the momentum vector p^μ is *space-like*. The simplest "standard state" one can choose is $p_s^{\ \mu} = (0, 0, 0, Q)$, where we introduced the quantity Q defined by $Q^2 = -C_1 > 0$. The generators of the associated little group are:

$$\begin{aligned} W^0 &= Q\,J_3 \\ W_1 &= Q\,J_{20} = Q\,K_2 \\ W_2 &= Q\,J_{01} = -Q\,K_1 \end{aligned} \qquad (10.4\text{-}26)$$

The second Casimir operator is

$$C_2 = Q^2(K_1^{\ 2} + K_2^{\ 2} - J_3^{\ 2}) \qquad (10.4\text{-}27)$$

The Lie algebra consists of the commutation relations:

$$\begin{aligned} [K_2, J_3] &= i\,K_1 \\ [J_3, K_1] &= i\,K_2 \\ [K_1, K_2] &= -i\,J_3 \end{aligned} \qquad (10.4\text{-}28)$$

With the substitution $K_{1,2} \to J_{1,2}$, this algebra is the same as that of SO(3) except for the negative sign of the last equation. This difference is important as the corresponding little group, called SO(2, 1), becomes non-compact, and all its irreducible unitary representations are infinite-dimensional.

Space-like representations of the Poincaré group have not yet found direct applications to physical systems as do time-like and light-like ones. However, space-like vectors, such as momentum-transfer vectors in scattering processes, do play useful roles in the formulation of physical problems. Thus, the subject of space-like unitary irreducible representations of the Poincaré group is relevant to some branches of theoretical physics. Possible applications of these representations in yet unidentified ways certainly cannot be excluded, as is also the case with representations corresponding to $c_1 = 0$, $c_2 \neq 0$, mentioned in the previous subsection.

The unitary irreducible representations of SO(2, 1) are labelled by the eigenvalue c_2 which can either take on continuous values and be in the range $0 < c_2 < \infty$, or be negative and assume the discrete values $c_2 = -j(j+1)$, $j = 0, 1, 2, \ldots$. (If double-valued representations are admitted, then $j = 1/2, 3/2, \ldots$ are also permitted.) The basis vectors are labelled by $|p_s \lambda\rangle_{c_2}$ where $\lambda = 0, \pm 1, \ldots$ in the case of positive (continuous) c_2; and $\lambda = j+1, j+2, \ldots$ or $\lambda = -j-1, -j-2, \ldots$ in the case of negative (discrete) c_2. The derivation of these representations is straightforward and is left as an exercise. [cf. Problem 10.9] Given any of these representations, a unitary irreducible representation of the Poincaré group can be built, again by the application of homogeneous Lorentz transformations beyond those in the little group. In order to transform the standard momentum $p_s^{\,\mu}$ to a general vector p^μ, we can, for instance, adopt the following procedure:

$$\begin{aligned}(0,0,0,Q) &\xrightarrow{L_3(\xi)} (Q\mathrm{sh}\xi, 0, 0, Q\mathrm{ch}\xi)\\ &\xrightarrow{L_1(\zeta)} (Q\mathrm{sh}\xi\mathrm{ch}\zeta, Q\mathrm{sh}\xi\mathrm{sh}\zeta, 0, Q\mathrm{ch}\xi)\\ &\xrightarrow{R_3(\phi)} (Q\mathrm{sh}\xi\mathrm{ch}\zeta, Q\mathrm{sh}\xi\mathrm{sh}\zeta\cos\phi, Q\mathrm{sh}\xi\mathrm{sh}\zeta\sin\phi, Q\mathrm{ch}\xi)\end{aligned} \tag{10.4-29}$$

where the parameters (ξ, ζ, ϕ) are to be determined by identifying the last 4-vector with (p^0, p^1, p^2, p^3) and sh and ch are the hyperbolic sine and cosine functions. The general basis vector is defined as

$$|\mathbf{p}\,\lambda\rangle = H(p)\,|p_s\,\lambda\rangle \quad \text{where} \tag{10.4-30}$$

$$H(p) = R_3(\phi)\,L_1(\zeta)\,L_3(\xi) \quad . \tag{10.4-31}$$

As before, we have:

$$T(b)\,|\mathbf{p}\,\lambda\rangle = |\mathbf{p}\,\lambda\rangle\, e^{-ib^\mu p_\mu}$$

$$\Lambda\,|\mathbf{p}\,\lambda\rangle = |\Lambda\mathbf{p}\,\lambda'\rangle\, D^{c_2}[H^{-1}(\Lambda p)\Lambda\, H(p)]^{\lambda'}{}_{\lambda}$$

where D^{c_2} is the representation matrix for the little group [SO(2, 1)] corresponding to the Casimir operator eigenvalue c_2.

10.4.6 Covariant Normalization of Basis States and Integration Measure

In applying the induced representation method we require all generators to be represented by hermitian operators. The basis vectors, defined as eigenvectors of a maximal set of commuting generators, are orthogonal to each other by construction. We shall now consider the proper normalization of these vectors.

When basis vectors have one or more discrete labels, it is most convenient to normalize all vectors to unity, thereby obtaining an orthonormal basis. When the basis vectors, such as $\{|\mathbf{p}\,\lambda\rangle\}$, depend on continuous variables, the proper choice of normalization requires a little more thought. Since in our approach all basis vectors are defined in terms of those associated with a "standard vector" $\tilde{p}$ (p_n, p_t, p_l, or p_s, as the case may be) by unitary transformations,

$$|\mathbf{p}\,\lambda\rangle = H(p)\,|\tilde{p}\,\lambda\rangle$$

the normalization of $|\mathbf{p}\,\lambda\rangle$ cannot be completely arbitrary. For instance, if the definition of the scalar product $\langle \mathbf{p}'\lambda'|\mathbf{p}\,\lambda\rangle$ is to be Lorentz invariant, we must have[6]

(10.4-32)
$$\langle \mathbf{p}'\lambda'|\mathbf{p}\lambda\rangle = \langle \mathbf{p}'\lambda'|\Lambda^\dagger\Lambda|\mathbf{p}\lambda\rangle$$
$$= D^{s\dagger}[R(\Lambda,p')]^{\lambda'}{}_{\sigma'}\langle\Lambda\mathbf{p}'\sigma'|\Lambda\mathbf{p}\sigma\rangle D^s[R(\Lambda,p)]^\sigma{}_\lambda$$

for all $\Lambda \in \tilde{L}_+$. Because basis vectors corresponding to distinct eigenvalues must be mutually orthogonal, we should have

(10.4-33)
$$\langle \mathbf{p}'\lambda'|\mathbf{p}\lambda\rangle = N(p)\,\delta^3(\mathbf{p}-\mathbf{p}')\,\delta^{\lambda'}{}_\lambda \quad .$$

where $N(p)$ is a normalization factor yet to be determined. Substituting into Eq. (10.4-32), we obtain the condition:

(10.4-34)
$$N(p)\,\delta^3(\mathbf{p}-\mathbf{p}') = N(\Lambda p)\,\delta^3(\Lambda\mathbf{p}-\Lambda\mathbf{p}') \quad .$$

Any definition of $N(p)$ which satisfies this requirement is said to provide a *covariant normalization* for the states.

The normalization factor $N(p)$ is related to the integration measure when the continuous variables $\{p^i\}$ are to be summed over. Consider expanding an arbitrary state-vector $|\psi\rangle$ in terms of the basis vectors $\{|\mathbf{p}\lambda\rangle\}$,

(10.4-35)
$$|\psi\rangle = \sum_\lambda \int |\mathbf{p}\lambda\rangle\,\psi^\lambda(p)\,\tilde{d}p$$

where $\psi^\lambda(p)$ is the c-number "wave-function" and $\tilde{d}p$ is a yet-to-be-determined integration measure. If $\{|\mathbf{p}\lambda\rangle\}$ is an orthonormal basis, we expect to have

(10.4-36)
$$\psi^{\lambda'}(p') = \langle \mathbf{p}'\lambda'|\psi\rangle \quad .$$

Evaluating the right-hand side, using Eqs. (10.4-33) and (10.4-35), we obtain:

$$\psi^{\lambda'}(p') = \int \psi^{\lambda'}(p)\,N(p)\,\delta^3(\mathbf{p}-\mathbf{p}')\,\tilde{d}p \quad .$$

Since this must hold for all possible states $|\psi\rangle$, we conclude,

(10.4-37)
$$\tilde{d}p = \frac{1}{N(p)}\,d^3p = \frac{1}{N(p)}\,dp^1\,dp^2\,dp^3 \quad .$$

If $N(p)$ is *covariant*, as specified by Eq. (10.4-34), then Eq. (10.4-37) implies

(10.4-38)
$$\tilde{d}p = \tilde{d}\Lambda p \quad .$$

Hence, the integration measure defined in this way is *Lorentz invariant*.

We can now derive the appropriate form for the normalization factor $N(p)$. Since the Lorentz transformation matrix Λ has unit determinant, the 4-dimensional volume element d^4p is Lorentz invariant, i.e.

(10.4-39)
$$d^4(\Lambda p) = (\det\Lambda)\,d^4p = d^4p \quad .$$

[6] For definiteness, we use notation appropriate for the case $c_1 = M^2 > 0$. The reader can verify for himself quite easily that the end result holds for the other cases also.

For our applications, however, the component p^0 is not an independent variable; it is determined by the "mass-shell" condition:

(10.4-40) $$c_1 + p^2 = c_1 + \mathbf{p}^2 - (p^0)^2 = 0 \quad .$$

This equation has two roots, $p^0 = \pm[\mathbf{p}^2 + c_1]^{1/2}$. For irreducible representations of the time-like and light-like cases (which have ready physical applications), only the positive root is of interest to us. (Note that all proper Lorentz transformations leave the sign of $\underset{\sim}{p}^0$ unchanged, cf. Problem 10.11.) These results suggest that a suitable choice of $\tilde{d}p$ is

(10.4-41a) $$\tilde{d}p = \frac{1}{N}\,\theta(p^0)\,\delta(c_1 + p^2)\,d^4p = \frac{1}{N}\frac{d^3p}{2p^0} \quad .$$

where N is an arbitrary constant and in the last expression, p^0 is understood to mean $[\mathbf{p}^2 + c_1]^{1/2}$. It is customary to choose $N = (2\pi)^3$, hence

(10.4-41b) $$\tilde{d}p \equiv \frac{1}{(2\pi)^3}\frac{d^3p}{2p^0} \quad .$$

Correspondingly, the covariant normalization convention is given by

(10.4-42) $$\langle \mathbf{p}'\lambda' | \mathbf{p}\lambda \rangle = (2\pi)^3\,2p^0\,\delta^3(\mathbf{p} - \mathbf{p}')\,\delta^{\lambda'}{}_{\lambda} \equiv \tilde{\delta}(p - p')\,\delta^{\lambda'}{}_{\lambda} \quad .$$

which defines the Lorentz invariant δ-function $\tilde{\delta}(p - p')$. Aside from being covariant, this normalization convention has the distinct advantage that it applies equally well to both massless ($M = 0$) and massive ($M \neq 0$) cases. Most traditional books in physics do not use the covariant normalization; hence they must adopt different conventions for different states.

10.5 Relation between Representations of the Lorentz and Poincaré Groups—Relativistic Wave Functions, Fields, and Wave Equations

We emphasized in the last section how physical states of definite mass and spin, labelled by their momenta p_μ and helicity λ, arise naturally from the irreducible representations of the symmetry group of space-time—the Poincaré group. Traditionally, such states are not derived this way. Rather, they arise as elementary solutions to *relativistic wave equations*, the most well-known among these are the Maxwell's Equations in electromagnetism (for the photon), the Klein-Gordon Equation (for spin 0 bosons), and the Dirac Equation (for spin 1/2 fermions). As we have mentioned a number of times in previous sections, the components of these *relativistic wave functions* transform under Lorentz transformations as finite-dimensional representations of the Lorentz group. It is therefore of interest, both physically and mathematically, to formalize the relation between the two approaches in order to gain a deeper understanding of both.

10.5.1 Wave Functions and Field Operators

In Sec. 7.6 we explored the transformation properties of wave functions and fields under the rotation group, both in their c-number form and as second-quantized operators. Those results can be directly generalized to the relativistic case.

Definition 10.11 (Relativistic Wave Function): Let $\{D[\Lambda]\}$ be a finite dimensional $(n \times n)$ matrix representation of the proper Lorentz group. A c-number *relativistic wave function* is a set of n functions of space-time $\{\psi^{\sigma}(x)\}$ which transform under an arbitrary proper Lorentz transformation Λ as

$$\psi \xrightarrow{\Lambda} \psi' \qquad \psi'^{\alpha}(x) = D[\Lambda]^{\alpha}{}_{\beta}\,\psi^{\beta}(\Lambda^{-1}x) \quad . \tag{10.5-1}$$

Examples: (i) The simplest relativistic wave function is the single-component Klein-Gordon wave function $\phi(x)$ which transforms as the $(u,v) = (0,0)$ irreducible representation, and which is the most natural candidate to describe the physical states of a spin 0 particle; (ii) The most well known example of relativistic wave functions, which predates the theory of special relativity, are the electromagnetic fields $(\mathbf{E},\mathbf{B})$ which can be grouped into the second-rank anti-symmetric tensor $F^{\mu\nu}(x)$. $\{F^{\mu\nu}\}$ transform as the $(1,0)\oplus(0,1)$ representation of the proper Lorentz group; (iii) The 4-vector field $A^{\mu}(x)$ which describes a spin 1 particle ("vector boson") transforms as the $(1/2,1/2)$ representation; and (iv) The 4-component Dirac wave function $\psi^{\alpha}(x)$ transforms as the $(0,1/2)\oplus(1/2,0)$ representation.

Definition 10.12 (Relativistic Field Operators): For a given matrix representation $\{D[\Lambda]\}$ as above, a *relativistic field operator* is a set of n operator valued functions of space-time $\{\Psi^{\alpha}(x)\}$ which transforms under an arbitrary proper Lorentz transformation Λ as:

$$U[\Lambda]\,\Psi^{\alpha}(x)\,U[\Lambda^{-1}] = D[\Lambda^{-1}]^{\alpha}{}_{\beta}\,\Psi^{\beta}(\Lambda x) \tag{10.5-2}$$

where $U[\Lambda]$ is the operator representing Λ on the Hilbert space where Ψ is defined.[7]

Examples of relativistic field operators are the second-quantized versions of the wave functions (i)-(iv) described in the previous paragraph.

Our subsequent investigation can be formulated either in the c-number wave function language or in the field operator language. For definiteness, and because of a slight notational advantage, we shall use the field operator formulation.

10.5.2 Relativistic Wave Equations and the Plane Wave Expansion

How is a field operator $\Psi(x)$, transforming as Eq. (10.5-2), made to describe a "particle" of definite *mass m* and *spin s*? The answer lies in the "wave equation" that $\Psi(x)$ satisfies. Let us write the wave equation in the generic form:

$$\Pi\left(m, \frac{1}{i}\partial\right)^{\alpha}{}_{\beta}\Psi^{\beta}(x) = 0 \tag{10.5-3}$$

where Π is a linear differential operator (usually of the first or second degree in $\partial_{\mu} = \partial/\partial x^{\mu}$) and it is a *matrix* with respect to the Lorentz index of the wave function. An archtypical example of Eq. (10.5-3) is the *Dirac Equation* [Messiah, Schiff],

$$\left(\frac{1}{i}\gamma^{\mu}\partial_{\mu} + m\right)\Psi(x) = 0 \tag{10.5-4}$$

[7] In this section, we are reinstating the operator symbol U for the operator $U[\Lambda]$ representing a Lorentz transformation Λ to emphasize the difference between the two quantities.

where the 4-component indices on the γ matrices and on $\Psi(x)$ have been suppressed. The differential operator is linear in ∂ in this case. The simplest relativistic wave equation is, however, the *Klein-Gordon equation* for spin 0 particles. The field operator $\phi(x)$ has only one component and the differential operator Π is quadratic in ∂:

(10.5-5) $$(-\partial^\mu \partial_\mu + m^2)\phi(x) = 0 \quad .$$

The differential equation (10.5-3) can be converted into an algebraic equation by taking the Fourier transform,

(10.5-6) $$\Psi^\alpha(x) = \int \frac{d^4 p}{(2\pi)^3} \Phi^\alpha(p)\, e^{ipx}.$$

We obtain

(10.5-7) $$\Pi(m,p)\,\Phi^\alpha(p) = 0$$

where the matrix indices are again suppressed. Since the coefficients linking $\Phi(p)$ to $\Psi(x)$ in Eq. (10.5-6) are all Lorentz scalars, it should be obvious that $\Phi(p)$ transforms under proper Lorentz transformations just like $\Psi(x)$ in Eq. (10.5-2) with x replaced by p.

In order that Eq. (10.5-3) be a satisfactory relativistic wave equation for spin s and mass m, the matrix $\Pi(m,p)$ must have the following properties:

(i) It is relativistically covariant, or

(10.5-8) $$D(\Lambda)\,\Pi(m,p)\,D(\Lambda^{-1}) = \Pi(m,\Lambda p)$$

so that Eq. (10.5-7) is unchanged under Lorentz transformations, i.e. the validity of Eq. (10.5-7) should guarantee [cf. Problem 10.12]

(10.5-9) $$\Pi(m,\Lambda p)\,\Phi(\Lambda p) = 0 \quad .$$

(ii) The "mass-shell condition",

(10.5-10a) $$(p^2 + m^2)\Phi(p) = 0$$

hence

(10.5-10b) $$\Phi(p) = \delta(p^2 + m^2)\tilde{\Phi}(p)$$

must follow from Eq. (10.5-7).

(iii) If Φ transforms as the (u,v) representation of the Lorentz group, then it has angular momentum content $|u-v| \le j \le (u+v)$, as discussed in Subsection 10.3.2. If neither u nor v is zero, the field operator $\Phi(p)$ has multiple spin content. In order for the solutions of the field equation to correspond to particle states with a single spin (or helicity, if the particle is massless), $\Pi(m,p)$ must act like a projection matrix to select out the desired spin components of $\Phi(p)$ by means of Eq. (10.5-7). Among more familiar examples, this consideration is relevant only in the case of electromagnetic theory where the electromagnetic 4- vector potential A^μ has four components (with possible spin content 0 and 1) but the photon states only carry two helicities (± 1).

The last subsection will be devoted to a detailed analysis of point (iii). For the moment, we simply acknowledge that all acceptable relativistic wave equations satisfy the above requirements and proceed to explore the consequences of such a general equation. For definiteness, we restrict ourselves to the case $m \neq 0$, although most of what we say will apply to the massless case as well.

Eq. (10.5-10) implies that $\Phi(p)$ is non-vanishing only when its argument satisfies the mass-shell condition $p^2 + m^2 = 0$. There are two solutions to this equation,

$$p^0 = \pm(\mathbf{p}^2 + m^2)^{1/2}$$

referred to as positive and negative energy solutions, respectively. Separating the two types of solutions and making use of the invariant measure on the mass shell, Eq. (10.4-41), we can rewrite Eq. (10.5-6) as

$$\Psi(x) = \int \tilde{d}p\,[\Phi_+(p)e^{-ipx} + \Phi_-(p)e^{ipx}] \tag{10.5-11}$$

where

$$\Phi_\pm(p) = \tilde{\Phi}\,[p^0 = \pm(\mathbf{p}^2 + m^2)^{1/2}, \pm\mathbf{p}] \tag{10.5-12}$$

and $\tilde{\Phi}$ is defined in Eq. (10.5-10b). The matrix equations satisfied by $\Phi_\pm(p)$ are

$$\Pi(m, \pm p)\,\Phi_\pm(p) = 0 \tag{10.5-13}$$

where it is understood that any occurrence of p^0 in Π is to be replaced by $(\mathbf{p}^2 + m^2)^{1/2}$. Hence $\Pi(m,p)$ is in reality only a function of the 3-vector $\mathbf{p}$. The occurrence of *negative energy solutions* in relativistic wave equations [Eqs. (10.5-11), (10.5-12)] is closely related to the existence of an *anti-particle* state for each ordinary particle state and the associated *charge conjugation symmetry*. [Sakurai] In order not to distract ourselves on this point, we shall focus our attention on the positive energy solutions in what follows.

Consider the case $p = p_t = (m, \mathbf{p}{=}0)$ (the "rest frame" of the system). In order that the wave equation describes *spin s* particle states, the matrix equation (10.5-13) should have $(2s + 1)$ independent solutions corresponding to the $\lambda = -s, -s + 1, \ldots, s$ states of the system in its rest frame. We shall denote these elementary solutions by $u(\mathbf{0}\,\lambda)$,

$$\Pi(m, p_t)^\alpha{}_\beta\, u^\beta(\mathbf{0}\,\lambda) = 0 \qquad \lambda = -s, \ldots, s \tag{10.5-14}$$

where α and β are Lorentz indices. Once $\{u(\mathbf{0}\,\lambda)\}$ are specified, the general elementary solutions to Eq. (10.5-13) can be written down:

$$u^\alpha(\mathbf{p}\,\lambda) = D[H(p)]^\alpha{}_\beta\, u^\beta(\mathbf{0}\,\lambda) \tag{10.5-15}$$

where $H(p)$ is a Lorentz transformation which brings the rest-frame momentum vector $p_t = (m, \mathbf{0})$ to the given $p = (p^0, \mathbf{p})$, such as given by Eq. (10.4-6). To see that the wave function (10.5-15) does satisfy the wave equation (10.5-7), we note that

$$\begin{aligned}\Pi(m,p)\,u(\mathbf{p}\,\lambda) &= D[H(p)]\,\Pi(m,p_t)\,D[H(p)]^{-1}\,u(\mathbf{p}\,\lambda)\\ &= D[H(p)]\,\Pi(m,p_t)\,u(\mathbf{0}\,\lambda) = 0\end{aligned}$$

where the first step follows from Eq. (10.5-8), the second from (10.5-15), and the third from (10.5-14).

The elementary solutions given by Eq. (10.5-15) are usually called *plane wave solutions* to the wave equation. They are concrete realizations of the linear momentum basis states $\{|\mathbf{p}\,\lambda\rangle\}$ of the time-like irreducible representations of the Poincaré group we derived in abstract form in subsection 10.4.2. Notice that these wave functions carry both a set of Lorentz indices (denoted by the single superscript α) and a set of Poincaré labels $(\mathbf{p}, \lambda)$. Although not shown explicitly, they should also carry the Lorentz representation labels (u, v) (which define the range of α, and the Poincaré representation labels (m, s) (which define the mass shell condition for p^μ and the range of λ).

The general solution to the wave equation is a linear combination of the elementary solutions. Taking this fact into account, we rewrite Eq. (10.5-11) as

$$\Psi^\alpha(x) = \sum_\lambda \int \tilde{d}p\,[\mathrm{b}(\mathbf{p}\,\lambda)\,u^\alpha(\mathbf{p}\,\lambda)\,e^{ipx} + \text{negative energy term}] \tag{10.5-16}$$

where $\mathrm{b}(\mathbf{p}\,\lambda)$ is the expansion coefficient. This equation is usually referred to as the *plane wave expansion* of the field operator $\Psi(x)$.

10.5.3 The Lorentz-Poincaré Connection

Since we have chosen to consider $\Psi^\sigma(x)$ as operators (on the Hilbert space of physical states), we must ask: which factor on the right-hand side of Eq. (10.5-16) carries the operator value? Since $\tilde{d}p$, $u^\alpha(\mathbf{p}\,\lambda)$, and e^{ipx} are all c-numbers, the coefficient function $\mathrm{b}(\mathbf{p}\,\lambda)$ must be operator-valued. As a matter of fact, in Sec. 8.7 we already anticipated this result and interpreted these operator coefficients (for the 4- vector potential function) as the annihilation operators for the particle (photon) states. We review this point under the current circumstance. The Poincaré states, Eq. (10.4-5), can be written in terms of *creation operators* $\{a^\dagger(\mathbf{p}\,\lambda)\}$ as follows:

$$|\mathbf{p}\,\lambda\rangle = a^\dagger(\mathbf{p}\,\lambda)\,|0\rangle \tag{10.5-17}$$

where $|0\rangle$ is the *vacuum* state. The transformation properties of the states $|\mathbf{p}\,\lambda\rangle$, Eq. (10.4-8), imply for the operators

$$U[\Lambda]\,a^\dagger(\mathbf{p}\,\lambda)\,U[\Lambda^{-1}] = a^\dagger(\Lambda\mathbf{p}\,\lambda')\,D^{(s)}[\mathrm{R}(\Lambda, p)]^{\lambda'}{}_{\lambda} \quad . \tag{10.5-18}$$

The hermitian conjugates of Eqs. (10.5-17) and (10.5-18) are

$$\langle\mathbf{p}\,\lambda| = \langle 0|\,a(\mathbf{p}\,\lambda) \tag{10.5-19}$$

$$U[\Lambda]\,a(\mathbf{p}\,\lambda)\,U[\Lambda^{-1}] = D^{(s)}[\mathrm{R}(\Lambda, p)^{-1}]^{\lambda}{}_{\lambda'}\,a(\Lambda\mathbf{p}\,\lambda') \tag{10.5-20}$$

respectively, and $\{a(\mathbf{p}\,\lambda)\}$ are the *annihilation operators.*

The coordinate space (c-number) wave function of any physical state $|\phi\rangle$ can be expressed as matrix elements of the field operator [cf. Eq. (7.6-14)],

$$\phi^\alpha(x) = \langle 0|\,\Psi^\alpha(x)\,|\phi\rangle \tag{10.5-21}$$

where $|0\rangle$ is the vacuum state. Applying this connection to the linear momentum basis states, we obtain

$$u^\alpha(\mathbf{p}\,\lambda)e^{ipx} = \langle 0|\psi^\alpha(x)|\mathbf{p}\,\lambda\rangle \quad . \tag{10.5-22}$$

Substituting Eqs. (10.5-16) and (10.5-17) in the right-hand side, we obtain the condition

$$\langle 0|\, a(\mathbf{p}'\,\lambda')\, a^\dagger(\mathbf{p}\,\lambda)\,|0\rangle = \delta^{\lambda'}{}_{\lambda}\,\tilde{\delta}(\mathbf{p}-\mathbf{p}') = \langle \mathbf{p}'\,\lambda'\,|\,\mathbf{p}\,\lambda\rangle \tag{10.5-23}$$

where $\tilde{\delta}(\mathbf{p}-\mathbf{p}')$ is the invariant delta function on the mass shell complementary to the invariant measure of integration $\tilde{d}p$ introduced in Eq. (10.4-42). It is now clear that the operator-valued "coefficients" $b(\mathbf{p}\,\lambda)$ are nothing other than the annihilation operators for the corresponding basis states, as we expected:

$$b(\mathbf{p}\,\lambda) = a(\mathbf{p}\,\lambda) \quad . \tag{10.5-24}$$

We can now go back to the plane wave expansion, Eq. (10.5-16) and consider its significance. The field operator $\Psi^\alpha(x)$ (on the LHS) transforms as certain finite dimensional non-unitary representation of the Lorentz group, whereas the annihilation operator $a(\mathbf{p}\,\lambda)$ (on the RHS) transforms as the infinite dimensional unitary representation of the Poincaré group characterized by (m, s). The connection between the two is established by the elementary (c-number) wave functions $u^\alpha(\mathbf{p}\,\lambda)e^{ipx}$. [Note that the integration measure $\tilde{d}p$ has been chosen to be a Lorentz invariant.]

Theorem 10.15 (Connection Between Representations of Lorentz and Poincaré Groups): The c-number wave functions $u^\alpha(\mathbf{p}\,\lambda)e^{ipx}$ in the plane wave expansion formula Eq. (10.5-16) are the coefficient functions which connect the set of operators $\{a(\mathbf{p}\,\lambda)\}$, transforming as the irreducible unitary representation (m, s) of the Poincaré group, to the set of field operators $\Psi^\alpha(x)$, transforming as certain finite dimensional non-unitary representations of the Lorentz group.

To pursue this group theoretical interpretation of the "plane wave solutions" of the wave equation a little further, note that $u^\alpha(\mathbf{p}\,\lambda)\,e^{ipx}$ carries both the Poincaré indices $(\mathbf{p}\,\lambda)$ and the Lorentz indices (x, α). Applying a Lorentz transformation Λ to both sides of Eq. (10.5-16), we obtain:

$$\begin{aligned}
\text{LHS} &= U[\Lambda]\,\Psi^\alpha(x)\,U[\Lambda^{-1}] = D[\Lambda^{-1}]^\alpha{}_{\alpha'}\,\Psi^{\alpha'}(\Lambda x) \\
&= D[\Lambda^{-1}]^\alpha{}_{\alpha'} \sum_\lambda \int \tilde{d}q\,[a(\mathbf{q}\,\lambda)\,u^{\alpha'}(\mathbf{q}\,\lambda)\,e^{iq\Lambda x} + (-\text{energy term})] \\
&= D[\Lambda^{-1}]^\alpha{}_{\alpha'} \sum_\lambda \int \tilde{d}p\,[a(\Lambda\mathbf{p}\,\lambda)\,u^{\alpha'}(\Lambda\mathbf{p}\,\lambda)\,e^{ipx} + (-\text{energy term})]
\end{aligned}$$

where, in the last step, we made a change of integration variables from q to $p = \Lambda^{-1}q$; and

$$\text{RHS} = \sum_{\lambda,\lambda'} \int \tilde{d}p\,\{D^{(s)}[\mathrm{R}(\Lambda, p)^{-1}]^{\lambda'}{}_{\lambda}\,a(\Lambda\mathbf{p}\,\lambda)\,u^\alpha(\mathbf{p}\,\lambda')e^{ipx} + (-\text{energy term})].$$

Comparing the two expressions, we obtain

$$D[\Lambda^{-1}]^\alpha{}_{\alpha'}\,u^{\alpha'}(\Lambda\mathbf{p}\,\lambda) = D^{(s)}[\mathrm{R}(\Lambda, p)^{-1}]^{\lambda'}{}_{\lambda}\,u^\alpha(\mathbf{p}\,\lambda')$$

or, equivalently,

$$D[\Lambda]^\alpha{}_{\alpha'}\,u^{\alpha'}(\mathbf{p}\,\lambda) = u^\alpha(\Lambda\mathbf{p}\,\lambda')\,D^{(s)}[\mathrm{R}(\Lambda, p)]^{\lambda'}{}_{\lambda} \quad . \tag{10.5-25}$$

This equation can be compared with Eq. (10.4-8) and recognized as a "realization" of that general formula—since $u^\alpha(\mathbf{p}\,\lambda)$ is the plane wave solution corresponding to the state $|\mathbf{p}\,\lambda\rangle$ in the chosen Lorentz group representation (index α). The explicit expression for $u(\mathbf{p}\,\lambda)$ given by Eq. (10.5-15) for an irreducible Lorentz wave function satisfies Eq. (10.5-25), as can be readily verified. [cf. Problem 10.14]

We hope this discussion is helpful in illuminating the respective roles played by the (Lorentz) wave functions and fields, the (Poincaré) particle states, and the relativistic wave equations (or the associated "plane wave expansion") which connect them. The particle states are physical states, the associated representation (Poincaré) must be unitary. On the other hand, the field operators $\Psi(x)$ are not always direct physical observables, the corresponding representation (Lorentz) does not have to be unitary. The reason for using the operators $\Psi(x)$ in physics is that interactions between fundamental particles are most conveniently formulated in terms of these field operators if general requirements of covariance, causality,..., etc. are to be incorporated in a consistent way. The formulation of such theories lies, of course, outside the scope of this book. [Berestetskii, Streater]

10.5.4 "Deriving" Relativistic Wave Equations

We have seen that, from the group theoretical point of view, the role of a relativistic wave equation is to take a (momentum space) field operator and project out the physical degrees of freedom corresponding to 4-momenta *on the mass shell* and to a *unique spin*. By taking advantage of this understanding, we can (i) dissect known wave equations to their essentials, to gain further insight to their structure; and (ii) uncover systematic methods to derive new wave equations. We shall first assume that the mass shell condition is satisfied, and focus on the spin degree of freedom.

The wave function $u^\alpha(\mathbf{0}\,\lambda)$ transforms under Lorentz transformations either as an irreducible representation such as the vector field A^μ $(u = 1/2 = v)$, or as a reducible representation such as the Dirac field $(0, 1/2) \oplus (1/2, 0)$. For the sake of definiteness, we shall assume that the fields $\Psi(x)$, $\Phi(p)$, and the wave functions $u(\mathbf{p}\,\lambda)$ of the last subsection are all irreducible and transform as some (u, v) representation. Accordingly, the generic Lorentz index α carried by these will be replaced by the actual labels appropriate for this representation: either the regular set $\{k, l;\ k = -u, \ldots, u;\ l = -v, \ldots, v\}$ or the canonical set $\{j, \lambda;\ \lambda = -j, \ldots, j;\ j = |u - v|, \ldots, (u + v)\}$. Generalization to the reducible case is straightforward in principle and will be commented upon at the end.

Because a general solution of the (momentum space) wave equation (10.5-7) can be written in terms of the rest frame solution according to Eq. (10.5-15), we shall focus on the rest frame equation (10.5-14) at first. In the rest frame, the only degrees of freedom are those associated with rotations. Since the wave function $u^{j\lambda}(\mathbf{0}\,\lambda)$ has *a priori* angular momentum components $|u - v| \leq j \leq (u + v)$, the matrix $\Pi(m, p_t)$ must serve the purpose of projecting a single value of j, say $j = s$, out of all its possible values, i.e.

$$\Pi^{j'\lambda'}{}_{j\lambda}(p_t) \sim \delta^{j'}{}_s \delta^j{}_s \delta^{\lambda'}{}_\lambda \quad . \tag{10.5-26}$$

The symbol $\sim$ reads "proportional to", since an additional overall constant can be included if necessary. Since the connection between the two sets of bases is given by Eqs. (7.7-8) and (7.7-9), we can rewrite the matrix Π in the (k, l) basis as

$$\Pi^{k'l'}{}_{kl}(p_t) \sim \sum_{\lambda} \langle k'l'(uv)s\lambda \rangle \langle s\lambda(uv)k\,l \rangle \quad . \tag{10.5-27}$$

Thus, the form of the wave equation in the rest frame is fully determined by group theoretical considerations, once the representation (u, v) of the wave function is chosen.

We can now derive the general momentum space wave equation using the covariance property of Π, Eq. (10.5-8),

$$\Pi(m, p) = D[H(p)]\,\Pi(m, p_t)\,D[H(p)^{-1}] \tag{10.5-28}$$

where $H(p)$ has its usual meaning. Combining with Eq. (10.5-26), we obtain the explicit form of Π in the (jm) basis (up to a proportionality constant):

$$\Pi^{j'\lambda'}{}_{jl}(m, p) \sim \sum_{\sigma} D[H(p)]^{j'\lambda'}{}_{s\sigma}\, D[H(p)^{-1}]^{s\sigma}{}_{j\lambda} \quad . \tag{10.5-29}$$

Rewriting Π in the (k, l) basis is straightforward, but will not be done here.

The matrix Π given by Eq. (10.5-29) is both necessary and sufficient for the momentum space wave equation (10.5-7) to yield solutions having the required spin properties, if the wave function transforms as an irreducible representation of the Lorentz group. To have a satisfactory relativistic wave equation, however, one still has to make sure that the mass shell condition $p^2 + m^2 = 0$ is satisfied. This will be the case if the scalar "characteristic equation" of the matrix equation (10.5-7) (with Π given by Eq. (10.5-29)) coincides with the mass shell condition. To determine whether this actually happens, one needs to study in more detail the algebraic properties of Π given by Eq. (10.5-29). Since the purpose of our treatment of this subject is mainly to elucidate the meaning of relativistic wave equations, we shall not pursue this technical subject further. We only mention that in general $-p^2 = m^2$ is, indeed, a root of the characteristic equation. However, for higher values of (u, v), the characteristic equation may be a higher order polynomial of p^2, and have additional distinct roots which give rise to other branches of the mass shell. The requirement of having only solutions of a unique mass then restricts the possible representations (u, v) that can be used to describe a given spin s.[8]

We must still consider the case when the wave function transforms as a reducible representation of the Lorentz group. It suffices to discuss the case that two irreducible representations (u_1, v_1) and (u_2, v_2) are involved, such as the Dirac spinor. If we write the matrix $\Pi(m, p)$ in the block form

$$\Pi = \begin{pmatrix} \Pi_{11} & \Pi_{12} \\ \Pi_{21} & \Pi_{22} \end{pmatrix} \tag{10.5-30}$$

where Π_{ij} themselves are $(2u_i + 1)(2v_i + 1) \times (2u_j + 1)(2v_j + 1)$ matrices, then all previous discussion concerning spin projection is relevant here for the matrices

[8] For those interested in the subject of discovering new wave equations, details of this approach can be found in "Relativistic Wave Equations and Field Theory for Arbitrary Spin" by the author published in The Physical Review **156**, 1385 (1967).

Π_{ij} $(i, j = 1, 2)$ individually. The mass shell condition can be obtained from the characteristic equation associated with the complete matrix Π given above.

In this way, we can, for instance, derive the relativistic wave equation for a spin 1/2 particle using the $(0, 1/2) \oplus (1/2, 0)$ field from group theoretical arguments alone. It is not hard to verify that the result is just the Dirac Equation in the so-called γ_5 representation [Messiah]. To close, one should also mention that a full treatment of this subject must include proper discussion of the discrete symmetry transformations: space inversion, time reversal, and charge conjugation.[8]

Problems

10.1 From Eq. (10.1-9) derive the Lorentz transformation formula for (x, t) explicitly in terms of the velocity v between two coordinate frames moving relative to each other along the x-axis. (Compare the result with that given in any standard textbook containing a chapter on special relativity.)

10.2 Show that the Lie algebra of E_3 can be written in our new notation as

$$\begin{aligned} [P_k, P_l] &= 0 \\ [P_m, J_{kl}] &= i(P_k J_{ml} - P_l J_{km}) \\ [J_{mn}, J_{kl}] &= i(J_{kn}\delta_{ml} - J_{ln}\delta_{mk} + J_{mk}\delta_{nl} - J_{ml}\delta_{kn}) \quad . \end{aligned}$$

10.3 Verify the commutation relations involving K in Eqs. (10.2-22) and (10.2-23): (i) by explicit computation using 5×5 matrices derived from Eq. (10.1-9); and (ii) by applying the general formulas of Eqs. (10.2-17) and (10.2-18).

10.4 Express $L_m(\xi) J_n L_m(\xi)^{-1}$ in terms of generators of the Lorentz group.

10.5 Show that an anti-symmetric second-rank tensor in Minkowski space transforms as the $(1, 0) \oplus (0, 1)$ representation of the Lorentz group.

10.6 (i) Show that the trace of a second-rank tensor $t^{\mu}{}_{\mu}$ is invariant under all Lorentz transformations, so that it transforms as the $(0, 0)$ representation. (ii) Show that the traceless symmetric tensor $t^{\{\mu,\nu\}} - g^{\mu\nu} t^{\lambda}{}_{\lambda}/4$ transforms irreducibly under Lorentz transformations as the $(1, 1)$ representation.

10.7 Verify Eq. (10.3-6). [cf. Appendix VII]

10.8 Derive the finite-dimensional irreducible representations of the homogeneous Lorentz group in the canonical basis from considerations parallel to those used to derive the unitary representations (Subsection 10.3.3).

10.9 Using the same method developed for SO(3) and for the homogeneous Lorentz group, derive the finite-dimensional unitary irreducible representations of the group SO(2, 1) which has as its generators (K_1, K_2, J_3). [Subsection 10.4.5]

10.10 Verify Eqs. (10.4-12) and (10.4-13) using the Lie algebra of the Poincaré group.

10.11 Show that if p is a time-like or light-like 4-vector, then the sign of the time component of the vector Λp is the same as that of p, for all proper homogeneous Lorentz transformations Λ.

10.12 Verify that Eq. (10.5-9) is satisfied provided $\Pi(m, p)$ is covariant in the sense of Eq. (10.5-8).

10.13 Consider the following ambiguity associated with the $c_1 = c_2 = 0$ representation of the Poincaré group. The rotation $R_2(2\pi)$ leaves the standard vector $P_l = (\omega_0, 0, 0, \omega_0)$ invariant; hence it is a member of the little group. Let $R_2(2\pi)$ operate on the basis vector $|\mathbf{p}_l\,\lambda\rangle$ of the little group representation space. What do you expect the result to be: $|\mathbf{p}_l\,\lambda\rangle$, $|\mathbf{p}_l\,\lambda\rangle(-1)^{2\lambda}$, or another answer? Explain the reason for your choice.

10.14 Show that the construction of $u(p\,\lambda)$ given by Eq. (10.5-15) satisfies Eq. (10.5-25) which expresses the group-theoretic requirement on the plane wave solutions.

CHAPTER 11

SPACE INVERSION INVARIANCE

Space inversions are discrete transformations which involve changing the sign of one or more of the space coordinates. They are symmetry transformations for most physical systems, with the notable exception of those involving weak interactions.[1] By themselves, these operations are quite simple; in conjunction with the continuous space-time transformations, they lead to interesting, non-trivial, and useful consequences. It is this latter aspect which we shall concentrate on in this chapter. We shall consider, in turn, 2- and 3-dimensional Euclidean space and 4-dimensional Minkowski space. Many of the results from Chaps. 6–10 will be used and expanded when we adjoin the discrete space inversion operations to the continuous symmetry groups. Some general physical consequences of space inversion invariance on quantum mechanical states, scattering amplitudes, and multipole radiation processes are discussed in the last section.

Although the time reversal transformation may seem rather similar to space inversion in 4-dimensional Minkowski space, the representation theory incorporating time reversal which is consistent with established physical principles turns out to have certain unique features. Therefore, a separate chapter will be devoted to that topic.

11.1 Space Inversion in Two-Dimensional Euclidean Space

Let $\hat{\mathbf{e}}_1$ and $\hat{\mathbf{e}}_2$ be the two coordinate unit vectors in the 2-dimensional Euclidean space E_2. There are three distinct space inversion transformations defined as:

(11.1-1a) $$I_\alpha \hat{\mathbf{e}}_i = \hat{\mathbf{e}}_j (I_\alpha)^j{}_i \qquad \alpha = 1, 2, s$$

with

(11.1-1b) $$I_1 = \begin{vmatrix} -1 & 0 \\ 0 & 1 \end{vmatrix} \qquad I_2 = \begin{vmatrix} 1 & 0 \\ 0 & -1 \end{vmatrix} \quad \text{and} \quad I_s = \begin{vmatrix} -1 & 0 \\ 0 & -1 \end{vmatrix} \quad .$$

We see that I_1 inverts the l-axis, I_2 the 2-axis, and I_s both. Corresponding to (11.1-1), the components of any coordinate vector $\mathbf{x}$ transform as

(11.1-2) $$x^i \rightarrow x'^i = (I_\alpha)^i{}_j x^j \quad .$$

[1] Even though space inversion, or parity, invariance is not respected by the weak interaction, the study of the properties of weakly interacting physical systems under space inversion transformation is still of great interest because: (i) the violation of parity is "maximal"; (ii) the combined "charge-conjugation" and parity transformation, usually called CP, is very closely a symmetry transformation [Commins, Sakurai]; and (iii) according to one school of thinking, it could well be that the underlying laws of physics are actually invariant under parity, only to be broken "spontaneously" by the ground state of the physical world at currently studied energy ranges. [Commins]

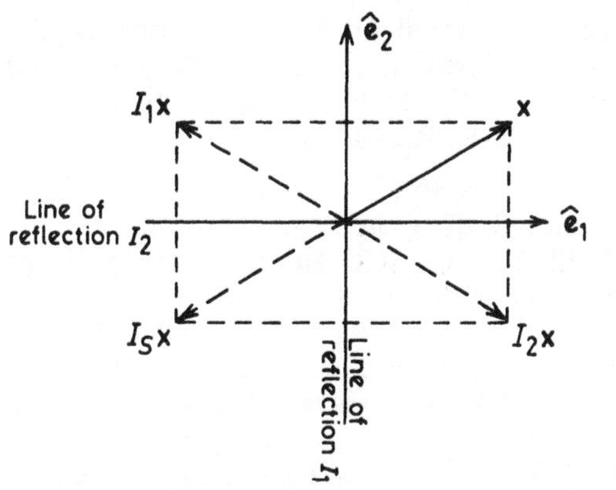

Fig. 11.1 Space Inversion transformations in two-dimensional Euclidean Space

Geometrically, under I_1, the transformed space is the *mirror image* of the original E_2 space with respect to the $x^1 = 0$ (vertical) axies. The same is true for I_2 with respect to the $x^2 = 0$ (horizontal) axis. The full inversion transformation I_s reverses each coordinate space vector with respect to the origin. (See Fig. 11.1)

Together with the identity E (represented by the 2×2 unit matrix in the above description), $\{I_\alpha\}$ form an order 4 group—the dihedral (or four-) group D_2. This group was studied in Chap. 2 [cf. Sec. 2.1, Table 2.3, and Fig. 2.1]. Note also that there are three order 2 subgroups consisting of $\{E, I_\alpha\}$ $\alpha = 1, 2, s$. They are, of course, all isomorphic to the group C_2 (Sec. 2.1), which has already appeared in many guises in other contexts.

The group C_2 has two one-dimensional irreducible representations characterized by $I_\alpha = \pm 1$. The group D_2 has four one-dimensional irreducible representations which are summarized in Table 3.2. The 2-dimensional defining matrices for $\{I_\alpha\}$ in Eq. (11.1-1) correspond to the direct sum of the irreducible representations labelled $\mu = 2$ and 3 in Table 3.2. These results will be used later.

11.1.1 The Group O(2)

The linear homogeneous transformations induced by $\{I_\alpha\}$ on 2-dimensional coordinate vectors preserve the length of the vectors: let $\mathbf{x}$ be an arbitrary vector and $\mathbf{x}' = I_\alpha \mathbf{x}$ [cf. Eq. (11.1-2)] then

$$|\mathbf{x}'|^2 = x_1'^2 + x_2'^2 = x_1^2 + x_2^2 = |\mathbf{x}|^2.$$

We know (from Chap. 6) that 2-dimensional rotations also have this property. In fact the 2-dimensional rotation group SO(2) consists of all such transformations that have unit determinant. A glance at Eq. (11.1-1b) reveals that I_s has unit determinant while the mirror reflections I_1 and I_2 have determinants equal to -1. I_s is therefore a member of the SO(2) group: it corresponds to a rotation by the angle π. I_1 and I_2 are not rotations.

Definition 11.1 (Two Dimensional Orthogonal Matrices): 2×2 matrices $\{A\}$ which satisfy the condition $A A^{\mathrm{T}} = E$ are called *2-dimensional orthogonal matrices.*

Theorem 11.1 (Two-Dimensional Orthogonal Group O(2)): (i) The set of all 2×2 orthogonal matrices forms a group, the orthogonal group O(2), with respect to matrix multiplication; (ii) Elements of O(2) belong to either one of two disjoint sets, $\{\mathrm{R}: \mathrm{R} \in \mathrm{SO}(2)\}$ and $\{I_2\mathrm{R}: \mathrm{R} \in \mathrm{SO}(2)\}$.

The proof of (i) is trivial. To verify (ii), we note that $A\,A^{\mathrm{T}} = E$ implies $\det A = \pm 1$. If $\det A = 1$, then $A = \mathrm{R} \in \mathrm{SO}(2)$ [Theorem 6.1]. If $\det A = -1$ then $\det I_2 A = 1$, hence $I_2 A = \mathrm{R} \in \mathrm{SO}(2)$ and $A = I_2\mathrm{R}$. The two sets are disjoint because they are distinguished by the value of det A.

It is obvious that the above results are equally valid if we substitute I_1 for I_2 everywhere. In fact, the same applies to any member of the class of O(2) elements having the form $I_\theta = \mathrm{R}(\theta) I_2 \mathrm{R}(\theta)^{-1}$, where $\mathrm{R}(\theta) \in \mathrm{SO}(2)$ is a rotation by the angle θ. Geometrically, I_θ represents the *reflection operator* with respect to the axis perpendicular to the direction $\mathrm{R}(\theta)\hat{\mathbf{e}}_2$. We see that all the reflections can be obtained from a given one by rotation. In the following investigation, we shall use "I" without a subscript to denote any member of the *class of reflections*.

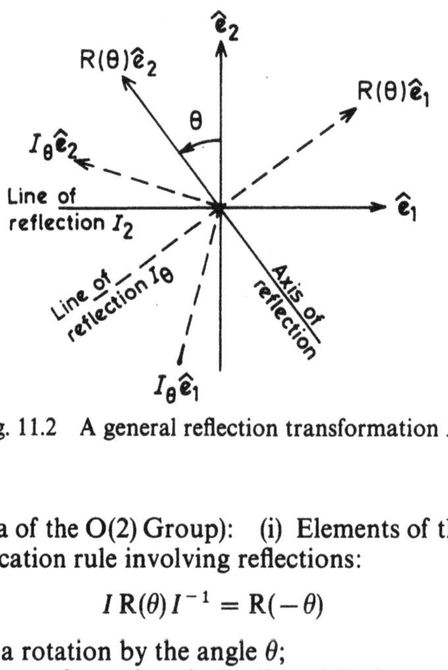

Fig. 11.2 A general reflection transformation I_θ

Theorem 11.2 (Algebra of the O(2) Group): (i) Elements of the group O(2) satisfy the following multiplication rule involving reflections:

$$I\,\mathrm{R}(\theta)\,I^{-1} = \mathrm{R}(-\theta) \tag{11.1-3}$$

where $\mathrm{R}(\theta) \in \mathrm{SO}(2)$ is a rotation by the angle θ;
(ii) Let J be the generator of rotations in E_2 (Sec. 6.2), then

$$I\,J\,I^{-1} = -J \quad . \tag{11.1-4}$$

Eq. (11.1-3) can be visualized geometrically as shown in Fig. 11.3: the mirror-image of a clockwise rotation is clearly a counter-clockwise one. Eq. (11.1-4) follows from Eq. (11.1-3), if account is taken of the connection between $\mathrm{R}(\theta)$ and J, Eq. (6.2-4). Both results can also be established algebraically by matrix multiplication, using Eqs. (6.1-3) and (6.2-5).

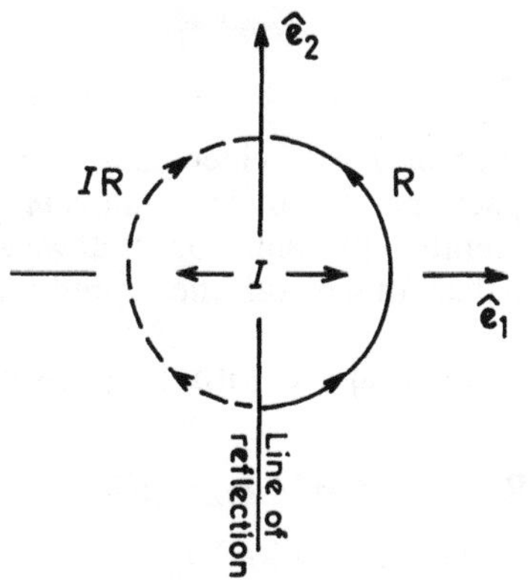

Fig. 11.3 A rotation is reversed by Space Reflection

One of the corollaries of Theorem 11.2 is that the subgroup of rotations SO(2) forms an invariant subgroup of O(2). The factor group O(2)/SO(2) has two elements: the two cosets mentioned in part (ii) of Theorem 11.1; it is isomorphic to C_2.

The operator for the reflection of an arbitrary axis can be obtained from that of a given axis by a rotation, as discussed a moment ago. If we pick I_2 as the "standard" reflection operator, then a general reflection operator can be written as

$$I_\theta = \mathrm{R}(\theta) I_2 \mathrm{R}(\theta)^{-1} = \mathrm{R}(2\theta) I_2 = I_2 \mathrm{R}(-2\theta) \tag{11.1-5}$$

where θ is the angle of rotation from the y-axis to the new axis of reflection [Fig. 11.2], and Theorem 11.2 is used in the last two steps. In particular, we have

$$I_1 = \mathrm{R}(-\pi) I_2 = I_2 \mathrm{R}(\pi) \quad . \tag{11.1-6}$$

11.1.2 Irreducible Representations of O(2)

Two one-dimensional *degenerate irreducible representations* of O(2) are induced by the factor group O(2)/SO(2). They involve assigning $\mathrm{R}(\theta) \to 1$ and $I\,\mathrm{R}(\theta) \to \pm 1$ for elements of the two cosets respectively.

To derive the *non-degenerate representations* we proceed as follows: Let V be the vector space on which some irreducible representation of O(2), labelled by μ, is realized. This representation must also be a representation of the subgroup of rotations SO(2), and of the C_2 subgroup of reflections $\{E, I\}$. (These representations can, of course, be reducible.) Let us focus on SO(2). Its irreducible representations are all one-dimensional [Sec. 6.3]; each one is characterized by an integer m and realized on a 1-dimensional vector space.

We shall find out what is the minimum number of such one-dimensional spaces that V must contain. When a given m-representation of SO(2) is in the μ-representation of O(2), let $|m\rangle$ be the basis vector defined by the eigenvalue equation [Eq. (6.3-5)]

$$J\,|m\rangle = |m\rangle\, m \quad .$$

Eq. (11.1-4) implies

$$J\,I\,|m\rangle = -I\,J\,|m\rangle = I\,|m\rangle(-m) \quad .$$

Hence $I|m\rangle$ is an eigenvector of J with eigenvalue $(-m)$—it does not belong to the one-dimensional subspace spanned by $|m\rangle$ unless $m = 0$. The exceptional case ($m = 0$) yields just the degenerate representations that we already mentioned earlier; we need not consider it further. In general, the representation space V must be at least two-dimensional.

Consider the two-dimensional space with $\{|m\rangle, |-m\rangle\}$ as basis. The above discussion implies [Eq. (6.3-6)]

$$\begin{aligned} R(\theta)\,|\pm m\rangle &= |\pm m\rangle \exp(\mp im\theta) \\ I\,|\pm m\rangle &= |\mp m\rangle a_{\pm} \end{aligned} \qquad (11.1\text{-}7)$$

where $a_\pm$ are complex numbers. Because I is a symmetry transformation, it is realized as a unitary operator, hence

$$a_\pm = \exp(i\alpha_\pm)$$

where $\alpha_\pm$ are real.

Furthermore, since $I \cdot I = E$, Eq. (11.1-7) requires

$$a_+ a_- = \exp[i(\alpha_+ + a_-)] = 1$$

or

$$\alpha_+ = -\alpha_- = \alpha \quad .$$

Therefore, the second equation in (11.1-7) becomes

$$I\,|\pm m\rangle = |\mp m\rangle \exp(\pm i\alpha) \qquad (11.1\text{-}8)$$

where α is an arbitrary real angle.

The first equation in Eq. (11.1-7) and Eq. (11.1-8) tell us that the two-dimensional space spanned by $\{|\pm m\rangle\}$ is invariant under O(2) transformations. It is also minimal [Definition 3.4], as the two linearly independent basis vectors are inextricably linked by the reflection operator I. Thus we have obtained a two-dimensional unitary irreducible representation of O(2) characterized by a positive integer m and an angle α.

The remaining task is to identify the *inequivalent irreducible representations* among those found above. We know that representations characterized by distinct values of the parameter m are inequivalent, since that is the case for the subgroup SO(2) of O(2). But what about those corresponding to different α?

Two representations are equivalent if they are related by a similarity transformation; or, in other words, if one can be obtained from the other by a change of basis. An inspection of Eq. (11.1-8) suggests the following change of basis:

$$\begin{aligned} |m\rangle' &= |m\rangle \\ |-m\rangle' &= |-m\rangle\, e^{i\alpha} \end{aligned} \qquad (11.1\text{-}9)$$

With respect to the primed basis, we obtain

$$\begin{aligned} R(\theta)\,|\pm m\rangle' &= |\pm m\rangle' \exp(\mp im\theta) \\ I\,|\pm m\rangle' &= |\mp m\rangle' \end{aligned} \qquad (11.1\text{-}10)$$

where the right-hand sides are independent of the parameter α. This result indicates that representations labelled by (m, α) are all equivalent to the one characterized by $(m, 0)$. In other words, there is only one inequivalent unitary irreducible representation of O(2) for each positive integer m.

We summarize the results discussed so far by the following theorem.

Theorem 11.3 (Unitary irreducible Representations of O(2)): The group O(2) has two types of inequivalent unitary irreducible representations: (i) There are two degenerate one-dimensional representations characterized by a *parity* eigenvalue $\eta\,(=\pm 1)$ with a single basis vector $|0\,\eta\rangle$ defined by

$$\begin{aligned} R(\theta)\,|0\,\eta\rangle &= |0\,\eta\rangle \\ I\,|0\,\eta\rangle &= |0\,\eta\rangle\,\eta \quad ; \end{aligned} \tag{11.1-11}$$

(ii) There are an infinite number of two-dimensional faithful representations characterized by an *angular momentum* eigenvalue $m\,(=1, 2, \ldots)$ with basis vectors $\{|\pm m\rangle\}$ defined by

$$\begin{aligned} R(\theta)\,|\pm m\rangle &= |\pm m\rangle \exp(\mp im\theta) \\ I\,|\pm m\rangle &= |\mp m\rangle \quad . \end{aligned} \tag{11.1-12}$$

The proof of these results has been given already in the discussions leading to the statement of the Theorem.

Having obtained the main result of this subsection, we turn to some details concerning *phase convention* for the basis vectors. In the above discussion, we did not specify precisely the spatial reflection operator I. The results hold in principle for any member of the class of reflections I_θ, Eq. (11.1-5). We should be aware, however, of possible dependence of the relative phases of the basis vectors on the choice of I in the defining equations (11.1-11) and (11.1-12).

Suppose we substitute $I_\theta = R(\theta)\,I\,R(\theta)^{-1} = I\,R(-2\theta)$ in place of I in Eq. (11.1-11). We obtain

$$I_\theta|0\,\eta\rangle = I\,R(-2\theta)\,|0\,\eta\rangle = I\,|0\,\eta\rangle = |0\,\eta\rangle\,\eta \quad .$$

The right-hand side is totally independent of the parameter θ. The same vector $|0\,\eta\rangle$ is obtained no matter which I is used for its definition in Eq. (11.1-11).

The situation is, however, different with Eq. (11.1-12). It is straightforward to see that

$$\begin{aligned} I_\theta|\pm m\rangle &= I\,R(-2\theta)\,|\pm m\rangle = I\,|\pm m\rangle \exp(\pm i2m\theta) \\ &= |\mp m\rangle \exp(\pm i2m\theta) \quad . \end{aligned} \tag{11.1-13}$$

Hence once the "relative phase" between the two eigenvectors $|m\rangle$ and $|-m\rangle$ is specified using one reflection operator I by Eq. (11.1-12), the effect on these vectors by other reflection operators I_θ is determined. For definiteness, we shall choose $I = I_2$ [reflection about the (horizontal) x-axis] in the defining equation (11.1-12) in all subsequent discussions where a specific choice is required. We have, in particular, then

$$\begin{aligned} I_2\,|\pm m\rangle &\equiv |\mp m\rangle \\ I_1\,|\pm m\rangle &= |\mp m\rangle\, e^{\pm im\pi} = |\mp m\rangle\,(-1)^m \quad . \end{aligned} \tag{11.1-14}$$

The first equation simply specifies our particular choice of I in (11.1-12); the second equation follows from (11.1-13) with the substitution $\theta = -\pi/2$.

We can form *eigenstates of the spatial reflection operators* by taking linear combinations of $|m\rangle$ and $|-m\rangle$. For instance, let us define

$$|m\,\tau\rangle = (|m\rangle + |-m\rangle\tau)/2^{1/2} \tag{11.1-15}$$

where $\tau = \pm 1$. Then, it is easy to see that

$$\begin{aligned} I_2\,|m\,\tau\rangle &= |m\,\tau\rangle\,\tau \\ I_1\,|m\,\tau\rangle &= |m\,\tau\rangle\,\tau(-1)^m \end{aligned} \tag{11.1-16}$$

We obtain, therefore, eigenstates of $I_{1,2}$ with eigenvalues $\tau(-1)^m$ and τ respectively.

So far, we have only considered single-valued representations of O(2). If O(2) is the full symmetry group of the system under consideration, we would expect these to be the only relevant representations for physical applications. As part of a larger symmetry in 3- or 4-dimensional space, however, we know double-valued representations of SO(2), corresponding to $m = 1/2, 3/2, \ldots$, are also relevant. In a double-valued representation, it is permissible to have $I^2 = -1$, in addition to $I^2 = 1$ (as considered above). We shall not discuss these representations in any detail here because the logical place to introduce double-valued representations is in the context of O(3) and O(3, 1) where they arise from single-valued representations of the "covering groups". [cf. Sec. 7.1]

It is worthwhile to call attention to some general conceptual points contained in the results summarized in Theorem 11.3. We note that the structure of the two types of irreducible representations are rather different. The inequivalent representations of the first kind are distinguished by the eigenvalue η of the space inversion (*Parity*) operator, whereas those of the second kind are characterized by the eigenvalue m of the (magnitude of) angular momentum operator. Since the parameter η determines the character of the irreducible representation, it will be called the *intrinsic parity* eigenvalue. This is to be contrasted with eigenvalues (τ and $\tau(-1)^m$) of spatial reflections in the second kind of irreducible representations labelled by m, such as given in Eq. (11.1-16), which are derived quantities. *Both* values of $\tau\,(\pm 1)$ are contained in the *same* irreducible representation.

11.1.3 The Extended Euclidean Group $\tilde{\mathrm{E}}_2$ and its Irreducible Representations

We shall now consider combining O(2) group operations with translations T(**b**) in the two-dimensional Euclidean Space.

Definition 11.2 (Extended Euclidean Group $\tilde{\mathrm{E}}_2$): The full symmetry group of the 2-dimensional Euclidean space is called the 2-dimensional *extended Euclidean group* $\tilde{\mathrm{E}}_2$. It consists of translations, rotations, and space reflections.

Since we have already studied the continuous group E_2 and its irreducible representations in some detail in Chap. 9, it is only necessary to consider the extensions due to the introduction of the discrete space reflection operators. The generators of continuous transformations are (P_1, P_2) for translations, and J for rotations. Simple geometrical considerations similar to that leading to Theorem 11.2 suggest the following algebraic relations between space inversion, transla-

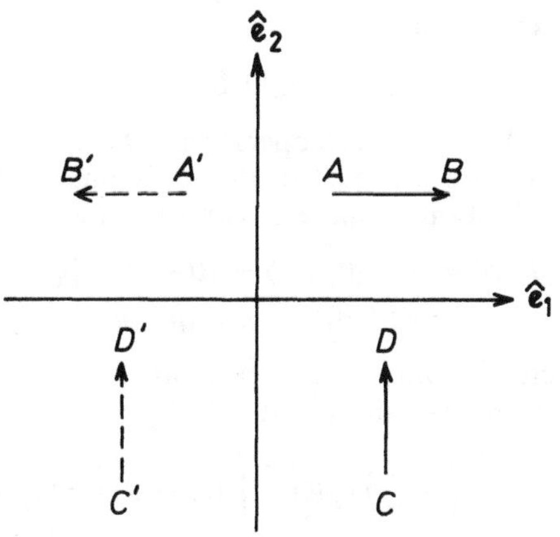

Fig. 11.4 Effect of reflection I_1 on translation $T(b\hat{e}_1)$ $(A \to B)$ and $T(b\hat{e}_2)$ $(C \to D)$

tions and their generators:

(11.1-17)
$$I\,T(\mathbf{b})I^{-1} = T(\mathbf{b}') \qquad b'^i = I^i{}_j b^j$$
$$I\,P_i I^{-1} = P_j I^j{}_i$$

where $I^i{}_j$ is the relevant reflection matrix (such as given in Eq. (11.1-1b)). Particular cases are $I_1 P_1 I_1{}^{-1} = -P_1, I_1 P_2 I_1{}^{-1} = P_2, \ldots$ etc. [cf. Fig. 11.4].

These results can also be verified algebraically using the 3×3 matrix representations of the operators as described in Sec. 9.1. [Problem 11.2]

Just as in the case of the continuous group E_2, the translations $T(\mathbf{b})$ form an invariant subgroup T_2. The factor group $\tilde{E}_2/T_2$ is isomorphic to O(2). The irreducible representations of $\tilde{E}_2$ are labelled by the eigenvalue p^2 of the Casimir operator $\mathbf{P}^2$. We shall derive the unitary irreducible representations by the induced representation method.

Degenerate irreducible representations are obtained in the case $p^2 = 0$ (hence $p_1 = p_2 = 0$). The little group for the $\mathbf{p} = 0$ vector is the full factor group O(2). The unitary irreducible representations of O(2) are given by Theorem 11.3. Each of these representations induces a representation of $\tilde{E}_2$, in which the translations are degenerate and are all represented by the identity operator.

The *faithful irreducible representations* are derived in the same way as described in Sec. 9.3. The little group of the standard vector $\mathbf{p}_0 \equiv (p, 0)$ is now the C_2 group consisting of $\{E, I_2\}$. There are two irreducible representations, both one-dimensional, which are characterized by the eigenvalue $\eta = \pm 1$ of the reflection operator I_2. The basis vector (for a given p and η) is defined by

(11.1-18)
$$\mathbf{P}\,|\hat{\mathrm{p}}_0\rangle = |\hat{\mathrm{p}}_0\rangle\,\mathbf{p}_0$$
$$I_2\,|\hat{\mathrm{p}}_0\rangle = |\hat{\mathrm{p}}_0\rangle\,\eta$$

where $\hat{\mathrm{p}}_0$ is the unit vector in the $\mathbf{p}_0$ direction (along the x-axis). As in Sec. 9.3, we define the general basis vector as

$$|\hat{p}\rangle \equiv R(\theta)|\hat{p}_0\rangle. \tag{11.1-19}$$

The matrix elements of the translation operators T(**b**) and rotation operators $R(\theta)$ with respect to this basis are identical to those obtained in Sec. 9.3. The matrix elements of the space reflection I_2 operator can be deduced as follows:

$$\begin{aligned} I_2|\hat{p}\rangle &= I_2 R(\theta)|\hat{p}_0\rangle = R(-\theta) I_2|\hat{p}_0\rangle \\ &= R(-\theta)|\hat{p}_0\rangle\eta = |\hat{p}_2\rangle\eta \end{aligned} \tag{11.1-20}$$

where θ is the polar angle of $\hat{p}$ and $-\theta$ is the polar angle of $\hat{p}_2$—the I_2 reflection of $\hat{p}$. [See Fig. 11.5] Similarly, we can show that

$$\begin{aligned} I_1|\hat{p}\rangle &= R\left(-\frac{\pi}{2}\right) I_2 R\left(\frac{\pi}{2}\right)|\hat{p}\rangle = R(-\pi) I_2|\hat{p}\rangle \\ &= R(-\pi)|\hat{p}_2\rangle\eta = |\hat{p}_1\rangle\eta \end{aligned} \tag{11.1-21}$$

where $\hat{p}_1$ is the I_1 reflection of $\hat{p}$. [See Fig. 11.5] These results, of course, conform to our expectations based on geometrical considerations. The precise derivation establishes the sign (phase factor) of the non-vanishing matrix elements for a given representation.

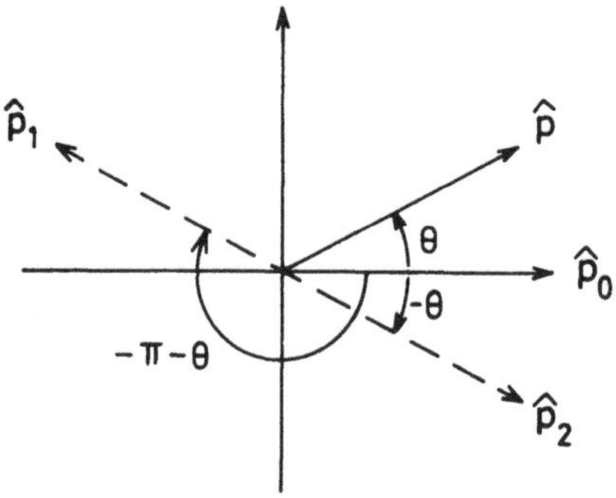

Fig. 11.5 Effects of reflections I_1 and I_2 on the momentum vector $\hat{\mathbf{p}}$

Theorem 11.4 (Faithful Unitary Irreducible Representations of $\tilde{E}_2$): The faithful unitary irreducible representations of $\tilde{E}_2$ are characterized by a continuous parameter (momentum) $p \in (-\infty, \infty)$ and a discrete parameter (parity) η $(= \pm 1)$. The representation matrices for elements of the E_2 subgroup are given by Eqs. (9.3-4), (9.3-5), and for space inversions by (11.1-20), and (11.1-21).

Let us turn our attention to the alternative *angular momentum basis* on the same representation space [cf. Sec. 9.2 and second half of Sec. 9.3] and establish the connection to irreducible representations of O(2) discussed in the last subsection. Following Eq. (9.3-8), we define (omitting the invariant labels p, η as usual)

$$|m\rangle = i^m \int R(\phi)|\hat{p}_0\rangle e^{im\phi}\frac{d\phi}{2\pi} \quad . \tag{11.1-22}$$

We know that

$$J\,|m\rangle = |m\rangle\, m$$

and

$$\mathrm{T}(\mathbf{b})\,|m\rangle = \sum_{m'} |m'\rangle\, e^{i(m-m')\phi}\, \mathrm{J}_{m-m'}(pb)$$

where ϕ is the polar angle of **b**. The only question is how do these basis vectors behave under reflections. Making use of Eq. (11.1-20), we have

$$\begin{aligned} I_2\,|m\rangle &= i^m \int \mathrm{R}(-\phi)\,|\hat{\mathrm{p}}_0\rangle\,\eta\, e^{im\phi}\frac{d\phi}{2\pi} \\ &= |-m\rangle\,\eta\,(-1)^m \end{aligned} \tag{11.1.23}$$

and

$$\begin{aligned} I_1\,|m\rangle &= \mathrm{R}(-\pi)\,I_2\,|m\rangle = \mathrm{R}(-\pi)\,|-m\rangle\,\eta\,(-1)^m \\ &= |-m\rangle\,\eta \quad . \end{aligned} \tag{11.1-24}$$

We conclude that, in a given (p,η) irreducible representation of $\tilde{\mathrm{E}}_2$, the two basis vectors $|\pm m\rangle$ span a subspace that is irreducible with respect to O(2) transformations (i.e. rotations and reflections). In this subspace, the matrices for rotations and reflections are:

$$\mathrm{R}(\theta) = \begin{pmatrix} e^{-im\phi} & 0 \\ 0 & e^{im\theta} \end{pmatrix} \qquad I_1 = \begin{pmatrix} 0 & \eta \\ \eta & 0 \end{pmatrix} \qquad I_2 = (-1)^m\, I_1 \quad . \tag{11.1-25}$$

11.2 Space Inversion in Three Dimensional Euclidean Space

In 3-dimensional Euclidean space, one can have space reflection with respect to the origin I_s (all three coordinates change sign), reflections with respect to a coordinate axis I_i (two of the coordinates change sign), and reflections with respect to a coordinate plane I_{ij} (one of the coordinates changes sign). It is a simple matter to see that I_i is equivalent to a rotation by π (around the same axis), and that I_{ij} is equivalent to the total reflection I_s followed by a rotation by π (around the normal to the coordinate plane). Therefore, it suffices to consider the single independent space reflection transformation I_s, which we shall refer to as *space inversion* or *parity transformation*,

$$\begin{aligned} I_s\hat{\mathbf{e}}_i &= -\hat{\mathbf{e}}_i \qquad i = 1, 2, 3 \quad ; \\ I_s\mathbf{x} &= -\mathbf{x} \qquad \text{for all } \mathbf{x} \quad . \end{aligned} \tag{11.2-1}$$

We shall study the consequences of combining this inversion operation with elements of the continuous transformation groups SO(3) (Chapters 7,8) and E_3 (Chap. 9). Since the general ideas and the methods used will be similar to those of the previous section, we shall not belabor the details too much.

11.2.1 The Group O(3) and its Irreducible Representations

The space inversion operation, Eq. (11.2-1), clearly preserves the length of all 3-dimensional vectors **x**, just as the rotations do.

Theorem 11.5 (The Group O(3)): (i) The set of all homogeneous linear transformations $\{A\}$ on 3-dimensional Euclidean space which preserve the length of vectors forms a group—*the orthogonal group* O(3); (ii) elements of the group O(3) are divided into two classes, $\{\mathrm{R}; \mathrm{R} \in \mathrm{SO}(3)\}$ and $\{I_s\mathrm{R}; \mathrm{R} \in \mathrm{SO}(3)\}$, distinguished by the sign of the determinant of the transformation matrix.

The necessary and sufficient condition for a homogeneous linear transformation matrix A to preserve the lengths of vectors on which it operates is, of course,

$$A^{\mathrm{T}} A = E$$

or, equivalently,

(11.2-2) $$A^i{}_k A^j{}_l \delta^{kl} = \delta^{ij} \quad .$$

As before, this implies $\det A = \pm 1$, the $\det A = 1$ class corresponds to 3-dimensional rotations and the $\det A = -1$ class represents non-trivial reflections and the space inversion. Because the determinant of A can assume both signs, the anti-symmetric unit tensor ε^{ijk} is no longer an invariant tensor like δ^{ij}. [cf. Eq. (7.1-6)] Elements of O(3) belonging to the class of non-trivial reflections and the inversion reverse the sign of ε^{ijk}.

Theorem 11.6 (Algebra of the O(3) Group): The space inversion transformation commutes with all 3-dimensional rotations and their generators, i.e.

(11.2-3) $$I_s \mathrm{R} I_s^{-1} = \mathrm{R} \qquad \text{for all } \mathrm{R} \in \mathrm{SO}(3)$$

(11.2-4) $$[I_s, J_i] = 0 \qquad \text{for } i = 1, 2, 3 \quad .$$

These relations, together with the algebra of SO(3) [Sec. 7.2], form the algebra of O(3).

Proof: Since I_s reverses the sign of all coordinate components, it is represented by the matrix $-E$ (the negative identity matrix):

$$I_s = \begin{pmatrix} -1 & & \\ & -1 & \\ & & -1 \end{pmatrix} \quad .$$

This matrix clearly commutes with all 3×3 matrices, including J_i and $\mathrm{R}(\alpha, \beta, \gamma)$. QED

The irreducible representations of O(3) can be derived readily from those of SO(3). Since I_s commutes with all generators of SO(3), it is a "Casimir operator"; and the basis vectors of the irreducible representations can be chosen as simultaneous eigenvectors of I_s and J_3:

(11.2-5) $$\begin{aligned} J_3 |m\rangle &= |m\rangle m \\ I_s |m\rangle &= |m\rangle \eta \end{aligned}$$

where $\eta = \pm 1$. Can the choice of η depend on m? The answer is "no", as

$$\begin{aligned} I_s |m \pm 1\rangle &= I_s J_\pm |m\rangle [j(j+1) - m(m \pm 1)]^{-1/2} \\ &= J_\pm I_s |m\rangle [j(j+1) - m(m \pm 1)]^{-1/2} \\ &= |m \pm 1\rangle \eta \end{aligned}$$

follows from Eq. (11.2-5). In other words, the same eigenvalue η for I_s is shared by all vectors in the canonical basis $\{|m\rangle, m = -j,\ldots,j\}$.

Theorem 11.7 (Unitary Irreducible Representations of O(3)): The unitary irreducible representations of O(3) are labelled by (j, η) where $j = 0, 1/2, 1, 3/2, \ldots$, and $\eta = \pm 1$. The matrix representation of rotations are the same as in SO(3) and the matrix for the space inversion I_s is η times the identity matrix. The parameter η is referred to as the *parity* of this representation.

It is interesting to note that the generalization from SO(3) to O(3) is much more straightforward than that from SO(2) to O(2)! The simplicity of the 3-dimensional case is, of course, due to the fact that the independent space inversion operator I_s is proportional to the identity. This, in turn, is related to the oddness of the space dimension. (The space inversion in 2-dimensional is not independent of rotations.) In general, as rotations can change the sign of coordinates in pairs, the total space inversion operator is useful only in odd-dimensional spaces.

Examples of physical realizations of representations of O(3) abound in all branches of physics, since most physical systems are invariant under space inversion as well as rotations. The solutions to classical and quantum mechanical equations of motion for spherically symmetric systems are usually classified according to parity and angular momentum eigenvalues. Specifically, consider the *spherical harmonics* $Y_{lm}(\hat{\mathrm{u}})$ where $\hat{\mathbf{u}}$ is a unit vector specified by two angles (θ, ϕ). We already know that Y_{lm} is the basis "wave function" of angular momentum states $|lm\rangle$, [Eq. (8.6-1)]

$$Y_{lm}(\hat{\mathrm{u}}) = \langle \hat{\mathrm{u}} | l\, m \rangle = \langle \hat{\mathrm{z}} | \mathrm{R}_2{}^{\dagger}(\theta) | l\, m \rangle\, e^{im\phi} \quad .$$

Now we wish to investigate its behavior under space inversion I_s:

$$Y_{lm}(\hat{\mathrm{u}}) \xrightarrow{I_s} Y_{lm}(-\hat{\mathrm{u}}) = \langle \hat{\mathrm{u}} | I_s | l\, m \rangle = \langle \hat{\mathrm{u}} | l\, m \rangle \eta = \eta\, Y_{lm}(\hat{\mathrm{u}})$$

where we made use of Eq. (11.2-5) in the second step. Since η is independent of m and $\hat{\mathrm{u}}$, we can find its value by specializing to the simple case $m = 0$ and $\hat{\mathrm{u}} = \hat{\mathrm{z}}$. We obtain:

$$\begin{aligned} Y_{l0}(-\hat{\mathrm{z}}) &= \langle -\hat{\mathrm{z}} | l\, 0 \rangle = \langle \hat{\mathrm{z}} | \mathrm{R}_2{}^{\dagger}(\pi) | l\, 0 \rangle = \langle \hat{\mathrm{z}} | l\, 0 \rangle (-1)^l \\ &= Y_{l0}(\hat{\mathrm{z}})(-1)^l \end{aligned}$$

where the explicit expression for $D^l[\mathrm{R}_2(\pi)]$ [cf. Problem 7.7] is used in the third step, and the rest of the derivation involves only definitions. We conclude from this result that $\eta = (-1)^l$ and, in general,

$$Y_{lm}(\hat{\mathrm{u}}) \xrightarrow{I_s} Y_{lm}(-\hat{\mathrm{u}}) = (-1)^l\, Y_{lm}(\hat{\mathrm{u}}) \quad . \tag{11.2-6}$$

We obtain thereby a group-theoretical derivation (and interpretation) of another well-known classical property of Y_{lm}. Physically, this implies that systems with "orbital angular momentum" l carry parity eigenvalue $(-1)^l$.

11.2.2 The Extended Euclidean Group $\tilde{\mathrm{E}}_3$ and its Irreducible Representations

The *extended Euclidean group* $\tilde{\mathrm{E}}_3$ consists of translations $\{\mathrm{T}(\mathbf{b})\}$ in addition to all the O(3) transformations. Alternatively, we can say that $\tilde{\mathrm{E}}_3$ is obtained by adjoining space inversion I_s to the proper Euclidean group E_3. Let $\mathbf{P} = (P_1, P_2, P_3)$ be generators of translations; then the same geometrical and algebraic considerations as presented in the last section imply that

$$I_s \mathrm{T}(\mathbf{b}) I_s^{-1} = \mathrm{T}(-\mathbf{b})$$
(11.2-7)
$$I_s \mathbf{P} I_s^{-1} = -\mathbf{P} \quad .$$

The translations $\{\mathrm{T}(\mathbf{b})\}$ remain an invariant subgroup of the extended group. The operator $\mathbf{P}^2$ remains a Casimir operator. But $\mathbf{J}\cdot\mathbf{P}$ is no longer invariant under all group operations: it changes sign under space inversion. (Quantities which are invariant under rotations and change sign under space inversion are often called *pseudo-scalars*.) It is clear, however, that $(\mathbf{J}\cdot\mathbf{P})^2$ is a natural Casimir operator.

The *degenerate representations* of $\tilde{\mathrm{E}}_3$ correspond to $\mathbf{P}^2 = 0$ (hence $P_1 = P_2 = P_3 = 0$). The little group coincides with the factor group $\tilde{\mathrm{E}}_3/\mathrm{T}_3$ which is isomorphic to O(3). The irreducible representations are the same as those of O(3) described in the previous sub-section. All translations are represented by the identity operator in this representation.

To derive representations of $\tilde{\mathrm{E}}_3$ with non-degenerate translations, we start, as in Sec. 9.7, with the standard vector $\mathbf{p}_0 = p\hat{\mathbf{e}}_z$. The little group is now the O(2) group associated with transformations of the x- and y-coordinates. Thus, we must use the irreducible representations of O(2) [Theorem 11.3] as the starting point. Two classes of representations emerge.

There are two one-dimensional irreducible representations of O(2) labelled by η $(= \pm 1)$. Neglecting the invariant irreducible representation labels (p, η), we denote the starting basis vector by $|\hat{p}_0\rangle$, $\hat{p}_0 = \mathbf{p}_0/p = \mathbf{e}_z$. It is defined by the eigenvalue equations:

$$\mathbf{P}\,|\hat{p}_0\rangle = |\hat{p}_0\rangle\,\mathbf{p}_0$$
(11.2-8a)
$$J_3\,|\hat{p}_0\rangle = 0$$
$$I\,|\hat{p}_0\rangle = |\hat{p}_0\rangle\,\eta$$

where I is any reflection operator in the x-y plane. The general basic vector is then defined as:

(11.2-8b)
$$|\hat{p}\rangle \equiv \mathrm{R}(\hat{p})|\hat{\mathrm{p}}_0\rangle = \mathrm{R}(\phi,\theta,0)\,|\hat{\mathrm{p}}_0\rangle$$

where (θ, ϕ) are the polar and azimuthal angles of $\hat{\mathbf{p}}$. We leave it as an exercise for the reader to verify the following general expressions of the representation matrices for elements of the $\tilde{\mathrm{E}}_3$ in the (p, η) representation (Problem 11.4):

$$\mathrm{T}(\mathbf{b})\,|\hat{p}\rangle = |\hat{p}\rangle\,\mathrm{e}^{-i\mathbf{b}\cdot\mathbf{p}}$$
(11.2-9)
$$\mathrm{R}(\alpha,\beta,\gamma)\,|\hat{p}\rangle = |\mathrm{R}\hat{p}\rangle$$
$$I_s\,|\hat{p}\rangle = |\hat{p}\rangle\,\eta \quad .$$

If we transform to the angular momentum basis by the usual method, we find the representation space naturally decomposes into a direct sum of subspaces on which the subgroup O(3) is realized exactly as described in the previous sub-section. [cf. Problem 11.5]

Next, we will use the two-dimensional *faithful representations* of O(2) to construct the corresponding induced representations of $\tilde{\mathrm{E}}_3$. Suppressing the representation labels[2] (p, λ), we obtain starting basis vectors $|\hat{p}_0 \pm\rangle$ defined by the eigenvalue equations [Eq. (11.1-12)]:

$$\begin{aligned} \mathbf{P}\,|\hat{p}_0 \pm\rangle &= |\hat{p}_0 \pm\rangle\,\mathbf{p}_0 \\ J_3\,|\hat{p}_0 \pm\rangle &= |\hat{p}_0 \pm\rangle(\pm\lambda) \\ I_2\,|\hat{p}_0 \pm\rangle &= |\hat{p}_0 \mp\rangle \end{aligned} \tag{11.2-10}$$

where I_2 is the reflection operator which reverses the sign of the y-coordinate. The general basis vectors $|\hat{p} \pm\rangle$ are, as usual, defined by:

$$|\hat{p} \pm\rangle \equiv \mathrm{R}(\hat{p})\,|\hat{p}_0 \pm\rangle \equiv \mathrm{R}(\phi, \theta, 0)\,|\hat{p}_0 \pm\rangle \tag{11.2-11}$$

where (θ, ϕ) are the direction angles of $\hat{\mathbf{p}}$. The representation matrices of $\mathrm{T}(\mathbf{b})$ and $\mathrm{R}(\alpha, \beta, \gamma)$ are the same as those for the continuous group E_3 given in Sec. 9.6 [Eqs. (9.7-9), (9.7-10)]. We need only consider the space inversion operator I_s. We begin by noting that

$$I_s = \mathrm{R}_2(\pi)\,I_2 \quad . \tag{11.2-12}$$

Using this decomposition, we obtain

$$I_s\,|\hat{p}_0 \pm\rangle = \mathrm{R}_2(\pi)|\hat{p}_0 \mp\rangle \quad .$$

Hence, the effect of I_s on a general basis vector is

$$\begin{aligned} I_s\,|\hat{p} \pm\rangle &= I_s\,\mathrm{R}(\hat{p})\,|\hat{p}_0 \pm\rangle = \mathrm{R}(\hat{p})\,I_s\,|\hat{p}_0 \pm\rangle \\ &= \mathrm{R}(\phi, \theta, 0)\,\mathrm{R}_2(\pi)\,|\hat{p}_0 \pm\rangle \quad . \end{aligned}$$

To proceed, we make use of

$$\mathrm{R}_3(\phi)\,\mathrm{R}_2(\pi + \theta) = \mathrm{R}_3(\phi)\,\mathrm{R}_2(-\pi + \theta) = \mathrm{R}_3(\pi + \phi)\,\mathrm{R}_2(\pi - \theta)\,\mathrm{R}_3(-\pi)$$

$$\mathrm{R}_3(-\pi)\,|\hat{p}_0 \mp\rangle = |\hat{p}_0 \mp\rangle\, e^{\mp i\lambda\pi} = |\hat{p}_0 \mp\rangle(-1)^{\lambda}$$

and

$$\mathrm{R}_3(\pi + \phi)\,\mathrm{R}_2(\pi - \theta)\,|\hat{p}_0 \mp\rangle = \mathrm{R}(-\hat{p})\,|\hat{p}_0 \mp\rangle \equiv |-\hat{p} \mp\rangle \quad .$$

Combining these results, we arrive at the useful result:

$$I_s\,|\hat{p} \pm\rangle = |-\hat{p} \mp\rangle(-1)^{\lambda} \quad . \tag{11.2-13}$$

We recall that the eigenvalue λ has the physical interpretation of being the helicity of the state [cf. Sec. 9.6]. Since the helicity is the projection of $\mathbf{J}$ along the direction of $\mathbf{p}$, it is understandable that it changes sign under I_s—as $\mathbf{p}$ changes sign while $\mathbf{J}$ remains invariant.

We summarize the main results as follows:

Theorem 11.8 (Unitary Irreducible Representations of $\tilde{\mathrm{E}}_3$): The unitary irreducible representations of the extended Euclidean group $\tilde{\mathrm{E}}_3$ are characterized by the

[2] In order to be consistent with the convention of Chap. 9, the representation label m for the O(2) irreducible representation will be replaced by the symbol λ in the following.

eigenvalues of the Casimir operators $\mathbf{P}^2$ and $(\mathbf{J}\cdot\mathbf{P})^2$:

(i) When $\mathbf{P}^2 = 0$ (hence $\mathbf{J}\cdot\mathbf{P} = 0$), the irreducible representations coincide with those of the factor group O(3); they are labelled by (j, η)—the "angular momentum" and "parity" eigenvalues respectively; these representations are degenerate in the translations.
(ii) When $\mathbf{P}^2 = p^2\,(p \neq 0)$ and $\mathbf{J}\cdot\mathbf{P} = 0$, the irreducible representations are labelled by (p, η)—the magnitude of linear momentum and intrinsic parity eigenvalues. The basis vectors for these representations are defined by Eqs. (11.2-8a,b) and the representation matrices are given by Eq. (11.2-9); these are the *zero helicity representations.*
(iii) When $\mathbf{P}^2 = p^2\,(p \neq 0)$ and $(\mathbf{J}\cdot\mathbf{P})^2/p^2 = \lambda^2$ $(\lambda = 1, 2, \ldots)$, the irreducible representations are labelled by (p, λ)—the magnitude of linear momentum and helicity eigenvalues. The basis vectors are defined by Eqs. (11.2-10), (11.2-11); and the representation matrices are given by Eqs. (9.7-9), (9.7-10), and (11.2-13).

Note that in part (iii) we only included single-valued representations (corresponding to integer-valued helicity eigenvalue λ) induced by the little group O(2). As remarked in connection with Theorem 11.3, multivalued representations of O(2) could be considered, which can induce multivalued representations of $\tilde{\mathrm{E}}_3$. However, only the double-valued representations, which naturally arise both from the O(3) subgroup of $\tilde{\mathrm{E}}_3$ and from its extension to the complete Poincaré group [next section], will be of interest to us.

Next, we turn attention to a basis consisting of *simultaneous eigenvectors of angular momentum and parity* for the faithful unitary irreducible representations (case (iii) above). The angular momentum basis is obtained by the standard projection method, as given in Eq. (9.8-6). Keeping in mind the suppressed invariant lables (p, λ), we have

$$|j\,m\,\pm\rangle = \int d\Omega_p\, \mathrm{R}(\hat{p})\,|\hat{p}_0\,\pm\rangle D_j^{\dagger}[\mathrm{R}(\hat{p})]^{\pm\lambda}{}_m \frac{2j+1}{4\pi} \quad .$$

In order to find out the action of I_s on these states, we begin in a similar way as earlier [Eq. (11.2-12)]:

$$I_s\,|j\,m\,\pm\rangle = \int \mathrm{d}\Omega_{\hat{p}}\, \mathrm{R}(\hat{p})\,\mathrm{R}_2(\pi)\,|\hat{p}_0\,\mp\rangle\, \mathrm{D}_j^{\dagger}[\mathrm{R}(\hat{p})]^{\pm\lambda}{}_m \frac{2j+1}{4\pi} \quad .$$

Defining $\mathrm{R}(\hat{p}') = \mathrm{R}(\hat{p})\,\mathrm{R}_2(\pi)$, changing the integration variables to $\mathrm{d}\Omega_{\hat{p}'}$, invoking the Rearrangement Lemma and the invariant group measure, and making use of[3]

$$\begin{aligned} D_j^{\dagger}[\mathrm{R}(\hat{p})]^{\pm\lambda}{}_m &= D^j[\mathrm{R}^{-1}(\hat{p})]^{\pm\lambda}{}_m = D^j[\mathrm{R}_2(\pi)\,\mathrm{R}^{-1}(\hat{p}')]^{\pm\lambda}{}_m \\ &= D^j[\mathrm{R}_2(\pi)]^{\pm\lambda}{}_{\lambda'}\, D_j^{\dagger}[\mathrm{R}(\hat{p}')]^{\lambda'}{}_m = (-1)^{j\pm\lambda}\, D_j^{\dagger}[\mathrm{R}(\hat{p}')]^{\pm\lambda}{}_m \end{aligned}$$

we obtain

$$(11.2\text{-}14) \qquad I_s\,|j\,m\,\pm\rangle = |j\,m\,\mp\rangle(-1)^{j\pm\lambda} = |j\,m\,\mp\rangle(-1)^{j+\lambda} \quad .$$

The last equality follows from $(-1)^{2\lambda} = 1$. (We consider integer λ only.)

[3] By the convention adopted in Appendix I, the representation label j is switched to the lower position on hermitian conjugate matrix. Its placement does not affect anything.

Since I_s commutes with all rotations, both angular momentum eigenvalues (j, m) remain invariant under I_s—in contrast to the linear momentum eigenvalue $\hat{\mathbf{p}}$ which changes sign, as in Eq. (11.2-13). Since the helicity eigenvalue $(\pm\lambda)$ is the only one that changes sign under I_s in Eq. (11.2-14), we can form *parity eigenstates* by taking linear combinations of positive and negative helicity states. Thus, if we define

(11.2-15) $$|j m \tau\rangle = [|j m +\lambda\rangle + |j m -\lambda\rangle \tau]/2^{1/2}$$

where $\tau = \pm 1$; and we reinstated the helicity label on the right-hand side in order to distinguish between the $\pm$ label associated with helicity λ and that with parity τ. Applying Eq. (11.2-14) to Eq. (11.2-15), we obtain:

(11.2-16) $$I_s |j m \tau\rangle = |j m \tau\rangle \tau(-1)^{j+\lambda} \quad .$$

Thus the *parity eigenvalue* of the $|j M \tau\rangle$ state is $\tau(-1)^{j+\lambda}$.

We again point to the conceptual distinction between the *intrinsic parity* eigenvalue η associated with the irreducible representations of the (j, η) and the (p, η) types [Case (i) and (ii) of Theorem 11.8 respectively] on the one hand, and the parity eigenvalue τ for the (p, λ) representation encountered in Eq. (11.2-16). [cf. discussion following Eq. (11.1-16)] The parameter η labels the relevant irreducible representations. Its allowed values are ± 1; its actual value is not specified—it depends on the intrinsic property of the physical system to which it is applied. In contrast, the parameter τ is not intrinsic to the irreducible representation; *both* values of $\tau(= \pm 1)$ occur in the *same* irreducible representation. In Eq. (11.2-16), the parity eigenvalue $\tau(-1)^{j+\lambda}$ depends on the particular linear combination we take in Eq. (11.2-15), as well as on the other eigenvalues j and λ. In some later applications, the derived parity eigenvalue can also depend on intrinsic parity parameters of sub-systems of the physical system. [Sec. 11.4]

11.3 Space Inversion in Four-Dimensional Minkowski Space

In Minkowski space $\{x^\mu\}$, the spatial dimensions $\mu = 1, 2, 3$ and the time dimension $\mu = 0$ are intimately related; but they are not treated equally, on account of the negative sign associated with the time component of the underlying metric. This fact leads to a number of similarities and differences in the way space and time dimensions affect the irreducible representations of the relevant continuous symmetry groups which we have studied in Chaps. 9 and 10. As we now try to incorporate the discrete symmetry operations of space inversion and time reversal in Minkowski space, we shall encounter a fundamental difference between the two. The representation theory involving space inversion is rather similar to those of previous sections. It will be developed in this section. The treatment of time reversal invariance, however, requires some important rethinking, if the mathematical result is to correspond to established physical principles. It will be taken up separately in Chap. 12.

11.3.1 The Complete Lorentz Group and its Irreducible Representations

Definition 11.3 (The Complete Homogeneous Lorentz Group $\tilde{\mathrm{L}}$): The set of all elements of the proper Lorentz group, together with the space inversion I_s and their products form the *Complete Lorentz Group.* The rules of multiplication for the group can be inferred from matrix multiplication of the 4×4 matrices which define the group elements.

In 4-dimensional space-time, the *space inversion* or *parity transformation* I_s is given by the matrix

(11.3-1)
$$I_s = \begin{pmatrix} 1 & & & \\ & -1 & & \\ & & -1 & \\ & & & -1 \end{pmatrix}$$

which is seen to coincide with the negative of the matrix representing the metric tensor $g_{\mu\nu}$. Since the determinant of I_s is -1, in contrast to that of proper Lorentz transformations, elements of the complete Lorentz group can again be divided into two non-overlapping classes distinguished by the sign of their determinant.

Correspondingly, in extending the proper Lorentz group to the complete Lorentz group, the totally anti-symmetric unit tensor $\varepsilon^{\mu\nu\lambda\sigma}$ is no longer strictly invariant [cf. Eq. (10.1-7)]; it changes sign under all transformations which belong to the same class as I_s. Thus, the complete Lorentz group $\tilde{L}$ consists of all linear homogeneous transformations $\{\Lambda\}$ with $\Lambda^0{}_0 \geq 1$ and one invariant tensor, the metric tensor $g_{\mu\nu}$. [Eq. (10.1-5)]

We already know that I_s commutes with all spatial rotations. It is only necessary to check its effect on the Lorentz boosts $\{L_i(\xi)\}$. From the explicit formulas for I_s [Eq. (11.3-1)] and L_i [Eq. (10.1-9)], it follows immediately that

(11.3-2)
$$I_s L_i(\xi) I_s^{-1} = L_i(-\xi) = L_i^{-1}(\xi) \quad .$$

This result is also intuitively obvious—under space inversion, all 3-vectors, such as the direction of a Lorentz boost, reverse sign. In terms of the generators $\{K_i\}$ of Lorentz boosts, the above equation can be rewritten as

(11.3-3)
$$I_s K_i I_s^{-1} = -K_i \quad .$$

We observe that: (i) any element belonging to the class with determinant equal to -1 can be rewritten as $I_s\Lambda$ where Λ is an element of the proper Lorentz group; (ii) the proper Lorentz group $\tilde{L}_+$ is an invariant subgroup of the complete group $\tilde{L}$: and (iii) the factor group $\tilde{L}/\tilde{L}_+$ is isomorphic to the reflection group of order 2, $\{E, I_s\}$. (Prove!) Hence we obtain immediately an *one-dimensional degenerate representation* of the complete Lorentz group induced by the factor group which assigns all elements of the proper group $\{\Lambda\}$ to the value 1 and all elements of the coset $\{I_s\Lambda\}$ to the value -1.

As any irreducible representation of the complete group is also a representation (reducible or irreducible) of the proper group, the non-trivial representations can be systematically derived using known representations of the proper Lorentz group [Sec. 10.3] in conjunction with algebraic relations between I_s and the generators of the continuous transformations [Eqs. (11.2-4), (11.3-3)]. We shall only consider the case of finite dimensional irreducible representations. The treatment of the unitary (hence, infinite dimensional) irreducible representations is not difficult, given the methodology developed in the previous chapters. A complete account of the mathematical theory can be found in the authoritative book by Naimark. [Naimark]

The *finite dimensional irreducible representations* of the proper Lorentz group were classified in Sec. 10.3 using the generator set $M_m = (J_m + iK_m)/2$, $N_m =$

$(J_m - iK_m)/2$, $m = 1, 2, 3$. As space inversion changes the sign of K_m and leaves J_m invariant, the effects of I_s on the new generators are:

$$\begin{aligned} I_s M_m I_s^{-1} &= N_m \\ I_s N_m I_s^{-1} &= M_m \end{aligned} \tag{11.3-4}$$

In other words, space inversion interchanges the two sets of generators $\{M_m\}$ and $\{N_m\}$. It follows that the Casimir operators of the proper group, $\mathbf{M}^2$ and $\mathbf{N}^2$, also transform into each other under I_s:

$$\begin{aligned} I_s \mathbf{M}^2 I_s^{-1} &= \mathbf{N}^2 \\ I_s \mathbf{N}^2 I_s^{-1} &= \mathbf{M}^2 \end{aligned} \tag{11.3-5}$$

This result implies, of course, that $\mathbf{M}^2$ and $\mathbf{N}^2$ are no longer separately invariant under the complete Lorentz group.

The above equations holds as operator equations on the representation space of the group, as they do for the 4×4 defining matrices. (Recall we use the same symbols to denote corresponding members of both sets.) Let $\{|k\,l\rangle\}$ be basis vectors of the (u, v) representation of the proper Lorentz group. [Eqs. (10.3-3), (10.3-4)] We shall find how the parity-transformed vectors $\{I_s|k\,l\rangle\}$ behave under the generators: we obtain

$$\begin{aligned} \mathbf{M}^2 I_s|k\,l\rangle &= I_s \mathbf{N}^2 |k\,l\rangle = I_s|k\,l\rangle\, v(v+1) \\ \mathbf{N}^2 I_s|k\,l\rangle &= I_s \mathbf{M}^2 |k\,l\rangle = I_s|k\,l\rangle\, u(u+1) \\ M_3 I_s|k\,l\rangle &= I_s N_3 |k\,l\rangle = I_s|k\,l\rangle\, l \\ N_3 I_s|k\,l\rangle &= I_s M_3 |k\,l\rangle = I_s|k\,l\rangle\, k \end{aligned} \tag{11.3-6}$$

We conclude that $I_s|k\,l\rangle$ transforms as basis vectors of the $|l\,k\rangle$ element of the basis for a (v, u) representation of the proper Lorentz group.

When $u = v$, the new vectors can belong to the original representation space of the proper group. We obtain the *self-conjugate irreducible representations* of the complete Lorentz group. Specifically, we must have

$$I_s|k\,l\rangle = |l\,k\rangle\, \eta_{kl}$$

where η_{kl} are possible phase factors. But η_{kl} must be independent of the labels (l, k) because we show that

$$\begin{aligned} I_s|k+1\,l\rangle &= I_s M_+ |k\,l\rangle\, C_k = N_+ I_s|k\,l\rangle\, C_k \\ &= N_+ |l\,k\rangle\, \eta_{kl}\, C_k = |l\,k+1\rangle\, \eta_{kl} \end{aligned}$$

which implies $\eta_{k+1,l} = \eta_{k,l}$, and similarly $\eta_{k,l+1} = \eta_{k,l}$. (The unimportant constant C_k in the above equation is a shorthand for $[u(u+1) - k(k+1)]^{-1/2}$.) In other words, the effect of I_s is

$$I_s|k\,l\rangle = |l\,k\rangle\, \eta \tag{11.3-7}$$

Furthermore, since $I_s^2 = 1$, we must have $\eta = \pm 1$. Hence, we obtain two distinct representations of the complete Lorentz group labelled by (u, η): the basis vectors behave as those of the (u, u) representation under proper Lorentz transformations and they transform according to Eq. (11.3-7) under space inversion.

If $u \neq v$, the vectors $\{I_s|k\,l\rangle\}$ cannot be in the original representation space labelled by (u, v)—they form the basis of a new representation space of the proper Lorentz group labelled by (v, u). The direct sum of these two spaces form a minimal invariant space under the complete Lorentz group. We may *define*

$$|l\,k\rangle_{v,u} \equiv I_s|k\,l\rangle_{u,v} \tag{11.3-8}$$

which fixes the relative phase between the vectors of the two subspaces.[4] Note that in general $|k\,l\rangle$ is not an eigenstate of space inversion, but $|k\,l\rangle_\pm = |k\,l\rangle \pm |l\,k\rangle$ is: $I_s|k\,l\rangle_\pm = |kl\rangle_\pm(\pm 1)$. However, $|kl\rangle_\pm$ do not have simple behavior under (M_m, N_m), or equivalently, (J_m, K_m).

We summarize these results in a theorem:

Theorem 11.9 (Finite Dimensional Irreducible Representations of the Complete Lorentz Group): The finite dimensional irreducible representations of the complete Lorentz group belong to two classes: (i) the *self-conjugate* representations are $(2u + 1)^2$-dimensional representations characterized by two parameters (u, η) ($u = 0, 1/2, 1 \ldots$; $\eta = \pm 1$) which behave under proper Lorentz transformations as the (u, u) representation of Sec. 10.3 and under I_s as in Eq. (11.3-7); and (ii) the *general representations* characterized by two distinct parameters (u, v) (where both $u, v = 0, 1/2, 1 \ldots$) which are $2(2u + 1)(2v + 1)$-dimensional, and which behave under the proper Lorentz group as the reducible $(u, v) \oplus (v, u)$ representation and under I_s as given in Eq. (11.3-8).

Just as explained in Chap. 10, finite dimensional representations of this kind are realized in nature as physical operators and operator fields rather than physical states. Let us examine some examples.

Example 1 (Dirac Spinor): The simplest irreducible representation of the Complete Lorentz group which is not self-conjugate corresponds to the $(0, 1/2) \oplus (1/2, 0)$ representation of the proper group. The physical realization of this representation is the famous Dirac spinor. Many elementary particles in nature (electron, muon, quarks,... etc.) are represented by Dirac spinors in quantum field theory. A brief discussion of Dirac spinors in terms of spinors of undotted $(0, 1/2)$ and dotted $(1/2, 0)$ indices is given in Appendix VI. We shall not elaborate on the subject here. [cf. Dirac, Messiah] In the following examples, when we mention the Dirac spinor, it will be denoted by ψ.

Example 2 (Scalars and Pseudo-scalars): The simplest self-conjugate representations have ($u = 0$, $\eta = \pm 1$). Quantities transforming as the $\eta = 1$ representation are called *scalars*, those as $\eta = -1$ are called *pseudo-scalars*. A scalar is invariant under both proper Lorentz transformations and space inversion, whereas a pseudo-scalar is invariant under the former but changes sign under the latter. In this sense, the metric tensor $\{g_{\mu\nu}\}$ is like a scalar and the totally antisymmetric tensor $\{\varepsilon_{\mu\nu\lambda\sigma}\}$ is like a pseudo-scalar. The operator C_1 $(= -P_\mu P^\mu)$ of Chap. 10 [Eq. (10.4-1)] is an

[4] Although it is permissible to have a different phase convention, such as an extra negative sign in Eq. (11.3-8), that would only amount to a change of basis, thus leading to an equivalent representation.

example of a scalar. In the Dirac theory of spin 1/2 fermions, $(\bar{\psi}\psi)$ is a scalar whereas $(\bar{\psi}\gamma_5\psi)$ is a pseudo-scalar. [Dirac, Messiah]

Example 3 (Vectors and Axial-vectors): Among the most familiar examples of the irreducible representations described in Theorem 11.8 are polar vectors, corresponding to $(u = 1/2,\ \eta = 1)$. The relevant representation for the proper Lorentz group is $(u = 1/2,\ v = 1/2)$. Physical examples of this representation already mentioned in Sec. 10.3 are the coordinate vector x^μ, the momentum vector P_μ, the electromagnetic 4-potential $A^\mu(x), \ldots$ etc. [cf. also next subsection and Appendix VI] Quantities which behave as the (1/2, 1/2) representation under proper Lorentz transformations, but opposite to the vectors under space inversion (i.e. $\eta = -1$) are called *axial vectors.* The Pauli-Lubanski vector W^λ [Eq. (10.4-9)] is an axial vector. In the Dirac theory, $(\bar{\psi}\gamma^\mu\psi)$ is a 4-vector whereas $(\bar{\psi}\gamma^\mu\gamma_5\psi)$ is an axial vector. [Dirac, Messiah]

Example 4 (Second Rank Tensors): The *anti-symmetric second rank tensors* $J_{\mu\nu}$ (generators of the Lorentz group) and $F_{\mu\nu}$ (electromagnetic field tensor) are realizations of the irreducible representation of the complete Lorentz group corresponding to the $(1,0) \oplus (0,1)$ representation of the proper group. So is $\{\bar{\psi}\,[\gamma^\mu, \gamma^\nu]\,\psi\}$ in Dirac theory. There is only one inequivalent representation of this kind. The relationship between the components of the antisymmetric tensors and the *symmetric bispinors* (which transform according to the representations (0, 1) and (1, 0) of the proper group) is discussed at the end of Appendix VI.

As mentioned in Sec. 10.3.2, a traceless second-rank symmetric tensor has 9 independent components and it transforms as the self-conjugate representation (1, 1) of the proper Lorentz group. When extended to the complete group, this leads to two inequivalent representations distinguished by $\eta = \pm 1$ respectively.

11.3.2 The Extended Poincaré Group and its Irreducible Representations

Definition 11.4 (The Extended Poincaré Group): Elements of the complete Lorentz group, space-time translations, and their products together form the *Extended Poincaré Group.*

The group structure is specified by the Lie algebra of the 10 generators of the Poincaré group; the already encountered relations $I_s J_i = J_i I_s$ [Eq. (11.2-4)], $I_s K_i = -K_i I_s$ [Eq. (11.3-3)], $I_s P_i = -P_i I_s$ [Eq. (11.2-7)], $(i = 1, 2, 3)$; and

(11.3-9) $$I_s P_0 = P_0 I_s \quad .$$

This new relation is intuitively obvious; it can also be verified using the 5×5 matrix representation of the group elements. Eq. (11.3-9), in conjunction with (11.2-7), implies that P_μ transforms in the same way under I_s as the coordinate vector x_μ: it is a polar vector.

In order to extend the study of irreducible representations of the Poincaré group of Chap. 10 to the present case, we need to know the space inversion behavior of the Casimir operators as well as the Pauli-Lubanski vector, in addition to that of the generators. It is straightforward to verify that W^λ is an axial vector (the $\varepsilon_{\mu\nu\lambda\sigma}$ factor contributes the extra negative sign under space inversion), and that both C_1 and C_2 are scalars. [Prove!]

The *degenerate irreducible representations* are those induced by the little group of the null vector $p_n = (0, \mathbf{0})$, which is the complete Lorentz group. The unitary irreducible representations of this group are known. [cf. Sec. 10.4] [Naimark] All translations $\{T(b)\}$ are represented by the identity operator. We shall examine the other cases in detail.

Time-Like Vector Case ($c_1 > 0$)

As in Sec. 10.4, we define $c_1 = M^2$ and adopt as the standard vector $p_t = (p^0, \mathbf{p}) = (M, \mathbf{0})$. The little group of p_t is, in the present case, the group O(3). According to Theorem 11.7, the irreducible representations are characterized by two numbers (s, η_p) in addition to M: $s(s+1)$ $(s = 0, 1/2, 1, \ldots)$ is the eigenvalue of the operator $\hat{C}_2 = W_\mu W^\mu / M^2$, and η_p $(= \pm 1)$ is the *intrinsic parity* of the representation. Suppressing the invariant labels (M, s, η), the rest frame basis vectors are characterized by

(11.3-10)
$$\begin{aligned} \hat{C}_2 |\mathbf{0}\,\lambda\rangle &= |\mathbf{0}\,\lambda\rangle\, s(s+1) \\ J_3 |\mathbf{0}\,\lambda\rangle &= |\mathbf{0}\,\lambda\rangle\, \lambda \\ I_s |\mathbf{0}\,\lambda\rangle &= |\mathbf{0}\,\lambda\rangle\, \eta_p \quad . \end{aligned}$$

A general basis vector is defined, as in Sec. 10.4, by [Eqs. (10.4-4), (10.4-5)]

(11.3-11)
$$|\mathbf{p}\,\lambda\rangle = R(\hat{\mathbf{p}})\,|p\hat{\mathbf{z}}\,\lambda\rangle$$

where

$$|p\hat{\mathbf{z}}\,\lambda\rangle = L_3(\xi)|\mathbf{0}\,\lambda\rangle \quad .$$

The behavior of $|\mathbf{p}\,\lambda\rangle$ under proper Lorentz transformations and translations is the same as given in Sec. 10.4 [Eqs. (10.4-6), (10.4-7)]. We need only to study the space inversion properties of these vectors. Since $|\mathbf{p}\,\lambda\rangle$ is the eigenvector of $\mathbf{P}$ and $\mathbf{J}\cdot\mathbf{P}/p$, and since $\mathbf{J}$ is invariant whereas $\mathbf{P}$ changes sign under space inversion, we anticipate $I_s|\mathbf{p}\,\lambda\rangle$ to be proportional to $|-\mathbf{p}\, -\lambda\rangle$. It remains, however, to determine the precise phase relationship. We consider first the states along the z-axis, $|p\hat{\mathbf{z}}\,\lambda\rangle$. It is convenient to use the combined operator $R_2(\pi)I_s$ which leaves the vector $p\hat{\mathbf{z}}$ invariant,

$$\begin{aligned} R_2(\pi)I_s|p\hat{\mathbf{z}}\,\lambda\rangle &= R_2(\pi)\,I_s\,L_3(\xi)\,|\mathbf{0}\,\lambda\rangle = L_3(\xi)R_2(\pi)I_s|\mathbf{0}\,\lambda\rangle \\ &= L_3(\xi)\,R_2(\pi)\,|\mathbf{0}\,\lambda\rangle\,\eta_p = L_3(\xi)\,|\mathbf{0}\, -\lambda\rangle\,\eta_p(-1)^{s-\lambda} \\ &= |p\hat{\mathbf{z}} - \lambda\rangle\,\eta_p(-1)^{s-\lambda} \quad . \end{aligned}$$

In the first step we used the definition of $|p\hat{\mathbf{z}}\,\lambda\rangle$; in the second step, the commutativity of $L_3(\xi)$ with $R_2(\pi)I_s$; in the third step, the last eigenvalue equation from Eq. (11.3-10); and in the fourth step, the formula for the rotation matrix $D^s[R_2(\pi)]$. It follows then,

(11.3-12)
$$I_s\,|p\hat{\mathbf{z}}\,\lambda\rangle = R_2(-\pi)\,|p\hat{\mathbf{z}}\, -\lambda\rangle\,\eta_p(-1)^{s-\lambda} \quad .$$

This derivation well illustrates the general procedure for deriving the transformation properties of state vectors under a discrete operator (in this case, I_s) given its defining properties on some standard vectors [Eq. (11.3-10)], in conjunction with its algebraic relationship with the generators of the continuous group.

We proceed, now, to the general case:

$$\begin{aligned} I_s|\mathbf{p}\,\lambda\rangle &= I_s \mathrm{R}(\phi,\theta,0)\,|p\hat{\mathbf{z}}\,\lambda\rangle = \mathrm{R}(\phi,\theta,0)\,I_s\,|p\hat{\mathbf{z}}\,\lambda\rangle \\ &= \mathrm{R}(\phi,\theta,0)\,\mathrm{R}_2(-\pi)\,|p\hat{\mathbf{z}}\,-\lambda\rangle\,\eta_p(-1)^{s-\lambda} \\ &= \mathrm{R}(\phi,\,-\pi+\theta,0)\,|p\hat{\mathbf{z}}\,-\lambda\rangle\,\eta_p(-1)^{s-\lambda} \\ &= \mathrm{R}(\pi+\phi,\,\pi-\theta,\,-\pi)\,|p\hat{\mathbf{z}}\,-\lambda\rangle\,\eta_p(-1)^{s-\lambda} \\ &= \mathrm{R}(\pi+\phi,\,\pi-\theta,\,0)\,|p\hat{\mathbf{z}}\,-\lambda\rangle\,\eta_p(-1)^{s-\lambda}e^{-i\pi\lambda} \\ &= \mathrm{R}(\pi+\phi,\,\pi-\theta,\,0)\,|p\hat{\mathbf{z}}\,-\lambda\rangle\,\eta_p e^{-i\pi s} \quad . \end{aligned}$$

In the third step, we used Eq. (11.3-12); in the fifth step, we used the identity $\mathrm{R}_2(-\beta) = \mathrm{R}_3(\pi)\,\mathrm{R}_2(\beta)\,\mathrm{R}_3(-\pi)$; in the last step, we used $(-1)^{s-\lambda} = e^{-i\pi(s-\lambda)}$; and all the other steps are straightforward.

From the above result, we deduce the useful conclusion

$$I_s|\mathbf{p}\,\lambda\rangle = |-\mathbf{p}\,-\lambda\rangle\,\eta_p\,e^{\mp i\pi s} \tag{11.3-13}$$

where the upper sign applies when $0 \le \phi < \pi$ (ϕ is the azimuthal angle of the vector $\mathbf{p}$) and the lower sign applies when $\pi \le \phi < 2\pi$. The reason for the difference in the two cases is that the azimuthal angle of $-\mathbf{p}$ is $\pi + \phi$ when ϕ is in the first two quadrants, but it is $\phi - \pi = (\pi + \phi) - 2\pi$ when ϕ is in the last two quadrants. Note that if s is an integer then the phase factor is independent of the sign of the exponent, and we have

$$I_s|\mathbf{p}\,\lambda\rangle = |-\mathbf{p}\,-\lambda\rangle\,\eta_p(-1)^s \qquad (s = \text{integer}). \tag{11.3-13a}$$

To summarize the main conclusions of this subsection, we state the following theorem:

Theorem 11.10 (Time-like Unitary Irreducible Representation of the Extended Poincaré Group): The time-like unitary irreducible representations of the extended Poincaré group are characterized by three invariant parameters (M, s, η_p) corresponding to the *mass*, *spin*, and *intrinsic parity* of the states respectively. The representation space for a given set of parameters (M, s, η_p) is the same as that of the (M, s) representation of the proper Poincaré group (Theorem 10.10). The intrinsic parity eigenvalue η_p takes on two distinct values, ± 1. The behavior or the basis vectors under space inversion is given by Eq. (11.3-13).

We see from the above results that the plane-wave basis states $\{|\mathbf{p}\,\lambda\rangle\}$ are not eigenstates of space inversion, except in the rest-frame. For those physical applications where invariance under space inversion plays an important role, it is desirable to use a basis incorporating the parity eigenvalue. Since the space inversion operator I_s commutes with rotations, it is natural that such a basis consist of eigenvectors of angular momenta. [cf. Secs. 7.5.3 and 8.4.2] We shall construct such a basis in Sec. 11.4 when we consider physical applications of the formalism developed here.

Light-Like Case ($c_1 = 0 = c_2$)

As discussed in Subsection 10.4.4, the physically interesting irreducible representations of the proper Poincaré group for massless states ($c_1 = M^2 = 0$) are those with $c_2 = W_\mu W^\mu = 0$. These representations are characterized by one non-trivial invariant parameter λ which is the eigenvalue of the helicity operator $\mathbf{J}\cdot\hat{\mathbf{P}}$ ($\lambda = 0$, $\pm 1/2$, $\pm 1, \ldots$). How is the previous analysis affected by the inclusion of the space inversion symmetry? To find out, we retrace the arguments of Subsection 10.4.4.

We choose the "standard vector" $p_l = (\omega_o, 0, 0, \omega_o)$. The little group of p_l is now $\{O(2)\colon R_3(\phi), R_3(\phi)R_2(\pi)I_s; 0 \le \phi \le 2\pi\}$. The two classes of transformations listed above correspond, respectively, to all rotations about the z-axis, and all reflections about a plane containing the z-axis. It is clear that both leave the standard vector p_l invariant. We shall consider, in turn, two types of irreducible representations induced by those of O(2) [Theorem 11.3, Subsection 11.1.2]. The basis vectors in the representation space of the little group satisfy, in both cases,

$$
\begin{aligned}
P^\mu |\mathbf{p}_l\rangle &= |\mathbf{p}_l\rangle p_l{}^\mu \\
W_i |\mathbf{p}_l\rangle &= 0 \qquad i = 1, 2 \quad .
\end{aligned} \tag{11.3-14}
$$

Zero-helicity Irreducible Representations

The representations of the little group in this case [Theorem 11.3] are one-dimensional and are labelled by an additional parameter η_p, the *intrinsic parity*. There are two inequivalent representations of this type, corresponding to the eigenvalues $\eta_p = \pm 1$ respectively. The basis vectors are defined by ($\eta_p = \pm 1$)

$$
\begin{aligned}
J_3 |\mathbf{p}_l \eta_p\rangle &= 0 \\
R_2(\pi) I_s |\mathbf{p}_l \eta_p\rangle &= |\mathbf{p}_l \eta_p\rangle \eta_p \quad .
\end{aligned} \tag{11.3-15}
$$

The last equation can be re-written in the form

$$
I_s |\mathbf{p}_l \eta_p\rangle = R_2(-\pi) |\mathbf{p}_l \eta_p\rangle \eta_p \quad . \tag{11.3-16}
$$

The full basis in the representation space of the whole group consists of vectors $\{|\mathbf{p}\,\eta_p\rangle\}$ defined by the usual prescription

$$
|\mathbf{p}\,\eta_p\rangle \equiv H(p) |\mathbf{p}_l \eta_p\rangle
$$

where $H(p) = R(\phi, \theta, 0)\, L_3(\xi)$ is the Lorentz transformation which brings $p_l{}^\mu$ to $p^\mu = (\omega, \mathbf{p})$. The action of continuous Poincaré transformations on the basis vectors is given in Subsection 10.4.4. We need only to determine the effect due to space inversion. Taking advantage of the similarity of Eq. (11.3-16) to Eq. (11.3-12), we can infer the result we need without repeating the intermediate steps in the proof of Eq. (11.3-13); we obtain

$$
I_s |\mathbf{p}\,\eta_p\rangle = |-\mathbf{p}\,\eta_p\rangle \eta_p \quad . \tag{11.3-17}
$$

As there is no apparent physical application of these representations, we shall not pursue this subject further.

General Helicity Irreducible Representations

The irreducible representations of the little group in the non-zero helicity case are two-dimensional [Theorem 11.3]; the basis vectors will be denoted by $\{|\mathbf{p}_l \lambda\rangle; \lambda = \pm m; m = 1/2, 1, 3/2, \ldots\}$. Here we include double-valued (odd-half integer m) representations because we know that they are relevant for the continuous Poincaré group [Sec. 10.4.4], and for physics applications. The basis vectors are defined by

(11.3-18) $$J_3|\mathbf{p}_l\,\lambda\rangle = |\mathbf{p}_l\,\lambda\rangle\,\lambda \qquad \lambda = \pm m$$

(11.3-19) $$R_2(\pi)\,I_s|\mathbf{p}_l\,m\rangle \equiv |\mathbf{p}_l\; -m\rangle \quad .$$

We have taken care to specify only one sign of λ in the second defining equation, since the effect of the reflection operator on $|\mathbf{p}_l\; -m\rangle$ can be determined from the above equations, it should not be freely assigned. This precaution is necessary because we cannot literally apply Theorem 11.3 [in particular, Eq. (11.1-12)], having included the extra double-valued representations. We see that

$$\begin{aligned} I_s|\mathbf{p}_l\,-m\rangle &= I_s R_2(\pi) I_s|\mathbf{p}_l\,m\rangle = R_2(\pi)|\mathbf{p}_l\,m\rangle \\ &= R_2(-\pi)|\mathbf{p}_l\,m\rangle(-1)^{2m} \quad . \end{aligned}$$

Comparing with Eq. (11.3-19), we observe a difference in the phase factor on the right-hand side. These two equations can be combined into a single one, applicable to both signs of the helicity:

(11.3-20) $$I_s|\mathbf{p}_l\,\lambda\rangle = R_2(-\pi)|\mathbf{p}_l\,-\lambda\rangle(-1)^{|\lambda|-\lambda} \quad .$$

Comparing with Eq. (11.3-12) for the $M > 0$ case, we see that Eq. (11.3-20) can be regarded as a limiting case of the former if we set $\eta_p = 1$ and $s = |\lambda|$. Had we included a factor η_p in the definition (11.3-19), the two cases would be even closer in appearance. The two choices, $\eta_p \equiv \pm 1$ would, however, lead to two equivalent irreducible representations when $M = 0$, in contrast to the $M > 0$ case. (The difference originates, of course, from the fact that the relative phases between the positive and negative helicity states are already fixed by rotations when $M > 0$, which is not the case when $M = 0$.)

Having observed the close similarity to the $M > 0$ case, it is straightforward to derive the behavior of an arbitrary state under space inversion. The result can be transcribed from Eq. (11.3-13),

(11.3-21) $$I_s|\mathbf{p}\,\lambda\rangle = |-\mathbf{p}\,-\lambda\rangle\,e^{\mp i\pi|\lambda|}$$

according to whether the azimuthal angle of $\mathbf{p}$ is in the first two quadrants (upper sign) or in the last two quadrants (lower sign).

Theorem 11.11 (Light-like Unitary Irreducible Representations of the Extended Poincaré Group): Unitary irreducible representations of the extended Poincaré group corresponding to zero mass states ($c_1 = 0 = c_2$) include: (i) $\lambda = 0$, $\eta_p = \pm 1$ which is characterized by Eqs. (10.4-23), (10.4-24) under the proper group and Eq. (11.3-17) under space inversion; and (ii) $\lambda = 1/2, 1, 3/2, \ldots$ which correspond to the direct sum representation $(M=0, \lambda) \oplus (M=0, -\lambda)$ of the proper group and behave according to Eqs. (11.3-20) and (11.3-21) under space inversion.

As mentioned earlier, it is possible to introduce an extra factor η_p (± 1) in the last two equations. This factor will not, however, carry any intrinsic significance—the two representations corresponding to $\eta_p = \pm 1$ will be equivalent to each other. It is convenient to take advantage of this freedom of choice of relative phase, especially if we wish to adopt a uniform notation for the $M = 0$ and the $M > 0$ cases. Hence we shall use, from now on,

(11.3-22) $$I_s|p\hat{\mathbf{z}}\,\lambda\rangle = R_2(-\pi)|p\hat{\mathbf{z}}\,-\lambda\rangle\,\eta_p(-1)^{|\lambda|-\lambda}$$

and

(11.3-23) $$I_s|\mathbf{p}\,\lambda\rangle = |-\mathbf{p}\,-\lambda\rangle\,\eta_p\,e^{\mp i\pi|\lambda|}$$

bearing in mind that η_p for massless states is chosen by convention.

In the physical world, the $\lambda = 1$ irreducible representation is realized by the photon states in Quantum Electrodynamics. In Sec. 8.7, we described the relationship between the creation and annihilation operators of these states to the electromagnetic fields **E** and **B** through the (polar) vector potential $\mathbf{A}(\mathbf{x}, t)$ in the Coulomb gauge. [cf. also Sec. 10.5] We can show that this formalism requires choosing the convention $\eta_p = -1$ for photon states in Eqs. (11.3-22) and (11.3-23). Indeed, on the one hand, we have

(11.3-24) $$I_s\mathbf{A}(\mathbf{x}, t)\,I_s^{-1} = -\mathbf{A}(-\mathbf{x}, t)$$

as the consequence of the polar vector nature of **A**; and, on the other hand, using the right-hand side of Eq. (8.7-7), the same quantity can be evaluated to be

(11.3-25)
$$\begin{aligned}
&\sum_\lambda \int d^3k\,[I_s a(\mathbf{k}, \lambda) I_s^{-1}\,\hat{\mathbf{e}}(\mathbf{k}, \lambda)\,e^{i\mathbf{k}\cdot\mathbf{x} - i\omega t} + h.c.] \\
&= -\eta_p \sum_\lambda \int d^3k\,[a(-\mathbf{k}, -\lambda)\,\hat{\mathbf{e}}(\mathbf{k}, \lambda)\,e^{i\mathbf{k}\cdot\mathbf{x} - i\omega t} + h.c.] \\
&= -\eta_p \sum_\lambda \int d^3k\,[a(\mathbf{k}, \lambda)\,\hat{\mathbf{e}}(-\mathbf{k}, -\lambda)\,e^{-i\mathbf{k}\cdot\mathbf{x} - i\omega t} + h.c.] \\
&= \eta_p \sum_\lambda \int d^3k\,[a(\mathbf{k}, \lambda)\,\hat{\mathbf{e}}(\mathbf{k}, \lambda)\,e^{-i\mathbf{k}\cdot\mathbf{x} - i\omega t} + h.c.] \\
&= \eta_p\,\mathbf{A}(-\mathbf{x}, t)
\end{aligned}$$

where in the second step we used Eq. (11.3-23) (transcribed for the annihilation and creation operators), in the third step we changed the signs of dummy summation and integration variables, in the fourth step we used the algebraic identity

(11.3-26)
$$\begin{aligned}
\hat{\mathbf{e}}(-\mathbf{k}, -\lambda) &= \mathrm{R}(\pi + \phi, \pi - \theta, 0)\,\hat{\mathbf{e}}(k\hat{\mathbf{z}}, -\lambda) \\
&= \mathrm{R}(\phi, \theta, 0)\,\mathrm{R}_3(\pi)\,\mathrm{R}_2(\pi)\,\hat{\mathbf{e}}(k\hat{\mathbf{z}}, -\lambda) \\
&= \mathrm{R}(\phi, \theta, 0)\,[-\hat{\mathbf{e}}(k\hat{\mathbf{z}}, \lambda)] \\
&= -\hat{\mathbf{e}}(\mathbf{k}, \lambda)
\end{aligned}$$

and the other steps involve only the use of definition (8.7-7). Comparing Eqs. (11.3-24) and (11.3-25), we conclude

(11.3-27) $$\eta_p = -1 \qquad \text{(for photon states).}$$

As a consistency check, we can examine the realization of Eq. (11.3-22) in terms of the helicity wave functions:

(11.3-28)
$$\begin{aligned}
\hat{\mathbf{e}}(k\hat{\mathbf{z}}, \lambda = \pm 1) = \mp\hat{\mathbf{x}} - i\hat{\mathbf{y}} \xrightarrow{I_s} \pm\hat{\mathbf{x}} + i\hat{\mathbf{y}} &= R_2(-\pi)\,(\mp\hat{\mathbf{x}} + i\hat{\mathbf{y}}) \\
&= -R_2(-\pi)\,\hat{\mathbf{e}}(k\hat{\mathbf{z}}, \lambda = \mp 1)
\end{aligned}$$

where an irrelevant factor of $2^{1/2}$ has been omitted from the intermediate steps. Comparing (11.3-28) with (11.3-22), we again obtain Eq. (11.3-27). We can write Eq. (11.3-28) and the corresponding realization of Eq. (11.3-23) symbolically as

$$I_s\,\hat{\mathbf{e}}(k\hat{\mathbf{z}},\lambda) = -R_2(-\pi)\,\hat{\mathbf{e}}(k\hat{\mathbf{z}},-\lambda)$$
$$I_s\,\hat{\mathbf{e}}(\mathbf{k},\lambda) = \hat{\mathbf{e}}(-\mathbf{k},-\lambda) \qquad (11.3\text{-}29)$$

respectively. This kind of notation is somewhat delicate to use, as can be seen from the possibility of confusing the last equation (which pertains to the space inversion transformation property of the state represented by the polarization vector $\hat{\mathbf{e}}(\mathbf{k},\lambda)$) with Eq. (11.3-26) (which only states an algebraic identity satisfied by $\hat{\mathbf{e}}(\mathbf{k},\lambda)$). Note the sign difference on the right-hand sides! We shall use the corresponding operator equations, such as Eq. (11.3-24), whenever possible. These are much less susceptible to such confusion, since *c*-number wave functions and operators corresponding to the states are clearly separated.

Although the neutrino states have helicity $\pm 1/2$ and also are believed to be massless, it has been known since 1957 that only $\lambda = -1/2$ (left-handed) neutrinos and $\lambda = +1/2$ (right-handed) anti-neutrinos exist in nature. The absence of states with the opposite helicity for the same particle (anti-particle) showed convincingly that space inversion is not a symmetry transformation for the theory of weak interactions in which neutrinos play an important role. On the other hand, the fact that the actual helicities of the neutrino and the anti-neutrino are opposite suggests that if space inversion and particle-antiparticle reversal are combined into a new transformation, called *CP* (*C* for *charge conjugation* and *P* for *parity*), it may become a symmetry of the theory. However, evidence has been found since 1964 that this combined symmetry is also violated, albeit only slightly, in nature. [Commins]

The above discussion illustrates the necessity of maintaining an open mind about relating mathematical space-time symmetries and the associated group representations to physical systems in nature. Although the mathematical theory is clear and definite, the physical applications are ever expanding and changing. Fresh discoveries often shatter old prejudices as well as open new horizons. The selection of the space-time symmetries and the range of irreducible representations studied here only reflect practical criteria appropriate for this time and for the special purpose of this book. The most important lessons to be learned from our expositions are the group-theoretical methods, which transcend the particular symmetries and representations that are of interest at any given time. As the next chapter (on time reversal) will reveal, occasions may arise when the group theoretical methods themselves will have to be scrutinized and modified as well.

11.4 General Physical Consequences of Space Inversion

Since most physical processes in nature do conserve parity, applications of the theory of space inversion symmetry as formulated in this chapter span most fields in physics. We shall consider some of the most general consequences, applicable to a variety of physical systems and physical processes. Among the generators of the Poincaré group, I_s commutes with $\mathbf{J}$ and P_0. It is natural, therefore, that parity considerations are most relevant and useful in the context of angular momentum and energy eigenstates. However, its application is not confined to this situation, as will become obvious when we discuss symmetry relations among scattering amplitudes in later parts of this section. Many topics treated here are follow-up subjects from earlier expositions involving continuous symmetries.

11.4.1 Eigenstates of Angular Momentum and Parity

We proceed to construct simultaneous eigenstates of the commuting operators I_s and $\mathbf{J}$ along the same lines as in Subsection 11.2.2. The general method for changing bases from $|\mathbf{p}\,\lambda\rangle$ to pure angular momentum states $|p\,J\,M\,\lambda\rangle$ has been described in Sec. 8.4. According to Eq. (8.4-9), the angular momentum states can be written as

$$|p\,J\,M\,\lambda\rangle = (2J+1)\int (\mathrm{dR})\,\mathrm{R}\,|p\hat{z}\,\lambda\rangle\, D_J{}^{\dagger}[\mathrm{R}]^{\lambda}{}_{M} \tag{11.4-1}$$

where R denotes a general rotation. The angular variables for R are suppressed and dR is the invariant measure over the rotation group such that $\int \mathrm{dR} = 1$. We can now examine the space inversion properties of these vectors:

$$\begin{aligned} I_s|p\,J\,M\,\lambda\rangle &= (2J+1)\int (\mathrm{dR})\,\mathrm{R}I_s|p\hat{z}\,\lambda\rangle\, D_J{}^{\dagger}[\mathrm{R}]^{\lambda}{}_{M} \\ &= (2J+1)\int (\mathrm{dR})\,\mathrm{R}\mathrm{R}_2(-\pi)|p\hat{z}-\lambda\rangle\,\eta_\lambda\, D_J{}^{\dagger}[\mathrm{R}]^{\lambda}{}_{M} \\ &= \eta_\lambda(2J+1)\int (\mathrm{dR}')\,R'|p\hat{z}-\lambda\rangle\, D_J{}^{\dagger}[\mathrm{R}'\mathrm{R}_2(\pi)]^{\lambda}{}_{M} \\ &= \eta_\lambda(2J+1)\int \mathrm{dR}'\,\mathrm{R}'|p\hat{z}-\lambda\rangle\, D_J{}^{\dagger}[\mathrm{R}_2(\pi)]^{\lambda}{}_{M'} D_J{}^{\dagger}[\mathrm{R}']^{M'}{}_{M} \\ &= \eta_\lambda(-1)^{J-\lambda}(2J+1)\int \mathrm{dR}'\,\mathrm{R}'|p\hat{z}-\lambda\rangle\, D_J{}^{\dagger}[\mathrm{R}']^{-\lambda}{}_{M} \end{aligned} \tag{11.4-2}$$

where in the first step we used $I_s\mathrm{R} = \mathrm{R}\,I_s$, in the second we used $I_s|p\hat{\mathrm{z}}\,\lambda\rangle = \mathrm{R}_2(-\pi)|p\hat{\mathrm{z}}\,-\lambda\rangle\eta_\lambda$ with a yet unspecified phase factor η_λ, in the third step we shifted the integration variables using the Rearrangement Lemma, in the fourth we applied the basic group property of the D matrix, and in the last step we used the explicit expression for $D^J[\mathrm{R}_2(\pi)]$. Comparing the right-hand side of the equation with the definition (11.4-1), we obtain

$$I_s|p\,J\,M\,\lambda\rangle = |p\,J\,M\,-\lambda\rangle\,\eta_\lambda(-1)^{J-\lambda} \quad . \tag{11.4-3}$$

For *single particle states* with non-zero mass, $\eta_\lambda = \eta_p(-1)^{s-\lambda}$ [Eq. (11.3-12)], hence

$$I_s|p\,J\,M\,\lambda\rangle = |p\,J\,M\,-\lambda\rangle\,\eta_p(-1)^{J-s} \tag{11.4-4}$$

where η_p is the intrinsic parity of the particle. For zero mass states, by the convention discussed in Subsection 11.3, we need only substitute s by $|\lambda|$ in the above derivation, hence

$$I_s|p\,J\,M\,\lambda\rangle = |p\,J\,M\,-\lambda\rangle\,\eta_p(-1)^{J-|\lambda|} \quad . \tag{11.4-5}$$

Since the helicity changes sign in Eqs. (11.4-3)-(11.4-5), unless $\lambda = 0$, these states are not eigenstates of parity. It is, however, quite trivial to form parity eigenstates out of these angular momentum states. With $\tau = \pm 1$, define

$$|p\,J\,M\,|\lambda|\,\tau\rangle = [|p\,J\,M\,\lambda\rangle + \tau|p\,J\,M\,-\lambda\rangle]/2^{1/2} \tag{11.4-6}$$

then

$$I_s|p\,J\,M\,|\lambda|\,\tau\rangle = |p\,J\,M\,|\lambda|\,\tau\rangle\,\tau\,\eta_p(-1)^{J-s} \quad . \tag{11.4-7}$$

By construction, of course, these states also satisfy

$$\mathrm{R}\,|p\,J\,M\,|\lambda|\,\tau\rangle = |p\,JM'\,|\lambda|\,\tau\rangle D^J[\mathrm{R}]^{M'}{}_M \tag{11.4-8}$$

hence they are the simultaneous eigenstates of angular momentum and parity that we need.

Example: Consider a free electron in some reference frame (say, that defined by a nucleus). The magnitude of the helicity is always 1/2, so we needn't be concerned about the label $|\lambda|$. For each value of the magnitude of the momentum p (or equivalently, energy), and total angular momenta $(J\,M)$, there are two states with opposite parity ($\tau = \pm 1$) with eigenvalues $(-1)^{J\mp 1/2}$ [$\eta_p = 1$ for the electron, by convention]. We can identify these states with those of the non-relativistic mechanical classification. According to the latter description, one begins with states of definite "orbital angular momentum" $l = 0, 1 \ldots$; to which one adds the "spin angular momentum" s. Since $s = 1/2$, there are two possible values of total angular momentum for each l: $J = l \pm 1/2$. Conversely, for each J there are two possible values of l: $l = J \pm 1/2$. Under space inversion, these states have parity eigenvalue $(-1)^l$; spin being unaffected by I_s. [Messiah, Schiff] Comparing eigenvalues, we can uniquely identify the $\tau = \pm 1$ states in the helicity formulation with the $l = J \mp 1/2$ states in the orbital angular momentum description.

It is worthwhile to emphasize that: (i) the association of the parity eigenstates in the helicity basis with those having definite orbital angular momenta is unique only when $s = 1/2$, the relationship becoming rather complicated when $s > 1/2$; and (ii) whereas the $|p\,J\,M\,|\lambda|\,\tau\rangle$ states are defined as eigenstates of a general set of commuting operators, the classification of states according to orbital and spin angular momenta makes sense only under restricted circumstances when "orbital" and "spin" angular momenta do not mix, and hence acquire separate meaning as physical operators.

The above analysis applies also to *two-particle states* in their center-of-mass frame. Referring to Subsection 8.4.2, we see that we only have to make the substitution $\lambda \to \lambda_1 - \lambda_2$, and to deduce the relevant η_λ phase factor in order to use Eq. (11.4-3). It is straightforward to derive, from Eq. (8.4-14),

$$\begin{aligned} I_s|p\hat{\mathbf{z}}\,\lambda_1\,\lambda_2\rangle &= I_s|p\hat{\mathbf{z}}_1\rangle \times I_s\mathrm{R}_2(\pi)\,|p\hat{\mathbf{z}}\,\lambda_2\rangle \\ &= \mathrm{R}_2(-\pi)|p\hat{\mathbf{z}}\,-\lambda_1\rangle\,\eta_1(-1)^{s_1-\lambda_1}\times\,|p\hat{\mathbf{z}}\,-\lambda_2\rangle\,\eta_2(-1)^{s_2-\lambda_2} \\ &= \mathrm{R}_2(-\pi)|p\hat{\mathbf{z}},\,-\lambda_1,\,-\lambda_2\rangle\,\eta_1\eta_2(-1)^{s_1+s_2-\lambda_1-\lambda_2} \end{aligned} \tag{11.4-9}$$

where s_1, s_2 and η_1, η_2 are the spin and intrinsic parity eigenstates of particles 1 and 2 respectively.[5] Substituting the phase factor on the right-hand side in its proper place in the derivation of Eq. (11.4-3), we obtain the following space inversion transformation property for the two-particle angular momentum states:

(11.4-10) $$I_s |p J M \lambda_1 \lambda_2\rangle = |p J M -\lambda_1 -\lambda_2\rangle \eta_1 \eta_2 (-1)^{J-s_1+s_2} \quad .$$

In deriving the final result, we made use of the identity $(-1)^{s-\lambda} = (-1)^{-s+\lambda}$ (for either particle) to eliminate all helicity labels on the phase factor. Again, simultaneous eigenstates of angular momentum and parity can be defined according to Eq. (11.4-6), but we shall not pursue the matter here.

11.4.2 Scattering Amplitudes and Electromagnetic Multipole Transitions

Consider a general two-body to two-body scattering process

(11.4-11) $$a + b \longrightarrow c + d$$

as first analyzed in Subsection 8.4.3 and depicted in Fig. 8.1. If space inversion is a symmetry of the physical system, what simplification of the scattering amplitudes can be deduced? We can apply the invariance principle to Eq. (8.4-21): using $T = I_s^{-1} T I_s$ and Eq. (11.4-10), we immediately obtain

(11.4-12) $$\langle -\lambda_c -\lambda_d \| T_J(E) \| -\lambda_a -\lambda_b\rangle = \eta \langle \lambda_c \lambda_d \| T_J(E) \| \lambda_a \lambda_b\rangle$$

where $\eta = \eta_a \eta_b \eta_c \eta_d (-1)^{s_a - s_b - s_c - s_d}$. To arrive at this result, use is made of the fact that the initial and final total angular momenta are equal, hence the J-dependent phase factor in Eq. (11.4-10) for the two states can be made to cancel out. To apply this result to the partial wave expansion formula (8.4-22), we note that

$$d^J(\theta)^{\lambda}{}_{\lambda'} = d^J(\theta)^{-\lambda}{}_{-\lambda'} (-1)^{\lambda-\lambda'} \quad .$$

Hence, denoting the scattering amplitude by $f(\theta, \phi)$, we obtain

(11.4-13) $$f_{-\lambda_c -\lambda_d; -\lambda_a -\lambda_b}(\theta, \phi) = \eta' f_{\lambda_c \lambda_d; \lambda_a \lambda_b}(\theta, -\phi)$$

where

$$\eta' = \eta_a \eta_b \eta_c \eta_d (-1)^{s_a - \lambda_a + s_b - \lambda_b + s_c - \lambda_c + s_d - \lambda_d} \quad .$$

In deriving the last result, we again freely used the identity $(-1)^{s-\lambda} = (-1)^{-s+\lambda}$ for each of the particles.

Eq. (11.4-13) indicates that, roughly speaking, half of the amplitudes for a general scattering process can be related to others by parity conservation. The simplicity of this equation, which applies to scattering amplitudes of arbitrary incoming and outgoing particles (a, b, c, and d), is one of the remarkable consequences of the helicity formalism.

We now turn to electromagnetic transition amplitudes. The general processes are:

(11.4-14) $$a \rightarrow \gamma + b \qquad \text{(photo-emission)}$$

[5] The phase factors appearing in these equations differ in detail from those of the original paper [Jacob & Wick], as can be traced to two origins: (i) the use of $R(\phi, \theta, 0)$ rather than $R(\phi, \theta, -\phi)$ to rotate from $\hat{\mathbf{z}}$ to $\hat{\mathbf{p}}$; and (ii) the omission of a "second particle factor" $(-1)^{s_2 - \lambda_2}$ [Jacob & Wick] in the definition of the two-particle state in Eq. (8.4-14). Both departures from the original definitions adopted here lead to simplifications in applications.

and

(11.4-15) $$\gamma + a \to b \qquad \text{(photo-absorption)}$$

where "a" and "b" are arbitrary atomic, nuclear, or elementary particle states. According to the formalism developed in Sec. 11.3.4, we can treat the (massless) photon states in the same way as massive states with s replaced by $|\lambda| = 1$, and η_p set equal to -1. Referring back to Sec. 8.7 on multipole wave functions $\mathbf{A}^{k\lambda}_{JM}(\mathbf{x})$ for the two ($\lambda = \pm 1$) helicity states, we begin by examining some of their properties under space inversion. Applying the space inversion operator I_s to both sides of Eq. (8.7-9), we obtain

(11.4-16) $$\text{LHS} = -\mathbf{A}(-\mathbf{x}, t) = -\sum_{J,M,\lambda} \int k^2 dk \left[a(k\, J\, M\, \lambda) \mathbf{A}^{k\lambda}_{JM}(-\mathbf{x}) e^{-i\omega t} + h.c. \right]$$

and

(11.4-17) $$\begin{aligned} \text{RHS} &= \sum_{J,M,\lambda} \int k^2 dk \left[(-1)^J a(k\, J\, M\, -\lambda) \mathbf{A}^{k,\lambda}_{JM}(\mathbf{x}) e^{-i\omega t} + h.c. \right] \\ &= \sum_{J,M,\lambda} \int k^2 dk \left[a(k\, J\, M\, \lambda) (-1)^J \mathbf{A}^{k,-\lambda}_{JM}(\mathbf{x}) e^{-i\omega t} + h.c. \right] \quad . \end{aligned}$$

Comparing these two expressions, we conclude that

(11.4-18) $$\mathbf{A}^{k,-\lambda}_{JM}(\mathbf{x}) = \mathbf{A}^{k\lambda}_{JM}(-\mathbf{x}) (-1)^{J+1} \quad .$$

In deriving (11.4-16) we used the space inversion property of $\mathbf{A}$ (first step) and a straightforward substitution using Eq. (8.7-9) (second step). In deriving (11.4-17) we used Eq. (11.4-5) (first step), and changed the sign of the dummy summation index λ (second step). Eq. (11.4-18) can also be inferred directly from the explicit formula for $\mathbf{A}^{k\lambda}_{JM}(\mathbf{x})$, Eq. (8.7-15). [Problem 11.12]

The wave function for photon states of definite angular momentum eigenvalues $(J\, M)$, energy $\hbar\omega$, and parity $\tau(-1)^J$ is, according to Eq. (11.4-6),

(11.4-19) $$\mathbf{A}^{k\tau}_{JM}(\mathbf{x}) = \left[\mathbf{A}^{k,\lambda=1}_{JM}(\mathbf{x}) + \tau\, \mathbf{A}^{k,\lambda=-1}_{JM}(\mathbf{x}) \right] / 2^{1/2} \quad .$$

It follows from Eq. (11.4-18) that

(11.4-20) $$\mathbf{A}^{k\tau}_{JM}(-\mathbf{x}) = \tau(-1)^{J+1} \mathbf{A}^{k\tau}_{JM}(\mathbf{x}) \quad .$$

The expansion of the vector potential field operator $\mathbf{A}(\mathbf{x}, t)$ in terms of the angular momentum and parity wave functions is:

(11.4-21) $$\mathbf{A}(\mathbf{x}, t) = \sum_{J,M,\tau} \int k^2 dk \left[a(k\, J\, M\, \tau) \mathbf{A}^{k\tau}_{JM}(\mathbf{x}) e^{-i\omega t} + h.c. \right] \quad .$$

In analogy to Eq. (8.7-19), one can define *multipole moment operators* with definite parity which are responsible for the electromagnetic transition (say, photo-absorption) from an arbitrary initial state $|i\rangle$ to a final state $|f\rangle$,

(11.4-22) $$H^{k\tau}_{JM} = \int d^3x\, \mathbf{J}(\mathbf{x}) \cdot \mathbf{A}^{k\tau}_{JM}(\mathbf{x}) \quad .$$

It follows then

$$I_s H^{k\tau}_{JM} I_s^{-1} = \int d^3x\, I_s\, \mathbf{J}(\mathbf{x})\, I_s^{-1} \cdot \mathbf{A}^{k\tau}_{JM}(\mathbf{x})$$

$$= -\int d^3x\, \mathbf{J}(-\mathbf{x}) \cdot \mathbf{A}^{k\tau}_{JM}(\mathbf{x})$$

(11.4-23)
$$= -\int d^3x\, \mathbf{J}(\mathbf{x}) \cdot \mathbf{A}^{k\tau}_{JN}(-\mathbf{x})$$

$$= \tau(-1)^J \int d^3x\, \mathbf{J}(\mathbf{x}) \cdot \mathbf{A}^{k\tau}_{JM}(\mathbf{x})$$

$$= \tau(-1)^J H^{k\tau}_{JM} \quad .$$

In other words, $\{H^{k\tau}_{JM}\}$ are *irreducible spherical tensor operators* with parity $\tau(-1)^J$. In deriving Eq. (11.4-23) one makes use of the definition (11.4-22) (first and last steps), the polar vector nature of $\mathbf{J}(\mathbf{x})$ (second step), change of the sign of dummy integration variable $\mathbf{x}$ (third step), and Eq. (11.4-20) (fourth step).

Since the electromagnetic interaction Hamiltonian, Eq. (8.7-17), is invariant under space inversion, the parity eigenvalues of the initial and final states (η_i and η_f respectively) must satisfy the selection rule

(11.4-24)
$$\eta_i \eta_f = \tau(-1)^J \quad .$$

Comparing this result with the conventional classification of multipole moments [Blatt & Weisskopf, Jackson, Rose], we can identify the $\tau = +1$ case as the usual *electric multipole* and the $\tau = -1$ case as the *magnetic multipole.* We remark that the selection rule (11.4-24) is obtained under the (prevailing) condition that the energy $\hbar\omega$ is small compared to the rest energies (mc^2) of the initial and final states, so that both systems "a" and "b" can be regarded as at rest (i.e. no recoil effect is taken into account).

We close this subject with a brief look at the multipole fields. According to Eqs. (11.4-19) and (8.7-15),

$$\mathbf{A}^{k,\tau}_{JM}(\mathbf{x}) = \frac{16\pi^2}{2J+1} \sum_l \left(\frac{2l+1}{8\pi}\right)^{1/2} i^l j_l(kx)\, \mathbf{T}_{JM}{}^l(\hat{\mathbf{x}})$$

$$\cdot [\langle J\,1\,(l\,1)\,0\,1\rangle + \tau \langle J, -1\,(l\,1)\,0, -1\rangle]$$

(11.4-25)
$$= \frac{16\pi^2}{2J+1} \sum_l \left(\frac{2l+1}{8\pi}\right)^{1/2} i^l j_l(kx)\, \mathbf{T}_{JM}{}^l(\hat{\mathbf{x}}) \langle J1\,(l1)\,01\rangle$$

$$\cdot [1 + \tau(-1)^{J-l-1}] \quad .$$

Since $l = J$ or $J \pm 1$, the last factor implies that magnetic multipole ($\tau = -1$) wave functions for $\mathbf{A}(\mathbf{x})$ involve only $l = J$, whereas electric multipole ($\tau = +1$) wave functions consist of a specific linear combination of $l = J \pm 1$ terms. In the former case

(11.4-26)
$$\mathbf{A}^{k,\tau=-1}_{JM}(\mathbf{x}) = u_J(kx)\, \mathbf{T}^J_{JM}(\hat{\mathbf{x}})$$

$$\mathbf{E}^{(\text{magnetic})}_{JM}(\mathbf{x}) = ik\, u_J(kx)\, \mathbf{T}^J_{JM}(\hat{\mathbf{x}})$$

$$\mathbf{B}^{(\text{magnetic})}_{JM}(\mathbf{x}) = \nabla \times [u_J(kx)\, \mathbf{T}^J_{JM}(\hat{\mathbf{x}})]$$

where the function $u_J(kx)$ can be read off from (11.4-25). These results agree with those given in standard references. [Blatt & Weisskopf, Jackson, Rose] In these references, it is shown (by various vector identities), that the corresponding expressions for $\tau = +1$ can be written in a way similar to the above with the roles of the **E** and **B** fields reversed, i.e.

$$\begin{aligned} \mathbf{E}_{JM}^{(\text{electric})}(\mathbf{x}) &= -\nabla \times [v_J(kx)\mathbf{T}_{JM}^{J}(\hat{\mathbf{x}})] \\ \mathbf{B}_{JM}^{(electric)}(\mathbf{x}) &= ikv_J(kx)\mathbf{T}_{JM}^{J}(\hat{\mathbf{x}}) \end{aligned} \tag{11.4-27}$$

which correspond to a vector potential wave function

$$\mathbf{A}_{JM}^{k\ \tau=+1}(x) = \frac{i}{k}\nabla \times [v_J(kx)\mathbf{T}_{JM}^{J}(\hat{\mathbf{x}})] \quad .$$

We should point out that the significance of these discussions goes beyond "reproducing" familiar classical radiation formulas by a different method. With the use of the group-theoretical approach, we have put the theory of radiation on the same footing as the helicity formalism for general processes. Hence, many general theorems based on continuous and discrete symmetries can be directly applied, often resulting in better understanding and much simplified derivation of previously obscure results. Furthermore, certain restrictive features of the traditional theory (such as the "no recoil" assumption) can be removed if necessary.

Problems

11.1 (i) Enumerate some of the subgroups of O(2); (ii) Is the subgroup $\{E, I\}$ ($I = I_1$ or I_2) an invariant subgroup? (iii) Is O(2) the direct product of SO(2) with one of the subgroup $\{E, I\}$? (iv) Describe the classes of O(2).

11.2 Write down the 3×3 matrix representation of the coordinate transformation operator (P_1, P_2) and (I_1, I_2) [Eq. (9.1-5)]. Verify Eq. (11.1-13) algebraically.

11.3 With respect to the angular momentum basis of the (p, η) representation of $\tilde{\mathrm{E}}_2$, the reflection matrices contain the factor η [Eqs. (11.1-18)–(11.1-21)]. In describing irreducible representations of the O(2) group, we indicated how such factors can be "transformed away" by a change of basis [Eqs. (11.1-7)–(11.1-10)]. Is it possible to do the same for the $\tilde{\mathrm{E}}_2$ group and to show that the $\eta = 1$ and $\eta = -1$ representations (for the same p) are actually equivalent representations, related to each other by a change of basis? Why?

11.4 Derive the representation matrices for the operators T(**b**), R(α, β, γ), and I_s in the irreducible representation corresponding to $\mathbf{P}^2 = p^2 \neq 0$, $(\mathbf{J}\cdot\mathbf{P})^2 = 0$ for the group $\tilde{\mathrm{E}}_3$.

11.5 Define the angular momentum basis of the (p, η) representation of $\tilde{\mathrm{E}}_3$ in terms of the linear momentum basis given by Eq. (11.2-8ab). Derive the representation matrices of elements of the subgroup O(3) in the new basis and compare them with the result of the subsection on irreducible representations of O(3).

11.6 Find eigenstates of the operator $I_\theta = \mathrm{R}(\theta)\, I_2\, \mathrm{R}(\theta)^{-1}$ in the vector space of the m-irreducible representation ($m = 1, 2, \ldots$) of the O(2) group and the associated eigenvalues.

11.7 Take the standard vector $|\mathbf{p}_l\,\lambda\rangle$ defined by Eq. (11.3-14) for the $c_1 = c_2 = 0$ representation of the Poincaré group. Show that the vector $I_s\,|\mathbf{p}_l\,\lambda\rangle$ is an eigenvector of the operators P^μ, J_3, and $W_{1,2}$ and evaluate the eigenvalues. Show explicitly why $I_s\,|\mathbf{p}_l\,\lambda\rangle$ does not lie in the vector space spanned by the basis Eq. (11.3-15).

11.8 An alternative proof of Eq. (11.3-18) can proceed as follows: Let $I_s\,|\mathbf{p}\,\lambda\rangle = |-\mathbf{p}\,-\lambda\rangle\,\eta(\mathbf{p},\lambda)$, then demonstrate that $\eta(\mathbf{p},\lambda)$ is independent of $\mathbf{p}$. Carry this proof out using the identity $I_s\,|\mathbf{p}\,\lambda\rangle = I_s H(p)\,|\mathbf{0}\,\lambda\rangle = H(-\mathbf{p})\,[H^{-1}(-\mathbf{p})\,I_s H(\mathbf{p})]\,|\mathbf{0}\,\lambda\rangle$ and show that the operator in the square bracket reverses the helicity but is independent of $\mathbf{p}$.

11.9 Enumerate the independent helicity amplitudes for elastic electron-proton scattering and express all the helicity amplitudes in terms of the independent ones.

CHAPTER 12

TIME REVERSAL INVARIANCE

12.1 Preliminary Discussion

In 4-dimensional Minkowski space, the time reversal transformation I_t is, as the terminology implies,

(12.1-1) $$x = (x^0, \mathbf{x}) \xrightarrow{I_t} x' = (-x^0, \mathbf{x}) \quad .$$

Hence, I_t is represented by the diagonal matrix

(12.1-2) $$I_t = \begin{pmatrix} -1 & & & \\ & 1 & & \\ & & 1 & \\ & & & 1 \end{pmatrix} .$$

Since this 4×4 matrix is just the sign-reversed matrix to I_s, Eq. (11.3-1), one might expect it to be straightforward to extend the representation theory of the previous section to the present case. In the mathematical sense, this expectation is true, at least in the context of the homogeneous (Lorentz) subgroup. If I_t is to be associated with a linear operator on the representation space, then the algebraic relation $I_t I_s = -E$ implies that:

(12.1-3) $$I_t \Lambda I_t^{-1} = I_s \Lambda I_s^{-1} \qquad \text{for all } \Lambda \in \tilde{L}_+ \quad .$$

Hence the two operators I_t, I_s are at least proportional to each other on the representation space. [Naimark]

In order to bring in translations $\{T(\mathbf{b})\}$ as well, the matrices (11.3-1), (12.1-2) must be extended to become 5×5 diagonal ones both with a positive 1 added to the last position. [Eq. (10.1-25)] We deduce from the algebra of these matrices that

(12.1-4) $$I_t\, T(b)\, I_t^{-1} = T(I_t b)$$

where $I_t b = (-b^0, \mathbf{b})$, in comparison to the result for space inversion

(12.1-5) $$I_s\, T(b)\, I_s^{-1} = T(I_s b)$$

where $I_s b = (b^0, -\mathbf{b})$. In other words, the product $I_s I_t$ does not commute with translations; rather,

(12.1-6) $$I_s I_t\, T(b) (I_s I_t)^{-1} = T(-b)$$

This is intuitively correct: the product $I_s I_t$ is the total inversion operator in 4-dimensional space-time, a translation by b^μ becomes a translation by $-b^\mu$ after all the space-time axes are reversed. The same result follows from the 5×5 matrix algebraic approach: the product $I_s I_t$ is represented by a diagonal matrix with elements $(-1,-1,-1,-1,1)$; hence it does not commute with the 5×5 translation matrices which have non-vanishing elements in all five columns.

Definition 12.1 (The Full Poincaré Group): The symmetry group consisting of proper Poincaré transformations $g(b,\Lambda)$, space inversion I_s, and time reversal I_t with multiplication rules are specified above forms the *Full Poincaré group.*

If we were to follow the methodology developed up to this point in a straightforward way, we would map I_t to a unitary operator on the representation space, just as for space inversion and the continuous symmetry transformations. We would then conclude from Eqs. (12.1-3) and (12.1-4) that the (hermitian) generators of the continuous transformations satisfy the following algebraic relations with I_t:

$$I_t \mathbf{J} I_t^{-1} = \mathbf{J} \qquad I_t \mathbf{K} I_t^{-1} = -\mathbf{K}$$
$$I_t P^0 I_t^{-1} = -P^0 \qquad I_t \mathbf{P} I_t^{-1} = \mathbf{P} \tag{12.1-7}$$

We might then start to identify suitable little groups for various "standard vectors" of the invariant subgroup of translations, and to derive the corresponding induced representations. This line of development will, however, quickly run into problems if we examine closely the physical consequences of the mathematical results so obtained. In fact, one can sense trouble already in Eq. (12.1-7): if time reversal is a good symmetry transformation, we expect P^0, the Hamiltonian, to be invariant under I_t; but (12.1-7) requires P_0 to change sign. Similarly, we would expect the 3-momentum to change sign under time reversal, but (12.1-7) indicates the opposite. In order to formulate these potential contradictions in precise terms, let us first review the meaning of time reversal invariance in classical physics.

12.2 Time Reversal Invariance in Classical Physics

It is well-known that all equations of motion in Classical Mechanics—for systems simple or complex (Newton's Law, Lagrange Equations, or Hamiltonian formulation)—are invariant under time reversal if the basic physical variables transform in the following way.

$$\mathbf{r} \xrightarrow{I_t} \mathbf{r}' = \mathbf{r} \qquad \text{(position)}$$
$$\mathbf{p} \xrightarrow{I_t} \mathbf{p}' = I_t(m\frac{d}{dt}\mathbf{r}) = -\mathbf{p} \qquad \text{(momentum)}$$
$$H \xrightarrow{I_t} H' = I_t\left[\frac{p^2}{2m} + V(\mathbf{r})\right] = H \qquad \text{(Hamiltonian)}$$
$$\mathbf{L} \xrightarrow{I_t} \mathbf{L}' = I_t(\mathbf{r}\times\mathbf{p}) = -\mathbf{L}. \qquad \text{(Angular Momentum)} \tag{12.2-1}$$

How does the formal invariance of Newton's Law relate to the real physical world, and how is it checked by actual experiments? The answer is provided by the following operational procedure:

(i) Perform some real experiment A (with definite initial conditions) in the laboratory and record the time evolution of the system on film.

(ii) Run the film backwards, we see a fictitious experiment A_t which we shall call the *time-reversed image* of A. We shall see that, at any instant, positions of objects will appear to be the same as before while directions of linear momenta (indicated by velocities) and angular momenta (indicated by the sense of rotation) will appear to be opposite to those of the original motion at the corresponding instant, in accord with Eq. (12.2-1).

(iii) If new initial conditions of the experiment are set exactly to what one observes for A_t (i.e. the time-reversed image of the final conditions of A), then this second real experiment, called A′, will develop in real time in a way identical to that of the fictitious experiment A_t, and the energy of the system will be the same as the original experiment (again in accord with Eq. (12.2-1)).

Symbolically, time reversal invariance in this sense will be expressed by $A' = A_t$. Note that time reversal invariance would be devoid of content without the third step: the first two are mere definitions, and it would be useless to compare A with A_t.

We remark that Classical Electromagnetism is also known to be invariant under time reversal if, in addition to Eq. (12.2-1), we let the field variables transform as

$$\begin{aligned} \mathbf{E} &\xrightarrow{I_t} \mathbf{E}' = \mathbf{E} \\ \mathbf{B} &\xrightarrow{I_t} \mathbf{B}' = -\mathbf{B} \quad . \end{aligned} \tag{12.2-2}$$

12.3 Problems with Linear Realization of Time Reversal Transformation

The time reversal transformation properties of classical physical variables given by Eq. (12.2-1) are expected to remain valid for their quantum mechanical counterparts, according to the Correspondence Principle [Messiah, Schiff]. Furthermore, the quantum mechanical 3-momentum and energy (Hamiltonian) operators have the group-theoretical significance of being the generators of (3-dimensional) spatial and time translations, respectively. However, the quantum-mechanical versions of Eq. (12.2-1) are in sharp contradiction with Eq. (12.1-7), which was derived from the geometrical transformation laws, Eqs. (12.1-3), (12.1-4), and the realization of I_t as an ordinary unitary operator on the space of physical states (like the other symmetry transformations). Which set of equations is wrong? Which of the general principles which lead to these equations must be re-examined and modified?

Another way of seeing the same problem is as follows. Consider the basic relation between the Hamiltonian (or energy) operator and time evolution in quantum mechanics:

$$i\hbar \frac{\partial}{\partial t} = H \quad . \tag{12.3-1}$$

This is the basis of the Schrödinger Equation. If the usual rule of linear transformation is applied, the left-hand side changes sign under time reversal. On the other hand, the Hamiltonian H on the right-hand side does not change sign, according to Eq. (12.2-1). This dilemma can be resolved in three possible ways: (i) the Hamiltonian does change sign under time reversal transformation, hence the Correspondence Principle does not hold; (ii) the left-hand side of (12.3-1) does not change sign under time reversal, therefore I_t is not realized as a usual linear transformation; or (iii) the Schrödinger Equation is not time-reversal-invariant.

Suppose the Hamiltonian changes sign under I_t. Then, every eigenstate of H (i.e. a stationary state with definite energy) must have a corresponding state (the time-reversed state) with energy the negative of the original one. We certainly do not see such pairing of states in the real world. Besides, if they exist, the time-reversed states of a state of arbitrarily high energy (such as a single particle with very high momentum) would have arbitrarily low energy. Such systems are intrinsically unstable: any small disturbance would cause a given physical configuration collapsing to the negative infinite energy states. This option is clearly unacceptable.

If we do not wish to give up time reversal invariance as a symmetry of Quantum Mechanics (possibility (iii) above), we must re-examine alternatives to the realization of I_t as an ordinary unitary linear operator. The best way to motivate a possible new approach is to study a simple, but non-trivial example. For this purpose, consider the Schrödinger Equation for a single free particle of mass m in the coordinate-space representation

$$i\hbar \frac{\partial}{\partial t} \psi(x,t) = -\frac{\hbar^2}{2m} \nabla^2 \psi(\mathbf{x},t) \quad . \tag{12.3-2}$$

If we attempt to implement time reversal by the linear mapping

$$\psi(\mathbf{x},t) \xrightarrow{I_t} \psi'(\mathbf{x},t') = \eta\psi(\mathbf{x},-t) \tag{12.3-3}$$

as an obvious first try, we find

$$\begin{aligned} i\hbar\frac{\partial}{\partial t'}\psi'(\mathbf{x},t') &= -i\hbar\frac{\partial}{\partial t}\eta\psi(\mathbf{x},-t) = \frac{\hbar^2}{2m}\nabla^2\eta\psi(\mathbf{x},-t) \\ &= \frac{\hbar^2}{2m}\nabla^2\psi'(\mathbf{x},t') \end{aligned} \tag{12.3-4}$$

Thereby, we lose the invariance of the Schrödinger equation as discussed earlier. The way out of his dilemma is relatively easy to see in this particular example, since the unwanted sign change in the transformed equation (12.3-4) can be compensated by taking the complex-conjugation of both sides of the equation. In other words, the Schrödinger Equation will be invariant under time reversal if, instead of (12.3-3), we adopt the following mapping of the wave function under I_t:

$$\psi(\mathbf{x},t) \xrightarrow{I_t} \psi'(\mathbf{x},t') = \eta\psi^*(\mathbf{x},-t) \tag{12.3-5}$$

where, as usual, η denotes an arbitrary phase factor. The verification of the invariance of Eq. (12.3-2) is straightforward. [Messiah]

What have we given up by adopting this new time reversal transformation on ψ? The answer is that (12.3-5) is not an ordinary linear mapping (as we have so far assumed for all other symmetry transformations). Complex conjugation spoils the *linearity* requirement

$$\alpha_1\psi_1 + \alpha_2\psi_2 \longrightarrow \alpha_1\psi_1' + \alpha_2\psi_2' \quad .$$

Rather, we now have

$$\alpha_1\psi_1 + \alpha_2\psi_2 \xrightarrow{I_t} \alpha_1^*\psi_1' + \alpha_2^*\psi_2' \quad . \tag{12.3-6}$$

This type of mapping is called an *anti-linear transformation.*

Does Eq. (12.3-5) define an acceptable time reversal transformation on the space of coordinate space Schrödinger wave functions? The answer is yes, since such a transformation preserves the absolute value of scalar products (which correspond to physically measurable quantities). [Messiah, Schiff] Instead of dwelling on this particular case further, we shall proceed to formulate time reversal invariance in general along the same line.

Anti-Linear and Anti-Unitary Operators

In Appendix VIII we give a systematic summary of the properties of anti-linear operators. For practical applications, it is sufficient to know that an anti-linear operator A can be used much in the same way as an ordinary linear operator with the following exceptions:

(i) It does not commute with all complex numbers c; instead, we have

(12.3-7) $$A\,c = c^*A$$

(ii) In contrast to the usual identity $\langle\phi|A\psi\rangle = \langle A^\dagger\phi|\psi\rangle$, we must use

(12.3-8) $$\langle\phi|A\psi\rangle = \langle\psi|A^\dagger\phi\rangle = \langle A^\dagger\phi|\psi\rangle^* \quad .$$

One practical consequence of Eq. (12.3-8) is that the commonly used expression $\langle\phi|A|\psi\rangle$ becomes ambiguous: $\langle\phi|A\psi\rangle \neq \langle A^\dagger\phi|\psi\rangle$ for anti-linear operators. Before taking the scalar product, one has to indicate explicitly to which vector ("ket" or "bra") is the operator (A or $A^\dagger$) being applied first.

(iii) An *anti-unitary* operator A, by definition, is an anti-linear operator which also satisfies the unitary condition

(12.3-9) $$A\,A^\dagger = E \quad .$$

It is easy to see that the mapping (12.3-5) is anti-unitary (in the wave function space) provided $|\eta|^2 = 1$. In contrast to the scalar-product-preserving feature of unitary transformations, anti-unitary transformations have the property

(12.3-10) $$\langle A\phi|A\psi\rangle = \langle\phi|\psi\rangle^* = \langle\psi|\phi\rangle \quad .$$

We must now ask whether substituting anti-unitary operators for unitary ones in the representation of time reversal transformation would be totally consistent with all other established basic principles. The answer is affirmative, as unitarity was originally motivated by the physical requirement of conservation of probability in Quantum Mechanics when the physical system undergoes a symmetry transformation A: i.e.

(12.3-11) $$|\langle A\phi|A\psi\rangle|^2 = |\langle\phi|\psi\rangle|^2 \qquad \text{for all } |\phi\rangle \text{ and } |\psi\rangle \quad .$$

For this condition to be satisfied, it is sufficient that A be unitary; but that is not necessary. It is obvious that the antiunitarity condition (12.3-10) also guarantees the validity of conservation of probability expressed by the above equation. In fact, because of the freedom to choose the phase of state vectors inherent in Quantum Mechanics, it is possible to prove that all operators representing symmetry transformations can be assigned either to unitary or to anti-unitary operators. [Messiah, Chap. 10, Sec. 6]

12.4 The Anti-Unitary Time Reversal Operator

The discussion of the previous few subsections can now be summarized in one theorem.

Theorem 12.1 (I_t as an Anti-unitary Operator): Consistency with the principles of Quantum Mechanics requires that the realization of the time reversal transformation I_t in physics be in terms of an anti-unitary operator (also denoted by I_t) on the space of state vectors.

We now analyze the consequences of this theorem in the context of the full space-time symmetry of Minkowski space encompassing proper Lorentz transformations, 4-translations, space inversion, and time reversal. Since the physical system forms a representation of this symmetry group, all the algebraic relationships involving group elements must be preserved on the space of state vectors of the system, even when anti-unitary operators are included. We re-assemble those relationships involving time reversal:

$$\begin{aligned} I_t\,\mathrm{R}_{\hat{n}}(\psi)\,I_t^{-1} &= \mathrm{R}_{\hat{n}}(\psi) \\ I_t\,\mathrm{L}_{\hat{n}}(\xi)\,I_t^{-1} &= \mathrm{L}_{-\hat{n}}(\xi) \\ I_t\,\mathrm{T}(b^0,\mathbf{b})\,I_t^{-1} &= \mathrm{T}(-b^0,\mathbf{b}) \\ I_t I_s &= I_s I_t \end{aligned} \tag{12.4-1}$$

where all quantities should be familiar. To convert the first three equations into ones involving I_t with the generators of the continuous Poincaré group, we note that, for an arbitrary linear operator B and an anti-linear operator A, we have

$$A e^{-iB} A^{-1} = e^{iABA^{-1}} \quad .$$

This differs from the corresponding equation involving linear operators by a sign in the exponent. (The factor i in the exponent changes sign when "passing through" the anti-linear operator A. [Eq. (12.3-7)]) As a result, we obtain

$$\begin{aligned} I_t\,\mathbf{J}\,I_t^{-1} &= -\mathbf{J} \\ I_t\,\mathbf{K}\,I_t^{-1} &= \mathbf{K} \\ I_t\,P^0\,I_t^{-1} &= P^0 \\ I_t\,\mathbf{P}\,I_t^{-1} &= -\mathbf{P} \quad . \end{aligned} \tag{12.4-2}$$

The results are, of course, now consistent with identities (12.2-1), which should be valid in quantum mechanics as well as in classical physics according to the Correspondence Principle. The use of the anti-unitary operator I_t also leads to a simple proof of time reversal invariance of the Schrödinger equation in its most general form, Eq. (12.3-1)—on the left-hand side, both i and dt change sign under I_t; hence it stays invariant as is the case for the right-hand side. We have, therefore, a self-consistent mathematical scheme that can be used to formulate the group theoretical consequences of time reversal invariance along the lines of Sec. 11.3.

Before getting down to specifics, it is worthwhile mentioning that we do not expect basis states in the irreducible representations of the full group to be distinguished by eigenvalues of the operator I_t, in the manner of intrinsic parity due to I_s. This is due to a special feature of anti-linear operators.

Lemma: The eigenvectors of an anti-linear operator A are divided into equivalent classes characterized by the magnitude of its eigenvalues. In each class, there are an infinity of eigenvectors, one for each $\theta (0 \leq \theta < 2\pi)$, the phase angle of the eigenvalue.

Proof: Let $|\lambda\rangle$ be an eigenvector of A with the eigenvalue λ (for arbitrary complex λ),

$$A\,|\lambda\rangle = |\lambda\rangle\,\lambda \quad . \tag{12.4-3}$$

Consider the action of A on the vector $e^{i\alpha/2}|\lambda\rangle$, where α is any real number,

$$\begin{aligned} A\,e^{i\alpha/2}|\lambda\rangle &= e^{-i\alpha/2}\,A\,|\lambda\rangle = e^{-i\alpha/2}\,|\lambda\rangle\,\lambda \\ &= e^{i\alpha/2}|\lambda\rangle\,\lambda e^{-i\alpha} \quad . \end{aligned} \tag{12.4-4}$$

We conclude: $e^{i\alpha/2}|\lambda\rangle$ is also an eigenvector of A, with the eigenvalue $\lambda e^{-i\alpha}$ (for any real α). Let the positive real number ρ be the magnitude of λ, i.e. $\rho = |\lambda|$, then there is one eigenvector for each eigenvalue $\rho e^{i\theta}$, $0 \leq \theta < 2\pi$. QED

Since the eigenvalues of an anti-unitary operator must have unit modulus, it follows from the above theorem that if an anti-unitary operator has any eigenvector, then it has an infinite number of eigenvectors with eigenvalues covering the whole unit circle. This result applies, in particular, to I_t. We conclude that:

Theorem 12.2 (Eigenstates of Time Reversal Operator I_t): The representation space of any group embracing time reversal must contain eigenstates of I_t in entire classes, the states in each class are distinguished by their relative phases, which are related to their eigenvalues under I_t according to Eq. (12.4-4).

Consequently, the eigenvalue of I_t is not relevant in the classification of irreducible representations of the full space-time symmetry group. However, we can make use of the time reversal eigenvalue to fix the relative phase factors of basis vectors in a way not possible with unitary operators. (For any linear operator changing the phase of an eigenvector does not change the eigenvalue.) This feature will be utilized in the following.

12.5 Irreducible Representations of the Full Poincaré Group in the Time-Like Case

When $c_1 = M^2 > 0$ we begin, as usual, with the representation space of the little group SO(3) if we start with the proper group (or O(3) if we start with the extended group) associated with the rest frame vector $p_t = (M, \mathbf{0})$. The basis vectors $\{|0\,\lambda\rangle\}$ are defined by Eq. (10.4-3) (or Eq. (11.3-10)). Let us now consider the properties of the time-reversed states $\{I_t|0\,\lambda\rangle\}$:

$$\begin{aligned} P^0 I_t\,|0\,\lambda\rangle &= I_t P^0\,|0\,\lambda\rangle = I_t\,|0\,\lambda\rangle M \\ \mathbf{P}\,I_t\,|0\,\lambda\rangle &= -I_t\mathbf{P}\,|0\,\lambda\rangle = 0 \\ \mathbf{J}^2 I_t\,|0\,\lambda\rangle &= I_t\mathbf{J}^2\,|0\,\lambda\rangle = I_t\,|0\,\lambda\rangle\,s(s+1) \\ J_3\,I_t\,|0\,\lambda\rangle &= -I_t J_3\,|0\,\lambda\rangle = I_t\,|0\,\lambda\rangle(-\lambda) \\ I_s\,I_t\,|0\,\lambda\rangle &= I_t I_s\,|0\,\lambda\rangle = I_t\,|0\,\lambda\rangle\,\eta_p \quad . \end{aligned} \tag{12.5-1}$$

N.B. Since all eigenvalues here are real, they commute with I_t; that is the reason for not inserting extra parentheses to indicate the order of multiplication on the extreme right-hand sides of the above equations. In general, when anti-linear operators and complex numbers both appear in an expression, the order in which multiplications are to be carried out has to be specified clearly. Eq. (12.5-1) states that the time reversal transformation changes the sign of the J_3 eigenvalue while leaving all other eigenvalues unchanged. Since the operator $R_2(\pi)$ has exactly the same effect on the rest frame basis vectors as I_t, the product $R_2(\pi)I_t$ leaves all eigenvalues $(M, s; \mathbf{p}, \lambda)$ (as well as η_p) invariant. Consequently, the "time-reversed state" obtained by acting with this compound operator is related to the original state by, at most, a phase factor:

$$R_2(\pi)\, I_t|\mathbf{0}\,\lambda\rangle = |\mathbf{0}\,\lambda\rangle\,\eta_T \tag{12.5-2}$$

where the phase factor η_T is independent of λ. [Problem 12.1] We obtain, therefore,

$$I_t|\mathbf{0}\,\lambda\rangle = R_2(-\pi)|\mathbf{0}\,\lambda\rangle\,\eta_T = |\mathbf{0}\,-\lambda\rangle\,\eta_T(-1)^{s+\lambda} \quad . \tag{12.5-3}$$

The phase factor η_T can be "absorbed" into the definition of the basis vectors: for any given choice of $\{|\mathbf{0}\,\lambda\rangle\}$ with the associated η_T, the new basis vectors $\{|\mathbf{0}\,\lambda\rangle'\}$ defined as $|\mathbf{0}\,\lambda\rangle' = |\mathbf{0}\,\lambda\rangle\,\eta_T{}^{1/2}$ will satisfy all the same equations in (12.5-1), together with the simplified time reversal property

$$I_t\,|\mathbf{0}\,\lambda\rangle' = |\mathbf{0}\,-\lambda\rangle'(-1)^{s+\lambda} \quad . \tag{12.5-4}$$

The proof depends on the anti-linear nature of I_t [Theorem 12.1], as well as on the fact that η_T is independent of λ. [Problem 12.1]

The situation concerning fixing the phase factors can be made explicit in the following way. Consider a canonical basis labelled by λ $(=s, \ldots, -s)$ listed in a vertical column. Multiply all the basis vectors by a phase factor $e^{i\alpha}$ to obtain another canonical basis. In Table 12.1 we list the alternative sets alongside each other horizontally; thus the horizontal lable is the phase angle α. Each entry in this table is a vector of the (rest frame) representation space and is denoted by a short arrow.

Table 12.1 List of canonical basis vectors differing by a phase factor, and fixing of the phase by the time reversal eigenvalue

$\lambda \backslash \alpha$	0	$\cdots$	θ	$\cdots$	2π
s	$\rightarrow$	$\cdots$	$\rightarrow$	$\cdots$	$\rightarrow$
$s-1$	$\rightarrow$	$\cdots$	$\rightarrow$	$\cdots$	$\rightarrow$
$\vdots$	$\vdots$	$\vdots$	$\vdots$	$\vdots$	$\vdots$
$-s$	$\rightarrow$	$\cdots$	$\rightarrow$	$\cdots$	$\rightarrow$
η_T	1	$\cdot\cdot$	$e^{-i2\theta}$	$\cdot\cdot$	1
η_p	$\longleftarrow$		(± 1)		$\longrightarrow$

Listed on the bottom row is the intrinsic parity quantum number $\eta_p (= \pm 1)$, if space inversion symmetry applies. This eigenvalue is unique for all vectors of this space, as indicated by the two-sided arrow drawn across all the columns. Next up is the time reversal eigenvalue η_T defined by Eq. (12.5-2). All possible values of η_T appear in this row as η_T is correlated with the phase of the vectors [Theorem 12.2]. Thus the equivalent sets of canonical bases (i.e. the various columns of Table 12.1) are only distinguished by their time-reversal eigenvalues. For definiteness and for simplicity we choose, by convention, the column corresponding to $\eta_T = 1$. This is equivalent to including Eq. (12.5-4) as one of the defining equations [along with Eq. (10.4-22)] of the canonical basis in the rest frame.

We now move on to the basis vectors in an arbitrary frame. First, consider states moving along the z-axis, $|p\hat{z}\,\lambda\rangle = L_3(\xi)|\mathbf{0}\,\lambda\rangle$. The time reversal operator I_t reverses the direction of the Lorentz boost, as does $R_2(\pi)$; hence it is again convenient to start with

$$R_2(\pi)I_t\,|p\hat{z}\,\lambda\rangle = L_3(\xi)\,R_2(\pi)I_t\,|\mathbf{0}\,\lambda\rangle = L_3(\xi)\,|\mathbf{0}\,\lambda\rangle = |p\hat{z}\,\lambda\rangle \tag{12.5-5}$$

where in the first step we used the commutativity of $L_3(\xi)$ with $R_2(\pi)\,I_t$, and in the second step we used Eq. (12.5-2) (with $\eta_T = 1$ as by our convention). Hence, we obtain

$$I_t|p\hat{z}\,\lambda\rangle = R_2(-\pi)\,|p\hat{z}\,\lambda\rangle \tag{12.5-6}$$

which leads to the general result

$$\begin{aligned} I_t|\mathbf{p}\,\lambda\rangle &= I_t R(\phi,\theta,0)\,|p\hat{z}\,\lambda\rangle = R(\phi,\theta,0)\,I_t|p\hat{z}\,\lambda\rangle \\ &= R(\phi,\theta,0)\,R_2(-\pi)\,|p\hat{z}\,\lambda\rangle = R(\phi,-\pi+\theta,0)\,|p\hat{z}\,\lambda\rangle \\ &= R(\pi+\phi,\pi-\theta,0)\,R_3(-\pi)\,|p\hat{z}\,\lambda\rangle = R(\pi+\phi,\pi-\theta,0)\,|p\hat{z}\,\lambda\rangle\, e^{i\pi\lambda}. \end{aligned}$$

In other words,

$$I_t|\mathbf{p}\,\lambda\rangle = |-\mathbf{p}\,\lambda\rangle\, e^{\pm i\pi\lambda} \tag{12.5-7}$$

where the upper (lower) sign applies when the azimuthal angle ϕ of $\mathbf{p}$ in the first two (last two) quadrants, respectively.

Like the parity operator, the time reversal transformation reverses the direction of the linear momentum of a state; but unlike the former, I_t does not change the sign of the helicity—the reason is that $\mathbf{J}\cdot\mathbf{P}$ remains invariant (although each factor separately changes sign).

As an useful exercise, we investigate the consistency of our implementation of space inversion and time reversal symmetries on the representation space of the full Poincaré group: we shall check the compatibility of Eq. (11.3-13) with Eq. (12.5-7). To this end, let us compare the effect of the operator $I_s I_t$ with that of $I_t I_s$ on a general basis vector:

$$\begin{aligned} I_s I_t|\mathbf{p}\,\lambda\rangle &= I_s|-\mathbf{p}\,\lambda\rangle\, e^{\pm i\pi\lambda} = |\mathbf{p}\,-\lambda\rangle\,\eta_p e^{\mp i\pi(s-\lambda)} \\ I_t I_s|\mathbf{p}\,\lambda\rangle &= I_t[|-\mathbf{p}\,-\lambda\rangle\,\eta_p e^{\mp i\pi s}] \\ &= [I_t|-\mathbf{p}\,-\lambda\rangle]\,\eta_p e^{\pm i\pi s} = |\mathbf{p}\,-\lambda\rangle\,\eta_p e^{\pm i\pi(s-\lambda)}. \end{aligned}$$

The right-hand sides agree since both phase factors are equal to $(-1)^{s-\lambda}$. Hence the representation is self-consistent. Notice that the anti-unitary nature of I_t is crucial in deriving the correct result on the right-hand of the second equation.

We should also note that the square of I_t as defined by Eq. (12.5-4) is not 1, but

$$I_t^2|\mathbf{0}\,\lambda\rangle = I_t|\mathbf{0}\,-\lambda\rangle(-1)^{s+\lambda} = |\mathbf{0}\,\lambda\rangle(-1)^{2\lambda} = |\mathbf{0}\,\lambda\rangle(-1)^{2s}$$

It is easily verified that Eqs. (12.5-6) and (12.5-7) are also consistent with this result [Problem 12.2]. Hence we conclude

(12.5-8) $$I_t^2 = (-1)^{2s} = e^{i2\pi s} \quad .$$

Three questions might be asked at this point. First, is it possible to simplify this result by redefining $I_t \to I_t' = e^{i\pi s} I_t$? The answer is no, since such a transformation does not alter the value of I_t^2:

$$I_t' I_t' = e^{i\pi s} I_t e^{i\pi s} I_t = e^{i\pi s} e^{-i\pi s} I_t I_t = I_t I_t \quad .$$

We see here another unusual feature of anti-linear operators. Secondly, is Eq. (12.5-8) acceptable as part of a "representation" of the full Poincaré symmetry group? The answer is yes, since two-valued representations are already introduced in the representations of the proper Lorentz and Poincaré groups. (In other words, we are really discussing representations of the covering group which covers the physical space-time group manifold twice.) Lastly, is it possible to find irreducible representations of the full group in which $I_t^2 = 1$ or $-(-1)^{2s}$ instead of $(-1)^{2s}$? The answer is that $I_t^2 = 1$ is not allowed, but $I_t^2 = -(-1)^{2s}$ is. In the latter case, however, the representation space must be doubled so that $I_t|\mathbf{p}\,\lambda\rangle$ is in a different subspace than $|\mathbf{p}\,\lambda\rangle$. The proof of these assertions can be found in [Wigner (63)]. We shall consider only the "minimal" case discussed above where the irreducible representation spaces of the proper group remain invariant.

The results of this subsection can be summarized as follows.

Theorem 12.3 (Time-like Irreducible Representations of the Poincaré Group with Time Reversal): The time-like irreducible representation spaces of the Poincaré group including time reversal coincide with those of the proper (or extended) Poincaré group; the basic vectors $\{|\mathbf{p}\,\lambda\rangle\}$ in the (M, s) (or (M, s, η_p)) representation of the proper (or extended) group transform under I_t as given by Eq. (12.5-7).

The reason for explicitly distinguishing the two possibilities, with or without space inversion, in the formulation and the derivation of this theorem is, as mentioned earlier, that I_s is not a symmetry for some physical systems. Therefore it is of physical interest to formulate the theory of time reversal invariance in both cases. As one may notice, however, the consequences of time reversal invariance are really quite independent of whether space inversion is part of the symmetry or not. This is because the two discrete transformations mutually commute; they do not interfere with each other.

Time-reversal properties of the angular-momentum basis states [Secs. 8.4.1, 8.4.2], and other useful physical applications of time reversal invariance will be discussed in the last section of this Chapter.

12.6 Irreducible Representations in the Light-Like Case ($c_1 = c_2 = 0$)

The "standard vector" in this case is $p_l = (\omega_0, 0, 0, \omega_0)$. The little group of p_l is the SO(2) of rotations about the z-axis if we start with the proper Poincaré group; and it is the O(2) of (the same) rotations plus reflections about planes containing the z-axis if we include space inversion. Unlike the previous subsection, we shall consider the two cases in sequence rather than in parallel because the irreducible representations of the two little groups are more different from one another than the previous case.

Let us consider adjoining time reversal to the proper Poincaré group. The time reversal operator I_t is not a member of the little group of the enlarged group (since it changes the sign of $\mathbf{p}_l$), but the anti-linear operator $R_2(\pi)I_t$ is. The vector $R_2(\pi)I_t|\mathbf{p}_l\,\lambda\rangle$ satisfies all the defining eigenvalue equations that the original basis vector $|\mathbf{p}_l\,\lambda\rangle$ satisfies [Eq. (10.4-21)]. Hence one must be proportional to the other through a phase factor

$$R_2(\pi)\,I_t|\mathbf{p}_l\,\lambda\rangle = |\mathbf{p}_l\,\lambda\rangle\,\eta_T \tag{12.6-1}$$

or equivalently,

$$I_t|\mathbf{p}_l\,\lambda\rangle = R_2(-\pi)\,|\mathbf{p}_l\,\lambda\rangle\,\eta_T \quad . \tag{12.6-2}$$

The general basis vector is given by $|\mathbf{p}\,\lambda\rangle = R(\hat{p})\,L_3(\xi)\,|\mathbf{p}_l\,\lambda\rangle$ as usual. Following the procedure of the previous subsection literally, we obtain

$$I_t|\mathbf{p}\,\lambda\rangle = |-\mathbf{p}\,\lambda\rangle\,e^{\pm i\pi\lambda}\eta_T \tag{12.6-3}$$

where the $\pm$ sign has the same meaning as before.

According to discussions of the previous subsection, the choice of the phase factor η_T is quite arbitrary. In the current case, since λ is a fixed number for each irreducible representation of the proper group, it may appear tempting to pick $\eta_T = e^{\mp i\pi\lambda}$ so that Eq. (12.6-3) will appear simple. There are, however, good reasons not to do so. First, in most applications it is more convenient to keep Eq. (12.6-2) as simple as possible, rather than Eq. (12.6-3); hence we would rather have $\eta_T = 1$. Secondly, as mentioned once before, it is advantageous (for the sake of uniformity) to adopt conventions for the light-like case which are as close as possible to those of the time-like case. Comparing with corresponding results of the previous subsection, we see that $\eta_T = 1$ is also preferred on this ground. A third reason has to do with the inclusion of space inversion which we now consider.

As we extend our investigation to include space inversion, the little group becomes the O(2) of the extended group plus the modified time reversal operator $R_2(\pi)I_t$ (and their products, of course). Since $R_2(\pi)I_t$ commutes with all elements of the O(2) group, the inclusion of time reversal, again, does not necessitate enlarging the representation space. In this case, the representation space is two-dimensional and it includes both positive and negative helicity states (unless $\lambda = 0$, which is a special case). Eq. (12.6-1) holds as before, but with two possible values of λ, $\lambda = \pm m$ ($m = 1/2, 1, \ldots$) [Eq. (11.3-18)]. The relevant question to ask is: Can the phase factor η_T in (12.6-1) depend on λ? More specifically, since the time reversal phase factor can usually be "absorbed" into the definition of basis vectors, can we do this independently for $\lambda = \pm m$ in any way we choose (e.g. in the way suggested in the previous paragraph)? The answer is that η_T in Eq. (12.6-1) cannot be chosen independently for the two λ eigenstates. Because the $\lambda = -m$ state is defined relative to the $\lambda = m$ state by $R_2(\pi)I_s$ [Eq. (11.3-19)] and this operator commutes with $R_2(\pi)I_t$, η_T must be the same for the two helicity states.

The general basis vectors $|\mathbf{p}\,\lambda\rangle$ is defined in the usual way and their time reversal behavior is given without modification by Eq. (12.6-3). The only condition is that η_T should be *the same for both helicity states* as discussed above.

We conclude from these considerations, with or without including space inversion, that it will be desirable to choose, in general, $\eta_T = 1$. Consequently, we shall use, henceforth,

$$I_t|\mathbf{p}_l\,\lambda\rangle = R_2(-\pi)|\mathbf{p}_l\,\lambda\rangle \qquad (12.6\text{-}4)$$
$$I_t|\mathbf{p}\,\lambda\rangle = |-\mathbf{p}\,\lambda\rangle\, e^{\pm i\pi\lambda}$$

where, again, the sign of the phase factor is determined by the value of the azimuthal angle of **p** as described before.

Since these equations are identical in form to those of the time-like case basis vectors, we can treat them together in most applications. This represents a great advantage of the "helicity formalism" over older methods.

We summarize the results of the current subsection:

Theorem 12.4 (Time Reversal Property of Light-like Representations of the Poincaré Group): The light-like irreducible representation spaces of the proper and the extended Poincaré groups remain invariant under the time reversal transformation. The basis vectors $\{|\mathbf{p}\,\lambda\rangle\}$ transform under I_t as in Eq. (12.6-4).

The time reversal properties of the angular momentum states applicable to both massless and massive states and other useful applications of the formalism developed above will be the subject of the last section of this Chapter.

12.7 Physical Consequences of Time Reversal Invariance

Because of the anti-linear nature of the realization of time reversal transformation I_t, physical consequences of time reversal invariance must be deduced with some care. We again divide our discussion into two parts: the behavior of the quantum mechanical states under I_t, and the symmetries of transition amplitudes due to time reversal invariance.

12.7.1 Time Reversal and Angular Momentum Eigenstates

The time reversal transformation I_t commutes with rotations, but it anti-commutes with the generators of rotations. Its action on the single-particle angular momentum eigenstates is

$$\begin{aligned} I_t|p\,J\,M\,\lambda\rangle &= (2J+1)\int dR\, R[I_t|p\hat{z}\,\lambda\rangle]\,[D_J{}^\dagger[R]^\lambda{}_M]^* \\ &= (2J+1)\int dR\, R\, R_2(-\pi)|p\hat{z}\,\lambda\rangle\,[Y\,D_J{}^\dagger[R]Y^\dagger]^\lambda{}_M \\ &= (2J+1)\int dR'\, R'|p\hat{z}\,\lambda\rangle\,[D_J{}^\dagger[R']Y^\dagger]^\lambda{}_M \\ &= (-1)^{J+M}(2J+1)\int dR'\, R'|p\hat{z}\,\lambda\rangle\, D_J{}^\dagger[R']^\lambda{}_{-M} \end{aligned} \qquad (12.7\text{-}1)$$

In the first step we used the commutativity of R and I_t as well as the antilinear property of I_t, in the second step we used Eq. (12.5-6) and Eq. (7.4-5) with $Y = D^J[R_2(\pi)]$, in the third step we shifted the variable of integration, and in the last step we used Eq. (7.4-4) for the matrix $Y^\dagger$. Hence, we obtain

$$I_t|p\,J\,M\,\lambda\rangle = |p\,J\,-M\,\lambda\rangle(-1)^{J+M} \quad . \qquad (12.7\text{-}2)$$

This result applies to both time-like and light-like states. In fact it also applies to two-particle states defined by Eqs. (8.4-14), (8.4-16), and (8.4-17), i.e.

(12.7-3) $$I_t|p\,J\,M\,\lambda_1\,\lambda_2\rangle = |p\,J\,-M\,\lambda_1\,\lambda_2\rangle(-1)^{J+M} \quad .$$

12.7.2 Time-Reversal Symmetry of Transition Amplitudes

The scattering amplitude for a physical system from an initial state $|i\rangle$ to a final state $|f\rangle$ is usually written as

(12.7-4) $$S_{fi} = \langle f|S|i\rangle$$

where the S-matrix (for "scattering") operator is closely related to the infinite-time limit of the time evolution operator $U(t_1, t_0)$ [Messiah],

(12.7-5) $$S = \lim_{\substack{t_0 \to -\infty \\ t_1 \to \infty}} U(t_1, t_0) \qquad U(t_0, t_1) = e^{-iH(t_1 - t_0)} \quad .$$

Intuitively, the time-reversal transformation reverses the time evolution of the physical system, hence we anticipate

(12.7-6) $$I_t\,U(t_1, t_0)\,I_t^{-1} = U(t_0, t_1) = U(t_0, t_1)^\dagger$$

which implies

(12.7-7) $$I_t\,S\,I_t^{-1} = S^\dagger$$

and

(12.7-8) $$I_t\,H\,I_t^{-1} = H \quad .$$

The last relation agrees with the analysis of Sec. 12.4 [cf. Eq. (12.4-2)].

When we apply time reversal invariance to a physical scattering process, we obtain

(12.7-9) $$\begin{aligned}\langle f|S|i\rangle &= \langle f|(I_t^\dagger S^\dagger I_t)|i\rangle = \langle I_t f|S^\dagger|I_t i\rangle^* \\ &= \langle I_t i|S|I_t f\,\rangle \quad .\end{aligned}$$

Thus, the amplitudes for the process $i \to f$ are related, not to themselves, but to the amplitudes for the inverse scattering process $f \to i$ with appropriate changes in the variables (such as momenta, helicities, ... etc.). Eq. (12.7-9) is sometimes called the Principle of Microreversibility. [Messiah, Sec. XV-20]

To be little more specific, consider the two-body scattering process

(12.7-10) $$a + b \longrightarrow c + d$$

where a, b, c, d can be any atomic, nuclear, or elementary particle states. The time-reversed scattering process is

(12.7-11) $$c + d \longrightarrow a + b$$

as shown in Fig. 12.1. Notice that in the time-reversed scattering, all linear momenta (denoted by $\bar{p}$ in Fig. 12.1) reverse their directions while the helicities remain unchanged [Eq. (12.5-7)].

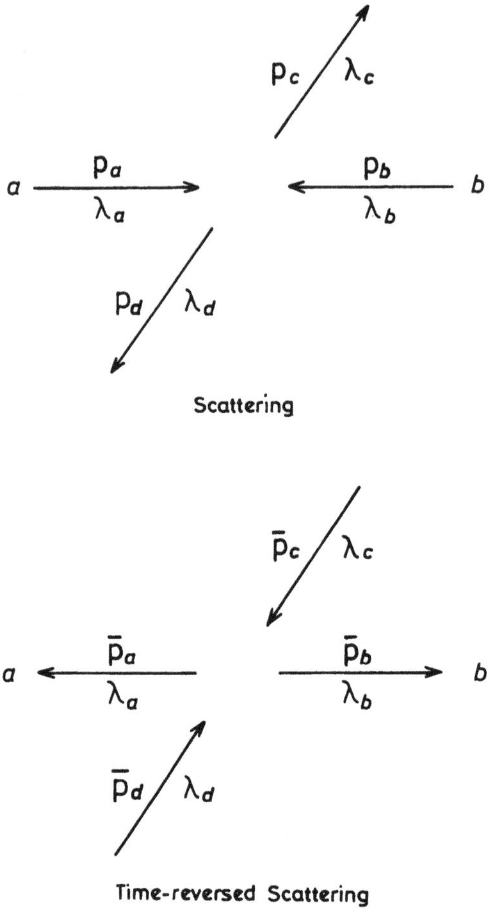

Fig. 12.1

Example: For a photo-emission process $a + b \to \gamma + c$ where γ denotes a photon, the time-reversed scattering is the photo-absorption process $\gamma + c \to a + b$. For instance, a, b, and c can be the proton, the neutron, and the deuteron. The time-reversed reaction, in this case, is often referred to as the photo-disintegration of the deuteron.

As in the case with parity conservation (Subsection 11.4.2), the most efficient way to deduce the consequences of time reversal invariance on the scattering amplitudes is to begin with the "partial wave amplitudes" (i.e. scattering in a definite state of angular momentum) using the results of the previous subsection. Since the partial wave amplitude is diagonal in (J,M) and it is independent of M [cf. Eq. (8.4-21)], Eqs. (12.7-3) and (12.7-9) together imply

$$\begin{aligned}&\langle \lambda_c \lambda_d \| \mathrm{T}_J^{a+b\to c+d}(E) \| \lambda_a \lambda_b \rangle \\ &\quad = \langle \lambda_a \lambda_b \| \mathrm{T}_J^{c+d\to a+b}(E) \| \lambda_c \lambda_d \rangle\end{aligned} \tag{12.7-12}$$

where we have indicated on the T operators the relevant scattering processes involved. Substituting this result in the partial wave expansion formula (8.4-22), we can deduce, for instance,

$$
\begin{aligned}
f^{a+b\to c+d}_{\lambda_c\lambda_d;\,\lambda_a\lambda_b}(\theta,\phi=0) &= \sum_J \langle\lambda_c\lambda_d\|\mathrm{T}_J^{a+b\to c+d}(E)\|\lambda_a\lambda_b\rangle\, d^J(\theta)^{\lambda_a-\lambda_b}_{\lambda_c-\lambda_d} \\
&= \sum_J \langle\lambda_a\lambda_b\|\mathrm{T}_J^{c+d\to a+b}(E)\|\lambda_c\lambda_d\rangle\, d^J(-\theta)^{\lambda_c-\lambda_d}_{\lambda_a-\lambda_b} \qquad (12.7\text{-}13) \\
&= (-1)^{\lambda_a-\lambda_b-\lambda_c+\lambda_d} f^{c+d\to a+b}_{\lambda_a\lambda_b;\,\lambda_c\lambda_d}(\theta,\phi=0)
\end{aligned}
$$

where in the second step we used Eq. (12.7-12) as well as the orthogonality condition on the d^J matrix [cf. Eq. (7.4-6)].

It is worth noting that symmetry conditions (12.7-12) and (12.7-13) do imply useful relations among amplitudes for the *same* process when applied to any elastic scattering process, for instance, $e+p\to e+p$, $\pi+p\to\pi+p$, $\gamma+a\to\gamma+a$, ... etc. In such cases, the combined application of parity conservation and time reversal invariance considerably reduces the number of independent scattering amplitudes.

Example: Consider electron-proton or neutron-proton scattering. Since each initial and final particle can have two states of polarization (helicity), there are nominally $2^4 = 16$ helicity amplitudes. Parity conservation [Eq. (11.4-13)] reduces the number of independent ones to 8—say only those with $\lambda_a = +1/2$. Time-reversal invariance leads to two new relations (among the eight), hence reduces the number of independent amplitudes to 6. [Problem 12.3]

12.7.3 Time Reversal Invariance and Perturbation Amplitudes

An important class of applications of time reversal invariance (and other symmetries) is to processes for which the transition amplitude can be approximated to a good degree of accuracy by the first few terms in a perturbation series expansion. Physical processes of this type mostly involve electromagnetic transitions, radioactive decays, or other weak-interaction reactions. (We have already discussed the general electromagnetic transition processes in Secs. 8.7 and 11.4 in the context of rotation and space inversion symmetries.) Specifically, the Hamiltonian of the physical system can be written, for these processes, in the form

$$H = H_0 + H_I \qquad (12.7\text{-}14)$$

where H_0 is the *unperturbed* or *strong Hamiltonian* and H_I is the *perturbing* or *weak Hamiltonian.* Standard perturbation theory implies that, to first order in H_I, the transition amplitude from an initial state $|a\rangle^0_{in}$ to a final state $|b\rangle^0_{out}$ is proportional to [cf. Messiah, Chaps. XVII and XIX; Sakurai, Secs. 4.3 and 4.5]

$$f_{a\to b} = {}^{\;0}_{\mathrm{out}}\langle b|H_I|a\rangle^0_{\mathrm{in}} \qquad (12.7\text{-}15)$$

where the superscript "0" on the states indicates that they are eigenstates of the unperturbed Hamiltonian H_0, and the subscripts "in" and "out" refer to states before (or "at $t=-\infty$") and after (or "at $t=\infty$") the transition takes place. (Roughly speaking, $|\psi\rangle_{\mathrm{out}} = S_0|\psi\rangle_{\mathrm{in}}$ where $S_0 = U(\infty,-\infty)$ is the *S-matrix* operator of Eq. (12.7-5) in the presence of H_0 alone.)

We are interested in examining the consequences of time reversal invariance of H_0 and H_I:

$$I_t H_I I_t^{-1} = H_I \qquad (12.7\text{-}16)$$
$$I_t H_0 I_t^{-1} = H_0 \quad .$$

The last equation implies $I_t S_0 I_t^{-1} = S_0^\dagger$ [Eq. (12.7-7)]. We obtain

$$\begin{aligned} f_{a\to b} &= {}^{0}_{\text{out}}\langle b| I_t^{-1} H_I I_t)|a\rangle^{0}_{\text{in}} = [{}^{0}_{\text{in}}\langle I_t b| H_I | I_t a\rangle^{0}_{\text{out}}]^* \\ &= f^*_{I_t a \to I_t b} \end{aligned} \qquad (12.7\text{-}17)$$

where the interchange of "in" and "out" status on the unperturbed (or strong interaction) states under I_t is to be noted.

In the simplest examples, there is no substantial distinction between the time-reversed and the (corresponding) original states. This happens if "a" and "b" are single-particle states at rest, or the vacuum state. In the former case, the time reversed state differs with the original one only by its spin projection and a phase factor [Eq. (12.7-1)]. In the latter case, there is no difference at all. Under this circumstance, Eq. (12.7-17) implies that either $f_{a\to b}$ or some linear combination of $f_{a\to b}$ must be real.

Example 1: Consider the decay of the strongly interacting π-meson to the pair of weakly interacting particles, the μ-meson and the neutrino ν. The strongly interacting part of the transition then involves the initial state "a" consisting of the spinless π-meson at rest, and the final state "b" being simply the vacuum. The transition amplitude f_π, often called the *pion decay constant*, is therefore real if time reversal invariance holds. [Commins]

Example 2: In a typical nuclear beta- or gamma-decay, the strongly interacting initial state "a" and the final state "b" each consists of a single-particle nuclear state of definite angular momentum and parity. In the basic beta-decay process

$$\text{neutron} \longrightarrow \text{proton} + \text{electron} + \text{neutrino} \qquad (12.7\text{-}18)$$

"a" is a neutron state and "b" is a proton state. The time-reversed states $I_t a$ and $I_t b$ can be inferred from Eq. (12.7-1). The requirement of time reversal Eq. (12.7-17), then implies that certain appropriately defined decay amplitudes or *form-factors* must be real. [Commins]

When the states "a" and "b" consist of more than one strongly interacting particles, one must take into account strong-interaction effects due to time reversal invariance ($I_t S_0 I_t^{-1} = S_0^\dagger$) in applying Eq. (12.7-17). Consider the case where "a" is a single-particle state but "b" consists of two strongly interacting particles. For instance, in the photo-disintegration of deuteron,

$$\text{photon} + \text{deuteron} \longrightarrow \text{proton} + \text{neutron}$$

"a" is the single particle deuteron state and "b" is the two-particle proton + neutron state. The time-reversed state $|I_t a\rangle$ remains simple: there is no distinction between $|I_t a\rangle_{\text{in}}$ and $|I_t a\rangle_{\text{out}}$; $|I_t a\rangle$ is obtained from $|a\rangle$ by simply reversing the momentum [Eq. (11.4-28)] or the spin-projection [Eq. (12.7-1)]. On the other hand, $|I_t b\rangle_{\text{in}}$ on the right-hand side of Eq. (12.8-17) is distinct from $|b\rangle_{\text{out}}$ even after making the necessary kinematic changes such as reversing linear and angular momentum components. For definite angular momentum states, we can use

$$|b\rangle_{\text{in}} = |b\rangle_{\text{out}}\, e^{i\delta_b} \tag{12.7-19}$$

where δ_b is the *phase shift* characterizing the elastic scattering matrix of the two-particle (proton-neutron) strongly interacting system. [Sakurai, Sec. 4.5] The correction factor due to the conversion from the "in" to the "out" state status is often referred to as the *final state interaction* factor.

Problems

12.1 (i) Prove that η_T in Eq. (12.5-2) is independent of λ. (ii) From Eq. (12.5-3) prove Eq. (12.5-4), keeping in mind the Lemma on anti-linear operators in Subsection 12.4.

12.2 Prove that $I_t^2 = (-1)^{2s}$ by applying the operator I_t to both sides of Eq. (12.5-6) and of Eq. (12.5-7).

12.3 Enumerate the independent helicity amplitudes for an elastic scattering process such as $e + p \to e + p$, taking into consideration space inversion and time reversal invariances. Specify how the dependent amplitudes are related to the independent ones.

CHAPTER 13

FINITE-DIMENSIONAL REPRESENTATIONS OF THE CLASSICAL GROUPS

In this chapter, we shall derive the finite-dimensional irreducible representations of the classical linear groups GL(m; C), GL(m; R), U(m_+, m_-), SL(m; C)), SU(m_+, m_-), O(m_+, m_-), and SO(m_+, m_-). There are two complementary approaches to investigate the irreducible representations of these classical Lie groups: the *canonical* approach of Cartan, using the Lie algebra; and the *tensorial* approach, using tensors of specific symmetry classes and other invariant properties. Our earlier treatment of the rotation and Lorentz groups, with covering groups SU(2) and SL(2) respectively, emphasized the canonical approach; whereas the tensor analysis introduced in connection with the symmetric group and with Lorentz spinors gave a taste of the tensorial approach. The current chapter will systematically develop the latter method. Since the theory and application of classical groups and their representations are very extensive and far-reaching, both in mathematics and in physics, many well-known books are primarily devoted to the subject [e.g. Boerner, Weyl [2], Wybourne]. Our treatment is restricted to presenting the general concepts and techniques necessary for deriving the irreducible representations of the various groups, and to establishing connections with results previously obtained.

The forum in which the tensorial method is applied is the tensor space first introduced in Sec. 5.5; it will be generalized to its natural extent in this chapter. The basic building blocks of the general tensor space will be established in Sec. 1. The irreducible representations of the classical groups will be obtained by decomposing the general tensor representations into their irreducible components. The principal idea behind the reduction technique is the same as always: find the maximal set of operators which commute with the group transformations on the general tensor space; classify elements of the space according to their transformation properties under these "invariant operations"; the resulting decomposition is then irreducible with respect to the group of interest. (As pointed out from Chap. 1 on, this general principle should be familiar to every student of quantum mechanics, in which one always seeks to diagonalize the Hamiltonian H by finding the eigenstates of a maximal set of operators which commute with H.) One important set of invariant operations on tensor spaces consists of elements of the group ring (algebra) associated with the symmetric group of the tensor indices, as studied in detail in Sec. 5.5. Another indispensable set of invariant operations on the general tensor space, not encountered previously, involves taking direct products and contractions with invariant tensors. We introduce this new tool in Sec. 2, in a simple setting in order to bring out the essential features more clearly. Using these tools in a systematic way, the irreducible representations of the general linear group are derived and discussed in Sec. 3. The other classical groups are subgroups of GL(m). Each one can be uniquely specified by the invariant tensors it admits. These invariant tensors lead to additional invariant operations which can be used to reduce further the tensor subspaces which are irreducible with respect to GL(m), or to establish equivalence relationships between irreducible representations which are inequivalent under GL(m). This is done systematically in Sec. 4 for each class of subgroups mentioned earlier. Whenever possible, we compare general results obtained in this approach to those derived in previous chapters for the specific groups SO(2) [Chap. 6], SO(3) [Chap. 7], SU(2) [Chap. 8], SO(3, 1) [Chap. 10], O(2), O(3), O(3, 1) [Chap. 11], and SL(2) [Appendix VI]. The last section consists of concluding remarks for the chapter and for the book.

13.1 GL(m): Fundamental Representations and the Associated Vector Spaces

The *general linear group* over the complex number field GL(m; C), or GL(m) in short, is most simply defined as the group of all invertible $m \times m$ matrices. These matrices occur naturally in the context of matrix transformations on an m-dimensional vector space V. It is useful to think of elements $\{g\}$ of GL(m) as transformations on V in two equivalent ways:

(i) Given a basis $\{\hat{e}_a; a = 1, 2, \ldots, m\}$ on V, g can be viewed as an invertible *linear transformation* defined by

(13.1-1) $$g\,\hat{e}_a = \hat{e}_b\, g^b{}_a \quad .$$

If $\mathbf{x} \in$ V and $\{x^a\}$ are components of $\mathbf{x}$ with respect to the basis $\{\hat{e}_a\}$, then g induces a mapping of each $\mathbf{x} \in$ V to another vector $\mathbf{x}' \in$ V:

(13.1-2) $$g\,\mathbf{x} = \mathbf{x}'$$

so that,

(13.1-3) $$x'^b = g^b{}_a x^a \quad .$$

This is the "*active* interpretation" of $g \in$ GL(m). [Sec. 5.5]

(ii) Alternatively, $g \in$ GL(m) can be viewed as a *coordinate transformation* associated with a change of basis from $\{\hat{e}_a\}$ to $\{\hat{e}_a'\}$ where

(13.1-4) $$\hat{e}_a' = g^{-1}\hat{e}_a = \hat{e}_b\,(g^{-1})^b{}_a \quad .$$

It follows that

(13.1-5) $$\hat{e}_a = \hat{e}_b'\, g^b{}_a$$

and that if $\{x^a\}$ and $\{x'^a\}$ are the components of the same vector $\mathbf{x} \in$ V with respect to the two bases $\{\hat{e}_a\}$ and $\{\hat{e}'_a\}$ respectively, then they are related by Eq. (13.1-3) again. (Proof: $\mathbf{x} = \hat{e}_a x^a = \hat{e}'_b g^b{}_a x^a = \hat{e}'_b x'^b$.) This is the "*passive* interpretation" of $g \in$ GL(m).

Since both interpretations of $\{g\}$ are useful in elucidating various points in subsequent discussions, we shall use them interchangably. Note that the invertibility of g is essential in making the two views equivalent [cf. Eqs. (13.1-4), (13.1-5)].

If we concentrate on the group properties of $\{g\}$, i.e. matrix multiplication (leaving aside other algebraic properties), then the following basic theorem holds.

Theorem 13.1 (Fundamental Representations of GL(m)): The general linear group GL(m) defined on an m-dimensional vector space V has four inequivalent m-dimensional matrix representations given by $\{g\}$, $\{g^*\}$, $\{(g^{-1})^T\}$ and $\{(g^{-1})^\dagger\}$. These are the *fundamental representations* of GL(m).

Proof: (i) The matrices $\{g\}$ obviously form a representation of the group; they are the defining matrices of the group. (ii) Consider the complex conjugate matrices $\{g^*\}$. They form a representation of the group since

$$g_1 \cdot g_2 = g_3 \quad \text{implies} \quad g_1^* \cdot g_2^* = g_3^* \quad \text{for all } g \in \mathrm{GL}(m)$$

where matrix multiplication is implied. This representation is not equivalent to the defining representation $\{g\}$; because if it were, there would exist a matrix S such that

$$g^* = S\,g\,S^{-1} \qquad \text{for all } g \in \mathrm{GL}(m).$$

This cannot be true as, by definition, $\{g\}$ consists of all non-singular $n \times n$ matrices with no other condition imposed. (iii) The matrices $\{(g^{-1})^T\}$ form a representation of the group since

$$(g_1^{-1})^T (g_2^{-1})^T = [g_2^{-1} g_1^{-1}]^T = [(g_1\, g_2)^{-1}]^T \tag{13.1-6}$$

This representation is not equivalent either to the original or the complex conjugate representation for the same reason as given in (ii). (iv) The arguments of (iii) can be repeated for the matrices $\{(g^{-1})^\dagger\}$. QED

The key idea of the tensorial approach is that all the finite dimensional representations of GL(m) can be obtained as irreducible components of repeated direct products of the above four fundamental representations. These direct product representations are realized on the direct product vector spaces obtained from V and three others related to it. In particular, the four fundamental representations can be regarded as realizations of the same group GL(m) on four distinct basic vector space V, V* (the conjugate), $\tilde{\mathrm{V}}$ (the dual), and $\tilde{\mathrm{V}}^*$ (the dual of the conjugate) respectively. We shall now define vectors in these spaces and establish a set of notations to be followed in the rest of this chapter.

Definition 13.1 (Vectors with a Covariant Index and $\tilde{\mathrm{V}}$): A set of numbers $\{y_a\}$ transforming according to $\{(g^{-1})^T\}$ under GL(m),

$$y_a \longrightarrow y'_a = [(g^{-1})^T]_a{}^b\, y_b = y_b (g^{-1})^b{}_a \tag{13.1-7}$$

form the *covariant components* of a vector **y**. These vectors reside in the *Dual Space* $\tilde{\mathrm{V}}$ of V.

The use of the term "dual space" relates to the observation that, given any $\mathbf{y} \in \tilde{\mathrm{V}}$ and $\mathbf{x} \in \mathrm{V}$, one can define a mapping from $(\mathrm{V} \times \tilde{\mathrm{V}})$ to the complex numbers C,

$$(y, x) = y_a x^a \tag{13.1-8}$$

which is linear in **x**. Consequently, each **y** defines a linear functional on V. In other words, $\{\mathbf{y}\}$ is a vector in the dual space $\tilde{\mathrm{V}}$ of the original vector space V. [cf.

Appendix II][1] The mapping (13.1-8) is a special case of *contraction* to be defined later on tensor spaces.

Lemma 1: The mapping defined by (13.1-8) is invariant under GL(m) transformations; or, equivalently, it is independent of the choice of basis in V.

This result in an immediate consequence of Eqs. (13.1-3) and (13.1-7).

Definition 13.2 (Vectors with a Dotted Covariant Index and V*): A set of numbers $\{z_{\dot{a}}; a = 1, 2, \ldots, m\}$ transforming according to $\{g^*\}$ under GL(m)

(13.1-9) $$z_{\dot{a}} \longrightarrow z'_{\dot{a}} = (g^*)_{\dot{a}}{}^{\dot{b}} z_{\dot{b}} = z_{\dot{b}} (g^\dagger)^{\dot{b}}{}_{\dot{a}}$$

form the *dotted covariant components* of a vector **z** in the *complex conjugate vector space* V* of V.

In Eq. (13.1-9) we have used the convention $(g^*)_i{}^j \equiv (g^i{}_j)^* \equiv (g^\dagger)^j{}_i$. [cf. Appendix I]

Definition 13.3 (Vectors with a Dotted Contravariant Index and $\tilde{\text{V}}$*): A set of numbers $\{w^{\dot{a}}; a = 1, 2, \ldots, m\}$ which transform according to $\{(g^{-1})^\dagger\}$ under GL(m)

(13.1-10) $$w^{\dot{a}} \longrightarrow w'^{\dot{a}} = [(g^{-1})^\dagger]^{\dot{a}}{}_{\dot{b}}\, w^{\dot{b}}$$

form the *dotted contravariant components* of the vector **w** which lies in $\tilde{\text{V}}$*, the dual space of the complex conjugate space V*.

We can show that the two spaces V* and $\tilde{\text{V}}$* are dual to each other by noting that, for given $z \in \text{V}^*$ and $w \in \tilde{\text{V}}^*$, the c-number

(13.1-11) $$(w, z) = w^{\dot{a}} z_{\dot{a}}$$

is bilinear in **w** and **z**, and it is invariant under GL(m).

The four mutually related vector spaces V, $\tilde{\text{V}}$, V*, and $\tilde{\text{V}}$*, each associated with one of the fundamental representations of GL(m), form the basic building blocks of the general tensor spaces in multi-linear algebra. The tensor spaces discussed in Sec. 5.5, corresponding to direct products of V, are an important subset of these general tensor spaces. Components of tensors in these spaces carry only undotted contravariant indices.

13.2 Tensors in V × $\tilde{\text{V}}$, Contraction, and GL(m) Transformations

To prepare further for the general analysis, we discuss one of the simplest and most important types of tensors, T^1_1, in this Section. With slight modifications in the statements, most concepts and results discussed here apply to general tensors as well. We choose to start with this special case for the sake of economy of tensor indices. In this way, the essential ideas can be seen without the distraction of irrelevant extra indices carried by general tensors. The features that we shall focus on in this section are complementary to those developed in Sec. 5.5. Together, they provide all the necessary techniques to tackle the general problem at hand.

[1] The linear functional defined by Eq. (13.1-8) is linear in y, in contrast to that of Definition II.15 which is anti-linear in y. Therefore, strictly speaking, we are using a different dual space here than that of Appendix II.

Definition 13.4 (Tensors of type T^1_1): The direct product space V × $\tilde{\text{V}}$ will be called the *tensor space* T^1_1. Elements of T^1_1 will be called *tensors of the type (1, 1).*

Given a basis $\{\hat{e}_a\}$ in V, we use the dual basis $\{\hat{e}^b\}$ in $\tilde{\text{V}}$, and the direct product basis $\{\hat{e}_a \times \hat{e}^b\}$ in T^1_1. The components of a typical element $t \in T^1_1$ transform under GL(m) as

$$t'^a{}_b = g^a{}_c t^c{}_d (g^{-1})^d{}_b, \qquad g \in \mathrm{GL}(m). \tag{13.2-1}$$

By comparison, the tensors we worked with in Sec. 5.5 involve n contravariant indices. They will be called tensors of type (n, 0). We shall not display the index m (the dimension of V associated with GL(m))—as we did in Sec. 5.5—since it remains fixed throughout the discussions of this chapter.

A special class of tensors of type (1, 1) is of the form

$$t^a{}_b = x^a y_b \qquad \mathbf{x} \in \mathrm{V},\ \mathbf{y} \in \tilde{\mathrm{V}} \quad . \tag{13.2-2}$$

$\{t^a{}_b\}$ transform under $g \in$ GL(m) according to Eq. (13.2-1), since $\{x^a\}$ transform according to Eq. (13.1-3) and $\{y_b\}$ according to Eq. (13.1-7). Not every tensor of type (1, 1) belongs to this class, but every tensor can be written as a linear combination of tensors belonging to this class.

Note that, just as in the case of vectors, Eq. (13.2-1) has two equivalent interpretations: (i) as the transformation of tensors $t \to t'$ on T^1_1 induced by $g \in$ GL(m); or (ii) as the transformation of components of the same tensor $t \in T^1_1$ resulting from a change of basis in V induced by $g \in$ GL(m).

Definition 13.5 (Contraction on T^1_1): The mapping from T^1_1 to C (the complex numbers)

$$t \in T^1_1 \qquad t^a{}_a = \mathrm{Tr}\, t = \sum_a t^a{}_a \tag{13.2-3}$$

is called the *contraction* of t.

Theorem 13.2 (Invariance of Contraction): (i) The contraction is invariant under transformations of GL(m), or equivalently, the definition (13.2-3) is independent of the choice of basis (which determines the numerical values of the individual components); (ii) For the class of tensors of the direct product form (13.2-2), the contraction coincides with the value of the linear functional y evaluated with the argument x, (y, x) [Eq. (13.1-8)].

The proofs of (i) and (ii) are obvious, and hence will be omitted.

Corollary: The operation of taking the contraction of a tensor commutes with all GL(m) transformations on the space T^1_1. [Problem 13.1]

Because of the invariance of contraction under GL(m) transformations (or commutativity of the two kinds of operations), contraction of tensors plays an important role (just as the permutations did in Sec. 5.5) in the representation theory that is to follow.

Theorem 13.3 (Tensors and Linear Operators): There is a one-to-one correspondence between elements of T^1_1 and the space of linear operators on V.

Proof: (i) Given a basis in V, an element $t \in T^1_1$, and an element $\mathbf{x} \in$ V, we can easily see that the mapping

(13.2-4) $$\mathbf{x} \xrightarrow{t} \mathbf{x}' \quad \text{with} \quad x'^a = t^a{}_b x^b$$

defines a linear transformation (operator). Note that the transformation property of t [Eq. (13.2-1)] is essential to ensure that the definition of this transformation be independent of the choice of basis.

(ii) Conversely, given a basis in V, any linear operator t can be written in the form (13.2-4) where $\{t^a{}_b\}$ are elements of the matrix realization of the linear transformation. [cf. Eq. (II.3-3)] These numbers form the components of a tensor of type (1, 1), since under a change of basis of V, the matrix of the linear operator transforms exactly as given by Eq. (13.2-1) [Definition 13.4]. (Prove!) QED

Corollary: When regarded as tensors corresponding to invertible linear transformations, elements of GL(m) form a subset of T^1_1 tensors.

We remark that by establishing a connection between tensors and linear operators (including $g \in$ GL(m)), we have identified a dual role played by the tensors—as "vectors" in a vector space (T^1_1) on the one hand, and as "operators" on a related vector space (V) on the other—which is reminiscent of the dual role played by elements of the group ring (algebra) in the representation theory of finite groups. This analogy is interesting in that all irreducible representations of a finite group can be obtained from the reduction of the "regular representation" defined on the group algebra space [Sec. 3.7], and our purpose here is to obtain all the (finite dimensional) irreducible representations of GL(m) from the reduction of tensor representations of this group defined on the general tensor space.

The *identity transformation*, $\mathbf{x} \to \mathbf{x}$ for all $\mathbf{x} \in$ V, has the matrix representation $\delta^a{}_b$ (the Kronecker delta) with respect to any basis. This means that the tensor corresponding to this operator has elements (i.e. $\delta^a{}_b$) which are invariant under GL(m) transformations. Applying Eq. (13.2-1), one can see directly that

(13.2-5) $$\delta^a{}_b \xrightarrow{g} \delta'^a{}_b = g^a{}_c \delta^c{}_d (g^{-1})^d{}_b = (g g^{-1})^a{}_b = \delta^a{}_b \quad .$$

Theorem 13.4 (Identity as the Only Invariant Tensor): The tensor $\{\delta^a{}_b\}$, which corresponds to the identity operator, is the only one in T^1_1 which is invariant under the full group GL(m).

Proof: If another invariant tensor with components $\{t^a{}_b\}$ existed, then the transformation formula

(13.2-6) $$t^a{}_b = g^a{}_c t^c{}_d (g^{-1})^d{}_b$$

would impose an additional constraint on the matrix elements of g for all $g \in$ GL(m). But we know that the only condition on all elements of GL(m) is that their inverses exist. (This condition is what makes Eq. (13.2-5), and hence $\delta^a{}_b$, special.) Therefore, the theorem holds. QED

Although stated explicitly here for tensors of type (1, 1) only, Theorem 13.4 generalizes to all tensor types when the wording is suitably modified. Invariant tensors can, and do, exist for important subgroups of GL(m). This is understandable on the intuitive level: on the one hand, any invariance condition such as Eq. (13.2-6) restricts the group elements to a subset of GL(m), and hence defines a subgroup; on the other hand, any definition of a linear subgroup of GL(m) must be independent of the basis chosen, and hence can be expressed in the form of an invariant tensor. Examples on these points can be found in SO(3) [Sec. 7.1] where the invariant tensors are δ^{ab}, ε^{abc} [Eqs. (7.1-5) and (7.1-6)]; in SO(3, 1) where they are $g^{\mu\nu}$, $\varepsilon^{\mu\nu\lambda\sigma}$ [Eqs. (10.1-5) and (10.1-6)]; and in SL(2) where the only invariant tensor is $\varepsilon^{\alpha\beta}$ [Appendix VI]. We shall use this characterization to define the important subgroups in general, and to identify their irreducible representations in Sec. 13.4. The invariants also provide powerful tools to evaluate many useful quantities in applications such as Clebsch-Gordan coefficients, eigenvalues of Casimir operators, . . . etc.

Let us now examine the representation of GL(m) realized on the space T^1_1. The mapping $t \xrightarrow{g} t'$, $g \in$ GL(m) given by Eq. (13.2-1) certainly forms a representation of the group GL(m). [Problem 13.2] It is the direct product representation of the two fundamental representations $\{g\}$ and $\{(g^{-1})^{T}\}$ (realized on the two spaces V and $\tilde{\text{V}}$ respectively). We would like to know: Is this representation reducible or is it irreducible?

To answer this question, we observe that: (i) a general tensor of this type has m^2 independent components; (ii) a certain combination of these components—its contraction, Eq. (13.2-3)—is invariant under GL(m) transformations. This implies that the contracted tensor (consisting of one number) transforms independently from the rest of the tensor (consisting of $m^2 - 1$ independent components). Hence, we expect the representation realized on T^1_1 to be reducible. How do we remove the contracted tensor $t^c{}_c$ from the full tensor $t^a{}_b$ when the former is of type (0, 0) (since there is no free tensor index of either kind) and the latter is of type (1, 1)? In order to "subtract" the contracted tensor from the full tensor, we must promote the former to the rank (1, 1) without altering its transformation property. This is achieved by taking the direct product of $t^c{}_c$ with the invariant tensor $\delta^a{}_b$: $\{t^c{}_c\delta^a{}_b;\ a, b = 1, 2, \ldots, m\}$ form components of a tensor of type (1, 1) which is invariant under GL(m) transformations. [Problem 13.3]

Theorem 13.5 (The Decomposition of the Tensor Space T^1_1): Each tensor $t \in T^1_1$ can be decomposed uniquely into two parts; the first, denoted by $\hat{t}$, has vanishing contraction and the second is proportional to $\delta^a{}_b$:

$$t^a{}_b = \hat{t}^a{}_b + \delta^a{}_b\left(\frac{1}{m}t^c{}_c\right) \tag{13.2-7a}$$

where

$$\hat{t}^a{}_b \equiv t^a{}_b - \delta^a{}_b\left(\frac{1}{m}t^c{}_c\right) \quad . \tag{13.2-7b}$$

Proof: Let $t = \tilde{t} + \alpha\,\delta$ where $\tilde{t}$ has vanishing contraction, δ is the invariant tensor, and α is a constant. By taking the contraction, we obtain

$$t^c{}_c = \alpha\,\delta^c{}_c = m\,\alpha$$

or

$$\alpha = \frac{1}{m} t^c{}_c \quad .$$

Substituting into the equation $\hat{t} = t - \alpha\,\delta$ we obtain Eq. (13.2-7). QED

Theorem 13.6 (Irreducibility of Tensors of Type (1, 1) with Vanishing Contraction): The set of tensors $\{\hat{t}\}$ of type (1, 1) with vanishing contraction are irreducible under GL(m).

Proof: Intuitively, the validity of this result follows from the fact that taking the contraction is the only operation on tensors of type (1, 1) which commutes with all GL(m) transformations. Once this operation is invoked to achieve the decomposition (13.2-7), the remaining tensors cannot be further reduced. More precisely, one can argue as follows: If $\{\hat{t}\}$ could be further decomposed into the direct sum of two invariant subspaces with respect to GL(m) then let I be the projection operator on T^1_1 which projects out one of these subspaces. The fact that I is a projection operator of a GL(m)-invariant subspace yields

(13.2-8) $$g^a{}_{a'}\, I^{a'c}_{b'd}\, (g^{-1})^{b'}{}_b = I^{ab'}_{ba'}\, g^{a'}{}_d (g^{-1})^c{}_{b'} \quad .$$

This equation is obtained from the invariance statement $g\,I t\, g^{-1} = I\, g t g^{-1}$, for arbitrary $t \in T^1_1$, by eliminating t. It can be re-written as

(13.2-9) $$g^a{}_{a'}\, g^c{}_{c'}\, I^{a'c'}_{b'd'}\, (g^{-1})^{b'}{}_b (g^{-1})^{d'}{}_d = I^{ac}_{bd} \quad .$$

Eq. (13.2-9) is equivalent to the statement that I^{ab}_{cd} is an invariant tensor. According to Theorem 13.4, the only invariant tensors of this type are:

(13.2-10) $$I^{ac}_{bd} = \delta^a{}_b\, \delta^c{}_d$$

and

(13.2-11) $$I^{ac}_{bd} = \delta^a{}_d\, \delta^c{}_b \quad .$$

In the first case, $(I\hat{t})^a{}_b = \delta^a{}_b(\mathrm{Tr}\,\hat{t}) = 0$, hence I is zero; and in the second case $(I\hat{t})^a{}_b = \hat{t}^a{}_b$, hence I is the identity operator. Any other form of I would lead to a non-trivial condition, Eq. (13.2-8), on $\{g \in \mathrm{GL}(m)\}$ which cannot be satisfied by all elements of this group. We conclude that further reduction of $\{\hat{t}\}$ is impossible. Therefore the theorem holds. QED

Note that on the full space T^1_1, the operator (13.2-10) is just the projection operator which projects out the part of $t \in T^1_1$ which has non-vanishing contraction. Hence, in principle, the last two theorems can be combined into one; and the above proof covers the contents of both.

To close, we remark that everything in this section can be made to apply to tensors with dotted indices—one needs only to replace V by V*, (g) by (g)*, and each contravariant (covariant) tensor index by a corresponding covariant (contravariant) dotted index.

13.3 Irreducible Representations of GL(m) on the Space of General Tensors

The most general tensor carries four distinct types of indices, as described in Sec. 13.1. In order to focus on essentials, we shall discuss in detail those only with undotted indices for the major part of this section. We shall see that all matters of principle can be addressed in this sector. Generalization to tensors with dotted indices is straightforward, and it will be done near the end. This Section concludes in Theorem 13.12 which describes the realization of all finite dimensional representations of GL(m) on general tensor spaces.

Definition 13.6 (Tensors of the type (i, j)): Given two integers (i, j), the direct product vector space of i factors of V and j factors of $\tilde{V}$ is called the *tensor space* T^i_j. Elements of this space are referred to as *tensors of type* (i, j).

With a given choice of basis $\{\hat{e}_a\}$ in V, and the associated natural basis on T^i_j, a typical tensor of this type will have components

$$t^{a_1 a_2 \cdots a_i}_{b_1 b_2 \cdots b_j} \equiv t^{\{a\}_i}_{\{b\}_j} \equiv t^{\{a\}}_{\{b\}} \tag{13.3-1}$$

where the second and third expressions are just abbreviated notations, which we shall use whenever appropriate, for the full expression on the left-hand side.

Tensors of type (i, j) are obvious generalizations of that of type (1, 1) discussed in the previous section, and of type $(n, 0)$ in Sec. 5.5. What can we do with these new classes of tensors? We can use them to generate irreducible representations of GL(m) and all its subgroups, of course! The tools which are needed to do this have all been introduced in the two sections mentioned above. All that we need to do now is, so to speak, to apply them systematically and watch the results come out.

Definition 13.7 (Contractions on the Tensor Space T^i_j): The mapping from T^i_j to T^{i-1}_{j-1}, in which a pair of contravariant and covariant indices is identified and summed over,

$$t^{\{a\}_i}_{\{b\}_j} \longrightarrow t^{\{a\}_{i-1}}_{\{b\}_{j-1}} = \sum_{a_k, b_l} \delta^{b_l}_{a_k} \, t^{a_1 \cdots a_k \cdots a_i}_{b_1 \cdots b_l \cdots b_j} \tag{13.3-2}$$

is called the *contraction* of t. The indices (a_k, b_l) can be any pair from the set $\{a\}_i$ and $\{b\}_j$.

This definition is an obvious generalization of Definition 13.5. Although stated in terms of components, the mapping is independent of the choice of basis, hence invariant under all GL(m) transformations. [cf. Theorem 13.2] Borrowing a familiar term in matrix theory, we shall refer to a tensor with vanishing contractions as *traceless*.

Anticipating that invariant tensors will play an important role in the representation theory of linear groups, we must naturally ask: What are the generalizations of the invariant tensor δ^a_b and Theorem 13.4 of Sec. 13.2?

Theorem 13.7 (Invariant Tensors of Type (i, j)): (i) Only tensor spaces of the type (i, i) admit invariant tensors under GL(m); (ii) On T^i_i all invariant tensors are linear combinations of direct products of δ^a_b

$$\delta^{a_1}_{b_{p1}} \delta^{a_2}_{b_{p2}} \cdots \delta^{a_i}_{b_{pi}} \tag{13.3-3}$$

where $(p_1, \ldots, p_i)$ is some permutation of $(1, 2, \ldots, i)$.

Proof: Let $I^{\{a\}}_{\{b\}}$ be an invariant tensor of the type (i, j). Then

$$g^{\{a\}}_{\{c\}} I^{\{c\}}_{\{d\}} (g^{-1})^{\{d\}}_{\{b\}} = I^{\{a\}}_{\{b\}} \qquad \text{for all } g \in \mathrm{GL}(m) \tag{13.3-4}$$

where

(13.3-5) $$g^{\{a\}}_{\{c\}} = g^{a_1}_{c_1} g^{a_2}_{c_2} \cdots g^{a_i}_{c_i} \quad .$$

Choose $g^a{}_b = r\,\delta^a{}_b$, hence $(g^{-1})^a{}_b = \delta^a_b/r$, then Eq. (13.3-4) implies

(13.3-6) $$r^{j-i} = 1 \qquad \text{for all } r \quad .$$

This requires $j - i = 0$ or $j = i$. Next, on T^i_j rewrite Eq. (13.3-4) in the form $g\,I - I\,g = 0$ and rearranging indices, we obtain

(13.3-7) $$g^{\{c\}}_{\{d\}}\, t^{\{d\},\{a\}}_{\{c\},\{b\}} = 0 \qquad \text{for all } g \in \mathrm{GL}(m)$$

where

(13.3-8) $$\begin{aligned} t^{\{d\},\{a\}}_{\{c\},\{b\}} &= \delta^{\{a\}}_{\{c\}}\, I^{\{d\}}_{\{b\}} - I^{\{a\}}_{\{c\}}\, \delta^{\{d\}}_{\{b\}} \\ \delta^{\{a\}}_{\{c\}} &= \delta^{a_1}_{c_1}\, \delta^{a_2}_{c_2} \cdots \delta^{a_i}_{c_i} \quad . \end{aligned}$$

Since $g^{\{c\}}_{\{d\}}$ is of the product form, Eq. (13.3-5), which is unchanged if the upper and lower indices are simultaneously permuted, and since $g^a{}_b \in \mathrm{GL}(m)$ is totally arbitrary, Eq. (13.3-7) implies

(13.3-9) $$\sum_p t^{p\{d\},\{a\}}_{p\{c\},\{b\}} = 0$$

where the sum is over all permutations ($p \in S_i$), and $p\{c\}$ denotes the set of indices obtained by applying p to $\{c\}$. On account of (13.3-8), Eq. (13.3-9) is a set of homogeneous linear equations on $I^{\{a\}}_{\{b\}}$, and it can be solved (within an overall factor) in terms of products of the invariant type-(1, 1) tensor δ. QED

There are four operations we can do on tensors which are of interest:

(i) We can take *direct products* of tensors of type (i, j) with those of type (i', j') to obtain tensors of type $(i + i', j + j')$. The total rank of the tensors are raised from $(i + j)$ and $(i' + j')$ to $(i + i' + j + j')$ in this process. All tensors of higher ranks are built from the basic ones, of type $(1, 0)$ and $(0, 1)$, by this operation;

(ii) We can take *contractions* of tensors of type (i, j) and obtain tensors of type $(i - 1, j - 1)$. This operation reduces the total rank of the tensor by 2 each time it is performed;

(iii) We can perform *permutations* on the contravariant and/or the covariant indices of a tensor of type (i, j) and obtain a tensor of the same type:

(13.3-10) $$t^{\{a\}}_{\{b\}} \xrightarrow{p,\,q} t'^{\{a\}}_{\{b\}} = t^{p\{a\}}_{q\{b\}}$$

where $p \in S_i$, $q \in S_j$, $p\{a\}$ is the set of integers resulting from applying the permutation p to the set $\{a\}$, and, similarly, $q\{b\}$ is the set obtained from $\{b\}$ by q. More generally, we shall also let p, q be elements of the group algebras $\tilde{S}_i$ and $\tilde{S}_j$ respectively. In that case, the right-hand side of Eq. (13.3-10) stands for the appropriate *linear combination* of tensor components specified by the elements p and q. This operation has been discussed in detail for the contravariant indices in Sec. 5.5. All results obtained there can be transcribed for the covariant indices;

(iv) We can perform $\mathrm{GL}(m)$ *transformations* on the tensors and get back tensors of the same type:

$$t^{\{a\}}_{\{b\}} \xrightarrow{g} t'^{\{a\}}_{\{b\}} = g^{\{a\}}_{\{c\}}\, t^{\{c\}}_{\{d\}}\, g^{-1\{d\}}_{\{b\}} \tag{13.3-11}$$

where $g^{\{a\}}_{\{c\}}$ is given by Eq. (13.3-5).

Eq. (13.3-11) indicates that general tensors of the type (i, j) provide a representation of the group GL(m). Except for the special cases $(i, j) = (0, 0), (0, 1)$, and $(1, 0)$, the representation is reducible. Our goal is to decompose this representation into its irreducible components in the general case.

In Sec. 5.5 we showed that representations in terms of tensors of type $(n, 0)$ can be systematically decomposed into their irreducible components by forming symmetry classes of tensors using Young symmetrizers. The underlying reason for this complete decomposition is that the symmetric group S_n is the maximal group of transformations which commutes with GL(m) on T^n_0. Similarly, in Sec. 13.2 we applied the invariant operation of contraction to decompose the representation on the T^1_1 space into its irreducible parts. In that case, taking contraction is the only operation on T^1_1 which commutes with all GL(m) transformations.

Applying the same principle to the more general case at hand, we shall decompose the reducible representation of GL(m) on T^i_j by systematic application of the following operations which commute with (i.e. are invariant under) GL(m) transformations: Young symmetrizers for contravariant indices from the group algebra $\tilde{S}_i$, Young symmetrizers for convariant indices from $\tilde{S}_j$, taking contractions (which reduces the rank of tensors), and taking direct products with invariant tensors (which enhances the rank of tensors). As these operations are all those invariant under GL(m), the decomposition so obtained will be complete, and the components of the decomposition will correspond to irreducible representations of the group GL(m).

To construct *symmetry classes of tensors* of the type (i, j) using Young symmetrizers, pick a Young tableau λ from those of the group S_i and another one σ from those of S_j and apply the method of Sec. 5.5 separately to the contravariant and convariant indices of the tensors. Denote by $t^{\lambda\{a\}}_{\sigma\{b\}}$ a tensor so constructed. It will be referred to as a *tensor of the symmetry* (λ, σ). Tensors of a given symmetry are, in general, not yet irreducible under GL(m), as they can be further reduced by taking contractions. When $\{a\}$ and $\{b\}$ contain more than one index, there are many ways to take contractions on $t^{\{a\}}_{\{b\}}$. (When discussing contractions, we shall suppress the "symmetry labels" (λ, σ) on t to avoid distraction. All results hold with arbitrary (λ, σ).) How can we systematically remove all those components of $t^{\{a\}}_{\{b\}}$ which have some nonvanishing contractions? We need the generalization of Theorem 13.5 to the space T^i_j.

Theorem 13.8 (Reduction of T^i_j by Contraction): Every tensor $t^{\{a\}}_{\{b\}}$ can be uniquely written as a sum of terms, each consisting of the direct product of a traceless tensor and an invariant tensor of the form (13.3-3). More explicitly, assuming $i < j$, the decomposition formula is:

$$\begin{aligned} t^{a_1\cdots a_i}_{b_1\cdots b_j} &= r^{a_1\cdots a_i}_{b_1\cdots b_j} \\ &+ \delta^{a_1}_{b_1} s^{a_2\cdots a_i}_{b_2\cdots b_j} + \text{other terms with one-}\delta \\ &+ \text{all two-}\delta \text{ terms} + \cdots \\ &+ \delta^{a_1}_{b_1}\delta^{a_2}_{b_2}\cdots\delta^{a_i}_{b_i} u_{b_{i+1}\cdots b_j} + \text{other terms with } i - \delta \text{ factors} \end{aligned} \tag{13.3-12}$$

where the tensors $\{r, s, \ldots, u\}$ have vanishing contractions, and "other terms" in the formula means "distinct terms obtained from the previous one by permutations of $\{a\}$ and $\{b\}$".

Proof: We already know that this theorem holds in T^1_1. [Theorem 13.5] In Problem 13.4 we ask the reader to prove the formula for (2, 1) tensors. In order to understand the general proof clearly, it is helpful to work out the next non-trivial case, $(i, j) = (2, 2)$. In this case, Eq. (13.3-12), in its entirety, reads

$$\begin{aligned} t^{ac}_{bd} &= r^{ac}_{bd} \\ &\quad + \delta^a_b s1^c_d + \delta^a_d s2^c_b + \delta^c_b s3^a_d + \delta^c_d s4^a_b \\ &\quad + \delta^a_b \delta^c_d u1 + \delta^a_d \delta^c_b u2 \end{aligned} \tag{13.3-13}$$

where r, $s1$, $s2$, $s3$, and $s4$ are traceless. Taking one contraction of this equation in all possible ways and rearranging terms, we obtain

$$\begin{aligned} m\, s1^a_b + s2^a_b + s3^a_b &= t^{ca}_{cb} - (m\, u1 + u2)\, \delta^a_b \\ s1^a_b + m\, s2^a_b + s4^a_b &= t^{ca}_{bc} - (u1 + m\, u2)\, \delta^a_b \\ s1^a_b + m\, s3^a_b + s4^a_b &= t^{ac}_{cb} - (u1 + m\, u2)\, \delta^a_b \\ s2^a_b + s3^a_b + m\, s4^a_b &= t^{ac}_{bc} - (m\, u1 + u2)\, \delta^a_b \quad . \end{aligned} \tag{13.3-14}$$

Contracting the remaining pair of indices, we obtain two independent equations which, after a trivial rearrangement, become

$$\begin{aligned} m(m\, u1 + u2) &= t^{ac}_{ac} \\ m(u1 + m\, u2) &= t^{ac}_{ca} \end{aligned} \tag{13.3-15}$$

The pair of equations in (13.3-15) (corresponding to the two ways that t can be fully contracted) unambiguously determines the two constants $u1$ and $u2$ in terms of t^{ac}_{ac} and t^{ac}_{ca}. Substituting these results in the right-hand sides of the equations in (13.3-14), we obtain a set of linear equations which can be solved uniquely to determine $s1$, $s2$, $s3$, and $s4$ in terms of the once-contracted and fully contracted t's. The solution is guaranteed to yield traceless s's since the right-hand sides of (13.3-14) are manifestly traceless. Substituting all these results in Eq. (13.3-13), we prove the theorem for this case, and also find the expression of r^{ac}_{bd} in terms of t^{ac}_{bd} and its contractions.

The above exercise clearly indicates how the general theorem can be established. Key to the proof is the observation that there is a one-to-one correspondence between the terms in the expansion (13.3-12) and all possible contractions of $t^{\{b\}}_{\{b\}}$— each factor of δ corresponds to a possible contraction. By taking all possible contractions of Eq. (13.3-12), we always arrive at just the right number of equations to determine the traceless coefficients on the right-hand side uniquely. In practice, the coefficients of terms with the maximum number of δ-factors are determined first from the fully-contracted t's. Next, the coefficients of terms with one less δ-factor are determined by the once-less-than-fully-contracted t's (in addition to the fully-contracted ones). This process is continued until the coefficients of terms with one δ-factor are determined from the once-contracted t's (plus all the higher terms). QED

Since we have established all the tools necessary to reduce tensors of type (i, j) by invariant operations (permutations of the contravariant indices, permutations of the covariant indices, and all possible contractions of these indices), we can state the main theorem of the representation theory of GL(m) on the tensor space of type (i, j).

Theorem 13.9 (Irreducible Representations of GL(m) on T^i_j): The irreducible representations of GL(m) realized on the tensor space T^i_j are obtained by first selecting a Young tableau λ associated with the symmetric group algebra $\tilde{S}_i$ of the contravariant indices, another tableau σ associated with $\tilde{S}_j$ of the covariant indices. Then, the subspace of traceless tensors of the symmetry (λ, σ), $t^{\lambda\{a\}}_{\sigma\{b\}}$, is invariant and irreducible under GL(m) transformations.

Since the reasoning behind this theorem has been spelled out several times already and the individual steps needed for the proof have all been developed in detail, we shall not repeat the arguments again here. We turn, instead, to the next obvious question: Of the irreducible representations obtained in this way, which ones are equivalent to one another? To answer this question, we need a lemma which will also prove to be useful later.

Lemma 2 (Equivalence of Tensor Representations and Invariant Tensors): Let G be any of the classical linear groups (GL(m) or its subgroups), $t^{\lambda\{a\}}_{\lambda\{b\}}$, $s^{\tau\{c\}}_{\kappa\{d\}}$ be tensors of the symmetry (λ, σ) and (τ, κ) respectively. If the two representations on G realized on these two symmetry classes of tensors are equivalent to each other, then there exists an invariant tensor I (of rank equal to the sum of those of t and s) under the group G.

Proof: The equivalence of the two representations means that (i) there exists a transformation I from s to t,

$$t^{\lambda\{a\}}_{\sigma\{b\}} = I^{\lambda\{a\}\,\kappa\{d\}}_{\sigma\{b\}\,\tau\{c\}}\, s^{\tau\{c\}}_{\kappa\{d\}} \tag{13.3-16}$$

which satisfies the equation (with tensor indices suppressed)

$$g_t I s = I g_s s \tag{13.3-17}$$

where $g \in$ G and the subscripts t and s refer to the tensor representation of g on the t- and s-space respectively. Rewrite Eq. (13.3-17) as

$$(I - g_t^{-1} I g_s) s = 0 \quad . \tag{13.3-18}$$

Since the tensor inside the parenthesis has the specified index symmetries, Eq. (13.3-18) holds for a general s-tensor $s^{\{c\}}_{\{d\}}$, not necessarily with the symmetry (τ, κ)—because if s is of the wrong symmetry type then (13.3-18) is automatically satisfied due to summation over indices of mismatched symmetries. We conclude therefore,

$$I = g_t^{-1} I g_s \quad . \tag{13.3-19}$$

This is just the statement that I is an invariant tensor with respect to the group G. QED

Note that this lemma can be used in reverse: if one knows that an invariant tensor I exists, then, for a given representation of G on the space of s-tensors, the transformation defined by Eq. (13.3-16) provides an equivalent representation of G on the space of t-tensors. In subsequent sections, we shall use this method to establish the equivalence of irreducible representations for the subgroups of GL(m) (which are characterized by specific invariant tensors).

For the moment, we shall use this lemma on the general linear group which only admits invariants of the form (13.3-3). First, let us consider two irreducible representations realized on the spaces T^i_0 and T^0_j, and of the symmetries $(\lambda, 0)$ and $(0, \sigma)$ respectively. If the two representations are equivalent we must have

$$t^{\lambda\{a\}} = I^{\lambda\{a\}\sigma\{b\}} s_{\sigma\{b\}} \tag{13.3-20}$$

and I must be an invariant tensor of type $(i + j, 0)$ according to the above lemma. But Theorem 13.7 states that there is no invariant tensor on T^{i+j}_0; hence two representations realized on the spaces T^i_0 and T^0_j respectively cannot be equivalent under GL(m). Next consider the case where the two irreducible representations are realized on the spaces T^i_0 and T^j_0, respectively. The equivalence of these representations then implies the existence of an invariant tensor of the type $I^{\{a\}i}_{\{b\}j}$. According to Theorem 13.7, such invariant tensors exist only if $i = j$ and

$$I^{\{a\}}_{\{b\}} = \delta_r{}^{\{a\}}_{\{b\}} \tag{13.3-21}$$

where $\delta_r{}^{\{a\}}_{\{b\}}$ denotes a linear combination of invariants of the form (13.3-3) (i.e. r is a member of the group ring $\tilde{S}_i$). Since $I^{\{a\}}_{\{b\}}$ has the symmetry (λ, σ)

$$I^{\{a\}}_{\{b\}} = I^{e_\lambda\{a\}}_{e_\sigma\{b\}} \tag{13.3-22}$$

where e_λ and e_σ are Young symmetrizers associated with the two tableaux λ and σ respectively. Applying this symmetry condition to the right-hand of Eq. (13.3-21), one can conclude that, in order for I to be non-zero, we must have some $r \in \tilde{S}_i$ such that

$$e_\lambda r e_\sigma \neq 0 \quad . \tag{13.3-23}$$

According to Theorems 5.4-5.6, this means that the Young diagrams associated with the tableaux λ, σ are the same. Conversely, if the Young diagrams associated with λ and σ are the same, then Eq. (13.3-23) holds for some r, then the invariant tensor (13.3-21) is non-zero and it establishes the equivalence of the two irreducible representations. These results are synthesized in the following theorem.

Theorem 13.10 (Equivalence of Irreducible Representations of GL(m)): Two irreducible representations of GL(m) realized on the space of type (i, j) tensors of symmetry (λ, σ), and of type-(i', j') tensors of symmetry (λ', σ') respectively are equivalent if and only if: (a) $(i, j) = (i', j')$, (b) λ and λ' correspond to the same Young diagram, and (c) σ and σ' correspond to the same diagram.

Example: On the tensor space of type (2, 2), four inequivalent irreducible representations of GL(m) ($m \geq 2$) can be obtained. The representation spaces consist of traceless tensors with symmetries associated with the following combinations of Young diagrams for the contravariant and covariant indices:

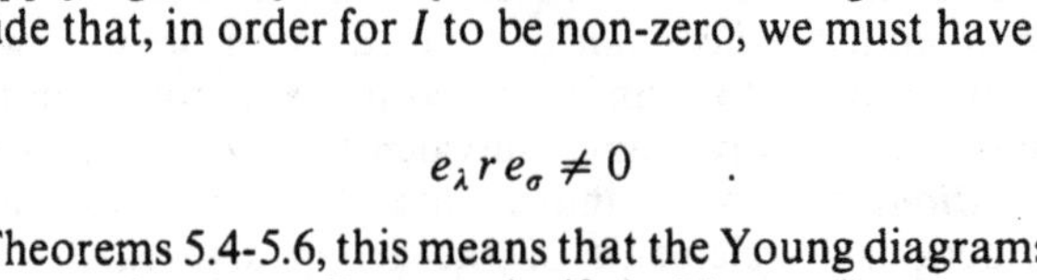

These are traceless tensors with symmetrized and anti-symmetrized indices in the four combinations indicated.

This completes our discussion of the representation theory of the group GL(m) on tensor spaces with undotted indices.

What about tensors with dotted indices that arise from taking direct products of V*, $\tilde{\mathrm{V}}$* of Sec. 13.1? We can extend the above theory to include tensors with dotted indices in a straightforward manner because of two basic facts. First, everything obtained above for tensors with undotted indices can be transcribed to apply to tensors with dotted indices with only minor changes of wording. Secondly, the dotted and undotted indices on a tensor of mixed type act completely independently because there is no invariant tensor of any mixed type.

Definition 13.8 (Tensors of Type $(i,j;k,l)$): Given four integers $(i,j;k,l)$, the direct product vector space of i factors of V, j factors of $\tilde{\mathrm{V}}$, k factors of $\tilde{\mathrm{V}}$*, and l factors of V* is called the *tensor space* $T^{i,k}_{j,l}$. Elements of this space are referred to as *tensors of type* $(i,j;k,l)$. Components of tensors of type $(i,j;k,l)$ have i undotted contravariant, j dotted covariant, k dotted contravariant, and l dotted covariant indices.

Theorem 13.11 (Invariant Tensors with Dotted Indices): (i) There is no invariant tensor with mixed dotted and undotted indices; (ii) The only invariant tensors with dotted indices are of the type $(0,0;i,i)$ and they must be some linear combination of products of δ's of the form (13.3-3) with all indices replaced by dotted ones.

The proof of these results can be formulated in analogous ways to some of the previously established theorems. We shall leave it to the reader. [Problem 13.5]

The *contraction of dotted indices* can be defined in an obvious way. Note that contraction of a dotted index with an undotted index is not permitted—such an operation would not be GL(m) invariant (equivalently, it would be basis-dependent). The *invariant operations* on dotted indices are therefore identical to those of undotted indices: actions by elements of the group algebra $\tilde{\mathrm{S}}_k$ on the contravariant indices, actions by elements of the group algebra $\tilde{\mathrm{S}}_l$ on the covariant indices, contractions of pairs of contravariant and covariant indices, and taking direct products with invariant tensors.

Without further ado, we state the grand theorem of the representation theory of GL(m) on general tensor spaces.

Theorem 13.12 (Irreducible Representations of GL(m) on the Space $T^{i,k}_{j,l}$): (i) The irreducible representations of GL(m) on the tensor space $T^{i,k}_{j,l}$ are obtained by selecting four Young tableaux $(\lambda,\sigma;\tau,\kappa)$ corresponding to the four kinds of indices of tensor type $(i,j;k,l)$. Then, the subspace consisting of traceless tensors of the symmetry $(\lambda,\sigma;\tau,\kappa)$, $t^{\lambda\{a\},\,\tau\{c\}}_{\sigma\{b\},\,\kappa\{d\}}$, are invariant and irreducible with respect to GL(m); (ii) Two irreducible representations of the above description are equivalent if and only if the two quartets of Young tableaux $(\lambda,\sigma;\tau,\kappa)$, $(\lambda',\sigma';\tau',\kappa')$ correspond to pairwise (i.e. $\lambda \leftrightarrow \lambda', \sigma \leftrightarrow \sigma', \ldots$, etc.) identical Young diagrams.

Since $\{T^{i,k}_{j,l}\}$ exhaust all direct products of the basic vector spaces V, V*, $\tilde{\mathrm{V}}$, and $\tilde{\mathrm{V}}$*, it is not surprising that all finite-dimensional representations of GL(m) are obtained by these tensor constructions.

Since the tensor space $T^{l,j}_{k,i}$ is the conjugate vector space of $T^{i,k}_{j,l}$, the irreducible representations on one are just the complex conjugate of those on the other (with the corresponding symmetry). Although these conjugate representations are not equivalent under the complex GL(m) group, one kind can be obtained from the other by a simple complex conjugation. We may remark that the distinction between V and V* disappears if we are interested in the *real general linear group*, GL(m; R). In that case, there is no need to introduce the dotted indices, and all interesting irreducible representations of the group are covered by Theorems 13.9 and 13.10.

13.4 Irreducible Representations of Other Classical Linear Groups

Various subgroups of GL(m) arise naturally in mathematical and physical applications. The finite dimensional irreducible representations of these subgroups can be derived by the tensorial method as given above, with proper attention given to the defining properties of the subgroup in question. Alternatively, one may start with the irreducible representations GL(m) described in Theorem 13.12 (they are automatically representations of the subgroup), and ask which of these remain irreducible, and which ones become equivalent with respect to the subgroup. In the following, we shall investigate several classes of subgroups of GL(m). In each case, we shall identify the invariant tensors which characterize the subgroup. We make use of these invariant tensors in two ways: to form additional invariant operations to help in further reducing the tensor subspaces previously found to be irreducible under GL(m); and to establish equivalence relations between irreducible representations previously found to be inequivalent with respect to GL(m) [Lemma 2].

13.4.1 Unitary Groups U(m) and U(m_+, m_-)

Commonly, a *unitary group* is defined as a matrix group $\{u\}$ satisfying the unitarity condition

(13.4-1) $$u\,u^\dagger = u^\dagger u = E$$

where E is the unit matrix. Displaying the indices explicitly, the equation is

(13.4-2) $$u^a{}_b\,(u^\dagger)^b{}_c = \delta^a{}_c \quad .$$

Recalling that $\{u^\dagger\}$ are the transformation matrices on the conjugate vector space [Eq. (13.1-9)], and that (when regarded as such) our convention [Definition 13.2] is to use dotted indices for its matrix elements, we can re-write Eq. (13.4-2) as

(13.4-3) $$u^a{}_b\,\delta^b_{\dot d}\,(u^\dagger)^{\dot d}{}_{\dot c} = \delta^a_{\dot c}$$

where we have introduced a tensor δ of type (1,0; 0,1) whose components with respect to the basis chosen are numerically the same as the Kronecker delta function δ^a_b, i.e.

(13.4-4) $$\delta^a_{\dot c} = \delta^a_c \quad .$$

We emphasize that whereas Eq. (13.4-3) is written as a covariant tensor equation which is valid with any choice of basis, Eq. (13.4-4) is a basis-dependent relation defining the *numerical values* of $\delta^a_{\dot{c}}$ in a particular basis. The mismatch of index types in Eq. (13.4-4) is a telltale sign that this is a basis-dependent statement.[2]

The unitarity condition as expressed by (13.4-3) is equivalent to the statement that the $U_{(m)}$ group admits an invariant tensor $\delta^a_{\dot{c}}$ (in addition to δ^a_b). The dual $\tilde{\delta}$ of δ, defined by the condition

$$\delta^a_{\dot{c}}\, \tilde{\delta}^{\dot{c}}_b = \delta^a_b \tag{13.4-5}$$

is a tensor of type (0, 1; 1, 0) which is also invariant with respect to group transformations. [Problem 13.6] Since by the particular definition of $\delta^a_{\dot{c}}$, (13.4-3), $\delta^a_{\dot{c}} = \tilde{\delta}^a_{\dot{c}}$ and since the positions of the dotted and undotted indices identify the invariant tensors uniquely, we shall drop the tilde on $\tilde{\delta}$, thus denote both invariant tensors by the same symbol δ. These tensors should not be confused with the universal invariant tensor δ^a_b—also denoted by the same symbol—because the latter carries only undotted indices.

In order to put the definition of the unitary groups on a general footing, we shall focus on the basis-independent features of the above description. Although the specific relation (13.3-4) will no longer be valid under an arbitrary change of basis, three general properties of the tensor will be unaltered: its invertibility, hermiticity[3], and positive definiteness. The first two attributes are clearly essential in order to have a unique invariant tensor [cf. Eqs. (13.4-3), (13.4-5)]. There is no obvious, imperative reason to have the third. Hence we shall relax this condition.

An invertible, hermitian tensor $\delta^a_{\dot{c}}$ (together with its dual $\delta^{\dot{a}}_c$) will be called a *metric tensor*. A metric tensor, even if not required to be positive definite, has the following characteristic property: given its components with respect to any basis, it is possible to find a suitable new basis such that $\delta^a_{\dot{c}}$ is brought to a diagonal form with diagonal elements equal to either $+1$ or -1. The pair of positive integers (m_+, m_-), where $m_\pm$ is the number of ± 1's (respectively), is called the *signature* of the metric. Obviously, $m_+ + m_- = m$. For example, the signature of the metric defined by Eq. (13.4-4), or any other metric which is positive definite, is $(m, 0)$. By forsaking positive definiteness, we open up the possibilities for the other signatures.

Definition 13.9 (The Unitary Group $\mathrm{U}(m_+, m_-)$): The group of linear transformations on V whose elements leave invariant a metric tensor $\delta^a_{\dot{c}}$ of signature (m_+, m_-) is called the *unitary group of signature* (m_+, m_-). It is denoted by $\mathrm{U}(m_+, m_-)$. If the metric tensor is positive definite, the signature is $(m, 0)$. The group $\mathrm{U}(m, 0)$ will be abbreviated as $\mathrm{U}(m)$.

The existence of an additional invariant tensor $\delta^a_{\dot{c}}$ has a number of important implications on the derivation of the irreducible representations of $\mathrm{U}(m_+, m_-)$ by the tensorial method. For instance, we now have additional operations on the tensor space which commute with group transformations (as compared to Sec. 13.3): taking

[2] Recall that under a change of basis, the components of $\delta^a_{\dot{c}}$ transform according to the left-hand side of Eq. (13.4-3) where u is replaced by g, the transfer matrix between the two bases. In that case, $g \in \mathrm{GL}(m)$; thus δ does not have to be invariant.

[3] Note that, it is sensible to talk about a "hermitian" second rank tensor only if it is of the type (1, 0; 0, 1) or (0, 1; 1, 0). For second rank tensors of all other types, the term is ill defined. [Problem 13.7]

direct products of tensors with invariant tensors constructed out of factors of $\delta^a_{\dot{c}}$, followed by contractions.

Consider, in particular, the following operation: multiplication by $\delta^b_{\dot{c}}$ and contracting b with an existing covariant index,

$$t^{a\ldots}_{b\ldots} \longrightarrow t'^{a\ldots}_{\dot{c}\ldots} = \delta^b_{\dot{c}}\, t^{a\ldots}_{b\ldots} \quad . \tag{13.4-6}$$

This operation has the effect of converting an undotted covariant index (b) to a dotted covariant index ($\dot{c}$). With the same multiplication but contracting the $\dot{c}$ index instead, we obtain an operation which converts a contravariant dotted index into a contravariant undotted index. Similarly, multiplying by $\delta^{\dot{c}}_b$ and contracting one of the indices with an existing one on a tensor either converts a covariant dotted index into an undotted one, or converts a contravariant undotted index into a dotted one. Thus, by repeated action of the above four operations, an arbitrary tensor of the type $(i, j; k, l)$ can be converted into other types $(i', j'; k', l')$ with the constraints $i + k = i' + k'$ and $j + l = j' + l'$. In particular, all tensors can be converted to the following four types: $(i + k, j + l; 0, 0)$, $(i + k, 0; 0, j + l)$, $(0, j + l; i + k, 0)$, or $(0, 0; i + k, j + l)$. In other words, the distinction between dotted and undotted indices is unnecessary for studying the representation theory of unitary groups.

We can see this already at the level of the four fundamental vector spaces: for the unitary group,

$$u^{-1} = u^{\dagger} \qquad (u^{-1})^{\dagger} = u \tag{13.4-7}$$

hence only two of the fundamental representations are independent. There is no need to involve all four vector spaces in the construction of irreducible tensors. For definiteness, let us only use the vector spaces V and $\tilde{\mathrm{V}}$, and hence restrict ourselves to tensors with undotted indices. On a general tensor space of this type, $(i, j; 0, 0)$, the only independent invariant tensors are products of δ^a_b. Thus the representation theory for the group $\mathrm{U}(m_+, m_-)$ is identical to that given in Sec. 13.3 up to Theorem 13.10. We conclude that the following theorem holds.

Theorem 13.13 (Irreducible Representations of $\mathrm{U}(m_+, m_-)$: (i) The finite dimensional representations of the group $\mathrm{U}(m_+, m_-)$ can be obtained by selecting two integers (i, j) and two associated symmetries (λ, μ) (i.e. Young tableaux), and realizing the group transformations on the subspace of traceless tensors of symmetry (λ, μ) in the tensor space T^i_j; (ii) Two such representations are equivalent if and only if $(i, j) = (i', j')$, λ and λ' correspond to the same Young diagram, and μ and μ' correspond to the same Young diagram.

Note that the above results in no way depend on the signature of the metric. This does not mean that the latter is not important in the general representation theory of $\mathrm{U}(m_+, m_-)$. To make the point, consider the case where the metric is positive definite. The unitarity condition then guarantees that the group manifold is compact (i.e. bounded) [cf. Sec. 8.1 for the parametrization of the group U(2)]. Then, all irreducible representations are finite dimensional. Theorem 13.13, therefore, provides all the irreducible representations of the group $\mathrm{U}(m)$. This is far from the case when the signature is other than $(m, 0)$. In general, many types of infinite dimensional irreducible representations of $\mathrm{U}(m_+, m_-)$ exist. These irreducible representations are not covered by the above tensorial method. We have seen examples of this phenomenon in the case of SO(3, 1), which is a subgroup of U(3, 1), in Sec. 10.3.3 and Appendix VII—all unitary irreducible representations are finite dimensional.

13.4.2 Special Linear Groups SL(m) and Special Unitary Groups SU(m_+, m_-)

The usual definition of the *special linear group* SL(m) is that it is the matrix group $\{s\}$ whose elements are invertible $m \times m$ matrices with unit determinant, $(\det s) = 1$. In terms of the matrix elements, the condition reads

$$s^{a_1}_{b_1} \cdots s^{a_m}_{b_m} \varepsilon^{b_1 \ldots b_m} = \varepsilon^{a_1 \ldots a_m} \tag{13.4-8}$$

where $\varepsilon^{a_1 \cdots a_m}$ is the unit totally anti-symmetric tensor of rank m. As pointed out in previous chapters when we encountered such a condition [Eqs. (7.1-6), (10,1-6)], it can be interpreted as stating the invariance of the unit anti-symmetric tensor $\varepsilon^{a_1 \cdots a_m}$.

Does the *unit totally anti-symmetric tensor* have a unique meaning? If ε is such a tensor with respect to some basis, what happens when we change the basis? To answer these questions, let us assume only that we have a tensor $\varepsilon^{[a]}$ which has totally anti-symmetric indices $(a_1, \ldots, a_m)$ with respect to some basis, and investigate how its components transform under an arbitrary change of basis. (Square brackets are used to indicate a set of anti-symmetric indices.) If $g \in \mathrm{GL}(m)$ denotes the transfer matrix for the change of basis, we have, by definition,

$$\varepsilon^{[a]} = \varepsilon^{a_1 \cdots a_m} \xrightarrow{g} g^{a_1}{}_{b_1} \cdots g^{a_m}{}_{b_m} \varepsilon^{b_1 \cdots b_m} \quad . \tag{13.4-9}$$

The right-hand side is again totally anti-symmetric in the indices $[a]$. Therefore, it is proportional to the original components; i.e.

$$\varepsilon^{a_1 \cdots a_m} \xrightarrow{g} \eta_g \varepsilon^{a_1 \cdots a_m} \qquad \text{for all } g \in \mathrm{GL}(m) \tag{13.4-10}$$

where η_g is a constant. If the original non-vanishing components correspond to $\varepsilon^{1 \cdots m} = 1$, then $\eta_g = (\det g)$. Since $(\det g)$ can be any constant for $g \in \mathrm{GL}(m)$, Eqs. (13.4-9), (13.4-10) tell us that, although the totally anti-symmetric nature of $\varepsilon^{[a]}$ is preserved under a change of basis, there is no basis-independent way of specifying the normalization of such a tensor. Thus the term "unit totally anti-symmetric tensor" is not a basis-independent one.

In order to obtain a basis-independent definition of SL(m), we note that Eqs. (13.4-8), (13.4-9) are homogeneous in $\varepsilon^{[a]}$; hence if any totally anti-symmetric tensor of rank m is invariant under a set of linear transformations, then all multiples of that tensor (i.e. all totally anti-symmetric tensor of rank m) are invariant under the same set of transformations. Thus, it is not necessary to specify which totally anti-symmetric tensor $\varepsilon^{[a]}$ is used in Eq. (13.4-8).

Definition 13.10 (Special Linear Group SL(m)): The *special linear group* SL(m) is that subgroup of GL(m) which leaves *any* totally anti-symmetric tensor of rank m invariant.

The discussion preceeding this definition guarantees that this statement is basis-independent.

The fact that the SL(m)-invariant $\varepsilon^{[a]}$ is almost (i.e. up to a constant multiple) invariant under the full group GL(m) means that the condition (13.4-8) is not very restrictive. We can easily see that every element of GL(m) is a multiple of an element of SL(m):

$$s = g\eta_g^{-1/m} \in \mathrm{SL}(m) \qquad \text{for any } g \in \mathrm{GL}(m).$$

Hence we expect that the inequivalent irreducible representations of SL(m) will not be too different from those of GL(m). In fact, the irreducible representations of GL(m) remain irreducible when restricted to the subgroup SL(m). This is so because: (i) the proof of full reduction by contraction, Theorem 13.8, is not affected by the presence of the invariant $\varepsilon^{[a]}$; and (ii) the proof of irreducibility under (Young) symmetrization, Theorem 5.13, also remains valid—the key idea that all symmetry-preserving operators on T_0^n are linear combinations of the group operators holds true for SL(m), as for GL(m). The last point follows from the fact that every linear combination of $g \in$ GL(m) is also a linear combination of $s \in$ SL(m), a consequence of the proportionality of elements of the two groups established above. Thus the first part of Theorem 13.12 is valid for the group SL(m), as it is for the group GL(m).

The existence of the invariant tensor $\varepsilon^{[a]}$ (and its dual $\varepsilon_{[a]}$ on the dual tensor space) means we have additional invariant operations such as taking direct products with $\varepsilon^{[a]}$ followed by taking n contractions ($n \leq m$). Each such operation converts (the totally anti-symmetric part of) n indices of a certain type to $m-n$ indices of the dual type which are also anti-symmetric. Since the irreducible tensor subspaces of GL(m) remain irreducible under SL(m), and since the new invariant operations do not simplify the tensor index structure in general, we do not expect these operations to be useful in reducing the tensor spaces. (An exception is the case $m = 2$, about which we will have more to say later.) In view of Lemma 2, however, we should look for equivalences of irreducible representations of GL(m) when these are restricted to the subgroup SL(m) with the invariant $\varepsilon^{[a]}$.

Equivalence of a pair of irreducible representations described in Theorem 13.12 under SL(m) can be established if one irreducible tensor space can be reached from the other by the repeated application of the invariant operation involving $\varepsilon^{[a]}$ (or $\varepsilon_{[a]}$) described above. Since each operation converts a set of n anti-symmetric indices (contained in a column of the associated Young tableau) into $m-n$ such indices (which appear in a corresponding column of the Young tableau associated with the new tensor), it is useful to introduce the notion of the *dual diagram* $\tilde{\lambda}$ for each Young diagram λ, such that the lengths of the columns of $\tilde{\lambda}$ are the complements of those of λ with respect to m (i.e. the two lengths add up to m). According to Young's convention, the columns of $\tilde{\lambda}$ are, of course, arranged in reverse order from their complements in λ. We can then state the equivalence condition, along with irreducibility, in the following theorem.

Theorem 13.14 (Irreducible Representations of SL(m)): (i) The irreducible representations of GL(m) realized on the space of type $(i, j; k, l)$ tensors as described in Theorem 13.12, part (i), remain irreducible when restricted to the group SL(m); (ii) Two irreducible representations of SL(m) associated with the symmetries $(\lambda, \mu; \tau, \kappa)$ and $(\lambda', \mu'; \tau', \kappa')$ are equivalent if and only if the two Young diagrams obtained by combining the columns of λ and $\tilde{\mu}$, and τ and $\tilde{\kappa}$ respectively are identical to those obtained for the primed case.

The validity of part (i) has been discussed earlier. The proof of part (ii) is not hard, but fairly lengthy to establish. Since the detailed arguments will not be needed elsewhere, we shall leave it out.

It is of interest to examine the special case of the SL(*2*) *group* (i.e. $m = 2$) in some detail. Unlike the general situation, the invariant tensor ε^{ab} can be used effectively to simplify the tensor spaces. In fact, we carried out just such an exercise when we analyzed the finite dimensional representations of the SL(2) group (as the covering group of the homogeneous Lorentz group) in Appendix VI. We recall a few features from that treatment which are related to the present discussion.

The particular usefulness of the invariant tensor in this case originates from the possibility to raise and lower dotted and undotted indices using the operation of multiplying a tensor by ε^{ab}, ε_{ac}, $\varepsilon^{\dot{a}\dot{c}}$, or $\varepsilon_{\dot{a}\dot{c}}$ and contracting one of the indices [cf. Eqs. (VI-19) and (VI-26)]. (This is similar to the situation in the previous subsection where dotted and undotted indices are converted into each other by using one contraction with the metric tensor δ.) Thus, by repeated application of this operation, we can convert all indices on a tensor into contravariant ones or covariant ones. There is no need to use both. At the level of fundamental representations, the condition for the invariance of ε

(13.4-11) $$g^a{}_c\, g^b{}_d\, \varepsilon^{cd} = \varepsilon^{ab}$$

can be written in the form

(13.4-12) $$\varepsilon^{-1} g\, \varepsilon = \tilde{g}^{-1}$$

which establishes the equivalence of the fundamental representations realized on V and $\tilde{\mathrm{V}}$, respectively. The complex conjugate of Eq. (13.4-12) implies the equivalence of the fundamental representations realized on V* and $\tilde{\mathrm{V}}$*. Hence, to derive all finite dimensional irreducible representations of SL(2), it suffices to restrict our attention to tensors of the type $(i, 0; k, 0)$. When $m \neq 2$, this simplification does not occur, for obvious reasons.

Even after restricting ourselves to tensor spaces of contravariant indices, the invariant tensor ε provides an additional invariance operation which must be taken into account in order to avoid redundancy. This invariant operation is the full *contraction* of a tensor (with two or more contravariant indices of the same type) by ε_{ac} and/or $\varepsilon_{\dot{a}\dot{c}}$. This means, in practice, that in selecting Young diagrams associated with the contravariant dotted and undotted indices, only those with a single row need be considered. The reason is that any two tensor indices appearing in the same column are totally anti-symmetrized (for SL(2), each index can only take two values), and hence are effectively contracted with either ε_{ac} or $\varepsilon_{\dot{a}\dot{c}}$. Such a pair can be left out, because the contractions are invariant under SL(2) transformations. (In other words, they correspond to a multiplicative "spin 0" factor which has nothing to do with the transformation properties of the rest of the tensor.)

As an example, consider the tensor $t^{\lambda(abc)}$ with the symmetry

$$\lambda = \begin{array}{|c|c|}\hline a & c \\ \hline b & \multicolumn{1}{c}{} \\ \cline{1-1}\end{array} \,.$$

Since the two indices a and b are anti-symmetrized, and hence contracted with ε_{ab}, we have

$$t^{\lambda(abc)} = \varepsilon_{ab}\, t^{abc} \qquad .$$

The object transforms under SL(2) just like t^c. For SL(2), there are of course no non-zero tensors of symmetry associated with Young diagrams containing columns longer than two.

The final result on SL(2) is that all its finite dimensional irreducible representations can be found on tensor spaces with totally symmetric undotted and dotted indices, corresponding to two Young tableaux of precisely one row and lengths i, and k respectively. The two integers (i, k) uniquely identify each inequivalent irreducible representation of the group. This is just the result obtained in Chap. 10 and Appendix VI.

Next, we consider the special unitary groups $SU(m_+, m_-)$.

Definition 13.11 (Special Unitary Group $SU(m_+, m_-)$): The subgroup of $GL(m)$ which admits both a metric tensor of signature (m_+, m_-) and a totally anti-symmetric tensor of rank m as invariant tensors is called the *special unitary group* $SU(m_+, m_-)$.

The irreducible representations of $SU(m_+, m_-)$ can be inferred from previous results without further elaboration.

Theorem 13.15 (Irreducible Representations of the Special Unitary Group $SU(m_+, m_-)$): The irreducible representations of the unitary group $U(m_+, m_-)$, realized as traceless tensors of specific symmetry (λ, μ) [Theorem 13.13], remain irreducible when restricted to the special unitary group $SU(m_+, m_-)$. Two such representations, associated with symmetries (λ, μ) and (λ', μ') respectively, are equivalent with respect to $SU(m_+, m_-)$ when the Young diagram obtained by combining the columns of λ and $\tilde{\mu}$ is the same as that obtained from λ' and $\tilde{\mu}'$.

Turning to the special case of SU(2), which was the subject of intensive study in Chap. 8 [cf. also Chap. 10 and Appendix VI], we need only to carry the previous discussion on SL(2) one step further: because tensors with dotted indices are superfluous for unitary groups, all irreducible representations of SU(2) can be found by examining tensors of one particular type—say, that with totally symmetric undotted indices. The number of such indices, i, completely specifies the representations. In Sec. 8.1, we used precisely these tensors to evaluate the representation matrices of all the irreducible representations of SU(2).

13.4.3 The Real Orthogonal Group $O(m_+, m_-; R)$ and the Special Real Orthogonal Group $SO(m_+, m_-; R)$

We mentioned at the end of Sec. 13.3 that, for the general linear group on a real vector space $GL(m; R)$, it is only necessary to consider tensor spaces with undotted indices; all irreducible representations of the group are covered by Theorems 9 and 10. We shall now consider some useful subgroups of $GL(m; R)$. Recall that most symmetry groups in space-time are examples of real groups, because space-time variables are real. In chapters 6-12, we have considered the groups SO(2), SO(3), SO(3, 1), O(2), O(3), and O(3, 1) in varying degrees of detail.

To motivate a general definition of the orthogonal groups, recall that in each of the above cited examples we had an *invariant metric tensor of rank 2*—δ_{ab} for the groups O(2), O(3), and $g_{\mu\nu}$ for the group O(3, 1). These tensors were given in their Cartesian form, with non-zero elements only along the diagonal and of values ± 1.

As we should know by now, the specific expressions for these tensor components [e.g. Eq. (10.1-2)] are not guaranteed to be basis-independent. In fact, let ξ_{ab} be the components of the metric tensor with respect to some basis, then upon a change of basis effected by $g \in \mathrm{GL}(m)$, we obtain

$$\xi_{ab} \xrightarrow{g} \xi'_{ab} = \xi_{cd}(g^{-1})^c{}_a(g^{-1})^d{}_b \quad . \tag{13.4-13}$$

This can be written as a matrix equation

$$\xi' = (g^{-1})^{\mathrm{T}}\xi g^{-1} \qquad \text{or} \qquad \xi = g^{\mathrm{T}}\xi' g \quad . \tag{13.4-14}$$

Thus, even if $\xi_{ab} = \delta_{ab}$, $\xi'_{ab} = (gg^{\mathrm{T}})^{-1}{}_{ab}$ is, in general, not necessarily simple-looking. In order to arrive at a general definition of the metric tensor, henceforth denoted by ξ, we must identify its essential features which are independent of the choice of basis. Two such features are evident from Eq. (13.4-14): its invertibility, and the symmetry in its two tensor indices. A third feature, not as apparent as the others, is its *signature* (m_+, m_-). The situation is similar to that of Subsection 13.4.1 when we discussed the invariant tensor of the unitary groups. Hence we shall not dwell on any details further.

Definition 13.12 (The Real Orthogonal Group $\mathrm{O}(m_+,m_-)$): The set of all real general linear transformations on V which leaves an invertible, symmetric metric tensor of signature (m_+,m_-) invariant is called the *real orthogonal group of signature* (m_+,m_-). It is denoted by $\mathrm{O}(m_+,m_-;\mathrm{R})$, or $\mathrm{O}(m_+,m_-)$ in short. If the metric is positive definite, the signature is $(m,0)$; the group $\mathrm{O}(m,0;\mathrm{R})$ will be denoted simply by $\mathrm{O}(m)$.

Comparing the description of the $\mathrm{O}(m_+,m_-)$ with that of $\mathrm{U}(m_+,m_-)$, it should be clear that the orthogonal group is a special case of the unitary group when the latter is restricted to a real vector space.

The finite-dimensional irreducible representations of $\mathrm{O}(m_+,m_-)$ can be inferred from those of $\mathrm{GL}(m;\mathrm{R})$ by further reduction, utilizing additional invariant operations furnished by the metric tensor ξ_{ab} and its dual ξ^{ab} defined by

$$\xi^{ab}\xi_{bc} = \delta^a_c \quad . \tag{13.4-15}$$

Recall that the irreducible representations of $\mathrm{GL}(m;\mathrm{R})$ are defined on the tensor spaces T^i_j (with undotted indices only). What invariant operations can ξ_{ab} and ξ^{ab} provide on these spaces? Our previous discussion of the group SL(2), with invariant tensors ε_{ab} and ε^{ab}, provides the answer.

First, by multiplying ξ_{ab} with a given tensor and contracting one of the indices, we can lower a contravariant index to a covariant position, e.g.

$$\xi_{ab}\, t^{bc\ldots}_{d\ldots} \sim t^{c\ldots}_{ad\ldots} \tag{13.4-16}$$

where $\sim$ means "transforms under $\mathrm{O}(m_+,m_-)$ as". Similarly, one can raise a covariant index to a contravariant position by multiplying by ξ^{ab} and contracting one of the indices. Thus, by a succession of these operations, we can convert any tensor $t^{\{a\}}_{\{b\}}$ into one with only one type of indices, either fully contravariant or fully covariant. For definiteness, we will pick the former.

Secondly, given any tensor $t^{abc\cdots}$, we can *contract* it *by the metric tensor* and obtain

$$t^{abc\ldots} \longrightarrow \xi_{ab}\, t^{abc\ldots} \sim t^{c\ldots} \quad . \tag{13.4-17}$$

For example, on the space of second rank tensors, consider the contraction with ξ_{ab} of the group O(m). We can choose a basis so that ξ_{ab} is just the Kronecker delta function of the indices,

$$\xi_{ab}\, t^{ab} = t^{11} + t^{22} + \cdots + t^{mm} \quad . \tag{13.4-18}$$

This quantity, equal to the trace of the matrix formed by $\{t^{ab}\}$, is invariant under O(m) transformations. [Problem 13.8] Hence it transforms as a tensor of rank 0, a real number in this case.

Contraction by the metric tensor can be used to help decompose a tensor into its irreducible parts in the same way as done for the regular contraction [Sec. 13.3]. Thus, in the above example one can write [cf. Eq. (13.2-7)]

$$t^{ab} = \hat{t}^{ab} + \frac{1}{m}\,\xi^{ab}(\xi_{cd}\, t^{cd}) \tag{13.4-19}$$

where the first term on the right, $\hat{t}^{ab}$ is "traceless," i.e.

$$\xi_{ab}\hat{t}^{ab} = 0 \tag{13.4-20}$$

[cf. (13.4-18)], and the second term is proportional to the invariant tensor ξ^{ab}. The two terms transform independently under O(m_+, m_-) transformations. For a general tensor with i indices $t^{a_1 \cdots a_i}$, contraction by the metric tensor can be done for any pair of indices from $\{a\}$. A tensor with the property that all possible contractions by the metric tensor vanish is said to be *traceless*.

It is not hard to see that the complete reduction of a general tensor $t^{abc\cdots}$ by contraction with ξ_{ab} can be obtained by a decomposition similar to that summarized in Theorem 13.8 for the regular contraction: every tensor $t^{abc\cdots}$ can be written as a sum of terms, each consisting of the product of a "traceless" tensor (of lower or equal rank) and an invariant tensor formed from ξ^{ab}. The proof of this assertion is almost identical to that of Theorem 13.8, and hence will not be repeated here.

Theorem 13.16 (Irreducible Representations of O(m_+,m_-)): The finite dimensional irreducible representations of O(m_+,m_-) can be found on the space of type-(i, 0), traceless tensors of symmetry λ (where λ denotes a Young tableau with i squares). Two such representations are equivalent if and only if the associated tableaux correspond to the same Young diagram.

All necessary steps for the proof of this theorem can be patterned after corresponding ones given previously for GL(m) and U(m_+,m_-). Note that, once we limit ourselves to tensors of type (i, 0), the regular contraction (by δ^a_b) is no longer relevant. However, contraction by the metric tensors ξ_{ab} plays a role which is almost identical.

The invariant operations of raising and lowering tensor indices mentioned earlier establish equivalent relations between representations defined on tensors of type (i, j) with those of types ($i+1, j-1$) and ($i-1, j+1$), according to Lemma 2 of Sec. 13.3. A traceless tensor of type (i, j) and symmetries (λ, μ) (which is irreducible under GL(m; R)) is, in general, reducible with respect to O(m_+,m_-). For example, consider the 3rd rank tensor $t_c^{\{ab\}}$, corresponding to the symmetry $\lambda = \boxed{a}\boxed{b}$. Since the index c can be raised by the metric tensor, $t_c^{\{ab\}}$ transform equivalently as $t^{\{ab\}c} = t_d^{\{ab\}}\,\xi^{dc}$ under O(m_+, m_-). However, the latter is clearly not irreducible: it can be reduced further both by applying Young symmetrizers associated with tableaux of the larger symmetric group (S_3 vs. S_2), such as

$$\begin{array}{|c|c|c|}\hline a & b & c \\ \hline \end{array} \quad \text{or} \quad \begin{array}{|c|c|}\hline a & b \\ \hline c \\ \cline{1-1} \end{array}$$

and by contraction with ξ_{ac}.[4]

To make contact with results obtained in earlier chapters by an entirely different approach, let us consider an example—O(2). In particular, let us consider the space T_0^2 of second rank tensors t^{ab}. Its dimension is 4. We reduce it as follows:

(i) The "trace" of t, $\xi_{ab}t^{ab} = t^{11} + t^{22}$ [Eq. (13.4-18)], transforms irreducibly and invariantly. It corresponds to the identity representation;

(ii) The subspace specified by the symmetry

$$\lambda = \begin{array}{|c|}\hline a \\ \hline b \\ \hline \end{array}$$

is one-dimensional, it consists of multiples of the anti-symmetric combination $\tilde{t} = t^{12} - t^{21} = \varepsilon_{ab}t^{ab}$, where ε_{ab} is the unit anti-symmetric tensor (with respect to a specific basis). Under an O(2) transformation u, $\tilde{t}$ transform as $\tilde{t} \to \tilde{t}' = \tilde{t}$ (det u). But (det u) $= \pm 1$ for O(2) matrices, hence $\tilde{t}' = \pm\tilde{t}$ depending on the sign of (det u).

(iii) Now, consider the space of traceless tensors corresponding to the symmetry $\lambda = \begin{array}{|c|c|}\hline a & b \\ \hline \end{array}$,

$$\hat{t}^{\{ab\}} = (t^{ab} + t^{ba})/2 - \xi^{ab}(t^{11} + t^{22})/2 \tag{13.4-21}$$

[cf. Eq. (13.4-19)]. It consists of what is left of the space T_0^2 after the trace and the anti-symmetric part of t have been removed. It is two dimensional, and irreducible with respect to O(2).

Referring to Sec. 11.1 on the group O(2), we see that the first two representations in the above list are just the two one-dimensional representations mentioned in the first part of Theorem 11.3. The two-dimensional representation comprising of traceless symmetric tensor $\hat{t}^{\{ab\}}$ (part (iii) above) corresponds to the $m = 2$ representation described in part two of Theorem 11.3. (The two-dimensional $m = 1$ representation of Theorem 11.3 clearly corresponds to the fundamental representation realized on V or T_0^1.) Thus we get complete agreement with our previous results, which were obtained by the Lie algebra approach.

The *special orthogonal group* SO(m_+, m_-; R), or SO(m_+, m_-) in short, is the subgroup of O(m_+, m_-) which admits the totally anti-symmetric tensor $\varepsilon^{[a]}$ and its dual $\varepsilon_{[a]}$ as additional invariants. In the tensor spaces $\{T_0^n; n = 0, 1, \ldots\}$ these invariant tensors by themselves can do little to induce equivalences among the inequivalent irreducible representations of the parent group [Theorem 13.16]. (The only obvious operation is that of contracting all the indices of $\varepsilon_{[a]}$ with a set of totally

[4] Contraction with ξ_{bc} will not give new results as the a and b indices are already symmetrized. Since the tensor $t_c^{\{ab\}}$ came traceless with respect to regular contraction in the pairs (a, c), contraction by ξ_{ac} may or may not lead to further reduction, depending on the signature (m_+, m_-).

anti-symmetric indices of $t^{[a]\cdots}$. This amounts to establishing the equivalence of a representation with Young diagram of m rows to another with its Young diagram obtained from the former by removing one column of length m.) However, by the combined action of the totally anti-symmetric tensors and the metric tensors ξ^{ab} and ξ_{ab}, we can obtain a whole series of invariant operations on the spaces $\{T^n_0\}$ which lead to many non-trivial equivalences. Let us look at some examples.

Consider the group SO(2). Using the metric tensors for index raising and lowering operations, we can obtain new invariant tensors such as

$$\varepsilon_b{}^a = \varepsilon_{bc}\,\xi^{ca} \quad . \tag{13.4-22}$$

Given a basis $(\hat{e}_1, \hat{e}_2)$, the new basis vectors

$$\hat{e}'_a = \varepsilon_a{}^b\,\hat{e}_b$$

will transform the same way (i.e. equivalently) under SO(2) as the original basis vectors because $\varepsilon_a{}^b$ is an invariant. (It is not hard to show that $(\hat{e}'_1, \hat{e}'_2)$ are some multiples of $(\hat{e}_2, -\hat{e}_1)$.) This suggests that the 2-dimensional space is reducible under SO(2). Indeed, in Chap. 6 we have seen that the two linear combinations $\hat{e}_\pm = \mp\hat{e}_1 - i\hat{e}_2$ transform independently under the group SO(2). Note that the basis $\{\hat{e}'_a\}$ does not transform the same way as $\{\hat{e}_a\}$ under the full group O(2)—for instance, under reflection of one of the coordinate axes the two bases behave in opposite ways. They are the analogs of axial and polar vectors, respectively, in three-space. Another way of seeing this point is that the new basis vectors $\hat{e}_\pm$ which diagonalize SO(2) transformations are not individually invariant under reflections—they transform into each other. It is not surprising that SO(2) and reflection transformations cannot be simultaneously diagonalized: they do not commute in 2-dimensional Euclidean space [Sec. 11.1].

Now consider the second rank tensors discussed a few paragraphs back. The two contracted quantities $\xi_{ab}t^{ab}$ and $\varepsilon_{ab}t^{ab}$ are both invariant under SO(2). (N.B. $\varepsilon_{ab}t^{ab}$ gives rise to the irreducible representation with a single two-square column Young symmetry type.) They correspond to equivalent representations of the group (the $m = 0$ representation of Sec. 6.3) whereas, as discussed earlier, they are inequivalent with respect to O(2). They are the (true) *scalar* and the *pseudo-scalar*, respectively. Elements of the two dimensional invariant subspace comprised of symmetric traceless tensors [Eq. (13.4-21)] can be written in the matrix form

$$t^{\{ab\}} = \begin{pmatrix} x & y \\ y & -x \end{pmatrix} \tag{13.4-23}$$

where the two independent components are denoted by x and y. Using the invariant tensor (13.4-22), we can obtain a new tensor of the same genre

$$t'^{\{ab\}} = t^{\{ac\}}\,\varepsilon_c{}^b = \begin{pmatrix} -y & x \\ x & y \end{pmatrix} \tag{13.4-24}$$

which transforms identically to the original one under SO(2) but in opposite ways under reflections in O(2). (For instance, depending on which of the axes is reversed, either x or y changes sign; it is obvious from (13.4-23) and (13.4-24) that the two tensors behave differently under such a transformation.) Hence this 2-dimensional irreducible representation of O(2) can also be reduced with respect to the subgroup SO(2). The change of basis in V which decomposes the fundamental representation will, in fact, effect the reduction of the second-rank tensor as well.

Next, let us consider the group SO(*3*). In particular, we can construct the following invariant tensor:

$$\varepsilon_{ab}{}^{c} = \varepsilon_{abd}\,\zeta^{dc} \qquad (13.4\text{-}25)$$

and use it to establish equivalences of irreducible representations of O(3) [Theorem 13.16] when they are restricted to the subgroup SO(3). The fundamental representation, $\square$, is not affected by the extra invariant tensor; it remains irreducible. This is the $j = 1$ representation of Chap. 7.

The anti-symmetric second-rank tensor $t^{[ab]}$ (corresponding to the two-square column Young diagram $\begin{smallmatrix}\square\\\square\end{smallmatrix}$) is automatically traceless, and it corresponds to a 3-dimensional irreducible representation of O(3). It remains irreducible under SO(3). However, because of the existence of the invariant tensor (13.4-25), $t^{[ab]}$ can be transformed into a tensor with a single index:

$$t^{[ab]} \qquad v^{a} = t^{[bc]}\,\varepsilon_{bc}{}^{a}$$

This is a three component quantity which transforms as the fundamental representation under SO(3), i.e. it corresponds also to $j = 1$. It is, of course, actually an *axial vector* which behaves in the opposite way to the coordinate vector under space inversion in O(3). In other words, the two $j = 1$ representations of SO(3) are inequivalent with respect to O(3); they correspond to the $\eta = \mp 1$ representations of Theorem 11, respectively.

The traceless symmetric second-rank tensor $t^{\{ab\}}$, $\square\square$, is again not affected by the anti-symmetric invariant tensor (13.4-25), since the contraction of the two tensors will only yield a null result. It corresponds to the $j = 2$ representation of SO(3) [Chap. 7], and the $(j, \eta) = (2, +)$ representation of O(3) [Chap. 11].

The trace of t^{ab}, $\zeta_{ab}t^{ab}$, is an invariant under both O(3) and SO(3). It is a (true) *scalar*. The totally anti-symmetric invariant tensor ε_{abc} can be used to reduce a third-rank tensor of the single-column Young diagram symmetry class to obtain $\varepsilon_{abc}t^{abc}$. This quantity transforms as an invariant under SO(3), but it changes sign under space inversions in O(3). It is a *pseudo-scalar*. The scalar and the pseudo-scalar both correspond to the $j = 0$ representation of SO(3) [Chap. 7]. They correspond to two inequivalent representations—$(j, \eta) = (0, +)$, and $(0, -)$ respectively—with respect to O(3).

These examples suggest that, in odd dimensions (when the space inversion transformation commutes with rotations [Sec. 11.2]), the irreducible representations of the group $O(m_+, m_-)$ remains irreducible under $SO(m_+, m_-)$. Inequivalent representations of $O(m_+, m_-)$ which differ from each other only by their behavior under space inversions, however, become equivalent to each other under $SO(m_+, m_-)$. On the other hand, in even dimensions (when spatial reflection does not in general commute with rotations [Sec. 11.1]), equivalence can be established between certain irreducible tensors (with respect to $O(m_+, m_-)$) and others obtained from them by invariant operations of the subgroup $SO(m_+, m_-)$. When this happens, the representation can be decomposed with respect to $SO(m_+, m_-)$; the new irreducible components have non-trivial transformation properties under spatial reflections. The last statement follows from the fact that (block-) diagonalization of the $SO(m_+, m_-)$ operators results in non-diagonal forms for the spatial reflection operators as a consequence of non-commutativity of the two types of transformations. In addition to the examples of O(2) and SO(2) cited earlier, we have encountered this situation also in the case of SO(3, 1) in Chaps. 10 and 11. For instance, a second-rank anti-symmetric tensor $F^{\mu\nu}$ is irreducible with respect to O(3, 1); but it is reducible with respect to SO(3, 1), being equivalent to the direct sum representation $(1,0) \oplus (0,1)$ in the notation of Chaps. 10 and 11. If we change to a basis in which SO(3, 1) transformations are block-diagonal, the space inversion transformation becomes non-diagonal [Appendix VI].

13.5 Concluding Remarks

In Chapters 6-12 we developed the representation theory of a number of space-time symmetry groups using the Lie algebra approach. In each case, the algebra of a small number of operators, the *generators* of continuous transformations plus certain discrete (inversion) operators, determine the local behavior of the irreducible representations which are of interest. In this Chapter, we systematically derived the finite-dimensional irreducible representations of general classical groups using the global tensorial method. We shall conclude this book with a few remarks pertaining to the complementary nature of these two universal approaches.

It should be rather obvious from the results of this chapter that, in principle, the tensorial method is the simplest and most unambiguous for the general linear group. The basic reason for this is that GL(m) transformations are of such general form that the only invariant operations permitted on the tensor space are Young symmetrizations and contractions. The existence of invariant tensors for the various subgroups of GL(m) leads to additional invariant operations which need to be taken into account in the analysis of their irreducible representations. In some cases, such as $U(m_+, m_-)$ and GL(m;R), these invariant operations actually lead to simplification of the tensor space structure (e.g. full scale elimination of tensors with dotted indices). In other cases, such as SL(m) and $O(m_+, m_-)$, the situation remains fairly simple; although one has to watch out for some reductions and equivalences brought about by the additional invariants. In more extreme cases, such as $SO(m_+, m_-; R)$, the large number of invariants (three, in the example given, corresponding to the conditions real, special, and orthogonal) make the end result rather complicated. This phenomenon is the consequence of the "reduction" procedure, from the most general to the more specialized groups, which is inherent to this method.

When the problem is approached from the Lie algebra point of view, we find that the more specialized groups have fewer generators and discrete transformations, and their Lie algebras are simpler in structure than those of the more general groups. Hence the representation theory for the former is simpler. Each time a group is enlarged, the effects due to the additional generator(s) and/or discrete operator(s) need to be analyzed and taken into account. This is certainly the situation we discovered when we worked our way through the groups SO(2), SO(3), SU(2), SO(3, 1), SL(2), O(2), O(3), and O(3, 1) in Chapters 6-12. This process is a "constructive" one, building from the specialized, simpler groups to the more general and more complex ones.

One of the remarkable features of the Lie algebra approach from a physicist's point of view is that the generators of continuous transformations and the discrete operators all have direct physical meaning: the former correspond to hermitian operators representing physical variables (momentum, energy, ...); the latter play important roles also in the classification of states and in selection rules for transition amplitudes. [Chapters 11, 12] Does this mean that the Lie algebra approach is more "physical" then the tensorial method, since the latter does not use the generators? The question is really somewhat meaningless. From a different point of view, one can, in fact, argue that the tensorial method is more "physical". Consider, for example, isospin symmetry in nuclear physics. The symmetry group is SU(2); the basic constitutuents of nuclei, proton and neutron (p,n), transform as the fundamental representation of the group. The hundreds (thousands ?) of nuclear isotopic states are made of protons and neutrons; and their isospin group transformation properties can be naturally envisioned in terms of irreducible tensors corresponding to their actual physical constituents. Since most nuclei consist of many nucleons, and since the isospin group SO(2) is so simple, the above observation is only of academic interest. However, this correspondence is of far more practical importance in the field of elementary particle physics where the symmetry groups are SU(2) × U(1) (of "weak isospin and hypercharge" [Commins]), SU(3) (of strongly interacting "color symmetry" [Halzen]), SU(6) (of the static quark model [Dyson]), SU(5), SO(10) (of "grand unified theory" [Halzen]), ... etc. Because typically the physical states in these applications contain only a small number of the basic constituents ("quarks" or "leptons" which, again, transform as the fundamental representation of the group), their group properties are most conveniently inferred from the tensor structure of their "wave functions" in terms of their constituents.

Although from time to time we have stated certain general features of the representation theory of Lie groups in the course of studying specified examples, no attempt has been made to cover this immensely rich subject systematically in this introductory book. It should be mentioned, however, that far-reaching results can be obtained by formulating the local Lie algebra approach on a sound mathematical footing. [Chevalley, Gilmore, Gourdin, Hamermesh, Miller, Pontrjagin, Varadarajan, Weyl, Wybourne] In particular, it is possible to classify all semi-simple Lie groups and Lie algebras, and to construct systematically their finite-dimensional and infinite-dimensional irreducible representations. These results have a wide range of applications in other branches of mathematics and, increasingly, in many fields in physics. The material that we have covered should provide adequate background and concrete experience for the reader to explore both the more general mathematical theory and the diverse physical applications in many fields of interest.

Problems

13.1 Prove that on the tensor space T^1_1, the operation of taking the contraction commutes with that of performing a GL(m) transformation.

13.2 Prove that the transformation, Eq. (13.2-1), defines a representation of GL(m) on the tensor space T^1_1.

13.3 Prove that: (i) the direct product of a tensor of type (i, j) with the invariant tensor $\delta^a{}_b$ is a tensor of type $(i + 1, j + 1)$; (ii) if a certain set $\{t : t \in T^i_j\}$ transforms under GL(m) as representation D, then the $(i + 1, j + 1)$ tensors $\{t\delta^a{}_b\}$ provide a representation of GL(m) which is the same as D.

13.4 Consider the decomposition of T_1^2 tensors according to Theorem 13.7

$$t_b^{ac} = r_b^{ac} + u^a \delta_b^c + v^c \delta_b^a$$

where $r_a^{ac} = 0 = r_c^{ac}$. Take all possible contractions of both sides. Show that the resulting equations serve to determine the coefficients of $\{u, v\}$uniquely.

13.5 Prove Theorem 13.11.

13.6 Prove that: (i) the "inverse" of an invariant tensor [Eq. (13.4-5)] is an invariant tensor; (ii) under a general linear transformation g, an invertible hermitian, and positive definite second rank tensor $\delta_{\dot{c}}^a$ retains all these attributes.

13.7 Prove that, for second rank tensors, the term "hermitian" has a definitive meaning only if the tensor type is (1, 0; 0, 1) or (0, 1; 1, 0).

13.8 Prove in detail that, in the case of the O(m_+, m_-) group, the contraction of any second rank tensor t^{ab} with the metric tensor, $\xi_{ab} t^{ab}$, is an invariant under group transformations.

13.9 For the group O(3), examine the spaces of second rank tensors, and decompose each into their respective irreducible parts by the method of Sec. 13.4.3. Compare the results with those of Sec. 11.2.

13.10 Is there an invariant tensor which characterizes the subgroup GL(m; R) of GL(M; C)? If the answer is yes, then what is this tensor? Can you determine the inequivalent irreducible representations of GL(m; R) making use of this invariant tensor?

APPENDIX I

NOTATIONS AND SYMBOLS

This appendix contains a summary of notations used in this book. Definitions of the quantities encountered here can be found either in the following Appendix, or in the proper parts of the text where they are first introduced.

I.1 Summation Convention

A pair of repeated upper and lower indices in the same expression implies a summation over the range of the index even if a summation sign is not explicitly written (Einstein convention). A pair of repeated indices on the same level does not imply summation unless preceded by an explicit summation sign. Hence,

(I.1-1) $$\sum_i A_i B^i = A_i B^i \quad ;$$

but $A_i B_i$ indicates no summation.

The indices which are summed over do not explicitly appear in the expression after summation, hence are called *dummy indices.* The symbol for each pair of dummy indices can be changed without changing the value of the sum.

I.2 Vectors and Vector Indices

(a) Vectors in ordinary 2- or 3-dimensional Euclidean spaces will be denoted by boldface single Latin letters, e.g. $\mathbf{x}, \mathbf{y}, \ldots$ etc. Unit vectors, i.e. vectors of unit length, will be distinguished by an overhead caret, e.g. $\hat{\mathbf{e}}, \hat{\mathbf{u}}, \hat{\mathbf{z}} \ldots$ etc.

Orthonormal basis vectors (cf. Definition II.19) in n-dimensional Euclidean space will be denoted by $\{\hat{\mathbf{e}}_i, i = 1, 2, \ldots, n\}$. The components of $\mathbf{x}$ with respect to this basis are denoted by $(x^i\}$ where

(I.2-1) $$\mathbf{x} = \hat{\mathbf{e}}_i x^i \quad .$$

(b) Certain linear spaces have non-trivial invariant 'metric tensors', say g_{ij} (cf. Chap. 10 and Appendix VI). In that case, it is convenient to distinguish between *contravariant components* of a vector labelled by an upper index as above, and *covariant components* of the same vector labelled by a lower index defined by

(I.2-2) $$x_i = g_{ij} x^j$$

such that $x_i y^i$ is an invariant. The metric tensor for Euclidean spaces is the Kronecker delta function: $g_{ij} = \delta_{ij}$. Hence, for Euclidean spaces, $x_i = x^j$.

(c) Vectors in general linear vector spaces will be formally denoted by Greek or Latin letters inside Dirac's $|\rangle$ ('ket') or $\langle|$ ('bra') symbols, e.g. $|x\rangle$, $|\xi\rangle, \ldots$, or $\langle f|$, $\langle\psi|, \ldots$ etc. Whenever confusion is not a danger, we shall omit the bra and ket signs,

and use bold letters to denote the corresponding (general) vectors, as for ordinary vectors.
(d) Multiplication of a vector $|x\rangle$ by a number α can be written in three equivalent ways:

(I.2-3) $$|\alpha x\rangle = \alpha \cdot |x\rangle = |x\rangle \alpha \quad .$$

In general, the last form is the preferred one, as effects due to additional operations on the vector from the left can be visualized most directly.
(e) Lower indices are used to label 'ket' basis vectors, e.g. $\{|e_i\rangle; i = 1, \ldots n\}$; upper indices are used to label components of ket-vectors. Consequently, if x^i are components of $|x\rangle$ with respect to $\{|e_i\rangle\}$, then

(I.2-4) $$|x\rangle = \sum_{i=1}^{n} |e_i\rangle x^i = |e_i\rangle x^i \quad .$$

(f) Upper indices are used to label basis-vectors of the dual space, e.g. $\{\langle e^i|; i = 1, \ldots, n\}$; lower indices are used to label components of bra-vectors, i.e.

(I.2-5) $$\langle x| = \sum_{i=1}^{n} x_i \langle e^i| = x_i \langle e^i| \quad .$$

(If $\langle x|$ and $\langle e^i|$ are due to $|x\rangle$, $|e_i\rangle$ respectively, then $x_i{}^\dagger = x^{i*}$ where * indicates complex-conjugation.) The raising and lowering of the index in this way is a desirable convention, since the scalar product can be written as

(I.2-6) $$\langle x|y\rangle = \sum_i x_i{}^\dagger y^i = x_i{}^\dagger y^i \quad .$$

I.3 Matrix Indices

As usual, elements of a matrix will be labelled by a row index followed by a column index. (In rare occasions, each index may consist of more than one symbols.) The *transpose* of a matrix, indicated by the superscript T, implies the interchange of the row and column indices. We write,

(I.3-1) $$\begin{aligned} A^{\mathrm{T}}{}_{ij} &= A_{ji} \\ A^{\mathrm{T}}{}_i{}^j &= A^j{}_i \quad . \end{aligned}$$

Note that superscripts (subscripts) remain as superscripts (subscripts); they are not affected by transposition.

Because of the Einstein summation convention adopted above, both upper and lower indices are used to label matrix elements. The normal notation for matrix multiplication is

(I.3-2) $$(A\,B\,C)^i{}_j = A^i{}_k B^k{}_m C^m{}_j$$

which naturally follows from the convention adopted above for vectors—as is shown in Sec. II.3.

Just as in the case of vector components, it is desirable to switch upper and lower indices of a matrix when its complex conjugate is taken. As hermitian conjugation also implies taking the transpose, it is natural to incorporate also (I.3-1), and arrive at the convention:

$$A^{\dagger i}{}_j = A^*{}_j{}^i = (A^j{}_i)^* \quad . \tag{I.3-3}$$

If A carries any other indices (such as a representation label), we shall raise or lower them according to the same convention.

As indices may also be raised or lowered by contraction with a metric tensor, as mentioned in Sec. I.2, variants of Eq. (I.3-2) may look like:

$$\begin{aligned}(A\,B\,C)^i{}_j &= A^{ik}\,B_{km}\,C^m{}_j \\ &= A^i{}_k\,B^{km}\,C_{mj} \quad .\end{aligned} \tag{I.3-4}$$

All these forms are equivalent if the raising and lowering of indices are carried out consistently.

APPENDIX II

SUMMARY OF LINEAR VECTOR SPACES

This appendix contains a systematic summary of elements of the theory of linear vector spaces which form the foundation of group representation theory, quantum mechanics, as well as classical mathematical physics. This review also provides a natural way to supply the details on the notations used in the text and summarized in Appendix I. Motivation is provided for definitions and theorems, but detailed proofs are omitted in most cases. Where a result is more subtle than might appear on the surface, an exultation to the reader (prove!) is included. For details, the reader is referred to the classic book by Halmos [Halmos].

II.1 Linear Vector Space

Definition II.1: A *Linear Vector Space* V is a set $\{|x\rangle, |y\rangle, \ldots \text{etc.}\}$, on which two operations + (*addition*) and $\cdot$ (*multiplication by a number*) are defined, such that the following basic axioms hold:

(i) If $|x\rangle \in \mathrm{V}$ and $|y\rangle \in \mathrm{V}$, then $|x\rangle + |y\rangle \equiv |z\rangle \quad \in \mathrm{V}$;

(ii) If $|x\rangle \in \mathrm{V}$ and α is a (real or complex) number, then

$$|\alpha x\rangle \equiv \alpha \cdot |x\rangle \equiv |x\rangle \alpha \qquad \in \mathrm{V} \quad ;$$

(iii) There exists a *null vector* $|0\rangle$, such that

$$|x\rangle + |0\rangle = |x\rangle \qquad \text{for all } |x\rangle \in \mathrm{V} \quad ;$$

(vi) For every $|x\rangle \in \mathrm{V}$, there exists a $|-x\rangle \in \mathrm{V}$ such that

$$|x\rangle + |-x\rangle = |0\rangle \quad ;$$

(v) The operation + is *commutative* and *associative*, i.e.

$$|x\rangle + |y\rangle = |y\rangle + |x\rangle \quad \text{and}$$

$$(|x\rangle + |y\rangle) + |z\rangle = |x\rangle + (|y\rangle + |z\rangle) \equiv |x\rangle + |y\rangle + |z\rangle \quad ;$$

(vi) $1 \cdot |x\rangle = |x\rangle$;

(vii) Multiplication by a number is associative, i.e.

$$\alpha \cdot |\beta x\rangle = (\alpha\beta) \cdot |x\rangle \equiv |x\rangle (\alpha\beta) \quad ;$$

(viii) The two operations satisfy the *distributive* properties:

$$(\alpha + \beta)\cdot|x\rangle = |x\rangle\alpha + |x\rangle\beta \quad \text{and}$$
$$\alpha\cdot(|x\rangle + |y\rangle) = |x\rangle\alpha + |y\rangle\alpha \quad .$$

(Prove that $|-x\rangle = |x\rangle(-1)$, and $0|x\rangle = |0\rangle$.)

Examples of some frequently encountered vector spaces are: (i) The space C_1 of all complex numbers; (ii) The space of all vectors $\mathbf{x}$ in 3-dimensional Euclidean space, R_3; (iii) The space C_n of all ordered n complex numbers $(x_1, x_2, \ldots, x_n)$; (iv) All polynomials of a real number variable (say t) with complex coefficients and of order n or less, $P_n(t)$; and (v) All functions of a real variable t which are solutions to a linear homogeneous differential equation (such as those encountered in classical and quantum physics). In each of these cases, it is understood that the two operations $+$ and $\cdot$ are defined in the conventional way so that the axioms of Definition II.1 are satisfied.

Definition II.2 A set of vectors $\{\mathbf{x} \in V, i = 1, \ldots m\}$ are *linearly independent* if $|x_i\rangle\alpha^i = 0$ (N.B. summation over i) necessarily implies that $\alpha^i = 0$ for all i, conversely, the vectors $\mathbf{x}_i$ are *linearly dependent* if there exists a set of numbers $\{\alpha^i\}$, not all zero, such that $|x_i\rangle\alpha^i = 0$.

When a set of non-zero vectors $\{\mathbf{x}_i\}$ are linearly dependent, some vector of the set can be written as a *linear combination* of the vectors preceding it. Note, as an example, in 2-dimensional space: (i) Any three vectors are linearly dependent; and (ii) Two vectors are linearly dependent if and only if they are collinear.

Definition II.3: A set of vectors $\{\hat{\mathbf{e}}_i, i = 1, \ldots, n\}$ forms a *basis* of V if (i) They are linearly independent; and (ii) Every $\mathbf{x} \in V$ can be written as a linear combination of $\{\hat{\mathbf{e}}_i\}$, i.e. $|x\rangle = |e_i\rangle x^i$, where x^i are ordinary numbers.

The numbers $\{x^i, i = 1, \ldots, n\}$ are the *components* of $\mathbf{x}$ with respect to the basis $\{\hat{\mathbf{e}}_i\}$. Vector spaces which have a basis with a finite number of elements are said to be *finite dimensional.*

Theorem II.1: All bases of a finite dimensional vector space V have the same number of elements. (Prove!)

Definition II.4: The number of elements n in a basis of a finite dimensional vector space V is called the *dimension of V.*

The theory and application of linear vector spaces are greatly simplified by the fact that all n-dimensional vector spaces are essentially identical in structure. The terminology and condition for having the same structure are expressed in the following definition:

Definition II.5: Two vector spaces V and V′ are said to be *isomorphic* to each other if there exists a one-to-one mapping $\mathbf{x} \in V \to \mathbf{x}' \in V'$, such that $(|x\rangle + |y\rangle\alpha)' = |x'\rangle + |y'\rangle\alpha$ for all $\mathbf{x}$, $\mathbf{y}$, and α.

(Prove that all axiomatic relations of Definition II.1 can be identified for the two isomorphic vector spaces!) Isomorphism is an equivalence relation.

Theorem II.2: Every n-dimensional linear vector space V_n is isomorphic to the space of n ordered complex numbers C_n; hence all n-dimensional linear vector spaces are isomorphic to each other.

From given vector spaces, one can create smaller vector spaces in the form of *subspaces* or larger vector spaces in the form of *direct sums*.

Definition II.6: A subset V_n of a linear vector space V with the property that it forms a linear vector space (Definition II.1) with the same definitions of the two operations + and as in V is called a *subspace* of V.

The dimension of a non-trivial subspace of a n-dimensional vector space is less than n. A theorem of practical importance is the following:

Theorem II.3: Given V_n and a subspace V_m $(m < n)$, one can always choose a basis $\{\hat{\mathbf{e}}_i, i = 1, \ldots, n\}$ for V_n in such a way that the first m basis-vectors lie in V_m, i.e. $\hat{\mathbf{e}}_i \in V_m$ for $i = 1, \ldots, m$.

Example: The x-y plane is a subspace of the 3-dimensional space. The Cartesian unit vectors $(\hat{\mathbf{e}}_x, \hat{\mathbf{e}}_y, \hat{\mathbf{e}}_z)$ form a basis having the property of Theorem II.3.

Definition II.7: Let V_1 and V_2 be subspaces of V, we say V is the *direct sum* of V_1 and V_2, and write $V = V_1 \oplus V_2$, provided (i) $V_1 \cap V_2 = 0$ (disjoint); and (ii) Every vector $\mathbf{x} \in V$ can be written as $|x\rangle = |x_1\rangle + |x_2\rangle$, where $\mathbf{x}_1 \in V_1$ and $\mathbf{x}_2 \in V_2$.

One can prove that the above *decomposition of V* is unique, and that a basis for V can always be chosen such that $\hat{\mathbf{e}}_i \in V_1$, for all $i = 1, \ldots, m_1$, and $\hat{\mathbf{e}}_i \in V_2$ for $i = m_1 + 1, \ldots, n$. (Clearly $n = m_1 + m_2$ where m_1 and m_2 are the dimensions of V_1 and V_2 respectively.)

Given two arbitrary vector spaces V_1 and V_2 one can always form a new vector space, their *direct sum*, which has V_1 and V_2 as its subspaces and $V = V_1 \oplus V_2$. The elements of V can be denoted by $(\mathbf{x}_1, \mathbf{x}_2)$ where $\mathbf{x}_1 \in V_1$, and $\mathbf{x}_2 \in V_2$. The two operations are defined by:

$$(\mathbf{x}_1, \mathbf{x}_2) + (\mathbf{y}_1, \mathbf{y}_2) = (\mathbf{x}_1 + \mathbf{y}_2, \ \mathbf{x}_1 + \mathbf{y}_2)$$

$$\alpha(\mathbf{x}_1, \mathbf{x}_2) = (\alpha\mathbf{x}_1, \ \alpha\mathbf{x}_2) \quad .$$

It is seen that the subspaces consisting of $(\mathbf{x}_1, 0)$, and $(0, \mathbf{x}_2)$ are isomorphic to V_1 and V_2 respectively.

II.2 Linear Transformations (Operators) on Vector Spaces

Linear transformations on vector spaces form the basis for all analysis on vector spaces. Of particular interest to us is the fact that group transformations are naturally associated with linear transformations because the "multiplication" rules are the same.

Definition II.8: A *linear transformation* (operator) A is a mapping of the elements of one vector space, V, onto those of another, V′, such that

(i) $$|x\rangle \in V \xrightarrow{A} |Ax\rangle \in V'$$

(ii) if $|y\rangle = |x_1\rangle\alpha_1 + |x_2\rangle\alpha_2 \quad \in V$ then

$$|Ay\rangle = |Ax_1\rangle\alpha_1 + |Ax_2\rangle\alpha_2 \quad \in V'$$

Familiar examples of linear transformation of vector spaces onto themselves are: (i) rotations of vectors in R_3, (ii) multiplication by $n \times n$ matrices on column vectors of C_n, (iii) $\frac{d}{dt}$ or any linear differential operator on the space of polynomials $P_n(t)$,... etc. On any vector space, there are two trivial but important linear operators:

(i) the *null* operator $A = 0$; $\quad |x\rangle \to 0|x\rangle = |0\rangle \quad$ for all $\mathbf{x} \in V$;

(ii) the *identity* operator $A = E$: $|x\rangle \to E|x\rangle = |x\rangle$ for all $\mathbf{x} \in V$.

A very special class of linear transformations is the linear functional. It provides the conceptual foundation for many important basic constructs such as the dual vector space, generalized functions (or distributions), and the differential on general manifolds.

Definition II.9: *Linear Functionals* are scalar-valued linear functions over vector spaces.

In other words, they correspond to the particular case $V' = C$ (the space of complex numbers) in Definition II.8. A simple (but non-trivial) example of a linear functional in ordinary 3-dimensional Euclidean space is the first component of each 3-vector.

It is convenient to adopt the alternative notation $|Ax\rangle \equiv A|x\rangle$, introduced by Dirac. This is particularly useful for the frequently encountered case when $V = V'$.

Definition II.10: It is natural to define the *multiplication of linear transformations A* and B by the definition $(AB)|x\rangle = A|Bx\rangle$ for all $\mathbf{x} \in V$. (Prove that AB, so defined, is a linear transformation!) Similarly, it is natural to define the *addition of linear transformations* and the *multiplication by numbers* α, β as $(\alpha A + \beta B)|x\rangle = A|x\rangle\alpha + B|x\rangle\beta$. The set of all linear transformations on a given vector space V, endowed with the above-defined operations form the *algebra of linear transformations on V.*

The following remarks on linear transformations (operators) are in order:

(i) The operator 0 and E introduced earlier satisfy: $A0 = 0A = 0$, and $AE = EA = A$ for all A; (Prove!)

(ii) With respect to *addition* and *multiplication by numbers*, the set of operators forms a vector space (of operators); (Prove!)

(iii) The algebra of operators satisfies the usual algebraic laws $A(B + C) = AB + AC$ (distributive), $A + (B + C) = (A + B) + C$, and $(AB)C = A(BC)$ (associative);

(iv) However, the operation of multiplication of operators is not necessarily commutative, i.e. in general $AB \neq BA$;

Other interesting properties of linear transformations are revealed in the following definitions and examples.

Definition II.11: An operator A is said to be *idempotent* if $A^2 = A$, and $A \neq E$. Such operators are also called *projection operators.*

A simple example of a projection operator is the matrix $\begin{pmatrix} 1 & 0 \\ 0 & 0 \end{pmatrix}$ on the vector space of two-component column matrices (C_2).

Definition II.12: An operator is said to be *nilpotent* if $A \neq 0$, and there is a positive integer m such that $A^m = 0$.

We mention two familiar examples of nilpotent operators: (i) the matrix $\begin{pmatrix} 0 & 1 \\ 0 & 0 \end{pmatrix}$ on two-component vectors (i.e. the *raising operator* for spin 1/2 states), and (ii) the differential operator $\frac{d}{dt}$ in the space of n-th order polynomials $P_n(t)$. The existence of idempotent and nilpotent operators is a manifestation of the fact that not all operators have inverses.

Definition II.13: An operator is said to be *invertible* if: (i) $|Ax\rangle = |Ay\rangle$ implies $|x\rangle = |y\rangle$ for all $\mathbf{x}, \mathbf{y} \in V$; and (ii) for every $\mathbf{y} \in V$ there exists a $\mathbf{x} \in V$ such that $|Ax\rangle = |y\rangle$. The mapping defined by $\mathbf{y} \to \mathbf{x}$ in (ii) is a linear transformation. (Prove!) It is called the *inverse* of A, and is denoted by A^{-1}.

Theorem II.4: (i) If A is invertible then $AA^{-1} = A^{-1}A = E$; (ii) if $AB = CA = E$, then A is invertible and $A^{-1} = B = C$; and (iii) a necessary and sufficient condition for A to be invertible is that: $A|x\rangle = 0$ implies $|x\rangle = 0$.

Theorem II.5: If A and B are both invertible, then: (i) $(AB)^{-1} = B^{-1}A^{-1}$; (ii) $(\alpha A)^{-1} = \alpha^{-1}A^{-1}$; and (iii) $(A^{-1})^{-1} = A$.

II.3 Matrix Representation of Linear Operators

Since all n-dimensional vector spaces are isomorphic to each other (Theorem II.2), linear operators on vector spaces also have universal properties. In fact, given any two vector spaces V_n, V_m and bases $\{\hat{\mathbf{e}}_i, i = 1, \ldots, n\}$, $\{\hat{\mathbf{e}}'_i, i = 1, \ldots, m\}$ respectively, every linear operator A from V_n to V_m can be represented by a $m \times n$ matrix $(A^j{}_i)$ (which is the natural form for linear operators from C_n to C_m). The correspondence is easily established as follows:

(i) Since $\hat{\mathbf{e}}_i \in V_n$, each of the n vectors $A\hat{\mathbf{e}}_i \in V_m$ can be written as a linear combination of $\{\hat{\mathbf{e}}_i, i = 1, \ldots, m\}$, i.e.

(II.3-1) $$A|e_i\rangle = |e'_j\rangle A^j{}_i \quad .$$

(Recall the implicit summation over the *dummy index* j from 1 to m.) This equation defines the $m \times n$ matrix $(A^j{}_i)$ for given A, $\{\hat{\mathbf{e}}_i\}$, and $\{\hat{\mathbf{e}}'_i\}$.

(ii) Consider an arbitrary vector $\mathbf{x} \in V_n$. It has components $\{x^i\}$ with respect to the basis $\{\hat{\mathbf{e}}_i\}$. The vector $|y\rangle = A|x\rangle$ lies in V_m, it has components $\{y^i\}$ with respect to the basis $\{\hat{\mathbf{e}}'_i\}$. How are $\{y^i\}$ related to $\{x^i\}$? The answer lies in

(II.3-2) $$|y\rangle = A|x\rangle = A|\mathrm{e}_i\rangle x^i = |\mathrm{e}'_j\rangle A^j{}_i x^i = |\mathrm{e}'_j\rangle y^j \quad ;$$

which implies:

(II.3-3) $$y^j = A^j{}_i x^i \quad \text{or} \quad \begin{pmatrix} y^1 \\ \vdots \\ y^m \end{pmatrix} = \begin{pmatrix} A^1{}_1 & \cdots & A^1{}_n \\ \cdots & \cdots & \cdots \\ \cdots & \cdots & \cdots \\ \cdots & \cdots & \cdots \\ A^m{}_1 & \cdots & A^m{}_n \end{pmatrix} \begin{pmatrix} x^1 \\ \vdots \\ x^n \end{pmatrix}$$

on account of the linear independence of $\{\hat{\mathbf{e}}'_j\}$. In Eq. (II.3-2), the third step follows from Eq. (II.3-1) (the rest are definitions). This result is given in detail to illustrate the clarity of the Dirac notation used in this particular way [note the ordering of the indices in Eq. (II.3-2)], and to contrast the two ways that $(A^j{}_i)$ appears in Eq. (II.3-1) and Eq. (II.3-3).

In most applications the two vector spaces are the same, i.e. $m = n$ and $V_n = V_m$, hence A is represented by a square matrix. For clarity in notation, we shall confine the following discussions to this case, although essentially all results hold also for the general case. It is obvious that if (A), (B) are the matrices corresponding to linear operators A, B respectively, then the matrix $\alpha(A) + \beta(B)$ is the corresponding one to the operator $\alpha A + \beta B$ where α, β are arbitrary numbers.

Theorem II.6: The algebra of linear operators on V_n and the algebra of matrices on C_n are isomorphic.

The choice of basis on a vector space is quite arbitrary. How does the change to a different basis affect the matrix representation of vectors and linear operators? Let $\{\hat{\mathbf{e}}_i; i = 1,\ldots,n\}$ and $\{\hat{\mathbf{u}}_j; j = 1,\ldots,n\}$ be two different bases of V_n, then

(II.3-4) $$|u_j\rangle = |\mathrm{e}_i\rangle S^i{}_j \qquad |\mathrm{e}_i\rangle = |u_j\rangle (S^{-1})^j{}_i$$

where (S) is a non-singular (i.e. invertible) matrix. Consider an arbitrary vector $\mathbf{x} \in V_n$. Let $\{x_{\mathrm{e}}{}^i\}$ and $\{x_{\mathrm{u}}{}^i\}$ be the components of $\mathbf{x}$ with respect to the two bases, respectively. Since $|x\rangle = |\mathrm{e}_i\rangle x_{\mathrm{e}}{}^i = |\mathrm{u}_i\rangle x_{\mathrm{u}}{}^i$, we can use Eq. (II.3-4) to derive:

(II.3-5) $$x_{\mathrm{e}}{}^i = S^i{}_j x_{\mathrm{u}}{}^j \qquad x_{\mathrm{u}}{}^j = (S^{-1})^j{}_i x_{\mathrm{e}}{}^i \quad .$$

Similarly, if $A|\mathrm{e}_i\rangle = |\mathrm{e}_l\rangle (A_{\mathrm{e}})^l{}_i$ and $A|\mathrm{u}_j\rangle = |\mathrm{u}_k\rangle (A_{\mathrm{u}})^k{}_j$, then Eq. (II.3-4) implies,

(II.3-6) $$(A_{\mathrm{e}}) = (S)(A_{\mathrm{u}})(S^{-1}) \qquad (A_{\mathrm{u}}) = (S^{-1})(A_{\mathrm{e}})(S) \quad .$$

We have suppressed the indices in the matrix equations in (II.3-6); it is extremely instructive for uninitiated readers to go through the proof of these equations to see how the indices almost automatically take care of themselves in the present notation.

Theorem II.7: A change of basis on a vector space causes the matrix representation of the linear operators to undergo a *similarity transformation* given by Eq. (II.3-6). Note, the transformation matrix S is *the same for all operators A*.

Are there any features of the matrix representation of a linear operator which are independent of the choice of basis, hence are characteristic of the operator itself?

It is well known that the trace $[\mathrm{Tr}(A) = A^i{}_i]$ and the determinant $[\det(A)]$ are invariant under similarity transformations. This fact leads to the following definition:

Definition II.14: The *trace of an operator A*, denoted by Tr A, and the *determinant of A*, denoted by det A, are defined to be the corresponding quantities for its matrix representation with respect to any given basis on the vector space. The results are independent of the choice of basis.

With this definition, one can then formulate the condition for an operator to be invertible, using known results from matrix algebra.

Theorem II.8: A linear operator on V_n is invertible if and only if $\det A \neq 0$.

II.4 Dual Space, Adjoint Operators

The set of all linear functionals f on a vector space V forms a vector space $\tilde{V}$ which is intimately related to V—provided proper definitions for addition and for multiplication by a number are given. The following notation (due to Dirac) will be very useful: a linear functional f assigns a (complex) number to each $\mathbf{x} \in V$, we denote that number by $\langle f|x\rangle$, i.e.

(II.4-1) $$\mathbf{x} \in V \xrightarrow{f} \langle f|x\rangle \in C_1 \quad .$$

By definition, $\langle f|\, \alpha_1 x_1 + \alpha_2 x_2\rangle = \langle f|x_1\rangle\alpha_1 + \langle f|x_2\rangle\alpha_2$. Hence a linear functional is fully defined once its action on a set of basis vectors is given. (In fact, $\langle f|x\rangle = \langle f|\mathrm{e}_i\rangle x^i$.)

Definition II.15: The *addition* of linear functionals f_1, f_2 and the *multiplication* of linear functionals by numbers α_1, α_2 are defined by:

(II.4-2) $$\langle \alpha_1 f_1 + \alpha_2 f_2|x\rangle = \alpha_1{}^*\langle f_1|x\rangle + \alpha_2{}^*\langle f_2|x\rangle \text{ for all } \mathbf{x} \in V \quad .$$

The use of the complex conjugates of $\alpha_{1,2}$ on the right-hand-side of this equation is not required for $\{f\}$ to form a vector space (prove!), but this definition makes the correspondence between linear functionals and scalar products simple (see next section).

The dual vector space $\tilde{V}$, consisting of $\{f\}$ with the operations defined above, can be related to the original vector space V in the following way. Given any basis $\{\hat{\mathbf{e}}_i, i = 1,\ldots,n\}$ of V, one can define a set of n linear functionals $\{\tilde{\mathbf{e}}_j \in \tilde{V}, j = 1,\ldots,n\}$ by

(II.4-3) $$\langle \tilde{\mathrm{e}}^j|\mathrm{e}_i\rangle = \delta^j{}_i \quad .$$

Theorem II.9: (i) The linear functionals $\tilde{\mathbf{e}}^j$, so defined, are linearly independent, and (ii) every linear functional on V can be written as a linear combination of $\{\tilde{\mathbf{e}}^j\}$. In other words, $\{\tilde{\mathbf{e}}^j, j = 1,\ldots,n\}$ form a basis of $\tilde{V}$.

It follows then: (i) $\tilde{V}$ has dimension n, and (ii) it is isomorphic to V. $\{\tilde{\mathbf{e}}^j\}$ is called the *dual basis* to $\{\hat{\mathbf{e}}_i\}$.

The natural correspondence between V and $\tilde{V}$ extends to the operators defined on these spaces. Every linear operator A on V *induces* a corresponding operator on $\tilde{V}$ in the following way: Let f be a linear functional (i.e. $f \in \tilde{V}$) and $\mathbf{x} \in V$ be any vector. One can show that the mapping $\mathbf{x} \to \langle f|Ax\rangle$ defines another linear functional on $\tilde{V}$. Call if f'. One can then prove that the mapping $f \to f'$ (which depends on A) is a linear transformation on $\tilde{V}$. It is usually denoted by $A^\dagger$.

Definition II.16: For every linear operator A on V, the *adjoint operator* $A^\dagger$ on $\tilde{V}$ is defined by the equation:

$$\langle A^\dagger f|x\rangle = \langle f|Ax\rangle \qquad \text{for all } \mathbf{x} \in V \quad . \tag{II.4-4}$$

It is not hard to establish the following useful results concerning the adjoint operator: Let A, B be operators on V; $A^\dagger$, $B^\dagger$ be their adjoints, and α be any complex number, then:

$$\begin{aligned} (A + B)^\dagger &= A^\dagger + B^\dagger \\ (AB)^\dagger &= B^\dagger A^\dagger \\ (\alpha A)^\dagger &= A^\dagger \alpha^* \end{aligned} \tag{II.4-5}$$

and

$$(A^\dagger)^\dagger = A \qquad \text{(prove!)} \quad .$$

II.5 Inner (Scalar) Product and Inner Product Space

The operations defined on vector spaces, so far, do not allow the consideration of geometrical concepts such as *distances* and *angles*. The key which leads to those extensions is the idea of the inner (or scalar) product.

Definition II.17: Let V be a vector space. An *inner* (*or scalar*) *product* on V is defined to be a scalar-valued function of ordered pair of vectors, denoted by (x, y) such that:

$$(x, y) = (y, x)^* \tag{II.5-1a}$$

$$(x, \alpha_1 y_1 + \alpha_2 y_2) = \alpha_1(x, y_1) + \alpha_2(x, y_2) \tag{II.5-1b}$$

$$(x, x) \geq 0 \qquad \text{for all } \mathbf{x} \in V\text{, and} \tag{II.5-1c}$$

$$(x, x) = 0 \qquad \text{if and only if } \mathbf{x} = 0 \quad .$$

A vector space endowed with an inner (scalar) product is called an *inner product space.*

Note that Eq. (II.5-1c) is meaningful only if (x, x) is real. This is guaranteed by condition (II.5-1a), with the complex conjugation on the right-hand-side.

Definition II.18: (i) the *length* (or *norm*) of a vector $\mathbf{x}$ in an inner product space V_n, is defined to be:

$$|x| = (x, x)^{1/2} \tag{II.5-2}$$

(ii) the cosine of the angle between two vectors $\mathbf{x}$, and $\mathbf{y}$ is defined to be:

$$\cos\theta = (x, y)/|x|\,|y| \quad . \tag{II.5-3}$$

One can show that this nomenclature makes sense, as most ordinary properties associated with length and angle follow readily from these general definitions, e.g. $-1 \leq \cos\theta \leq 1$, $|x + y| \leq |x| + |y|$, and $|x - y| \geq |x| - |y|$. (Prove!)

Inner product spaces have very interesting features because the scalar product provides a natural link between the vector space V and its dual space $\tilde{V}$.

Theorem II.10: (i) For fixed **x**, the scalar product (x, y) is a linear functional (with y as the independent variable) on V. Call this linear functional f_x. Then $f_x(y) \equiv \langle f_x | y \rangle = (x, y)$;

(ii) Given any linear functional f on an inner product space V, there is always a vector $\mathbf{x}_f \in$ V, such that $\langle f | y \rangle = (x_f, y)$ for all $\mathbf{y} \in$ V;

(iii) The one-to-one correspondence between $\mathbf{x} \in$ V and $f \in \tilde{V}$ established by (i) and (ii) is an isomorphism.

Therefore, we can, for all practical purposes, identify the two spaces (V and $\tilde{V}$) and write:

(II.5-4) $$\langle f_x | y \rangle = (x_f, y) \equiv \langle x | y \rangle$$

where both **x** and **y** are vectors in V. From now on, the scalar product will be denoted by angle brackets $\langle | \rangle$.

Definition II.19: (i) Two vectors **x**, **y** $\in$ V are said to be *orthogonal* if $\langle x | y \rangle = 0$; (ii) A set of vectors $\{\mathbf{x}_i, i = 1, 2, \ldots\}$ are said to be *orthonormal* if $\langle x^j | x_i \rangle = \delta^j{}_i$ for all i, j. (N.B. We shall adopt the convention of using opposing upper and lower indices for a set of vectors and their dual partners respectively. The advantage for this notation should become evident after the following discussion.)

A familiar set of orthonormal vectors in ordinary 3-dimensional Euclidean space is the basis vectors $\{\hat{\mathbf{e}}_x, \hat{\mathbf{e}}_y, \hat{\mathbf{e}}_z\}$. Vectors in an orthonormal set are necessarily linearly independent.

Theorem II.11: Any set of n orthonormal vectors $\{\hat{\mathbf{u}}_i\}$ in n-dimensional vector space V_n forms an *orthonormal basis*, which has the following properties:

(i) $$|x\rangle = |u_i\rangle x^i, \qquad \text{with } x^i = \langle u^i | x \rangle$$

(ii) $$\langle x | y \rangle = x_i^\dagger y^i = \langle x | e_i \rangle \langle e^i | y \rangle$$

(iii) $$|x|^2 = x_i^\dagger x^i = \sum_{i=1}^{n} |x^i|^2 \quad .$$

Here **x**, **y** $\in V_n$ are arbitrary vectors.

Theorem II.12: Let $E_i = |e_i\rangle\langle e^i|$ (no summation) be the mapping $|x\rangle \to E_i|x\rangle = |e_i\rangle\langle e^i|x\rangle = |e_i\rangle x^i$ (no summation). Then,

(i) E_i, $i = 1, 2, \ldots, n$, are linear operators on V;

(ii) E_i are *projection operators* (idempotents);

(iii) $\sum_{i=1}^{n} E_i = E$ is the identity operator.

The last result (iii) is often termed the *completeness relation.*

Let $\{\hat{\mathbf{e}}_i\}$ and $\{\hat{\mathbf{u}}_i\}$ be two orthonormal bases on V_n. The transformation between these bases is particularly simple in form.

Theorem II.13: If $|u_k\rangle = |e_i\rangle\, S^i{}_k$, and $S^{\dagger k}{}_j = (S^j{}_k)^*$ then:

(i) $S^{\dagger l}{}_i S^i{}_k = \delta^l{}_k$ (orthonormality of $\hat{u}_i$, $i = 1,\ldots,n$)

(ii) $S^i{}_k S^{\dagger k}{}_j = \delta^i{}_j$ (completeness of $\hat{u}_i$, $i = 1,\ldots,n$)

(iii) $|e_i\rangle = |u_k\rangle (S^\dagger)^k{}_i$ hence $(S^\dagger) = (S^{-1})$, i.e. S is a unitary matrix.

The orthonormality and completeness conditions for group representation matrices are used extensively throughout the book.

Given an arbitrary basis in an inner product space, $\{\hat{v}_i,\ i = 1,\ldots,n\}$, an orthonormal basis can always be constructed by the *Schmidt orthonormalization procedure*, i.e.

(i) choose $|u_1\rangle = |v_1\rangle/|v_1|$

(ii) with $\hat{u}_1,\ldots,\hat{u}_k$ chosen, let $|u'_{k+1}\rangle = |v_{k+1}\rangle - \sum_{i=1}^{k} |u_i\rangle\langle u^i|v_{k+1}\rangle$

then choose $|u_{k+1}\rangle = |u'_{k+1}\rangle/|u'_{k+1}|$. Repeat this process from $k = 1$ to $k = n - 1$.

At each stage, one can show that $|u'_{k+1}\rangle \neq 0$, hence the normalization in (ii) can be carried out. It is easy to prove that $\hat{u}_{k+1}$ (hence also $\hat{u}'_{k+1}$) is orthonormal to all $\hat{u}_i$, $i = 1,\ldots,k$.

II.6 Linear Transformations (Operators) on Inner Product Spaces

A useful lemma for studying properties of linear operators on inner product space is:

Lemma: A linear operator A on an inner product space V is equal to zero if and only if $\langle x|Ax\rangle = 0$ for all $\mathbf{x} \in$ V. (Prove!)

Recall that, in the case of general vector spaces, for each operator A on V, the *adjoint operator* $A^\dagger$ was defined *on the dual space* $\tilde{V}$. Since on inner product spaces, there is a natural isomorphism between $\tilde{V}$ and V, it is logical to "pull $A^\dagger$ back" to V.

Definition II.20: Given the operator A on V, its *adjoint* $A^\dagger$ *on* V is defined by the equation,

$$\langle x|A^\dagger y\rangle \equiv \langle Ax|y\rangle \qquad \text{for all } \mathbf{x}, \mathbf{y} \in V \quad .$$

This defining equation should be compared with the original (general) definition of $A^\dagger$ on $\tilde{V}$, Def. II.16. Because of the symmetry exhibited by these definitions and the general result $(A^\dagger)^\dagger = A$ [Eq. (II.4-5)], it is consistent to use the same symbol $A^\dagger$ for the adjoint to A on $\tilde{V}$ and on V. This can be seen from the following series of relations,

(II.6-1) $$\langle x|Ay\rangle = \langle Ay|x\rangle^* = \langle y|A^\dagger x\rangle^* = \langle A^\dagger x|y\rangle \quad .$$

These results suggest further notational improvements. Since

(II.6-2) $$\langle x|A|y\rangle \equiv \langle x|Ay\rangle = \langle A^\dagger x|y\rangle$$

we can interpret $A|y\rangle = |Ay\rangle$, as well as $\langle x|A = \langle A^\dagger x|$. Similarly, $A^\dagger|y\rangle = |A^\dagger y\rangle$ and $\langle x|A^\dagger = \langle Ax|$.

The correspondence between linear operators and $n \times n$ matrices is particularly simple with respect to an orthonormal basis. Specifically, if $\{\hat{e}_i\}$ is such a basis and $A|e_i\rangle = |e_j\rangle A^j{}_i$ then,

$$A^j{}_i = \langle e^j|A|e_i\rangle \quad \text{and} \qquad \text{(II.6-3)}$$
$$(A^\dagger)^k{}_l = \langle e^k|A^\dagger|e_l\rangle = \langle e^l|Ae_k\rangle^* = (A^l{}_k)^* \quad .$$

Thus the matrix corresponding to the adjoint operator $A^\dagger$ is precisely the *hermitian conjugate* of the matrix corresponding to A. For this reason, the adjoint operator $A^\dagger$ (on an inner product space) is often referred to as the *hermitian conjugate operator* to A.

Definition II.21: If $A = A^\dagger$ on V, A is said to be *hermitian* or self-adjoint.

Hermitian operators play a central role in the mathematical formulation of physics. In particular, in Quantum Mechanics, all physical observables are represented by hermitian operators. They are operator generalizations of real numbers.

Theorem II.14: A linear transformation A on an inner product space V is hermitian if and only if $\langle x|A|x\rangle$ is real for all $\mathbf{x} \in$ V.

Theorem II.15: If A, and B are hermitian operators then,

(i) $A + B$ is hermitian;

(ii) αA is hermitian if and only if α is real;

(iii) AB is hermitian if and only if $AB = BA$.

It is well known that every hermitian matrix can be diagonalized by a similarity transformation (i.e. change of basis). The diagonal matrix elements represent eigenvalues of the corresponding hermitian operator, and they are all real.

Another important class of operators are generalizations of numbers of unit modulus, i.e. $|\alpha|^2 = \alpha^*\alpha = \alpha\alpha^* = 1$.

Definition II.22: An operator U on inner product space is said to be *unitary* if $UU^\dagger = U^\dagger U = E$.

On finite dimensional space, either $UU^\dagger = E$ or $U^\dagger U = E$ implies the validity of the other, but in general both relations are required. The key property of unitary transformations is that they leave the scalar product invariant.

Theorem II.16: Let U be a unitary operator on V, and $\mathbf{x}, \mathbf{y} \in$ V, then:

(i) $\langle Ux|Uy\rangle = \langle x|y\rangle$ for all $\mathbf{x}, \mathbf{y}$;
(ii) $|Ux| = |x|$ for all $\mathbf{x}$.

Hence "lengths" of vectors and "angles" between vectors are left *invariant* when they undergo unitary transformations. This property makes unitary operators the natural mathematical entities to represent *symmetry transformations* in physics. This is particularly obvious in quantum mechanics where measurable transition probabilities are always given by the square of scalar products such as $|\langle x|y\rangle|^2$, and these are required to be invariant under symmetry transformations.

It is easy to see that an orthonormal basis remains to be orthonormal under a unitary transformation. We have seen previously (Theorem II.13) that the converse is also true: the transformation from one orthonormal basis to another is a unitary one.

So far we have always assumed that the "numbers" α, β,... which enter the definition of the vector spaces are complex numbers. Certain physical vector spaces, such as the 3-dimensional Euclidean space R_3, are defined over the *real number field* (as opposed to the complex). Most of the results summarized in this appendix remain valid in that case. A notable exception is the Lemma of Sec. II.6. (Find a counter example to the Lemma in R_3!) On real vector spaces, hermitian operators are represented by symmetric matrices, hence are themselves called *symmetric operators.* Similarly, unitary operators correspond to orthogonal matrices, and hence are called *orthogonal operators.*

APPENDIX III

GROUP ALGEBRA AND THE REDUCTION OF REGULAR REPRESENTATION

This appendix serves two purposes: (i) it gives a systematic introduction to the *group algebra* and the *regular representation*, to supplement the very brief treatment of Sec. 3.7; (ii) it provides the mathematical framework for the construction of irreducible representations of the symmetric groups studied in Chap. 5 and Appendix IV.

Given a finite group $G = \{g_i; i = 1, 2, \ldots, n_G\}$ and the group multiplication rule $g_i g_j = g_k$, we introduced the *regular representation* matrices Δ by $g_i g_j = g_m \Delta^m_{ij}$ (Sec. 3.7). The right-hand side was interpreted as a "formal sum", since the original definition of a group does not involve the operation of taking linear combinations. In order to explore the detailed structure of the regular representation, it is necessary to be more precise about what we do.

III.1 Group Algebra

Although in "pure" group theory one only deals with a single operation—the group multiplication—it is natural to introduce the idea of *linear combinations of group elements* in group representation theory because the representation operators $\{U(g)\}$ have such an algebraic structure. This can lead to powerful techniques for constructing irreducible representations.

Definition III.1: For a given finite group G, the *group algebra* $\tilde{G}$ is defined to consist of all formal linear combinations of g_i, $r = g_i r^i$, where $g_i \in G$ and $\{r^i\}$ are complex numbers. Linear combinations of elements of the algebra are formed according to the obvious rule: $\alpha r + \beta q = g_i(\alpha r^i + \beta q^i)$ where α, β are arbitrary complex numbers. In addition, multiplication of one element of the algebra (q) by another (r) is given by $rq = g_i g_j\, r^i q^j = g_k(\Delta^k_{ij} r^i q^j)$, where Δ^k_{ij} are determined by the group multiplication rule as indicated.

The group algebra so defined has the mathematical structure of a *ring*. With respect to the operation of taking linear combinations, a group algebra obviously constitutes a linear vector space. In order to make this aspect of its properties explicit, we sometimes adopt the Dirac vector notation for elements of the algebra: $|r\rangle \in \tilde{G}$. By definition, the original group elements $\{g_i\}$ form a basis on this vector space. It is possible to define an inner product on this vector space, $\langle r|q\rangle = r^*_i q^i$ for $r, q \in \tilde{G}$. With respect to this scalar product, the basis $\{g_i\}$ is by definition orthonormal. We shall not need to make use of this scalar product in what follows.

Let $G = \{g_i\}$, and $r \in \tilde{G}$; the element r induces a natural mapping on the group algebra space $\tilde{G}$ by the rule of group multiplication. This can be seen most clearly using the vector notation for elements of the algebra and interpreting the identity $rg_i = g_j g_i r^j = g_k r^j \Delta^k_{ji}$ [cf. Eq. (3.7-1)] as

(III.1-1) $$r|g_i\rangle = |g_k\rangle r^j \Delta^k_{ji} \quad .$$

In general, for any $q \in \tilde{G}$,

(III.1-2) $$r|q\rangle = r|g_i\rangle q^i = |g_k\rangle [r^j \Delta^k_{ji} q^i] \quad .$$

Therefore, every element of the group algebra r also plays the role of an *operator* on the vector space $\tilde{G}$.

The dual role played by the elements of the group algebra—as vectors *and* operators—is the key feature of the regular representation and is primarily responsible for its remarkable properties.

Definition III.2: A *representation of the group algebra* $\tilde{G}$ is a mapping from $\tilde{G}$ to a set of linear operators $\{U\}$ on a vector space V which preserves the group algebra structure (Def. III.1): if $q, r \in \tilde{G}$, and $U(q)$, $U(r)$ are their images, then $U(\alpha q + \beta r) = \alpha U(q) + \beta U(r)$, and $U(qr) = U(q)U(r)$. An *irreducible representation* of $\tilde{G}$ is one which does not have any non-trivial invariant subspace in V.

Because, by definition, elements of the group G form a basis in the group algebra $\tilde{G}$, it is straightforward to establish the following theorem.

Theorem III.1: (i) A representation of $\tilde{G}$ is also a representation of G, and *vice versa*; (ii) An irreducible representation of $\tilde{G}$ is also irreducible with respect to G, and *vice versa*.

The construction of irreducible representations of the group algebra is facilitated by the possibility of taking linear combinations of group elements to form the appropriate projection operators.

III.2 Left Ideals, Projection Operators

The vector space of the regular representation D^R is the group algebra space $\tilde{G}$ itself. We know that every inequivalent irreducible representation D^μ is contained in D^R n_μ times, where n_μ is the dimension of the μ-representation [Theorem 3.8]. Therefore, G can be decomposed into a direct sum of irreducible invariant subspaces L^μ_a where $a = 1, 2, \ldots, n_\mu$. It is, in principle, possible to find basis vectors of $\tilde{G}$ such that the first one lies in L^1_1 (always of dimension 1), the next n_2 lie in $L^2_1, \ldots$ etc. With respect to such a basis, the regular representation matrices appear in block-diagonal form as shown, where all unfilled blocks consist of zero elements:

$$\begin{pmatrix} 1 & & & & & & \\ & D^2 & & & & & \\ & & D^2 & & & & \\ & & & \ddots & & & \\ & & & & D^{n_c} & & \\ & & & & & \ddots & \\ & & & & & & D^{n_c} \\ & n_2 \text{ blocks} & & \cdots & n_c \text{ blocks} & & \end{pmatrix}$$

In the group algebra space $\tilde{G}$, the subspaces discussed above are invariant under left multiplication, i.e. L consists of those elements $\{r\}$ such that $p|r\rangle \equiv |pr\rangle \in \mathrm{L}$ for all $p \in \tilde{\mathrm{G}}$ provided $|r\rangle \in \mathrm{L}$. Hence, they are also called *left ideals.* Left ideals which do not contain smaller left ideals are said to be minimal. Clearly, minimal left ideals correspond to irreducible invariant subspaces. If one can identify the minimal left ideals of the group algebra, all the inequivalent irreducible representations can be easily found.

A powerful method to identify the minimal left ideals is to find the corresponding projection operators. In Chap. 4 we discussed irreducible projection operators in general. However, the definition there requires knowledge of the irreducible representation matrices [cf. Theorem 4.2], hence it is not useful in the construction of these representations. We shall identify characteristic properties of projection operators on the group algebra space $\tilde{G}$, which can guide us in the construction of such operators for specific groups, such as the symmetric group S_n as discussed in Chap. 5.

If we denote the projection operator onto the minimal left ideal L_a^μ by P_a^μ, then we anticipate the following:

(i) $\mathrm{P}_a^\mu |r\rangle \in \mathrm{L}_a^\mu$ for all $r \in \tilde{G}$, in short, $\mathrm{P}_a^\mu \tilde{G} \doteq \mathrm{L}_a^\mu$

(ii) if $|q\rangle \in \mathrm{L}_a^\mu$, then $\mathrm{P}_a^\mu |q\rangle = |q\rangle$; hence

(iii) $\mathrm{P}_a^\mu r = r\,\mathrm{P}_a^\mu$ for all $r \in \tilde{G}$; and

(iv) $\mathrm{P}_a^\mu \mathrm{P}_b^\nu = \delta^{\mu\nu}\delta_{ab}\mathrm{P}_a^\mu$.

The commutativity condition (iii) can be established by applying each side of the equation to an arbitrary element of the algebra $|s\rangle \in \tilde{G}$ with $|s\rangle$ written in its fully decomposed form $|s\rangle = \sum_{\nu,b} |s_b^\nu\rangle$, $s_b^\nu \in \mathrm{L}_b^\nu$, and comparing the results. The other properties follow from the definition of projection operators.

In the following, we shall also denote the direct sum of all left ideals L_a^μ with the same μ by L^μ (recall that there are n_μ such minimal left ideals), and the corresponding projection operator by P^μ. We have, therefore, $\tilde{G} = \sum_\mu \mathrm{L}^\mu$ and $\mathrm{L}^\mu = \sum_a \mathrm{L}_a^\mu$.

III.3 Idempotents

The dual role of the group algebra elements as vectors and operators permits a particularly elegant realization of the projection operators discussed above. Let e be the identity element of the group G. Since $e \in \tilde{\mathrm{G}}$, it has a unique decomposition $e = \sum_\mu e_\mu$ where $e_\mu \in \mathrm{L}^\mu$.

Theorem III.2: The projection operator P^μ is realized by *right-multiplication* with e_μ, i.e. if we define $\mathrm{P}^\mu |r\rangle \equiv |re_\mu\rangle$ for all $r \in \tilde{\mathrm{G}}$, then P^μ has all the properties discussed in the previous section.

Proof: (i) One must first show that $\mathrm{P}^\mu |r\rangle = |re_\mu\rangle$ defines a linear operator. This is left as an exercise.

(ii) Let $r \in \tilde{G}$, then

(III.3-1)
$$r = \sum_\mu r_\mu \qquad \text{where } r_\mu \in L^\mu \quad .$$

We also have

(III.3-2)
$$r = re = r \sum_\mu e_\mu = \sum_\mu re_\mu$$

where $re_\mu \in L^\mu$ because L^μ is a left ideal. Since the decomposition of r is unique, we conclude, $P^\mu r = re_\mu = r_\mu$. This coincides with the definition of the required projection operator.

(iii) Let us compare the two operators $P^\mu q$ and qP^μ for any $q \in \tilde{G}$ by observing their action on an arbitrary $|r\rangle \in \tilde{G}$,

$$P^\mu q|r\rangle \equiv P^\mu|qr\rangle \equiv |(qr)e_\mu\rangle = |qre_\mu\rangle$$

$$qP^\mu|r\rangle \equiv q|re_\mu\rangle \equiv |q(re_\mu)\rangle = |qre_\mu\rangle \quad .$$

Therefore $P^\mu q = qP^\mu$ for all $q \in \tilde{G}$.

(iv) Comparing the decomposition of e_ν, $e_\nu = 0 + \cdots + e_\nu + 0 + \cdots + 0$, with $e_\nu = e_\nu e = e_\nu \sum_\mu e_\mu = e_\nu e_1 + \cdots + e_\nu e_\nu + e_\nu e_{\nu+1} + \cdots$, and making use of the uniqueness of the decomposition again, we conclude $e_\nu e_\mu = \delta_{\nu\mu} e_\mu$. This condition implies that $P^\mu P^\nu = \delta^{\mu\nu} P^\mu$. QED

Definition III.3: Elements of the group algebra e_μ which satisfy the condition $e_\mu e_\nu = \delta_{\mu\nu} e_\mu$ are called *idempotents.* Those which satisfy the above relation up to an additional normalization constant are said to be *essentially idempotent.*

The above discussion only required use of the uniqueness of the decomposition into direct sums and the fact that L^μ are left ideals. Therefore, the theorem also applies to projection operators P^μ_a (for the minimal left ideals) defined as right-multiplication by the corresponding identity operators e^μ_a.

Definition III.4: An idempotent which generates a minimal left ideal is said to be a *primitive idempotent.*

How can we tell whether a given idempotent is primitive or not? The following theorem provides the answer.

Theorem III.3: An idempotent e_i is primitive if and only if $e_i r e_i = \lambda_r e_i$ for all $r \in \tilde{G}$, where λ_r is some number (which depends on r).

Proof: (i) Assume that e is a primitive idempotent. Then the left ideal $L = \{re;\ r \in \tilde{G}\}$ is a minimal ideal. Hence, the realization of the group algebra on L is irreducible. Now, define an operator R on $\tilde{G}$ by $R|q\rangle \equiv |qere\rangle$ for all $q \in \tilde{G}$. Clearly $R|q\rangle \in L$ and $Rs = sR$ for all $s \in \tilde{G}$. Therefore R represents a projection into L; and, according to Schur's Lemma, in the subspace L it must be proportional to the unit operator. We conclude that $ere = \lambda_r e$.

(ii) Assume $ere = \lambda_r e$ for all $r \in \tilde{G}$, and $e = e' + e''$ where e' and e'' are both idempotents. We shall prove this leads to a contradiction. First, we have, by definition, $ee' = e'$. Multiplying by e on the right, we get $ee'e = e'$, hence $e' = \lambda e$ by our assumption. Using the last result in the defining condition for an idempotent, we obtain $e' = e'e' = \lambda^2 ee = \lambda^2 e$. Therefore $\lambda^2 = \lambda$, which implies $\lambda = 0$ or $\lambda = 1$. If $\lambda = 0$, then $e = e''$; if $\lambda = 1$, then $e = e'$. In either case, e is not decomposable as assumed. QED

Finally, we need a criterion to distinguish among primitive idempotents those which generate inequivalent representations.

Theorem III.4: Two primitive idempotents e_1 and e_2 generate equivalent irreducible representations if and only if $e_1 r e_2 \neq 0$ for some $r \in \tilde{G}$.

Proof: Let L_1 and L_2 be the two minimal left ideals generated by e_1 and e_2, respectively.

(i) If $e_1 r e_2 = s \neq 0$ for some $r \in \tilde{G}$, then consider the linear transformation $q_1 \in L_1 \xrightarrow{S} q_2 = q_1 s \in L_2$. Clearly, for all $p \in \tilde{G}$, $Sp|q_1\rangle = S|pq_1\rangle = |(pq_1)s\rangle = |p(q_1 s)\rangle = p|q_1 s\rangle = pS|q_1\rangle$. Therefore, acting on L_1, $Sp = pS$ for all $p \in \tilde{G}$. According to Schur's Lemma, the two representations $D^1(\tilde{G})$ and $D^2(\tilde{G})$ (realized on L_1 and L_2 respectively) must be equivalent.

(ii) If the two representations are equivalent, then there exists a linear transformation S such that $SD^1(p) = D^2(p)S$ (or, as linear mappings from L_1 to L_2, $Sp = pS$) for all $p \in \tilde{G}$. Now, $|s\rangle \equiv S|e_1\rangle \in L_2$, and $S|e_1\rangle = S|e_1 e_1\rangle = Se_1|e_1\rangle = e_1 S|e_1\rangle = e_1|s\rangle = |e_1 s\rangle$. Therefore $s = e_1 s$. Since $s \in L_2$, we also have $s = se_2$. Combining the two, we obtain $e_1 s = se_2 = s$, hence $s = e_1 s e_2$. QED

Example: The Reduction of the Regular Representation of C_3.

This will turn out to be a long-winded way of deriving the irreducible representations of C_3. But it is useful to work through a concrete example to gain a firm grip on the general technique. Since $G = C_3$ is abelian, all the irreducible representations are one-dimensional, and each occurs in the regular representation just once. The three elements of the group are (e, a, a^{-1}) and the group multiplication table is given in Table 2.2 (with $b = a^{-1}$).

(i) The idempotent e_1 for the identity representation is, as always,

$$e_1 = \frac{1}{3}(e + a + a^{-1}) \quad .$$

It is straightforward to show that $ge_1 = e_1 g = e_1$ for any $g \in G$, $e_1 e_1 = e_1$, and hence $e_1 g e_1 = e_1$ for all $g \in G$. Thus if $r = g_i r^i \in \tilde{G}$, then $e_1 r e_1 = e_1 \sum_i r^i = \lambda_r e_1$.

(ii) Let $e_2 = xe + ya + za^{-1}$ be a second idempotent, then we must have $e_1 e_2 = e_1(x + y + z) = 0$, and $e_2 e_2 = e_2 = xe + ya + za^{-1} = (x^2 + 2yz)e + (2xy + z^2)a + (2zx + y^2)a^{-1}$. Therefore, (a) $x + y + z = 0$, (b) $x = x^2 + 2yz$, (c) $y = z^2 + 2xy$, and (d) $z = y^2 + 2zx$. Combining (a) and (b), we obtain $y^2 + z^2 + 4yz + y + z = 0$; whereas combining (d) and (c), we obtain $3(y - z)(y + z) + (y - z) = 0$.

Three solutions emerge:

(1) $x = 2/3 \quad y = z = -1/3$

(2) $x = 1/3 \quad y = (1/3)e^{i2\pi/3} \quad z = (1/3)e^{-i2\pi/3}$

(3) $x = 1/3 \quad y = (1/3)e^{-i2\pi/3} \quad z = (1/3)e^{i2\pi/3}$

Do all these solutions correspond to primitive idempotents? Let us first check on $e' = (2e - a - a^{-1})/3$: $e'e = ee' = e'$, $e'a = ae' = (-e + 2a - a^{-1})/3$, $e'a^{-1} = a^{-1}e' = (-e - a + 2a^{-1})/3$, $e'ee' = e'$, and $e'ae' = (-ee' + 2ae' - a^{-1}e')/3 = e'a$. The last result indicates that e' is not a primitive idempotent (cf. Theorem III.3).

Next, let us try

$$e_+ = 1/3[e + ae^{i2\pi/3} + a^{-1}e^{-i2\pi/3}] \qquad ee_+ = e_+e = e_+$$

$$ae_+ = e_+a = [ee^{-i2\pi/3} + a + a^{-1}e^{i2\pi/3}]/3 = e^{-i2\pi/3}e_+$$

$$e_+a^{-1} = a^{-1}e_+ = [ee^{i2\pi/3} + ae^{-i2\pi/3} + a^{-1}]/3 = e^{i2\pi/3}e_+$$

$$e_+ee_+ = e_+ \qquad e_+ae_+ = e^{-i2\pi/3}e_+e_+ = e^{-i2\pi/3}e_+$$

$$e_+a^{-1}e_+ = e^{i2\pi/3}e_+e_+ = e^{i2\pi/3}e_+$$

Thus e_+ is a primitive idempotent. Similarly, one can show that $e_- = (e + ae^{-i2\pi/3} + a^{-1}e^{i2\pi/3})/3$ is a primitive idempotent.

Do e_+ and e_- generate equivalent representations?

Applying Theorem III.4, we find: $e_+ee_- = e_+e_- = 0$, $e_+ae_- = e^{-i2\pi/3}e_+e_- = 0$, and $e_+a^{-1}e_- = e^{i2\pi/3}e_+e_- = 0$. Hence, e_+, e_- generate inequivalent representations. Now, let us evaluate the representations. The left ideal L_2 is spanned by e_+; hence $e|e_+\rangle = |e_+\rangle 1$, $a|e_+\rangle = |ae_+\rangle = |e_+\rangle e^{-i2\pi/3}$, and $a^{-1}|e_+\rangle = |a^{-1}e_+\rangle = |e_+\rangle e^{i2\pi/3}$. Thus, the representation elements corresponding to (e, a, a^{-1}) are $(1, e^{-i2\pi/3}, e^{i2\pi/3})$. Similarly, the left ideal L_3 spanned by e_- gives rise to the representation $(e, a, a^{-1}) \rightarrow (1, e^{i2\pi/3}, e^{-i2\pi/3})$. To summarize, we exhibit the results in Table III.1.

Table III.1 IRREDUCIBLE REPRESENTATIONS OF THE GROUP C_3

μ	e	a	a^{-1}
1	1	1	1
2	1	$e^{-i2\pi/3}$	$e^{i2\pi/3}$
3	1	$e^{i2\pi/3}$	$e^{-i2\pi/3}$

It is straightforward to verify that these representation elements satisfy the orthonormality and completeness relations [Theorems 3.5 and 3.6] as they should. We note in passing that the non-primitive idempotent e' encountered earlier is equal to $e_+ + e_-$. It is therefore indeed decomposable.

III.4 Complete Reduction of the Regular Representation

Let us summarize the situation: (i) the group algebra can be decomposed into left ideals L^μ with μ running over all inequivalent irreducible representations of the group; (ii) each L^μ is generated by right multiplication with an idempotent e which satisfies the conditions, $e_\mu e_\nu = \delta_{\mu\nu} e_\mu$, $\sum_\mu e_\mu = e$; (iii) each L^μ (and the corresponding e_μ) can be decomposed into n_μ minimal left ideals L^μ_a, $a = 1, \ldots, n_\mu$, with associated primitive idempotents e^μ_a which satisfy $e^\mu_a r e^\mu_b = \delta_{ab} \lambda_r e^\mu_a$ for all $r \in \tilde{G}$. Therefore, the problem of the complete reduction of the regular representation of a group G is reduced to that of identifying all the inequivalent primitive idempotents. In Chap. 5 and Appendix IV, this technique is applied to the symmetric group S_n to derive all the inequivalent irreducible representations.

In closing, we mention that the left ideals $L^\mu \left(= \sum_a L^\mu_a \right)$ which are associated with definite irreducible representations μ are, in fact, minimal two-sided ideals. A *two-sided ideal* T is a subspace of $\tilde{G}$ such that if $r \in T$ then $qrs \in T$ for all $q, s \in \tilde{G}$. A minimal two-sided ideal is one which does not contain smaller two-sided ideals. If T is a minimal two-sided ideal and it contains a minimal left ideal L^μ_a, then it contains all the other minimal left ideals corresponding to the same μ, and only these. This interesting property is a natural consequence of Theorem III.4 as can be seen from the following observation. If L^μ_a and L^μ_b correspond to equivalent irreducible representations then there exists an element of $Gs \neq 0$ such that $s = e^\mu_a s e^\mu_b$ (cf. part (ii) of the proof of Theorem III.4). Thus if $r \in L^\mu_a$ and L^μ_a is in T, then $rs = rse^\mu_b$ is both in L^μ_b and in T. It follows then that L^μ_b is in T. Conversely, if L^μ_a and L^ν_b are both in T, there exists an s such that $L^\mu_b s = L^\nu_b$ and they generate equivalent representations. (Show that if s does not exist, then T cannot be minimal.) We see, therefore, the complete reduction of the regular representation corresponds to decomposing $\tilde{G}$ first into minimal two-sided ideals L^μ, one for each inequivalent irreducible representation, and then reducing L^μ into minimal left ideals L^μ_a.

APPENDIX IV

SUPPLEMENTS TO THE THEORY OF SYMMETRIC GROUPS S_n

This appendix consists of a collection of lemmas which are needed to establish the central theorems of Chap. 5 on the representations of the symmetric group S_n.

Lemma IV.1: Let $\{h_\lambda\}$ and $\{v_\lambda\}$ be horizontal and vertical permutations of the Young tableaux θ_λ, and s_λ, a_λ, and e_λ the associated symmetrizer, anti-symmetrizer, and irreducible symmetrizer respectively. [cf. Chap. 5] Then the corresponding quantities for the Young tableau θ_λ^p are given by

$$h_\lambda^p = p h_\lambda p^{-1} \qquad v_\lambda^p = p v_\lambda p^{-1} \qquad s_\lambda^p = p s_\lambda p^{-1}$$
$$a_\lambda^p = p a_\lambda p^{-1} \qquad e_\lambda^p = p e_\lambda p^{-1} \quad .$$

Proof: Obvious by inspection of a typical example.

Because of this lemma, all algebraic relations which hold for operators of a normal tableau automatically hold for the corresponding operators of any tableau associated with the same Young diagram. Without any loss of generality we can, therefore, concentrate on the normal tableaux in most of the subsequent discussion.

Lemma IV.2: For any given θ_λ, the two sets $\{h_\lambda\}$ and $\{v_\lambda\}$ each form a subgroup of S_n, and the following identities hold:

(i)
$$h_\lambda s_\lambda = s_\lambda h_\lambda = s_\lambda$$
$$v_\lambda a_\lambda = a_\lambda v_\lambda = a_\lambda(-1)^{v_\lambda}$$
$$h_\lambda e_\lambda v_\lambda = e_\lambda(-1)^{v_\lambda}$$

for all h_λ, v_λ; and

(ii)
$$s_\lambda \cdot s_\lambda = \xi_\lambda s_\lambda$$
$$a_\lambda \cdot a_\lambda = \eta_\lambda a_\lambda$$

where ξ_λ and η_λ are integer numbers.

Proof: The fact that $\{h_\lambda\}$ forms a subgroup of S_n follows from the following argument: (a) the identity permutation is an element of the set; and (b) the inverse of any element is also a member of the set. The same argument applies to $\{v_\lambda\}$. All the identities listed under (i) and (ii) are then consequences of the rearrangement lemma for these subgroups.

Lemma IV.3: Given θ_λ, and $p \in S_n$, a necessary and sufficient condition for $p \neq h_\lambda v_\lambda$ is that there exist at least two numbers in one row of θ_λ which appear in the same column of θ_λ^p.

Proof: (a) If $p = h_\lambda v_\lambda$, we can always write it in the form $p = v_\lambda^{h_\lambda} h_\lambda$ where $v_\lambda^{h_\lambda} = h_\lambda v_\lambda h_\lambda^{-1}$. Correspondingly, we can write $\theta_\lambda^p = p\theta_\lambda = v_\lambda^{h_\lambda}\theta_\lambda^{h_\lambda}$. Thus, θ_λ^p can be obtained from θ_λ in two steps: first $\theta_\lambda \to \theta_\lambda^{h_\lambda}$ by h_λ, then $\theta_\lambda^{h_\lambda} \to \theta_\lambda^p$ by $v_\lambda^{h_\lambda}$. In neither of these steps is it possible to bring two numbers belonging to the same row into the same column. In other words, if there are two numbers with the stated property, then $p \neq h_\lambda v_\lambda$.
(b) To prove the converse to the above, we assume that there are no two numbers shared by a row of θ_λ and a column of θ_λ^p. We can obtain the tableau θ_λ^p from θ_λ by the following steps: Start with the numbers appearing in the first column of θ_λ^p. They must all belong to different rows of θ_λ, hence they can be brought to the first column by a horizontal permutation. Repeating this exercise for the other columns in turn, we obtain a tableau $\theta_\lambda^{h_\lambda}$ which differs from θ_λ^p only by the order of elements in individual columns. Therefore, $\theta_\lambda^{h_\lambda}$ can be transformed into θ_λ^p by a vertical permutation $v_\lambda^{h_\lambda}$. We conclude, therefore, $\theta_\lambda^p = v_\lambda^{h_\lambda}\theta_\lambda^{h_\lambda} = v_\lambda^{h_\lambda} h_\lambda \theta_\lambda = h_\lambda v_\lambda \theta_\lambda$, i.e. $p = h_\lambda v_\lambda$. Equivalently, if $p \neq h_\lambda v_\lambda$, then there must be at least one pair of numbers which appear in one row of θ_λ and one column of θ_λ^p. QED

Lemma IV.4: Given θ_λ and $p \in S_n$ which is *not* of the form $h_\lambda v_\lambda$, there exist two transpositions $\tilde{h}_\lambda$ and $\tilde{v}_\lambda$ such that $p = \tilde{h}_\lambda p \tilde{v}_\lambda$:

Proof: Since $p \neq h_\lambda v_\lambda$, by the preceding lemma, there exists a pair of numbers in a row of θ_λ which appear in the same column of θ_λ^p. Let t be the transposition of these two numbers. By definition, t is a member of the subgroup of horizontal permutations $\{h_\lambda\}$ as well as of the subgroup of vertical permutations $\{v_\lambda^p\}$. Denote this specific element by $t = \tilde{h}_\lambda = \tilde{v}_\lambda^p$. We can now define a vertical transposition associated with θ_λ, $\tilde{v}_\lambda = p^{-1}\tilde{v}_\lambda^p p = p^{-1}tp$, and verify the simple identity: $\tilde{h}_\lambda p \tilde{v}_\lambda = t\cdot p\cdot p^{-1}tp = p$. QED

Lemma IV.5: Given a Young tableau θ_λ, if an element r of the group algebra satisfies

$$h_\lambda r v_\lambda = (-1)^{v_\lambda} r \qquad \text{for all } h_\lambda \text{ and } v_\lambda$$

then r must be a multiple of the irreducible symmetrizer e_λ, i.e. $r = \xi e_\lambda$.

Proof: Let us write r as a linear combination of the group elements, $r = \sum_p \alpha_p p$. We shall show that (i) $\alpha_p = 0$ if p is not of the form $h_\lambda v_\lambda$; and (ii) α_p is proportional to $(-1)^{v_\lambda}$ if $p = h_\lambda v_\lambda$. To this end, substitute the expression for r in both sides of its defining equation,

$$\text{LHS} = h_\lambda r v_\lambda = \sum_q \alpha_q (h_\lambda q v_\lambda) = \sum_p (\alpha_{h_\lambda^{-1} p v_\lambda^{-1}}) p$$

$$\text{RHS} = \sum_p (-1)^{v_\lambda} \alpha_p p$$

and conclude $\alpha_{h_\lambda^{-1} p v_\lambda^{-1}} = (-1)^{v_\lambda}\alpha_p$ for all h_λ and v_λ. If $p \neq h_\lambda v_\lambda$, then $p = \tilde{h}_\lambda p \tilde{v}_\lambda$ where $\tilde{v}_\lambda$ is a transposition (Lemma IV.4), and

$$\alpha_{\tilde{h}_\lambda^{-1} p \tilde{v}_\lambda^{-1}} = \alpha_e = (-1)^{\tilde{v}_\lambda}\alpha_p = -\alpha_p \quad .$$

Therefore, $\alpha_p = 0$. On the other hand, if $p = h_\lambda v_\lambda$, then

$$\alpha_{h_\lambda^{-1} p v_\lambda^{-1}} = \alpha_e = (-1)^{v_\lambda}\alpha_p \quad .$$

Therefore, $\alpha_p = \xi(-1)^{v_\lambda}$ where $\xi = \alpha_e$ is a constant independent of p. We conclude that

$$r = \xi \sum_{h_\lambda, v_\lambda} (-1)^{v_\lambda} h_\lambda v_\lambda = \xi e_\lambda \quad .$$

QED

Lemma IV.6: Given two distinct Young diagrams labelled by λ and μ, assume $\lambda > \mu$. It follows that, for all $p, q \in S_n$,

(i) $$a^q_\mu s^p_\lambda = s^p_\lambda a^q_\mu = 0$$

(ii) $$e^q_\mu e^p_\lambda = 0 \quad .$$

Proof: (a) By arguments identical to those of Lemma IV.4, one can show that there exists at least one pair of numbers which appears simultaneously in one row of θ^p_λ and one column of θ^q_μ.
(b) Call the transposition of these two numbers t, then $t = \tilde{h}^p_\lambda = \tilde{v}^q_\mu$ and by Lemma IV.2

$$t\, s^p_\lambda = s^p_\lambda\, t = s^p_\lambda$$

and

$$t\, a^q_\mu = a^q_\mu\, t = -a^q_\mu \quad .$$

Therefore, we can deduce

$$s^p_\lambda a^q_\mu = (s^p_\lambda t)\, a^q_\mu = s^p_\lambda (t\, a^q_\mu) = -s^p_\lambda a^q_\mu = 0$$

and

$$a^q_\mu s^p_\lambda = -(a^q_\mu t)\, s^p_\lambda = -a^q_\mu (t\, s^p_\lambda) = -a^q_\mu s^p_\lambda = 0 \quad .$$

(c) Since $e^q_\mu e^p_\lambda = (s^q_\mu a^q_\mu)(s^p_\lambda a^p_\lambda) = s^q_\mu (a^q_\mu s^p_\lambda)\, a^p_\lambda$, it vanishes on account of the above. QED

The following lemma is needed in Sec. 5.5 in the proof of Theorem 5.13.

Lemma IV.7: The linear group transformations $\{D(g), g \in G_m\}$ on V^n_m given by Eq. (5.5-6) span the space of all symmetry-preserving linear transformations K.

Proof: $A \in K$ implies that

$$A^{\{i\}}{}_{\{j\}} = A^{\{i_p\}}{}_{\{j_p\}} \qquad \text{for all } p \in S_n.$$

$\{g \in G_m\}$ is a subset of K. A necessary and sufficient condition for $\{g \in G_m\}$ to span K is that the only linear functional on K which yields $L(g) = 0$ for all $g \in G_m$ is $L = 0$. We shall show that this is indeed satisfied. Let

$$L(A) = L^{\{j\}}{}_{\{i\}}\, A^{\{i\}}{}_{\{j\}}$$

where $L^{\{j\}}{}_{\{i\}}$ are components of L with respect to the dual basis to that which defines the components of A. Without loss of generality, we can take L to be symmetry-preserving. For, if it is not, we can show that

$$\tilde{L}^{\{j\}}{}_{\{i\}} = \sum_{p \in S_n} \frac{1}{n!} L^{\{j_p\}}{}_{\{i_p\}}$$

produces the same effect on all $A \in K$ and it is symmetry-preserving. Assume

$$L(g) = L^{ab\cdots c}_{rs\cdots t}\, g^r_a g^s_b \cdots g^t_c$$

for all $g \in G_m$. Consider the case $g = \bar{g} + \varepsilon\phi$ where $\bar{g}$ and ϕ are both invertible $m \times m$ matrices, and ε is an arbitrary infinitesimal parameter. Substituting this sum in the above equation, expanding in powers of ε, and making use of the symmetry of L, we obtain

$$\mathrm{L}^{ab\cdots c}_{rs\cdots t}\,\phi^r_a\,\bar{g}^s_b\cdots\bar{g}^t_c = 0$$

to first order in ε. Since $\{\phi\}$ is arbitrary, we must have:

$$\mathrm{L}^{ab\cdots c}_{rs\cdots t}\,\bar{g}^s_b\cdots\bar{g}^t_c = 0 \quad .$$

By repeated use of this argument, we arrive at the conclusion:

$$\mathrm{L}^{ab\cdots c}_{rs\cdots t} = 0$$

hence $\mathrm{L} \equiv 0$. QED

APPENDIX V

CLEBSCH–GORDAN COEFFICIENTS AND SPHERICAL HARMONICS

Numerical Tables of Clebsch-Gordan Coefficients $\langle JM(jj')mm'\rangle$

NOTE: A $\sqrt{\ }$ is to be understood over <u>every</u> coefficient; e.g., for $-8/15$ read $-\sqrt{8/15}$

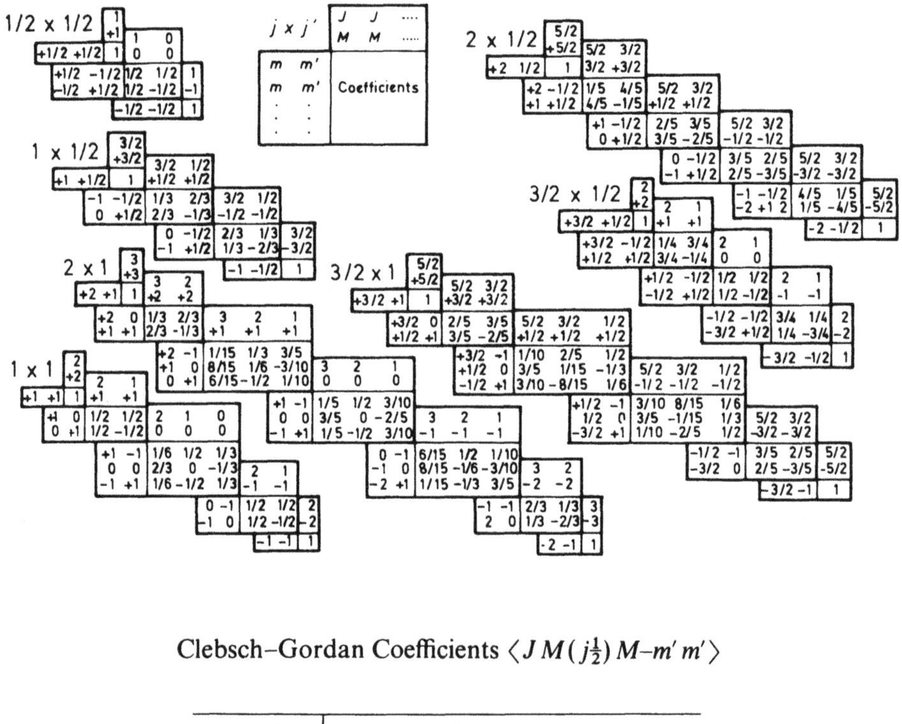

Clebsch–Gordan Coefficients $\langle JM(j\tfrac{1}{2})M\text{–}m'm'\rangle$

$j' = \frac{1}{2}$	$m' = \frac{1}{2}$	$m' = -\frac{1}{2}$
$J = j + \frac{1}{2}$	$\left(\dfrac{j + M + \frac{1}{2}}{2j+1}\right)^{\frac{1}{2}}$	$\left(\dfrac{j - M + \frac{1}{2}}{2j+1}\right)^{\frac{1}{2}}$
$J = j - \frac{1}{2}$	$-\left(\dfrac{j - M + \frac{1}{2}}{2j+1}\right)^{\frac{1}{2}}$	$\left(\dfrac{j + M + \frac{1}{2}}{2j+1}\right)^{\frac{1}{2}}$

Clebsch–Gordan Coefficients $\langle J\,M(j\,1)M{-}m'\,m'\rangle$

$j'=1$	$m'=1$	$m'=0$	$m'=-1$
$J=j+1$	$\left[\frac{(j+M)(j+M+1)}{(2j+1)(2j+2)}\right]^{\frac{1}{2}}$	$\left[\frac{(j-M+1)(j+M+1)}{(2j+1)(j+1)}\right]^{\frac{1}{2}}$	$\left[\frac{(j-M)(j-M+1)}{(2j+1)(2j+2)}\right]^{\frac{1}{2}}$
$J=j$	$-\left[\frac{(j+M)(j-M+1)}{2j(j+1)}\right]^{\frac{1}{2}}$	$\frac{M}{[j(j+1)]^{\frac{1}{2}}}$	$\left[\frac{(j-M)(j+M+1)}{2j(j+1)}\right]^{\frac{1}{2}}$
$J=j-1$	$\left[\frac{(j-M)(j-M+1)}{2j(2j+1)}\right]^{\frac{1}{2}}$	$-\left[\frac{(j-M)(j+M)}{j(2j+1)}\right]^{\frac{1}{2}}$	$\left[\frac{(j+M+1)(j+M)}{2j(2j+1)}\right]^{\frac{1}{2}}$

Spherical Harmonics $Y_{lm}(\hat{n})$

Definition:	Eq. (8.6-1)
Transformation Property:	Eq. (8.6-2)
Addition Theorem:	Eq. (8.6-3)
Decomposition of Product:	Eq. (8.6-4)
Recursion Formulas:	Eqs. (8.6-5), (8.6-6), (8.6-7)
Symmetry in *m*:	Eq. (8.6-8)
Symmetry in $\hat{\mathbf{n}}$ (Parity):	Eq. (11.2-6)
Connection to Legendre Functions:	Eq. (7.4-8)
Orthonormality:	Eq. (8.6-9)
Completeness:	Eqs. (8.3-14), (8.3-15), (8.6-10)

Table of the First Few Spherical Harmonics

$$Y_{00}=\frac{1}{\sqrt{4\pi}}\qquad Y_{10}=\sqrt{\frac{3}{4\pi}}\cos\theta\qquad Y_{20}=\sqrt{\frac{5}{16\pi}}(3\cos^2\theta-1)$$

$$Y_{30}=\sqrt{\frac{7}{16\pi}}(5\cos^3\theta-3\cos\theta)$$

$$Y_{11}=-\sqrt{\frac{3}{8\pi}}\sin\theta\,e^{i\varphi}\qquad Y_{21}=-\sqrt{\frac{15}{8\pi}}\sin\theta\cos\theta\,e^{i\varphi}$$

$$Y_{31}=-\sqrt{\frac{21}{64\pi}}\sin\theta(5\cos^2\theta-1)\,e^{i\varphi}$$

$$Y_{22}=\sqrt{\frac{15}{32\pi}}\sin^2\theta\,e^{2i\varphi}\qquad Y_{32}=\sqrt{\frac{105}{32\pi}}\sin^2\theta\cos\theta\,e^{2i\varphi}$$

$$Y_{33}=-\sqrt{\frac{35}{64\pi}}\sin^3\theta\,e^{3i\varphi}$$

APPENDIX VI

ROTATIONAL AND LORENTZ SPINORS

The intimate relationship between the group SO(3) of rotations and SU(2), as well as between the group SO(3, 1) of proper Lorentz transformations and SL(2), are of great importance both for the theory of group representations and for its physical applications. In each case, the correspondence is one-to-two and the 2×2 "special" matrices provide the lowest-dimensional non-degenerate representations of the orthogonal group. Basis vectors in the 2-dimensional representation space are commonly called *spinors*—to emphasize their distinction from the "vectors" (either 3- or 4-dimensional) which provide natural single-valued representations of the orthogonal group in question. One of the important features of the spinors is that all finite-dimensional representations of the group, such as the physically important vectors and tensors, can be obtained by taking direct products of spinors. For this reason, the spinor representations are called *fundamental representations* of the relevant groups. This Appendix supplements text material in chapters 8 and 10 on some basic properties of spinors.

We recall that the matrix A in the spinor representation corresponding to a proper Lorentz transformation Λ is defined by the equations (cf. Sec. 10.1.4):

(VI-1) $$x^\mu \longleftrightarrow X = \sigma_\mu x^\mu$$

(VI-2) $$x'^\mu = \Lambda^\mu{}_\nu x^\nu \longleftrightarrow X' = \mathrm{A}\, X\, \mathrm{A}^\dagger \quad .$$

The 2×2 matrices $\{X\}$ are hermitian; and $\{\mathrm{A}\}$ are "special", satisfying

(VI-3) $$\mathrm{A}^\alpha{}_{\alpha'}\, \mathrm{A}^\beta{}_{\beta'}\, \varepsilon^{\alpha'\beta'} = \varepsilon^{\alpha\beta}$$

or as a matrix equation,

(VI-3a) $$\mathrm{A}\, \varepsilon\, \mathrm{A}^{\mathrm{T}} = \varepsilon$$

where $\varepsilon^{\alpha\beta}$ is the two-dimensional unit anti-symmetric tensor. In matrix notation,

(VI-4) $$\varepsilon = \begin{pmatrix} 0 & 1 \\ -1 & 0 \end{pmatrix} \quad .$$

It satisfies the following conditions:

(VI-5) $$\varepsilon^\dagger = \varepsilon^{\mathrm{T}} = \varepsilon^{-1} = -\varepsilon = -\varepsilon^* \quad .$$

Note that the left-hand side of Eq. (VI-3) is equal to $\varepsilon^{\alpha\beta}\,\det\mathrm{A}$, and thus this equation is equivalent to $\det\mathrm{A} = 1$. Taking Eq. (VI-5) into account, Eq. (VI-3) can be cast in a variety of equivalent forms, such as

(VI-6a) $$\varepsilon^{T}A^{-1}\varepsilon = A^{T} = \varepsilon A^{-1}\varepsilon^{T}$$

(VI-6b) $$\varepsilon^{T}A^{\dagger}\varepsilon = (A^{*})^{-1} = \varepsilon A^{\dagger}\varepsilon^{T}$$

(VI-6c) $$\varepsilon^{T}A^{*}\varepsilon = (A^{\dagger})^{-1} = \varepsilon A^{*}\varepsilon^{T} \quad .$$

We shall use some of these results later.

If we confine our attention to 3-dimensional space, then X is, in addition to the above, traceless; and the A-matrices (corresponding to rotations) are unitary: i.e. they are SU(2) matrices.

Definition VI.1 (Lorentz Spinor): A *spinor* is a two component (complex) object $\{\xi^{\alpha}; \alpha = 1, 2\}$ which transform under Lorentz transformations as

(VI-7) $$\xi^{\alpha} \xrightarrow{\Lambda} \xi'^{\alpha} = A^{\alpha}{}_{\beta}\,\xi^{\beta}$$

where A(Λ) is the SL(2) matrix corresponding to Λ as specified by Eq. (VI-2).

When we restrict ourselves to the 3-dimensional space and to rotations, this definition gives the usual Pauli spinors; the components $\xi^{1,2}$ refer to those of "spin up" and "spin down" states (denoted in Chap. 7 by $|\pm\rangle$). We shall now establish the connection to the representation theory of Chaps. 7 and 10 by deriving the generators of rotations and Lorentz boosts in the spinor representation.

Consider an infinitesimal rotation around, say, the z-axis; then

(VI-8) $$x'^{0} = x^{0} \qquad x'^{3} = x^{3} \qquad x'^{1} = x^{1} - \delta\theta\, x^{2} \qquad x'^{2} = x^{2} + \delta\theta\, x^{1} \quad .$$

Define the generator of this rotation in the spinor representation, called J_3, by the usual formula

(VI-9) $$A = E - i\,\delta\theta\, J_3 \quad .$$

We obtain, on the one hand,

$$X' = \sigma_{\mu}x'^{\mu} = \sigma_{\mu}x^{\mu} + \delta\theta(-\sigma_1 x^2 + \sigma_2 x^1)$$

and, on the other hand,

$$X' = A X A^{\dagger} = X - i\,\delta\theta(J_3 X - X J_3{}^{\dagger}) \quad .$$

It follows that

(VI-10) $$J_3 X - X J_3{}^{\dagger} = i(-\sigma_1 x^2 + \sigma_2 x^1) \quad .$$

Since this equation holds for any vector $\{x^{\mu}\}$, we conclude that

(VI-11)
$$\begin{aligned} J_3 - J_3{}^{\dagger} &= 0 \\ J_3\sigma_3 - \sigma_3 J_3{}^{\dagger} &= 0 \\ J_3\sigma_1 - \sigma_1 J_3{}^{\dagger} &= i\sigma_2 \\ J_3\sigma_2 - \sigma_2 J_3{}^{\dagger} &= -i\sigma_1 \quad . \end{aligned}$$

Hence J_3 is a hermitian 2×2 matrix (first equation) which satisfies the usual SU(2) Lie algebra with $\sigma_1/2$ and $\sigma_2/2$ (last two equations). The unique solution to

Eq. (VI-11) is, expectedly,[1]

$$J_3 = \frac{1}{2}\sigma_3 = \frac{1}{2}\begin{pmatrix} 1 & 0 \\ 0 & -1 \end{pmatrix} \quad . \tag{VI-12}$$

By an identical argument, the other two generators for rotations, J_1 and J_2, must be equated to $\sigma_1/2$ and $\sigma_2/2$ respectively.

We now turn to an infinitesimal Lorentz boost along the z-axis. By definition, we have

$$x'^0 = x^0 + \delta\xi\, x^3 \qquad x'^1 = x^1 \qquad x'^2 = x^2 \qquad x'^3 = x^3 + \delta\xi\, x^0 \tag{VI-13}$$

and

$$\mathrm{A} = E - i\,\mathrm{d}\xi\, K_3 \quad . \tag{VI-14}$$

Comparing two equivalent expressions for X', as is done in the derivation of J_3 above, we obtain

$$\begin{aligned} X' &= \sigma_\mu x'^\mu = X + \delta\xi\,(E x^3 + \sigma_3 x^0) \\ &= \mathrm{A}\, X\, \mathrm{A}^\dagger = X - i\,\mathrm{d}\xi\,(K_3 X - X K_3{}^\dagger) \end{aligned}$$

hence,

$$K_3 X - X K_3{}^\dagger = i(E x^3 + \sigma_3 x^0) \quad .$$

Identifying coefficients of x^μ, we conclude that K_3 must satisfy the following conditions:

$$\begin{aligned} & K_3 - K_3{}^\dagger = i\sigma_3 \\ & K_3\sigma_1 - \sigma_1 K_3{}^\dagger = 0 = K_3\sigma_2 - \sigma_2 K_3{}^\dagger \\ & K_3\sigma_3 - \sigma_3 K_3{}^\dagger = iE \quad . \end{aligned} \tag{VI-15}$$

The unique solution to this set of equations is (cf. footnote 1):

$$K_3 = \frac{i}{2}\sigma_3 \quad . \tag{VI-16}$$

Again, identical arguments lead to the conclusion that $K_1 = i\sigma_1/2$ and $K_2 = i\sigma_2/2$.

To identify this representation with those described in Sec. 10.3.2, we note that

$$\begin{aligned} M_l &= (J_l + iK_l)/2 = 0 \\ N_l &= (J_l - iK_l)/2 = \sigma_l/2 \quad . \end{aligned} \qquad (l = 1, 2, 3) \tag{VI-17}$$

Hence, $\{\mathrm{A}\}$ correspond to the $(u, v) = (0, 1/2)$ representation of the Lorentz group as described in Sec. 10.3.2.

Theorem VI.1 (Spinor Representation of SL(2) and $\tilde{L}_+$): The spinors $\{\xi\}$, transforming by the formula (VI-7), provides a fundamental irreducible represen-

[1] Strictly speaking, both Eqs. (VI-11) and (VI-15) allow the generator to contain a real multiple of the identity matrix. But the condition detA = 1 on A requires the generators to be traceless. Hence the additional term is excluded.

tation of the Lorentz group. It corresponds to the irreducible representation labelled by (0, 1/2) in Sec. 10.3.2.

Scalars, or invariants, can be formed from spinors. Indeed, if $\varepsilon_{\alpha\beta}$ is the covariant unit anti-symmetric tensor defined by $\varepsilon^{\alpha\beta}\varepsilon_{\beta\gamma} = \delta^{\alpha}_{\gamma}$, then

(VI-18) $$\xi \cdot \eta \equiv \xi^{\alpha} \eta^{\beta} \varepsilon_{\alpha\beta} = \xi^2 \eta^1 - \xi^1 \eta^2$$

is a *Lorentz invariant* (or a *Lorentz scalar*). This is an immediate consequence of Eqs. (VI-3) and (VI-4). The result should be familiar when we restrict our attention to rotations—from Sec. 7.7, we know that, for two spin-1/2 systems, the anti-symmetric combination corresponding to (VI-18), $|+\ -\rangle - |-\ +\rangle$ [cf. Eq. (7.7-3)], is *rotationally invariant*. Note that: (i) the right-hand side of Eq. (VI-18) is the determinant of the 2×2 matrix formed with the components of ξ, η as rows; (ii) the anti-symmetric tensor $\varepsilon_{\alpha\beta}$ plays a role similar to a metric tensor, i.e. it defines an invariant; (iii) the invariant so formed is, however, *indefinite* and it is *anti-symmetric* under the interchange of ξ and η, i.e. $\xi \cdot \eta = -\eta \cdot \xi$; (iv) $\xi \cdot \xi = 0$ for all ξ; and (v) as a matrix, $\varepsilon_{\alpha\beta}$ is the inverse of $\varepsilon^{\alpha\beta}$ which, according to (VI-5) is the same as ε^{T}, or $-\varepsilon$.

As in the case of 4-vectors (Definition 10.7), it is convenient to introduce *covariant components* ξ_α of the spinor ξ

(VI-19a) $$\xi_\alpha \equiv \varepsilon_{\alpha\beta} \xi^\beta \qquad (\text{i.e. } \xi_2 = \xi^1, \xi_1 = -\xi^2)$$

in conjunction with the original *contravariant components* ξ^α. The inverse of Eq. (VI-19a) is

(VI-19b) $$\xi^\alpha = \varepsilon^{\alpha\beta} \xi_\beta \quad .$$

The Lorentz invariant product, Eq. (VI-18), is then

(VI-20) $$\xi \cdot \eta = \xi^\alpha \eta_\alpha = -\xi_\beta \eta^\beta = -\eta \cdot \xi \quad .$$

Definition VI.2 (Scalar Product · and Contraction of Spinors): The Lorentz invariant defined by Eq. (VI-18) is called the *scalar Product* of the two spinors. The formula, Eq. (VI-20), which expresses the scalar product as summation over a pair of contravariant and covariant indices is said to be a *contraction* of the two conjugate spinors.

Theorem VI.2 (Transformation Formula for Covariant Spinors): Under Lorentz transformations, the covariant components of ξ transform as

(VI-21) $$\xi_\alpha \longrightarrow \xi'_\alpha = \xi_\beta (\mathrm{A}^{-1})^\beta{}_\alpha$$

Proof: Using Eqs. (VI-6abc), and $(\varepsilon_{\alpha\beta}) = (\varepsilon^{\alpha\beta})^{\mathrm{T}}$, one can establish that

$$\begin{aligned} \xi'_\alpha = \varepsilon_{\alpha\beta} \xi'^\beta &= \varepsilon_{\alpha\lambda} \mathrm{A}^\lambda{}_\sigma \xi^\sigma = \varepsilon_{\alpha\lambda} \mathrm{A}^\lambda{}_\sigma \varepsilon^{\sigma\beta} \xi_\beta \\ &= \xi_\beta (\mathrm{A}^{-1})^\beta{}_\alpha \quad . \end{aligned}$$

QED

Given the SL(2) matrices (A) as described above, the set of conjugate matrices $\{\mathrm{A}^*\}$ form a representation of the same group. This can easily be verified:

(i) Since $E^* = E$, the identity element exists;
(ii) Since $(\mathrm{A}^{-1})^* = (\mathrm{A}^*)^{-1}$, the inverse for every A^* exists;

(iii) If $A_1 A_2 = A_3$ then, taking the complex conjugation on both sides, it follows that $A_1^* A_2^* = A_3^*$.

Hence we have a homomorphism. In fact, the mapping from the SL(2) group matrices $\{A\}$ to the complex conjugate matrices $\{A^*\}$ is an isomorphism. It is also worth noting that

$$\det A^* = (\det A)^* = 1$$

hence the group $\{A^*\}$ is SL(2), as is $\{A\}$ itself.

If we confine ourselves to the subset of SU(2) matrices (rotations), then each of the matrices $\{A^*\}$ is related to the corresponding one in $\{A\}$ by a similarity transformation:

(VI-22) $$A = \varepsilon A^* \varepsilon^{-1} \quad .$$

This result is a particular case of Eq. (7.4-5). It can also be derived from the observation that $A = \exp(-i\theta^k\sigma_k/2)$ and $\varepsilon\sigma_k\varepsilon^{-1} = -\sigma_k^*$. Thus the two representations are equivalent; there is no need to distinguish SU(2) spinors transforming according to $\{A\}$ from those according to $\{A^*\}$. That is why there was no reason to introduce the covariant spinors and to call attention to the $\{A^*\}$ matrix representation in Chap. 8.

However, the situation with the full SL(2) group is different. If we consider the SL(2) matrices representing Lorentz boosts, $A = \exp(\xi^k\sigma_k/2)$, it is easy to see that

(VI-23) $$\varepsilon A^* \varepsilon^{-1} = A^{-1}$$

in contrast to Eq. (VI-22). Therefore, the irreducible representation provided by the matrices $\{A^*\}$, or equivalently the matrices $\{\varepsilon A^* \varepsilon^{-1}\}$, is distinct from and *inequivalent* to $\{A\}$. We see that the generators of Lorentz transformations in the new representation $\{\varepsilon A^* \varepsilon^{-1}\}$ are:

(VI-24a) $$J_i = \sigma_i/2 \qquad K_i = -i\sigma_i/2$$

or equivalently,

(VI-24b) $$M_i = \sigma_i/2 \qquad N_i = 0 \quad .$$

Hence, this is the $(u, v) = (1/2, 0)$ representation of $\tilde{L}_+$ described in Sec. 10.3.2.

Theorem VI.3 (Conjugate Spinor Representation of SL(2) and $\tilde{L}_+$): The mapping

$$A \in SL(2) \longrightarrow \varepsilon A^* \varepsilon^{-1}$$

defines a second fundamental representation of SL(2). If the matrix A corresponds to a Lorentz transformation according to (VI-2), then this representation is the same as that labelled by $(1/2, 0)$ in Sec. 10.3.2.

In view of the above result, it is useful to introduce a second type of spinor which transforms according to the new (conjugate) representation.

Definition VI.3 (Spinor with Dotted Index): A *spinor with covariant dotted index* is a two-component complex quantity $(\xi_{\dot{\alpha}};\, \dot{\alpha} = 1, 2\}$ which transforms under Lorentz transformations as

(VI-25) $$\xi_{\dot\alpha} \xrightarrow{\Lambda} \xi'_{\dot\alpha} = A^{*}{}_{\dot\alpha}{}^{\dot\beta}\,\xi_{\dot\beta} = \xi_{\dot\beta}\,A^{\dagger\dot\beta}{}_{\dot\alpha}$$

where A(Λ) is determined from Eq. (VI-2) as before. (The placement of the various indices conforms to our convention explained in Appendix I.) The *contravariant dotted components* of the same spinor are given by

(VI-26a) $$\xi^{\dot\alpha} = \xi_{\dot\beta}\,\varepsilon^{\dot\beta\dot\alpha} \qquad (\text{i.e. } \xi^{\dot 1} = -\xi_{\dot 2},\ \xi^{\dot 2} = \xi_{\dot 1}) \quad .$$

The inverse of this equation is

(VI-26b) $$\xi_{\dot\alpha} = \xi^{\dot\beta}\,\varepsilon_{\dot\beta\dot\alpha} \quad .$$

Theorem VI.4 (Transformation Formula for Contravariant Components of Dotted Spinors): The contravariant components of dotted spinors transform as

(VI-27) $$\xi'^{\dot\alpha} = (A^{\dagger})^{-1\dot\alpha}{}_{\dot\beta}\,\xi^{\dot\beta}$$

under SL(2) and Lorentz transformations.

Proof: We have

$$\begin{aligned}\xi'^{\dot\alpha} &= \xi_{\dot\beta}'\,\varepsilon^{\dot\beta\dot\alpha} = \xi_{\dot\sigma}(A^{\dagger}\,\varepsilon)^{\dot\sigma\dot\alpha} = \xi^{\dot\beta}\,(\varepsilon^{T}A^{\dagger}\varepsilon)_{\dot\beta}{}^{\dot\alpha}\\ &= (\varepsilon^{T}A^{*}\varepsilon)^{\dot\alpha}{}_{\dot\beta}\,\xi^{\dot\beta} = (A^{\dagger})^{-1\dot\alpha}{}_{\dot\beta}\,\xi^{\dot\beta}\end{aligned}$$

where the first equality follows from Eq. (VI-26), the second from Eq. (VI-25), the third from the inverse of Eq. (VI-26), the fourth from transposing [cf. Appendix I.3 for notation], and the fifth from Eq. (VI-6c). QED

It follows from Eqs. (VI-25) and (VI-27) that the *contraction*

(VI-28) $$\dot\xi\cdot\dot\eta \equiv \xi_{\dot\alpha}\eta^{\dot\alpha} = -\xi^{\dot\alpha}\eta_{\dot\alpha} \equiv -\dot\eta\cdot\dot\xi$$

is also a Lorentz scalar, just as in the case of undotted spinors. Since for rotations $\varepsilon A^{*}\varepsilon^{T} = A$ [Eq. (VI-22)], it follows from Eq. (VI-27) that $\xi^{\dot\alpha}$ and ξ^{α} transform in exactly the same way under 3-dimensional rotations. Under Lorentz boosts, however, $\xi^{\dot\alpha}$ is transformed by the matrix $\exp(-\zeta^{k}\sigma_{k}/2)$ whereas ξ^{α} is transformed by the matrix $\exp(\zeta^{k}\sigma_{k}/2)$.

Spinors with undotted and with dotted indices do not mix under proper Lorentz transformations; they form separate invariant spaces (labelled by (0, 1/2) and (1/2, 0) respectively) independent of each other. We know, however, that these spaces are not separately invariant under the spatial inversion (Sec. 11.3); only the direct sum (0, 1/2) ⊕ (1/2, 0) is. We can ask: How do contravariant and covariant spinors with undotted and dotted indices transform under spatial inversion I_s? Since I_s commutes with rotations and reverses the direction of Lorentz boosts, the discussions of the last paragraph suggest that

(VI-29) $$I_s\,\xi^{\alpha} \sim \eta^{\dot\alpha} \qquad I_s\,\eta^{\dot\alpha} \sim \xi^{\alpha}$$

where ~ means "transform under proper Lorentz transformations as". This is of course expected in view of the general result $(u, v) \xleftrightarrow{I_s} (v, u)$ obtained in Sec. II.3. Assuming $I_s^2 = 1$ and adopting the convention on phase factors discussed there, we are led to the result

(VI-30) $$I_s \begin{pmatrix} \xi^{\alpha} \\ \eta^{\dot{\beta}} \end{pmatrix} = \begin{pmatrix} \eta^{\dot{\alpha}} \\ \xi^{\beta} \end{pmatrix} \quad .$$

Since spinors transform as the $j = 1/2$ representation under rotations, it is possible to consider an alternative to Eq. (VI-30). Instead of demanding $I_s{}^2 = 1$, one can also have $I_s{}^2 = -1$ since $R(2\pi) = -1$. With this choice, and utilizing the freedom to define the relative phase between ξ^{α} and $\eta^{\dot{\alpha}}$, we obtain

(VI-31) $$I_s \begin{pmatrix} \xi^{\alpha} \\ \eta_{\dot{\beta}} \end{pmatrix} = i \begin{pmatrix} \eta^{\dot{\alpha}} \\ \xi^{\beta} \end{pmatrix} \quad .$$

Which one of these [i.e. Eq. (VI-30) or Eq. (VI-31)], if any, is realized in nature depends on the physical system in question. Specifically, it depends on a proper consideration of the interplay between particle—anti-particle symmetry (charge conjugation) and space inversion. The subject matter goes beyond the scope of this book. Interested readers are referred to [Berestetskii] for a systematic treatment of this topic. The four component spinors described above are just the standard *Dirac Spinors.*

The covariant components of spinors transform under spatial inversion in a predictable way:

(VI-32) $$I_s \begin{pmatrix} \xi_{\alpha} \\ \eta_{\dot{\beta}} \end{pmatrix} = I_s \begin{pmatrix} \xi^{\alpha'} & \varepsilon_{\alpha'\alpha} \\ \eta^{\dot{\beta}'} & \varepsilon_{\dot{\beta}'\dot{\beta}} \end{pmatrix} = \lambda \begin{pmatrix} \eta^{\dot{\alpha}'} & \varepsilon_{\dot{\alpha}'\dot{\alpha}} \\ \xi^{\beta'} & \varepsilon_{\beta'\beta} \end{pmatrix} = \lambda \begin{pmatrix} \eta_{\dot{\alpha}} \\ \xi_{\beta} \end{pmatrix}$$

where $\lambda = 1$ or i depending on whether Eq. (VI-30) or (VI-31) applies.

We mentioned earlier that all finite dimensional representations of the Lorentz group can be obtained from direct products of the two "fundamental representations" (0, 1/2), (1/2, 0) which correspond to the spinors ξ^{α} and $\xi^{\dot{\alpha}}$ respectively. (Whether we use the contravariant or covariant components is irrelevant—they are obtained from each other by the transfer matrix ε.) We consider a few examples to illustrate the point. To begin with, the scalar representation (0, 0) can be obtained by forming the invariants $S_1 = \xi^{\alpha}\eta_{\alpha} = -\xi_{\alpha}\eta^{\alpha}$ and $S_2 = \xi^{\dot{\alpha}}\eta_{\dot{\alpha}} = -\xi_{\dot{\alpha}}\eta^{\dot{\alpha}}$, as discussed earlier in this Appendix. These quantities do not, however, have definite transformation properties under space inversion. In order to construct irreducible quantities under I_s, we must have,

(VI-33) $$S_{\pm} = S_1 \pm S_2 = \xi^{\alpha}\eta_{\alpha} \pm \eta_{\dot{\alpha}}\xi^{\dot{\alpha}}$$

where ξ and η transform into each other according to Eqs. (VI-29)–(VI-31). Depending on whether Eq. (VI-30) or Eq. (VI-31) applies, we obtain

(VI-34) $$I_s S_{\pm} = \pm S_{\pm} \quad \text{or} \quad \mp S_{\pm}$$

respectively.

Next consider the mixed spinor consisting of the product

(VI-35) $$\zeta^{\alpha}{}_{\dot{\beta}} = \xi^{\alpha}\eta_{\dot{\beta}} \quad .$$

Under a proper Lorentz transformation, we have according to Eqs. (VI-7) and

(VI-25):

$$\zeta^{\alpha}{}_{\dot\beta} \longrightarrow \zeta'^{\alpha}{}_{\dot\beta} = \mathrm{A}^{\alpha}{}_{\alpha'}\,\xi^{\alpha'}\,\eta_{\dot\beta'}\,\mathrm{A}^{\dagger\dot\beta'}{}_{\dot\beta}$$

or, suppressing implicit matrix indices,

(VI-36) $$\zeta \longrightarrow \zeta' = \mathrm{A}\,\zeta\,\mathrm{A}^{\dagger} \quad .$$

We see that components of ζ transform just like elements of the coordinate matrix X, Eq. (VI-1), corresponding to the 4-vector x^{μ}. Since the mixed spinors ζ, with one dotted and one undotted index each, transform manifestly as the $(1/2, 1/2)$ representation of the proper Lorentz group, the above correspondence with 4-vectors explicitly demonstrates that the latter transform as $(1/2, 1/2)$ as well. [cf. Sec. 10.3.2]

Under spatial inversion, we apply, say Eq. (VI-31) as follows:

(VI-37) $$I_s\zeta^{\alpha}{}_{\dot\beta} = -\eta^{\dot\alpha}\,\xi_{\beta} = -\varepsilon_{\beta\beta'}\,\xi^{\beta'}\,\eta_{\dot\alpha'}\,\varepsilon^{\dot\alpha'\dot\alpha} = (\varepsilon\zeta^{\mathrm{T}}\varepsilon^{\mathrm{T}})^{\dot\alpha}{}_{\beta} \quad .$$

Explicitly, we have

(VI-38) $$\begin{aligned} I_s\zeta^{1}{}_{\dot 1} &= \zeta^{2}{}_{\dot 2} \qquad & I_s\zeta^{2}{}_{\dot 2} &= \zeta^{1}{}_{\dot 1} \\ I_s\zeta^{1}{}_{\dot 2} &= -\zeta^{1}{}_{\dot 2} \qquad & I_s\zeta^{2}{}_{\dot 1} &= -\xi^{2}{}_{\dot 1} \quad . \end{aligned}$$

This is perfectly consistent with the behavior of the usual 4-vectors $(x^0, \mathbf{x}) \to (x^0, -\mathbf{x})$ as

$$\zeta \sim \begin{pmatrix} x^0 + x^3 & x^1 - ix^2 \\ x^1 + ix^2 & x^0 - x^3 \end{pmatrix}.$$

If our basic spinors behave under I_s according to Eq. (VI-30), instead, then the right-hand sides of Eqs. (VI-37) and (VI-38) change sign. We obtain an *axial-vector*, which behaves the same way as the coordinate vector under $\tilde{\mathrm{L}}_+$ but opposite to the latter under I_s.

We now consider *bi-spinors* consisting of the symmetric products

(VI-39) $$f^{\alpha\beta} = \xi^{\alpha}\xi^{\beta}, \qquad g_{\dot\alpha\dot\beta} = \eta_{\dot\alpha}\eta_{\dot\beta}.$$

Under proper Lorentz transformations, the three independent components of f and the three components of g transform separately as the $(0,1)$ and $(1,0)$ representations of $\tilde{\mathrm{L}}_+$. Under spatial inversions they transform into each other. In Sec. 10.3.2 we argued that a second rank anti-symmetric tensor (such as the electromagnetic field tensor $F^{\mu\nu}$) also transforms as the $(0,1) \oplus (1,0)$ representation of $\tilde{\mathrm{L}}_+$. The six independent components of $F^{\mu\nu}$ can be chosen conveniently as $E^k = F^{0k}$, and $B^k = \varepsilon^{kjm}F_{jm}/2$. We state without proof that the combinations $E^k \pm iB^k$ transform independently under all proper Lorentz transformations. Hence they correspond to the bi-spinor quantities f, g of Eq. (VI-39). Under spatial inversion, $E^k \to -E^k$ and $B^k \to B^k$, hence $E^k + iB^k \leftrightarrow -(E^k - iB^k)$, just as $f \leftrightarrow g$. For details, consult [Berestetskii].

In general, to obtain higher dimensional representations of the proper or the complete Lorentz group from the fundamental spinors, we need to form tensors with definite permutation symmetries, as discussed in chapters 5 and 12.

APPENDIX VII

UNITARY REPRESENTATIONS OF THE PROPER LORENTZ GROUP

Because the Lorentz group is non-compact, all its non-trivial unitary representations are necessarily infinite dimensional. This Appendix provides the details of the derivation of these representations. The presentation follows the steps outlined in the text, Sec. 10.3.3.

(i) The basis vectors of the representation space are chosen to be "canonical" with respect to the rotation subgroup in the sense of Sec. 7.3. They carry the representation label (j_0, j_1) [cf. Subsections 10.3.2, 10.3.3], and the individual vector label (j, m). We know that j is an integer or half-odd-integer and $m = -j, \ldots, j$. The task is to determine the values of (j_0, j_1) (which fix the range of j) allowed by the requirement that the representation be unitary.

(ii) The action of the generators of rotations $\{J_m\}$ on a typical basis vector $|j, m\rangle$ follows the canonical prescription of Sec. 7.3, Eqs. (7.3-12)–(7.3-14). The value of j does not change upon such action. The effect of the generators of Lorentz boosts $\{K_m\}$ on the basis vectors is partially determined by the Wigner-Eckart theorem as given by Eq. (10.3-5), which we repeat here

$$\text{(VII-1)} \qquad \begin{aligned} \langle j'm'|K_3|jm\rangle &= A^{j'}{}_j \langle j'm'(1,j)0\,m\rangle \\ \langle j'm'|K_\pm|jm\rangle &= \mp\sqrt{2}\,A^{j'}{}_j \langle j'm'(1,j)\pm 1\,m\rangle \end{aligned} \quad .$$

The reduced matrix elements, $\{A^{j'}{}_j\}$, which are the only unknowns in these expressions, are the target of our study. Taking the Clebsch-Gordan coefficients from Appendix V, and redefining

$$\begin{aligned} A_j^+ &= A^{j+1}{}_j/[(j+1)(2j+1)]^{1/2} \\ A_j &= A^j{}_j/[j(j+1)]^{1/2} \\ A_j^- &= A^{j-1}{}_j/[j(2j+1)]^{1/2} \end{aligned}$$

we can rewrite Eq. (VII-1) as

$$\begin{aligned} K_3|jm\rangle &= |j-1\,m\rangle[(j+m)(j-m)]^{1/2}A_j^- + |jm\rangle m A_j \\ &\quad + |j+1\,m\rangle[(j+m+1)(j-m+1)]^{1/2}A_j^+ \end{aligned}$$

$$\text{(VII-2)} \qquad \begin{aligned} K_\pm|jm\rangle &= \mp|j-1\,m\pm1\rangle[(j\mp m)(j\mp m-1)]^{1/2}A_j^- \\ &\quad + |j\,m\pm1\rangle[(j\mp m)(j\pm m+1)]^{1/2}A_j \\ &\quad \pm|j+1\,m\pm1\rangle[(j\pm m+1)(j\pm m+2)]^{1/2}A_j^+ \end{aligned} \quad .$$

(iii) To obtain constraints on the coefficients A_j, we must first require that the Lie algebra of the group be satisfied; in particular, $[K_\pm, K_3] = \pm J_\pm$ and $[K_+, K_-] = -2J_3$. A straightforward but tedious calculation yields the following conditions: [cf. Problem 10.7]

(VII-3)
$$[(j-1)A_{j-1} - (j+1)A_j]A_j^- = 0$$
$$[(j+2)A_{j+1} - jA_j]A_j^+ = 0$$
$$(2j-1)A_j^- A_{j-1}^+ - A_j^2 - (2j+3)A_{j+1}^- A_j^+ = 1 \quad .$$

Since the allowed values for j are 0, 1/2, 1, ..., there exists a least value of j which we denote, as usual, by j_0. An inspection of Eq. (VII-2) indicates that we must have $A_{j_0}^- = 0$. In general, when $A_j^\pm \neq 0$, the square brackets in the first two equations of (VII-3) must vanish; hence we obtain a recursion formula for the coefficient A_j,

(VII-4)
$$A_{j+1} = jA_j/(j+2) \quad .$$

It has the solution

(VII-5)
$$A_j = i\frac{\nu j_0}{j(j+1)}$$

where ν is an arbitrary (complex) constant. Substituting this result in the last equation of (VII-3), we obtain a recursion formula for $A_j^- = A_{j-1}^+ \equiv -B_j^2$:

(VII-6)
$$(2j+3)B_{j+1}^2 = (2j-1)B_j^2 + 1 - \left[\frac{\nu j_0}{j(j+1)}\right]^2 .$$

Since we already know that $B_{j_0} = 0$ [cf. discussion above Eq. (VII-4)], this equation can be solved to yield [cf. Problem 10.7],

(VII-7)
$$B_j^2 = \frac{(j^2 - j_0^2)(j^2 - \nu^2)}{j^2(4j^2 - 1)},$$

(VII-8)
$$A_j^- = B_j\xi_j \qquad A_{j-1}^+ = -B_j\xi_j^{-1}$$

where ξ_j is an arbitrary number.

(iv) We have yet to determine the allowed values for ν and ξ_j. They are constrained by the requirement of unitarity of the representation and the orthonormality of the canonical basis. Unitarity dictates that the matrix for K_3 be hermitian and the matrix for K_+ be the hermitian conjugate of K_-. Making use of Eq. (VII-2), we can show that the requisites for these conditions are:

(VII-9)
$$A_j = A_j^*$$
$$A_j^- = -A_{j-1}^{+*} \quad .$$

Substituting Eqs. (VII-5) and (VII-7) in the above, we obtain

(VII-10)
$$j_0(\nu + \nu^*) = 0$$

(VII-11)
$$|B_j|(|\xi_j|^2 - e^{-2i\beta_j}) = 0$$

where β_j is the phase of B_j (i.e. $B_j = |B_j| e^{i\beta_j}$). Provided $|B_j| \neq 0$, the second equation implies that $\beta_j = 0$ ($B_j^2 > 0$) and $|\xi_j|^2 = 1$. We see that ξ_j is an (arbitrary) relative phase factor for basis vectors belonging to subspaces with adjacent values of j. We can, by convention, choose $\xi_j = 1$ for all j.

Eq. (VII-10) requires that either, (a) $\nu = -\nu^*$ (ν imaginary), or (b) $j_0 = 0$. The unitary irreducible representations of case (a) are said to belong to the *principal series*, and those of case (b) belong to the *complementary series.*

(a) The Principal Series: Let $\nu = -iw$ (w real), then

$$A_j = w j_0/j(j+1)$$
$$B_j^2 = (j^2 - j_0^2)(j^2 + w^2)/j^2(4j^2 - 1) \quad . \tag{VII-12}$$

Since the condition $B_j^2 > 0$ is automatically satisfied, w can assume any real value.

(b) The Complementary Series: If $j_0 = 0$, then

$$A_j = 0$$
$$B_j^2 = (j^2 - \nu^2)/(4j^2 - 1) \quad . \tag{VII-13}$$

By definition $B_0 = B_{j_0} = 0$. We need to require that B_j^2 be real and positive for $j = 1, 2, \ldots$, etc. This will be satisfied if and only if $(1 - \nu^2)$ is real and positive or $-1 \leq \nu \leq 1$.

This completes the derivation of the unitary irreducible representations of the proper Lorentz group. Note that these representations are radically different from the unitary irreducible representations of the group SU(2) × SU(2) with which it shares the same Lie algebra. The results of this Appendix are summarized as Theorem 10.9 in Chap. 10. As mentioned in Sec. 10.3.3, the parameter ν is the same as the one called j_1 in Sec. 10.3.2 (and the beginning of this Appendix). A new symbol is used in the course of this derivation because the usual values it is to assume, as a consequence of unitarity of the representations. The identification of ν with j_1 will become obvious when the reader works out Problem 10.7.

APPENDIX VIII

ANTI-LINEAR OPERATORS

Anti-linear operators on a vector space share most properties of linear operators. Differences arise when complex conjugations or adjoints are involved. We shall summarize the important properties of anti-linear operators in the same order as they were presented for linear operators in Appendix II.

An *anti-linear operator* A is a mapping $|x\rangle \rightarrow |Ax\rangle$ on a vector space V such that if

$$|y\rangle = |x_1\rangle \alpha_1 + |x_2\rangle \alpha_2$$

then

(VIII-1) $$|Ay\rangle = |Ax_1\rangle \alpha_1{}^* + |Ax_2\rangle \alpha_2{}^*$$

where $\alpha_{1,2}$ are ordinary complex numbers. We shall also adopt the notation

(VIII-2) $$A|x\rangle \equiv |Ax\rangle \quad .$$

But care must be exercised in using this notation because, if α is any c-number, then

(VIII-3) $$A\alpha|x\rangle = A(|x\rangle \alpha) = |Ax\rangle \alpha^* = (A|x\rangle)\alpha^* = \alpha^* A|x\rangle$$

where Eq. (VIII-1) is used in the second step. Notice that the parentheses in the second and fourth expression in the above equation are absolutely necessary. The expression $A|x\rangle\alpha$ has no unambiguous meaning for anti-linear operators, in contrast to the case with linear operators.

Since Eq. (VIII-3) holds for all $|x\rangle \in$ V, it follows that

(VIII-4) $$A\,\alpha = \alpha^* A \quad .$$

This defines *multiplication by a number* for anti-linear operations. The *product* of A with another operator B is defined in the natural way [Definition II.10]

(VIII-5) $$(AB)|x\rangle = A\,|Bx\rangle \qquad \text{for all } |x\rangle \in \mathrm{V}.$$

It is easy to show that: if B is linear, then AB is anti-linear; if B is anti-linear, as A, then AB is a linear operator. The *sum* of two anti-linear operators can also be defined in the usual way. The *inverse* of A, if it exists, can be defined just as in Definition II.13. It can be shown that A^{-1} is also anti-linear. Most algebraic relations involving A^{-1} [cf. Theorems II.4, II.5] are the same as those for linear operators, with the exception of the following formula:

(VIII-6) $$(\alpha A)^{-1} = \alpha^{*-1} A^{-1} \quad .$$

The *adjoint* of A, denoted by $A^\dagger$, is defined by the equation

(VIII-7) $$\langle A^\dagger y|x\rangle = \langle y|Ax\rangle^*$$

for all $x \in \mathrm{V}$ and $y \in \tilde{\mathrm{V}}$. The complex conjugation on the right-hand side is essential; without it $A^\dagger y$ would not be a linear functional, hence would not belong to $\tilde{\mathrm{V}}$. [Prove!] One can show that $A^\dagger$ is anti-linear, the same as A. The adjoint operator $A^\dagger$ satisfies the algebraic relations given by Eq. (II.4-5). Note, however,

(VIII-8) $$(\alpha A)^\dagger = A^\dagger \alpha^* = \alpha A^\dagger \quad .$$

On an inner product space, the action of $A^\dagger$ on $x \in \mathrm{V}$ is defined by

(VIII-9) $$\langle y | A^\dagger x \rangle = \langle Ay | x \rangle^*$$

which is symmetrical to Eq. (VIII-7). The appearance of the complex conjugation on the right-hand sides of Eqs. (VIII-7) and (VIII-9), again, requires caution when manipulating anti-linear operators. For instance, Eq. (II.6-1) becomes, in the present case,

(VIII-10) $$\langle x | Ay \rangle = \langle Ay | x \rangle^* = \langle y | A^\dagger x \rangle = \langle A^\dagger x | y \rangle^* \quad .$$

As a consequence, the expression $\langle x | A | y \rangle$ cannot be interpreted unambiguously as in the case of linear operators: the two quantities $\langle x | (A | y \rangle) = \langle x | Ay \rangle$ and $(\langle x | A) | y \rangle = \langle A^\dagger x | y \rangle$ are complex conjugates of each other, rather than being identical previously. In order to be precise, one has either to use the parentheses to indicate the order of operations, or to enclose the operators in the bra or ket vector symbols as done above.

A *hermitian* or *self-adjoint* anti-linear operator is one which satisfies

(VIII-11) $$A = A^\dagger \quad .$$

Theorems II.14 and II.15 on hermitian operators remain valid.

An *anti-unitary* operator is one which is anti-linear and which satisfies

(VIII-12) $$AA^\dagger = A^\dagger A = E$$

or equivalently,

(VIII-13) $$A^\dagger = A^{-1} \quad .$$

Under an anti-unitary transformation, we have

(VIII-14) $$\langle x | y \rangle \longrightarrow \langle Ax | Ay \rangle = \langle x | A^\dagger Ay \rangle^* = \langle x | y \rangle^* \quad .$$

Hence, scalar products are transformed into their complex conjugates, rather than staying invariant as for unitary transformations. Let B be any operator. Let it transform under the anti-unitary transformation A as

(VIII-15) $$B \longrightarrow ABA^\dagger$$

so that group properties are preserved. We examine how matrix elements of B transform under A:

(VIII-16) $$\begin{aligned} \langle x | B | y \rangle \longrightarrow \langle Ax | (ABA^\dagger) | Ay \rangle &= [(\langle Ax | A) B (A^\dagger | Ay \rangle)]^* \\ &= \langle A^\dagger Ax | B | A^\dagger Ay \rangle^* = \langle x | B | y \rangle^* . \end{aligned}$$

We see that, again, these quantities are transformed into their complex conjugates. Eq. (VIII-14) is a special case of (VIII-16) when B is taken to be the identity operator.

Note that anti-unitarity transformations do preserve the modulus of the matrix elements $\langle x|B|y\rangle$, i.e.

(VIII-17) $$|\langle x|B|y\rangle| \xrightarrow{A} |\langle x|B|y\rangle| \quad .$$

In quantum mechanical applications, measurable quantities are always expressed in terms of probabilities which are the absolute value squared of "expectation values" of the above form. The invariance of these quantities under anti-unitary, as well as unitary, transformations [Eq. (VIII-17)] is the underlying reason why both types of operators are useful in the formulation of symmetry principles in physics.

REFERENCES AND BIBLIOGRAPHY

Berestetskii, V. B., E. M. Lifshitz, and L. P. Pitaevskii, *Relativistic Quantum Theory,* Pergamon Press, Oxford, New York (1971).

Biedenharn, L. C., and H. Van Dam, eds., *Quantum Theory of Angular Momentum,* Academic Press, New York (1965).

Blatt, J., and V. Weisskopf, *Theoretical Nuclear Physics,* Wiley, New York (1952).

Boerner, H., *Representations of Groups,* North-Holland Publ., Amsterdam (1969).

Carruthers, P., *Spin and Isospin in Particle Physics,* Gordon and Breach, New York (1971).

Chevalley, C., *Theory of Lie Groups,* Princeton Univ. Press, Princeton NJ. (1946).

Commins, E. D., and P. H. Bucksbaum, *Weak Interactions of Leptons and Quarks,* Cambridge Univ. Press, Cambridge (1983).

Courant, R., and D. Hilbert, *Methods of Mathematical Physics,* Vol. I, Wiley, New York (1953).

Dyson, F., *Symmetry Groups in Nuclear and Particle Physics,* Benjamin, New York (1966).

Edmonds, A. R., *Angular Momentum in Quantum Mechanics,* Princeton Univ. Press, Princeton NJ. (1968).

Elliot, J. P., and P. G. Dawber, *Symmetry in Physics,* Vols. I & II, Oxford Univ. Press, New York (1979).

Feynman, R. P., R. B. Leighton, and M. Sands, *The Feynman Lectures on Physics,* Vol. III-Quantum Mechanics, Addison-Wesley, Reading MA. (1965).

Gasiorowicz, S., *Quantum Physics,* Wiley, New York (1974).

Gel'fand, I., R. Minlos, and Z. Shapiro, *Representations of the Rotation and Lorentz Groups and Their Applications,* English Transl., Macmillan, New York (1963).

Georgi, H., *Lie Algebras in Particle Physics,* Benjamin/Cummings, Reading, MA. (1982).

Gilmore, R., *Lie Groups, Lie Algebras, and Some of Their Applications,* Wiley, New York (1974).

Goldstein, H., *Classical Mechanics,* 2nd ed., Addison-Wesley, Reading MA. (1980).

Gourdin, M., *Basics of Lie Groups,* Editions Frontieres, Gif-sur-Yvette, France (1982).

Halmos, P. R., *Finite Dimensional Vector Spaces,* 2nd ed., Van Nostrand, Princeton NJ. (1958).

Halzen, F., and A. D. Martin, *Quarks and Leptons: An Introductory Course in Modern Particle Physics,* Wiley, New York (1984).

Hamermesh, M., *Group Theory and Its Applications to Physical Problems,* Addison-Wesley, Reading MA. (1962).

Jacob, M., and G. Wick, "On the General Theory of Collisions for Particles with Spin," *Annals of Physics* (New York) 7, 401-428 (1959).

Joshi, A. W., *Elements of Group Theory for Physicists,* 3rd ed., Wiley, New York (1982).

Kahan, T., *Theory of Groups in Classical and Quantum Physics,* American Elsevier, New York (1965).

Landau, L. D., and E. M. Lifshitz

[1] *Mechanics,* 3rd ed. *Course of Theoretical Physics,* Vol. I., Pergamon Press, Oxford (1976).

[2] *The Classical Theory of Fields,* 4th ed. *ibid.,* Vol. II (1975).

[3] *Quantum Mechanics-Non-relativistic Theory,* 3rd ed. *ibid.,* Vol. III (1977).

Lichtenberg, D. B., *Unitary Symmetry and Elementary Particles,* Academic Press, New York (1970).

Lipkin, H. J., *Lie Groups for Pedestrians,* North-Holland, Amsterdam (1965).

Lyubarskii, G., *The Application of Group Theory in Physics,* English Transl., Pergamon, Oxford (1960).

Messiah, A., *Quantum Mechanics,* Vols. I & II, North-Holland, Amsterdam (1962).

Miller, W., *Symmetry Groups and Their Applications,* Academic Press, New York (1972).

Naimark, M., *Linear Representations of Lorentz Group,* English Transl., Macmillan, New York (1964).

Parikh, J. C., *Group Symmetries in Nuclear Structure,* Plenum Press, New York (1978).

Petrashen, M. I. and E. D. Trifonov, *Applications of Group Theory in Quantum Mechanics,* MIT Press, Cambridge MA (1969).

Pontrjagin, L., *Topological Groups,* Princeton Univ. Press, Princeton NJ. (1958).

Rose, M. E., *Elementary Theory of Angular Momentum,* Wiley, New York (1957).

Sakurai, J. J., *Invariance Principles and Elementary Particles,* Princeton Univ. Press, Princeton NJ. (1964).

Schiff, L. I., *Quantum Mechanics,* 3rd ed., McGraw-Hill, New York (1968).

Streater, R. F., and A. S. Wightman *PCT, Spin and Statistics, and All That,* Benjamin, New York (1978).

Talman, J. D., *Special Functions,* Benjamin, New York (1968).

Tinkham, M., *Group Theory and Quantum Mechanics,* McGraw-Hill, New York (1964).

Varadarajan, V. S., *Lie Groups, Lie Algebras and Their Representations,* Prentice-Hall, Englewood Cliffs NJ. (1974).

Vilenkin, N., "Special Functions and the Theory of Group Representations, *Amer. Math. Soc. Transl.,* Amer. Math. Soc., Providence, Rhode Island (1968).

Waerden, B. L., van der, *Group Theory and Quantum Mechanics,* Springer-Verlag, Berlin, New York (1974).

Watson, G. N., *A Treatise on the Theory of Bessel Functions,* Cambridge Univ. Press, Cambridge (1958).

Whittaker, E. T., and G. N. Watson, *A Course of Modern Analysis,* 4th ed., Cambridge Univ. Press, Cambridge (1958).

Weyl, H.,

[1] *Group Theory and Quantum Mechanics,* Dover, New York (1950).

[2] *Classical Groups, Their Invariants and Representations,* Princeton Univ. Press, Princeton NJ. (1946).

Wigner, E.,

[1] "On Unitary Representations of the Inhomogeneous Lorentz Groups," *Annals of Mathematics* **40**, 149-204 (1939).

[2] *Group Theory and Its Application to the Quantum Mechanics of Atomic Spectra,* Academic Press, New York (1959).

[3] Contribution in *Group Theoretical Concepts and Methods in Elementary Particle Physics,* ed. F. Gürsey, Gordon and Breach, New York (1964).

Wybourne, B., *Classical Groups of Physics,* Wiley, New York (1974).

INDEX

CPSIA information can be obtained
at www.ICGtesting.com
Printed in the USA
BVHW090225100720
583335BV00005B/95

9 789971 966577